BRIDGE
TO ABSTRACT
MATHEMATICS
Mathematical
Proof and
Structures

The Random House/Birkhäuser Mathematics Series:

BRIDGE TO ABSTRACT MATHEMATICS

Mathematical Proof and Structures

Ronald P. Morash

University of Michigan, Dearborn

The Random House/Birkhäuser Mathematics Series

Random House, Inc. New York

First Edition

987654321

Copyright © 1987 by Random House, Inc.

Library of Congress Cataloging in Publication Data

Morash, Ronald P.
   Bridge to abstract mathematics.

   Includes index.
   1. Logic, Symbolic and mathematical.   2. Mathematics
—1961–   .   I. Title.
QA9.M74   1987   511.3   86-21931

ISBN 0-394-35429-X

Manufactured in the United States of America

to my family

Preface

This text is directed toward the sophomore through senior levels of university mathematics, with a tilt toward the former. It presumes that the student has completed at least one semester, and preferably a full year, of calculus. The text is a product of fourteen years of experience, on the part of the author, in teaching a not-too-common course to students with a very common need. The course is taken predominantly by sophomores and juniors from various fields of concentration who expect to enroll in junior-senior mathematics courses that include significant abstract content. It endeavors to provide a pathway, or bridge, to the level of mathematical sophistication normally desired by instructors in such courses, but generally not provided by the standard freshman-sophomore program. Toward this end, the course places strong emphasis on mathematical reasoning and exposition. Stated differently, it endeavors to serve as a significant first step toward the goal of precise thinking and effective communication of one's thoughts in the language of science.

Of central importance in any overt attempt to instill "mathematical maturity" in students is the writing and comprehension of proofs. Surely, the requirement that students deal seriously with mathematical proofs is the single factor that most strongly differentiates upper-division courses from the calculus sequence and other freshman-sophomore classes. Accordingly, the centerpiece of this text is a substantial body of material that deals explicitly and systematically with mathematical proof (Article 4.1, Chapters 5 and 6). A primary feature of this material is a recognition of and reliance on the student's background in mathematics (e.g., algebra, trigonometry, calculus, set theory) for a context in which to present proof-writing techniques. The first three chapters of the text deal with material that is important in its own right (sets, logic), but their major role is to lay groundwork for the coverage of proofs. Likewise, the material in Chapters 7 through 10 (relations, number systems) is of independent value to any student going on in mathematics. It is not inaccurate, however, in the context of this book, to view it primarily as a vehicle by which students may develop further the incipient ability to read and write proofs.

IMPORTANT FEATURES

Readability. The author's primary pedagogical goal in writing the text was to produce a book that students can read. Since many colleges and universities in the United States do not currently have a "bridging" course in mathematics, it was a goal to make the book suitable for the individual student who might want to study it independently. Toward this end, an introduction is provided for each chapter, and for many articles within chapters, to place content in perspective and relate it to other parts of the book, providing both an overall point of view and specific suggestions for working through the unit. Solved examples are distributed liberally throughout the text. Abstract definitions are amplified, whenever appropriate, by a number of concrete examples. Occasionally, the presentation of material is interrupted, so the author can "talk to" the reader and explain various mathematical "facts of life." The numerous exercises at the end of articles have been carefully selected and placed to illustrate and supplement material in the article. In addition, exercises are often used to anticipate results or concepts in the next article. Of course, most students who use the text will do so under the direction of an instructor. Both instructor and students reap the benefit of enhanced opportunity for efficient classroom coverage of material when students are able to read a text.

Organization. In Chapter 1, we introduce basic terminology and notation of set theory and provide an informal study of the algebra of sets. Beyond this, we use set theory as a device to indicate to the student what serious mathematics is really about, that is, the discovery of general theorems. Such discovery devices as examples, pictures, analogies, and counterexamples are brought into play. Rhetorical questions are employed often in this chapter to instill in the student the habit of thinking aggressively, of looking for questions as well as answers. Also, a case is made at this stage for both the desirability of a systematic approach to manipulating statements (i.e., logic) and the necessity of abstract proof to validate our mathematical beliefs.

In Chapters 2 and 3, we study logic from a concrete and common-sense point of view. Strong emphasis is placed on those logical principles that are most commonly used in everyday mathematics (i.e., tautologies of the propositional calculus and theorems of the predicate calculus). The goal of these chapters is to integrate principles of logic into the student's way of thinking so that they are applied correctly, though most often only implicitly, to the solving of mathematical problems, including the writing of proofs.

In Chapter 4, we begin to <u>do</u> some mathematics, with an emphasis on topics whose understanding is enhanced by a knowledge of elementary logic. Most important, we begin in this chapter to deal with proofs, limiting ourselves at this stage to theorems of set theory, including properties of countably infinite collections of sets. The main emphasis here is on standard approaches to proving set inclusion (e.g., the "choose" method) and set equality (e.g., mutual inclusion), but we manage also, through the many solved examples, to anticipate additional techniques of proof that are studied in detail later. The chapter concludes by digressing to an optional, and perhaps somewhat offbeat, second look at the limit concept, directed toward an understanding of the epsilon-delta definition.

Chapters 5 and 6 provide the text's most concentrated treatment of proof writing per se. The general organization of these chapters is in order of increasing complexity, with special emphasis on the logical structure of the conclusion of the proposition to be proved. In Articles 5.1, 5.2, and 6.1, we progress from conclusions with the simplest logical structure [i.e., $(\forall x)(p(x))$], to conclusions with a more complex form [i.e., $(\forall x)(p(x) \to q(x))$], and then to the most complex case [$\forall$ followed by $\exists$]. Additional techniques, including induction, indirect proof, specialization, division into cases, and counterexample, are also studied. Solved examples and exercises calling for the writing of proofs are selected from set theory, intermediate algebra, trigonometry, elementary calculus, matrix algebra, and elementary analysis. Of course, instructors must gear the assignment of exercises to the students' background. Solved examples, together with starred exercises (whose solutions appear in the back of the book) provide numerous models of proofs, after which students may pattern their own attempts. An additional source of correctly written proofs (as well as some that were deliberately written incorrectly) is a "Critique and Complete" category of exercise that occurs in Article 4.1 and throughout Chapter 5.

Chapters 7 and 8 deal with the most common kinds of relations on sets, equivalence relations, partial orderings, and functions. Chapter 8 includes an introduction to cardinality of sets and a brief discussion of arbitrary collections of sets. Chapters 9 and 10 study the standard number systems encountered in undergraduate mathematics. Chapter 9 emphasizes the properties that distinguish the real numbers from other familiar number systems. Chapter 10 provides an outline of an actual construction of the real numbers, which would perhaps be most appropriately used in a class of seniors or as an independent study project for a well-motivated and relatively advanced student. In addition to treating material that is of considerable value in its own right, Chapters 7 through 10 provide ample opportunity for students to put into practice proof-writing skills acquired in earlier chapters. In keeping with the advancing abilities of students, proofs are deliberately written in an increasingly terse fashion (with less detailed explanation and less psychological support) in the later chapters. This may provide a smooth transition from this text to the "real world" of typical texts for standard junior-senior courses.

Flexibility. Bridging courses in mathematics are by no means an established or standardized part of the undergraduate curriculum. Indeed, among colleges and universities where such courses exist, the subject matter varies considerably. For this reason, an attempt has been made to include in this text a wide variety of topics and to avoid interdependence among topics whenever possible. Furthermore, a conscious decision was made to avoid any primary focus on material that is the specific content of mainstream junior-senior courses.

A number of articles in Book One (1.5, 2.4, 3.5, 4.3, 6.3, 6.4) are designated "optional." The nonoptional material in Book One (i.e., Articles 1.1–1.4, 2.1–2.3, 3.1–3.4, 4.1, 4.2, 5.1–5.4, 6.1, and 6.2) constitutes what the author regards as the core content for achieving the objectives of a bridging course and for permitting passage to Book Two. Though no topics in Book Two have been explicitly designated as optional, they can be covered selectively to fit the needs of a particular course. Many different syllabi can be based on this text, depending on the number of available class sessions, the initial level of the students, and the judgment of individual instructors or curriculum committees. For example, a two-credit course focused on sets, logic, and proof could cover the core material from Book One. A three-credit course for sophomores, in which a relatively leisurely pace and strong focus on fundamentals is desired, might proceed:

[Core plus 1.5, 2.4, 3.5] → [Ch. 7] → [8.1, 8.2]

or

[Core plus 2.4, 4.3, 6.1 ($\varepsilon - \delta$ proofs)] → [7.1, 7.2, 7.3] → [8.1, 8.2].

Possibilities for three-credit courses with a more advanced or accelerated point of view include:

[Core plus 1.5, 2.4, 6.3] → [Ch. 7] → [Ch. 8]

and

[Core plus 6.3] → [7.1, 7.2, 7.3] → [Ch. 9] → [10.1].

A number of alternative syllabi are contained in the instructor's manual, available free from the publisher to instructors using the text. This manual also provides a list of objectives for each article, as well as commentary on pedagogical issues related to various portions of the text.

ACKNOWLEDGMENTS

A large number of people contributed in important ways to the inception, development, and completion of this text. First among these was my editor at Random House/Birkhäuser, Wayne Yuhasz, without whose early encouragement my set of class notes would have remained in that state. I am indebted to him also for highly professional support, as the project progressed.

We began the project with an extensive survey of opinions about the teaching of mathematical proof writing, and we want to thank all who shared their thoughts and experiences:

William Berlinghoff, Southern Connecticut State University

Charles Biles, Humboldt State University

Richard Chandler, North Carolina State University

Orin Chein, Temple University

Bradd Clark, University of Southwestern Louisiana

William Coppage, Wright State University

Carl Cowen, Purdue University

Robert G. Dean, Stephen F. Austin University

Thomas Dence, Ashland College

Michael Evans, North Carolina State University

Daniel Farkas, Virginia Polytechnic and State University

Dorothy Goldberg, Kean College of New Jersey

Joel Haack, Oklahoma State University

Kenneth E. Hummel, Trinity University

John Lawlor, University of Vermont

Douglas Nance, Central Michigan University

Gregory B. Passty, Southwest Texas State University

Gail Ratliff, University of Missouri, St. Louis

Robert B. Reisel, Loyola University of Chicago

Donald F. Reynolds, Indiana State University

David Sprows, Villanova University

Louis A. Talman, Metropolitan State College

Raymond D. Terry, California Polytechnic State University

Richard Thompson, University of Arizona

James Vance, Wright State University

Robert W. West, University of California, Irvine

The suggestions of many reviewers had a strong influence on the development of the manuscript. I would like to thank Professors William Berlinghoff, Charles Biles, Orin Chein, Robert Dean, Michael Evans, Joel Haack, John Lawlor, David Sprows, Richard Thompson, and James Vance, for an extraordinarily conscientious job of reviewing, criticizing, enhancing, and sometimes praising my work. In particular, Professors Biles, Evans, and Vance provided material, including several fine exercises, that I incorporated into the text. I am grateful to Professor Berlinghoff and his students at Southern Connecticut State University, who used a late version of the manuscript in their course and made a number of helpful suggestions.

Colleagues and students at the University of Michigan, Dearborn, deserve thanks for important suggestions and feedback. Professors Stephen Milles, James Ward Brown, Frank Papp, Michael Lachance, and Manuel Esteban, as well as Larry Polnicky, were of particular help. Sandra Flack and Joyce Moss of the U. M. D. mathematics department provided clerical support, for which I am grateful.

Helene Neu, of the University of Michigan, Ann Arbor, gave me much advice and many helpful insights, as did Professors Ted Giebutowski and Keith Ferland of Plymouth State College in Plymouth, New Hampshire, and Dr. Robert Haberstroh of Computervision in Woburn, Massachusetts. Special thanks for valuable support and encouragement go to my friends and colleagues in biomedical research, Dr. Ruth Maulucci and Dr. Richard Eckhouse, of MOCO, Inc., Scituate, Massachusetts.

Finally, I would like to take this opportunity to thank two of my own teachers from my years as a Ph. D. candidate at the University of Massachusetts, Amherst: Dr. Samuel S. Holland, Jr., and Dr. David J. Foulis. Professor Holland, who directed my doctoral dissertation, taught me a great deal about doing mathematics but, through his example, even more about teaching mathematics and writing it. Professor Foulis not only influenced my research in that period through his pioneering work in the field of orthomodular lattice theory, but also introduced me to the concept of a bridging course for undergraduates through his excellent text, *Fundamental Concepts of Mathematics*.

RONALD P. MORASH
October 1986   *University of Michigan, Dearborn*

Contents

BRIDGE
TO ABSTRACT
MATHEMATICS

Mathematical
Proof and
Structures

BOOK ONE

The Foundation: Sets, Logic, and Mathematical Argument

Sets
CHAPTER 1

The purpose of this chapter is twofold: to provide an introduction to, or review of, the terminology, notation, and basic properties of sets, and, perhaps more important, to serve as a starting point for our primary goal—the development of the ability to discover and prove mathematical theorems. The emphasis in this chapter is on *discovery*, with particular attention paid to the kinds of evidence (e.g., specific examples, pictures) that mathematicians use to formulate conjectures about general properties. These conjectures become theorems when the mathematician provides a rigorous proof (methods of proof start in Chapter 4).

The information on set theory contained in this chapter is important in its own right, but the spirit of discovery—proceeding with caution from the particular to the possibly true general, which we emphasize in discussing sets—applies to all areas of mathematics and is indeed what much of mathematics is about! We will continue to stress its importance in later chapters, even as we concentrate increasingly on the mechanics of theorem-proving.

The formal development of set theory began in 1874 with the work of Georg Cantor (1845–1918). Since then, motivated particularly by the discovery of certain paradoxes (e.g., Russell's paradox, see Exercise 10), logicians have made formal set theory and the foundations of mathematics a vital area of mathematical research, and mathematicians at large have incorporated the language and methods of set theory into their work, so that it permeates all of modern mathematics. Formal, or axiomatic, set theory is not normally studied until the graduate level, and appropriately so. But the undergraduate student of mathematics at the junior-senior level needs a good working knowledge of the elementary properties of sets, as well as facility with a number of set theoretic approaches to proving theorems. As stated earlier, our treatment of the latter begins in Chapter 4. Here we encourage you to develop the habit of making conjectures about potential theorems of set theory, as suggested by the various types of evidence you encounter.

1.1 Basic Definitions and Notation

The notion of set is a primitive, or undefined, term in mathematics, analogous to point and line in plane geometry. Therefore, our starting point, rather than a formal definition, is an informal description of how the term "set" is generally viewed in applications to undergraduate mathematics.

REMARK 1   **A set** may be thought of as a well-defined collection of objects. The objects in the set are called **elements** of the set.

The elements of a set may be any kinds of objects at all, ranging from, most familiarly, numbers to names of people, varieties of flowers, or names of states in the United States or provinces in Canada. A set may even have other sets as some or all of its elements (see Exercise 9).

We will adopt the convention that capital letters A, B, X, Y, are used to denote the names of sets, whereas lowercase a, b, x, y, denotes objects viewed as possible elements of sets. Furthermore, the expression $a \in A$ ($\in$ is the Greek letter "epsilon" in lower case) represents the statement "the object a is an element of the set A," and $x \notin X$ represents the assertion that the object x is <u>not</u> an element of the set X. The convention about the use of upper- and lowercase letters may occasionally be dispensed with in the text when inconvenient (such as in an example in which an element of a given set is itself a set). However, it is especially valuable and will be adhered to in setting up proofs of theorems in later chapters.

One advantage of having an informal definition of the term *set* is that, through it, we can introduce some other terminology related to sets. The term *element* is one example, and the notion *well-defined* is another. The latter term relates to the primary requirement for any such description: *Given an object, we must be able to determine whether or not the object lies in the described set.* Here are two general methods of describing sets; as we will soon observe, well-definedness has a particular bearing on the second method.

METHODS OF DESCRIBING SETS

The roster method. We describe a set by listing the names of its elements, separated by commas, with the full list enclosed in braces. Thus $A = \{1, 2, 3, 4\}$ or $B = \{$Massachusetts, Michigan, California$\}$ are sets consisting of four and three elements, respectively, described by the roster method. Note that $2 \in A$ and Michigan $\in B$, but $5 \notin A$ and Ohio $\notin B$.

Two important facts are: (1) the order in which elements are listed is irrelevant and (2) an object should be listed only once in the roster, since listing it more than once does not change the set. As an example, the set $\{1, 1, 2\}$ is the same as the set $\{1, 2\}$ (so that the representation $\{1, 1, 2\}$ is never used) which, in turn, is the same as the set $\{2, 1\}$.

The rule, or description, method. We describe a set in terms of one or more properties to be satisfied by objects in the set, and by those objects only. Such a description is formulated in so-called *set-builder* notation, that is, in the form $A = \{x \mid x$ satisfies some property or properties$\}$, which we read "*A* is the set of all objects *x* such that *x* satisfies ...." Typical representations of sets by the rule method are:

$$C = \{x \mid x \text{ is a natural number and } x \leq 100.\}$$

or $D = \{x \mid x$ is the name of a state in the United States beginning with the letter *M*.$\}$

or $X = \{x \mid x$ is a male citizen of the United States.$\}$

In all these examples the vertical line is read "such that" and the set is understood to consist of <u>all</u> objects satisfying the preceding description, and <u>only those objects</u>. Thus $57 \in C$, whereas $126 \notin C$. The set *D* can also be described by the roster method, namely, as the set $\{$Maine, Maryland, Massachusetts, Michigan, Minnesota, Missouri, Mississippi, Montana$\}$. Although it's true that Maine $\in D$, it would be false to say that $D = \{$Maine$\}$; that is, the description of *D* must not be misinterpreted to mean that *D* has only one element. The same is true of the set *X* which is a very large set, difficult to describe by the roster method.

It is in connection with the description method that "well definedness" comes into play. The rule or rules used in describing a set must be (1) meaningful, that is, use words and/or symbols with an understood meaning and (2) specific and definitive, as opposed to vague and indefinite. Thus descriptions like $G = \{x \mid x$ is a goople$\}$ or $E = \{x \mid x!* \& 3\}$ or $Z = \{x \mid x$ is a large state in the United States$\}$ do not define sets. The descriptions of *G* and *E* involve nonsense symbols or words, while the description of *Z* gives a purely subjective criterion for membership. On the other hand, a set may be well defined even though its membership is difficult to determine or not immediately evident from its description (see Exercise 3).

COMPARISON OF THE ROSTER AND RULE METHODS. FINITE AND INFINITE SETS

The roster method has the obvious advantage of avoiding the problem of deciding well definedness. Whenever it's used (provided the objects named as elements have meaning), there can be no doubt as to which objects are, and are not, in the set. On the other hand, if the set to be described is large, the roster method can be impractical or impossible to employ. Clearly we would want to describe the set $F = \{x \mid x$ is a natural number and $x \leq 10^8\}$ by the rule method, although it's theoretically possible to list all the elements, whereas the set $I = \{x \mid x$ is a real number and $0 \leq x \leq 1\}$ cannot even theoretically be described by the roster method. Until we give a rigorous, or mathematically correct, definition in Article 8.3, we will view an *infinite set* as one that cannot, even theoretically, be described by the roster method. Stated differently, the elements of an infinite set are impossible to exhaust, and so cannot be listed. A *finite set*, on the other hand, is one that is not infinite. The set F, defined earlier, is finite, whereas I is infinite since it has the property that, between any two distinct elements of I, there is another element of I. A set may fail to have this property and still be infinite; the set of all positive integers is infinite because, whenever n is a positive integer, so is $n + 1$.

A widely used hybrid of the roster and rule methods is employed to describe both finite and infinite sets. The notation $Q = \{1, 3, 5, \ldots, 97, 99\}$ or $T = \{10, 20, 30, 40, \ldots\}$ implicitly uses the rule method by establishing a *pattern* in which the elements occur. It uses the appearance of the roster method, with the symbol "$\ldots$" being read "and so on" in the case of an infinite set such as T and "$\ldots,$" meaning "and so on, until" for a finite set like Q. As with any application of the rule method, there is a danger of misinterpretation if too little or unclear information is given. As one example, the notation $\{1, 2, \ldots\}$ may refer to the set $\{1, 2, 3, 4, 5, \ldots\}$ of all positive integers or to the set $\{1, 2, 4, 8, 16, \ldots\}$ of all nonnegative powers of 2. On the other hand, given the earlier pattern descriptions of Q and T, most readers would agree that $47 \in Q$, $2 \notin Q$, $50 \in T$, $50^{10} \in T$, and $15 \notin T$.

There is one other important connection between the roster method and the rule method. In a number of mathematical situations *solving a problem* means essentially to convert a description of a set by the rule method into a roster method description. In this context we often refer to the roster representation as the *solution set* of the original problem (see Exercise 1).

UNIVERSAL SETS

Although the idea of a "universal set" in an absolute sense, that is, a set containing all objects, leads to serious logical difficulties (explored in Exercise 10) and so is not used in set theory, the concept, when applied in a more limited sense, has considerable value. For our purposes a *universal set* is the set of all objects under discussion in a particular setting.

A universal set will often be specified at the start of a problem involving sets (in this text the letter U will be reserved for this purpose), whereas in other situations a universal set is more or less clearly, but implicitly, understood as background to a problem. We did the latter when we pointed out that Ohio $\notin B = \{$Massachusetts, Michigan, California$\}$ but did not explicitly say that $5 \notin B$ or that Harry Jones $\notin B$. The implicit understanding was that, in the discussion involving this set B, the objects under consideration, or the potential elements, were states, with the universal set U being a set of 50 elements.

The role then of a universal set is to put some bounds on the nature of the objects that can be considered for membership in the sets involved in a given situation.

SOME SPECIAL SETS

In mathematics the sets of greatest interest are those whose elements are mathematical objects; included among these are sets whose elements are numbers. In this context there are certain sets of numbers that serve as a universal set so frequently that we assign them (widely used and recognized) names and symbols.

DEFINITION 1

Throughout this text, we will denote by:

(a) **N** the set $\{1, 2, 3, 4, \ldots\}$ of all positive integers (natural numbers)
(b) **Z** the set $\{0, \pm 1, \pm 2, \ldots\}$ of all integers (signed whole numbers)
(c) **Q** the set of all rational numbers (quotients of integers)
(d) **R** the set of all real numbers (the reals)
(e) **C** the set of all complex numbers

These names are commonly used in the description of sets whose elements are numbers. It is of vital importance, also, to realize that the *universal set specified in the description of a set is as important as the rest of the definition.* For example, the set $J = \{x \in \mathbf{Q} \,|\, x^2 \geq 2\}$ is different from the set $L = \{x \in \mathbf{R} \,|\, x^2 \geq 2\}$, even though the descriptions of both sets use the same inequality (since, e.g., $\sqrt{2} \in L$, but $\sqrt{2} \notin J$). Considering these remarks, we may streamline the notation used in our descriptions of some sets earlier, writing

$$C = \{x \in \mathbf{N} \,|\, x \leq 100\}, \qquad F = \{x \in \mathbf{N} \,|\, x \leq 10^8\},$$

and

$$I = \{x \in \mathbf{R} \,|\, 0 \leq x \leq 1\}$$

We will study the sets **N**, **Z**, **Q**, **R**, and **C** as number systems in Chapters 9 and 10.

INTERVALS

Within the context of **R** as the universal set (the understanding throughout most of elementary and intermediate calculus), there are other special sets, known as *intervals*, which we will frequently encounter. Intervals are described by widely used notation, which we will soon introduce. Before doing so, we give a definition of interval that provides our first example of an abstract mathematical definition of the type we will often work with later in the text.

DEFINITION 2
A set *I*, all of whose elements are real numbers, is called an **interval** if and only if, whenever *a* and *b* are elements of *I* and *c* is a real number with $a < c < b$, then $c \in I$.

Intervals are characterized among other sets of real numbers by the property of containing any number between two of its members. All intervals must do this and intervals are the only sets of real numbers that do this. In particular, any set of real numbers such as $\{0, 1, 2\}$, or **Z** or **Q**, which fails to have this property, is not an interval. Intervals are easy to recognize; indeed, we will prove in Chapter 9 that every interval in **R** has one of nine forms.

DEFINITION 3
Nine types of intervals are described by the following terminology and notation, in which *a* and *b* denote real numbers:

1. $\{x \in \mathbf{R} \mid a \leq x \leq b\}$, a *closed and bounded* interval, denoted **[a, b]**,
2. $\{x \in \mathbf{R} \mid a < x < b\}$, an *open and bounded* interval, denoted **(a, b)**,
3. $\{x \in \mathbf{R} \mid a \leq x < b\}$, a *closed-open and bounded* interval, denoted **[a, b)**,
4. $\{x \in \mathbf{R} \mid a < x \leq b\}$, an *open-closed and bounded* interval, denoted **(a, b]**,
5. $\{x \in \mathbf{R} \mid a \leq x\}$, a *closed and unbounded above* interval, denoted **[a, ∞)**,
6. $\{x \in \mathbf{R} \mid a < x\}$, an *open and unbounded above* interval, denoted **(a, ∞)**,
7. $\{x \in \mathbf{R} \mid x \leq b\}$, a *closed and unbounded below* interval, denoted **(−∞, b]**,
8. $\{x \in \mathbf{R} \mid x < b\}$, an *open and unbounded below* interval, denoted **(−∞, b)**,
9. **R** itself is an interval and is sometimes denoted **(−∞, ∞)**.

Intervals arise in a large variety of mathematical contexts and in particular are involved in the statement of numerous theorems of calculus. A familiar application of interval notation at a more elementary level is in expressing the solution set to inequalities encountered in elementary algebra.

EXAMPLE 1   Assuming that the universal set is **R**, solve the following inequalities and express each solution set in interval notation:

(a) $7x - 9 \leq 16$
(b) $|2x + 3| < 5$
(c) $2x^2 + x - 28 \leq 0$

Solution   (a) $7x - 9 \leq 16$ is equivalent to $7x \leq 25$, which is equivalent to $x \leq \frac{25}{7}$. The set of solutions is $\{x \in \mathbf{R} \,|\, x \leq \frac{25}{7}\} = (-\infty, \frac{25}{7}]$.

(b)   If $a \in \mathbf{R}$, then $|x| < a$ is equivalent to $-a < x < a$. Hence $|2x + 3| < 5$ is equivalent to $-5 < 2x + 3 < 5$, or $-8 < 2x < 2$, or $-4 < x < 1$, which is expressed in interval notation as $(-4, 1)$.

(c)   If $a > 0$, the quadratic inequality $ax^2 + bx + c \leq 0$ is satisfied by precisely those numbers between and including the roots of the equation $ax^2 + bx + c = 0$. We find the latter by factoring $2x^2 + x - 28$ into $(2x - 7)(x + 4)$, yielding $x = \frac{7}{2}$ and $x = -4$ as roots. Thus we arrive at the solution set $-4 \leq x \leq \frac{7}{2}$, which is expressed in interval notation as $[-4, \frac{7}{2}]$. $\square$

The assumption that $U = \mathbf{R}$ in problems like the preceding example is usually made implicitly, that is, without specific mention. As a final remark on intervals, bearing on notation, we observe that it is necessary to distinguish carefully between $\{0, 1\}$, a two-element set, and $[0, 1]$, an infinite set. This remark suggests a general caveat for beginning students of abstract mathematics: A small difference between two notations representing mathematical objects can understate a vast difference between the objects themselves. The conclusion to be drawn is that we need always to read and write mathematics with great care!

THE EMPTY SET

Certain special cases of Definition 3 lead to rather surprising facts. For instance, if we let $a = b$ in (1), we see that $[a, a] = \{a\}$, a *singleton* or single-element set, is an interval. If we do the same thing in (2), we arrive at an even less intuitive situation, namely, no real number satisfies the criterion for membership in the open interval (a, a), since no real number is simultaneously greater than and less than a. Thus if this special case of (2) is to be regarded as a set, much less an interval, we must posit the existence of a set with no elements. This we do under the title of the *empty set* or *null set*, denoted either $\varnothing$ (a derivative of the Greek letter *phi* in lower case) or $\{ \ \}$. The empty set is, in several senses we will discuss later in this chapter, at the opposite end of the spectrum from a universal set. It is an exception to many theorems in mathematics; that is, the hypotheses of many theorems must include the proviso that some or all the sets involved should not be empty (i.e., be *nonempty*), and has properties that quickly lead to many brain-teasing questions (e.g., Exercise 10, Article 1.3). Another justification for the existence of an empty set, explored further in Article 1.2, is the desirability that the intersection of any two sets be a set. Still another justification is provided by examples such as Example 2.

EXAMPLE 2   Solve the quadratic inequality $5x^2 + 3x + 2 < 0$, $U = \mathbf{R}$.

Solution By completing the square, we can express $5x^2 + 3x + 2$ in the form $5(x + (\frac{3}{10}))^2 + (\frac{31}{20})$, which is clearly positive for any real x. Thus no real number satisfies the given inequality; we express this by saying that the solution set is $\varnothing$. □

RELATIONS BETWEEN SETS

Equality. Earlier we observed that the set $D = \{x \mid x$ is the name of a state in the United States beginning with the letter $M\}$ could also be described by means of the roster method. This observation implied an intimate relationship between D and the set $M = \{$Maine, Maryland, Massachusetts, Michigan, Minnesota, Missouri, Mississippi, Montana$\}$, a relationship identical to that existing between the sets $T = \{x \in \mathbf{R} \mid x^2 - 8x + 15 = 0\}$ and $P = \{3, 5\}$, or between the sets $G = \{x \mid x$ was the first president of the United States$\}$ and $W = \{$George Washington$\}$. The relationship is *set theoretic equality*. We will defer a formal definition of equality of sets until Chapter 4 (Definition 1(a), Article 4.1), contenting ourselves at this stage with an informal description.

REMARK 2   Let A and B be sets. We will regard the statement A **equals** B, denoted $A = B$, to mean that A and B have precisely the same elements.

Applying the criterion of Remark 2 to the preceding examples, we have $D = M$, $P = T$, and $G = W$. Equality of sets has such a deceptively simple appearance that it might be questioned at first why we even bother to discuss it. One reason is that our informal description of set equality highlights the basic fact that a set is completely determined by its elements. A second reason is that sets that are indeed equal often appear, or are presented in a form, quite different from each other, with the burden of proof of equality on the reader. Many of the proofs that the reader is given or challenged to write later in the text are, ultimately, proofs that two particular sets are equal. Such proofs are usually approached by the following alternative description of equality of sets:

Sets A and B are equal if and only if every element of A is also an element of B and every element of B is also an element of A.   (1)

In Chapters 2 through 4, on logic and proof, we will discuss why this characterization of equality carries the same meaning as the criterion from Remark 2. As examples of properties of set equality to be discussed in detail later, we note that every set equals itself; given sets A and B, if $A = B$, then $B = A$; and given sets A, B, and C, if $A = B$ and $B = C$, then $A = C$. These are called the *reflexive, symmetric,* and *transitive* properties of set theoretic equality, respectively. Finally, we note that $A \neq B$ symbolizes the statement that sets A and B are not equal.

Subset. Earlier we encountered a relationship of containment between an object and a set. Denoted $\in$, this relationship symbolizes membership, or elementhood, of the object as one of the elements in a set. There is also a concept of containment <u>between sets</u>, known as the *subset* relationship. As we did for set equality, we give an informal description of this concept now, with the formal definition provided in Definition 1(b), Article 4.1.

REMARK 3   Let A and B be sets. We regard the statement A **is a subset of** B, denoted $A \subseteq B$, to mean that every element of A is also an element of B. We write $A \nsubseteq B$ to denote that A is not a subset of B. Finally, we define B **is a superset of** A to mean $A \subseteq B$.

We observed earlier that the set D of the eight states whose names begin with the letter M is not the same as the set $S = \{\text{Maine}\}$. A correct relationship is $S \subseteq D$.

EXAMPLE 3   (a)   Find all subset relationships among the sets $H = \{1, 2, 3\}$, $N = \{2, 4, 6, 8, 10\}$, and $P = \{1, 2, 3, \ldots, 9, 10\}$.
(b)   Find all subset relationships among the sets $T = \{2, 4, 6, \ldots\}$, $V = \{4, 8, 12, \ldots\}$, and $W = \{\ldots, -8, -4, 0, 4, 8, \ldots\}$.

Solution   (a)   Clearly $H \subseteq P$ and $N \subseteq P$, as you can easily see by checking, one by one, that all the individual elements of H and N are elements of P. Don't be misled by the representation of P, which contains ten elements. Also, $P \nsubseteq H$ and $P \nsubseteq N$ (can you explain <u>precisely</u> why this is true?), whereas neither H nor N is a subset of the other (why?).
(b)   This problem is more difficult than (a) because the sets involved are infinite. Intuition about the connections among the underlying descriptions of these sets (e.g., V is the set of all positive integral multiples of 4) should lead to the conclusions $V \subseteq T$, $V \subseteq W$, $T \nsubseteq V$, $W \nsubseteq V$, and neither T nor W is a subset of the other. You should formulate an argument justifying the latter statement. $\square$

The five number sets designated earlier by name satisfy the subset relationships $N \subseteq Z$, $Z \subseteq Q$, $Q \subseteq R$, and $R \subseteq C$. The subset relation, like set theoretic equality, enjoys the reflexive and transitive properties. Put more directly, every set is a subset of itself, and for any sets A, B, and C, if $A \subseteq B$ and $B \subseteq C$, then $A \subseteq C$. The subset relation is not symmetric (try to formulate precisely what this statement means). Furthermore, Example 3 illustrates the fact that, given two sets, it may very well be that neither is a subset of the other. The reader will note that the transitivity of the subset relation has consequences for the examples in the previous paragraph, namely, a number of additional subset relationships among the five sets listed there are implied. You should write down as many of those relationships as possible.

Since "elementhood" and "subset" are both relationships of containment, it is important not to confuse the two. For instance, the set $A = \{1, 2, 3\}$ contains $\{2, 3\}$ and contains 2, but in different senses. As another example, we note that $3 \in A$ and $\{3\} \subseteq A$ are true statements, whereas $\{3\} \in A$ and $3 \subseteq A$ are false. Again, a basic feature of good mathematical writing is precision.

There is a special danger of confusion in dealing with the subset relationship in connection with the empty set $\varnothing$. Consider the question whether $\varnothing \in A$ and/or $\varnothing \subseteq A$, where $A = \{1, 2, 3\}$. These questions, especially the second, in view of the criterion given in Remark 3, are not easy to decide. This difficulty is one of several we meet in this chapter that highlight the need for a background in logic and proof. Chapters 2 through 4, providing such a background, discuss a more formal and precise approach to some of the informal "definitions" in this chapter, including that of Remark 3.

Finally, in view of our alternative statement (1) of the criterion for set equality in Remark 2, the connection between the relationships "subset" and "equality of sets" is: $A = B$ *if and only if* $A \subseteq B$ and $B \subseteq A$. This is a crucial fact that we will prove rigorously in Chapter 4 (Example 3, Article 4.1) and use repeatedly in formulating proofs from that point through the remainder of the text.

Proper subset. When we are told that $A \subseteq B$, the possibility that A and B are equal is left open. To exclude that possibility, we use the notation and terminology of *proper subset*.

DEFINITION 4

Let A and B be sets. We say that **A is a proper subset of B**, denoted $A \subset B$, if and only if $A \subseteq B$, but $A \neq B$. We write $A \not\subset B$ to symbolize the statement that A is not a proper subset of B (which could mean that either $A \not\subseteq B$ or $A = B$).

EXAMPLE 4   Explore various subset and proper subset relationships among the sets $A = \{1, 2, 3\}$, $B = \{1, 2, 3, 4\}$, $C = \{2, 3, 1\}$, and $D = \{2, 4, 6\}$.

Solution   The subset relationships are $A \subseteq B$, $C \subseteq B$, $A \subseteq C$, and $C \subseteq A$. As for proper subset relationships, we have $A \subset B$ and $C \subset B$. Note, however, that A is not a proper subset of C (nor C of A) since A and C are equal. Finally, note that even though A and D are not equal, A is not a proper subset of D since A is not a subset of D. $\square$

Some texts use the notation $A \subset B$ to denote "subset," at the same time using $A \subsetneqq B$ to denote "proper subset." This is an example of a problem with which all mathematicians and students of mathematics must deal, namely, the widespread nonuniformity of mathematical notation. The best rule to remember is that the burden of correct interpretation rests on you!

POWER SET

We suggested earlier that sets can themselves be elements of sets. One situation in which this always happens arises in the following definition.

DEFINITION 5

Let A be a set. We denote by $\mathscr{P}(A)$, the **power set of A**, the set of all subsets of A.

EXAMPLE 5   Discuss the structure of $\mathscr{P}(A)$, where $A = \{1, 2, 3, 4\}$.

Discussion   The elements of $\mathscr{P}(A)$ are precisely the subsets of A. So, for instance, the set $\{2, 4\}$ is an element of $\mathscr{P}(A)$. Also $\{1\} \in \mathscr{P}(A)$. Since $A \subseteq A$, then $A = \{1, 2, 3, 4\} \in \mathscr{P}(A)$. You should list 13 other elements of $\mathscr{P}(A)$. In the event that your list falls one short of the number we've specified, perhaps you have not considered the question, "is $\varnothing$ an element of $\mathscr{P}(A)$?" The answer clearly depends on an issue we raised, but did not settle, earlier, namely, whether $\varnothing \subseteq A$. You may want to look ahead to Article 4.1 (Example 1) for the final resolution of that problem.

Other questions about $\mathscr{P}(A)$ might easily be raised. For instance, is $1 \in \mathscr{P}(A)$? Is $\{2\} \subseteq \mathscr{P}(A)$? Is $\{\varnothing\} \subseteq \mathscr{P}(A)$? You should settle these questions and formulate similar ones.   □

Exercises

1. Express these sets via the roster method; that is list the elements in each:

(a) $A = \{x \in \mathbf{R} \mid x^3 + x^2 - 12x = 0\}$

★(b) $B = \{x \in \mathbf{R} \mid 3/(x + 1) + 3/(x^2 + x) = -2\}$

(c) $C = \{x \in \mathbf{N} \mid -12 \leq x < 25\}$

(d) $D = \{x \in \mathbf{N} \mid x \text{ is prime and divisible by } 2\}$

(e) $E = \{x \in \mathbf{Z} \mid -5 < x < 4\}$

(f) $F = \{x \mid x \text{ was or is a Republican president of the United States}\}$

(g) $G = \{x \mid x \text{ is a planet in the Earth's solar system}\}$

(h) $H = \{x \mid x \text{ is a month of the year}\}$

★(i) $I = \{a \in \mathbf{R} \mid f(x) = x/(x^2 - 3x + 2) \text{ is discontinuous at } x = a\}$

(j) $J = \{a \in \mathbf{R} \mid f(x) = |x| \text{ fails to have a derivative at } x = a\}$

(k) $K = \{a \in \mathbf{R} \mid f(x) = 3x^4 + 4x^3 - 12x^2 \text{ has a relative maximum at } x = a\}$

(l) $L = \{x \in \mathbf{R} \mid (x + 2)^{1/2} = (7 - x)^{1/2} - 3\}$

★(m) $M = \{x \in \mathbf{R} \mid |2x^2 + 2x - 1| = |x^2 - 4x - 6|\}$

(n) $N = \{z \in \mathbf{C} \mid z^2 = -1\}$

(o) $O = \{z \in \mathbf{C} \mid z^4 = 1\}$

2. Express the following sets by either interval notation (including $\varnothing$) or one of the symbols $\mathbf{N}$, $\mathbf{Z}$, $\mathbf{Q}$, $\mathbf{R}$, or $\mathbf{C}$:

★(a) $A = \{x \in \mathbf{R} \mid \sin 2x = 2 \sin x \cos x\}$

(b) $B = \{x \in \mathbf{R} \,|\, \sin \pi x = 0\}$

(c) $C = \{x \in \mathbf{R} \,|\, x^2 = -1\}$ (d) $D = \{x \in \mathbf{R} \,|\, x^2 - 5x + 7 < 0\}$

★(e) $E = \{x \in \mathbf{R} \,|\, 10x^2 - 7x - 12 \le 0\}$ (f) $F = \{x \in \mathbf{R} \,|\, |6x - 8| \le 4\}$

(g) $G = \{x \in \mathbf{R} \,|\, |7x - 12| < 0\}$ (h) $H = \{x \in \mathbf{R} \,|\, |9x + 13| \le 0\}$

(i) $I = \{x \in \mathbf{R} \,|\, x > 0 \text{ and } \cos \pi x = \cot \pi x\}$

(j) $J = \{x \in \mathbf{R} \,|\, \sec x / (\cos x + \tan x) = \sin x\}$

(k) $K = \{x \in \mathbf{R} \,|\, (2x + 7)^{1/2} \text{ is a real number}\}$

(l) $L = \{x \in \mathbf{Q} \,|\, x^2 + (3 - \sqrt{2})x + 3\sqrt{2} = 0\}$

★(m) $M = \{z \in \mathbf{C} \,|\, zz^* = |z|^2\}$ ★(n) $N = \{z \in \mathbf{C} \,|\, \text{Im}\,(z) = 0\}$

(*Note:* If a and b are real numbers and $z = a + bi$, then b is called the **imaginary part** of z, denoted Im (z), $z^* = a - bi$ is called the **complex conjugate** of z, and $|z| = (a^2 + b^2)^{1/2}$ is called the **modulus** of z.)

3. (a) Which of the following descriptions of sets are well defined?

   (i) $\{x \,|\, x$ is an American citizen on July 4, 1976$\}$

★(ii) $\{x \,|\, x$ is the 2171st digit in the decimal expansion of $\sqrt{2}\}$

★(iii) $\{x \,|\, x$ is an honest man$\}$

  (iv) $\{x \,|\, x$ is a month whose name in the English language ends in the letter $r\}$

   (v) $\{x \,|\, x$ is a day in the middle of the week$\}$

  (vi) $\{x \,|\, \sin 2x\}$

 (vii) $\{x \in \mathbf{N} \,|\, x$ is an integral multiple of 4$\}$

(viii) $\{x \,|\, x$ is an aardling$\}$

  (ix) $\{x \,|\, ((x^2 - 6x + 3)/(x^3 + 4))^{1/2}\}$

   (x) $\{x \in \mathbf{R} \,|\, x + y = 4\}$

(b) For each of the sets in (a) that is well defined, suggest an appropriate universal set.

4. Given the following "pattern" descriptions of infinite sets, list five additional elements of each:

(a) $A = \{1, \frac{1}{3}, \frac{1}{9}, \ldots\}$ (b) $B = \{1, 2, 3, 5, 8, 13, \ldots\}$

★(c) $C = \{-1, 2, -4, 8, \ldots\}$ (d) $D = \{\pi, 4\pi, 7\pi, 10\pi, \ldots\}$

(e) $E = \{\ldots, -8, -5, -2, 1, 4, 7\}$ (f) $F = \{\ldots, -8, -5, -2, 1, 4, 7, \ldots\}$

5. Given the following six sets, answer true or false to statements (a) through (n):

$$A = (-\infty, -7] \quad B = \{4, 8, 12, \ldots, 96, 100\} \quad C = [-1, 6]$$

$$D = (-1, 6) \qquad E = \{-1, 0, 1, 2, 3, 4, 5, 6\} \quad F = (-\infty, -6)$$

(a) $-7 \in A$ (b) $6 \in B$

(c) $D \subseteq C$ (d) $C \subseteq D$

(e) $D \subset C$ (f) $E \subseteq D$

(g) $D \subseteq E$ (h) $-6 \in A$

(i) $-6 \in F$ (j) $-\frac{13}{2} \in A$

(k) $-\frac{13}{2} \notin F$ (l) $100 \in B$

(m) $0 \in B$ (n) $-1 \notin D$

6. Given the following collections of sets, find in each of parts (a), (b), and (c) all relationships of equality, subset, and proper subset existing between pairs of them:

(a) $A = \{-1, 1, 4\}$, $B = (-1, 4)$, $C = \{x \in \mathbf{R} \mid x^3 - 4x^2 - x + 4 = 0\}$, $D = [-1, 4]$.

(b) $A = \{\varnothing, 0, 1\}$, $B = \{\varnothing, \{\varnothing\}\}$, $C = [0, 1]$, $D = \{\{0, 1\}, \{0\}, \{1\}, \varnothing, \{\varnothing\}\}$

(c) $A = \{x \in \mathbf{N} \mid |x| \le 4\}$, $B = \{-4, -3, -2, -1, 0, 1, 2, 3, 4\}$, $C = \{x \in \mathbf{Z} \mid |x| < 5\}$.

7. (a) Considering the definition of *interval* given in Article 1.1, explain precisely why the set $\{0, 1, 2\}$ is <u>not</u> an interval.

★(b) What statement can be made about the subsets $\mathbf{Z}$ and $\mathbf{Q}$ of $\mathbf{R}$, based on Definition 2 and the assertion (from the paragraph following Definition 2) that $\mathbf{Z}$ and $\mathbf{Q}$ are not intervals?

8. Considering the "definition" of *subset* given in Article 1.1 (cf., Remark 3), discuss the pros and cons of the statement $\varnothing \subseteq \{1, 2, 3\}$, that is, can you see arguments for both the truth and falsehood of this statement? What about $\varnothing \subseteq \varnothing$? What about $\varnothing \subseteq A$, where A is any set?

9. Throughout this problem, <u>assume</u> the statement "$\varnothing \subseteq A$ for any set A" is true:

(a) Calculate $\mathscr{P}(S)$ for:

    (i) $S = \{1, 2, 3\}$ ★(ii) $S = \{a, b, c, d\}$

    (iii) $S = \varnothing$ (iv) $S = \{\varnothing\}$

    (v) $S = \{\varnothing, \{\varnothing\}\}$ (vi) $S = \mathscr{P}(T)$ where $T = \{1, 2\}$

(b) Can you list all the elements of $\mathscr{P}(\{1, 2, 3, \ldots\})$? List ten such elements.

(c) Can you give an example of a finite set X such that $\mathscr{P}(X)$ is infinite?

★**10.** Suppose U were a truly universal set; that is, U contains all objects. Then, in particular, U would contain itself as an element, that is, $U \in U$. This is an unusual situation since most sets that one encounters do not contain themselves as an element (e.g., the set X of all students in a mathematics class is not a student in that class; that is, $X \notin X$ in this case.) Now consider the "set" A of all sets that are not elements of themselves; that is, $A = \{Y \mid Y \notin Y\}$. Discuss whether $A \in A$ or $A \notin A$.

1.2 Operations on Sets

As stated earlier, sets like $\mathbf{Z}$ or $\mathbf{R}$ or $\{1, 2, 3\}$, consisting of numbers, are of greater mathematical interest than most other sets, such as the set of all names in a telephone book. One reason is that numbers are mathematical objects; that is, numbers can be combined in various mathematically interesting ways, by means of *algebraic operations*, to yield other numbers. Among the operations on real numbers that are familiar are addition, subtraction, multiplication, and division. You should also know that these types of operations may satisfy certain well-known properties, such as commutativity, associativity, and distributivity. For example, addition and multiplication over the real numbers both satisfy the first two properties, while multiplication distributes over addition. On the other hand, subtraction over real numbers is neither commutative nor associative.

Just as there is an "algebra of numbers" based on operations such as addition and multiplication, there is also an *algebra of sets* based on several fundamental operations of set theory. We develop properties of set algebra later in this chapter; for now our goal is to introduce the operations by which we are able to combine sets to get another set, just as in arithmetic we add or multiply numbers to get a number.

UNION AND INTERSECTION

In the following definitions we assume that all sets mentioned are subsets of a universal set U.

DEFINITION 1

Let A and B be sets. We define a set formed from A and B, called the **intersection of A and B**, denoted $A \cap B$ (read "A intersection B") by the rule $A \cap B = \{x \mid x \in A$ and $x \in B\}$.

Note that $A \cap B$ is a set whose elements are the objects common to A and B; it may be thought of as the "overlap" of A and B.

DEFINITION 2

Let A and B be sets. We define the **union of A and B**, denoted $A \cup B$ (read "A union B") by $A \cup B = \{x \mid x \in A$ or $x \in B\}$.

Again, $A \cup B$ is a set and is formed from A and B. Its elements are any objects in either A or B, including any object that happens to lie in both A and B. (We will see in Chapter 2 that, in mathematical usage, the word "or" automatically includes the case "or both.") The operations of union and intersection are called *binary* operations because they are applied to two sets to make a third set.

EXAMPLE 1   Let $A = \{1, 3, 5, 7, 9\}$, $B = \{1, 4, 7, 10, 13, 16\}$, and $C = \{-5, -3, -1, 1, 3, 5\}$. Calculate $A \cap B$, $A \cup B$, $A \cap C$, $B \cap C$, and $B \cup (A \cap C)$.

Solution $A \cap B = \{1, 7\}$ since these two objects are common to both sets and are the only such objects. $A \cup B = \{1, 3, 4, 5, 7, 9, 10, 13, 16\}$ since this set results from "gathering into one set" the elements of A and B. Similarly, $A \cap C = \{1, 3, 5\}$ and $B \cap C = \{1\}$. To calculate $B \cup (A \cap C)$, we use our result for $A \cap C$ to arrive at $\{1, 4, 7, 10, 13, 16\} \cup \{1, 3, 5\}$, which equals $\{1, 3, 4, 5, 7, 10, 13, 16\}$. □

Note that, in listing the elements of $A \cup B$, we write 1 and 7 only once each, although each occurs in both A and B. As stated earlier, we never list an object more than once as an element of a set. Also, even though our solution to Example 1 lists numbers in increasing order, this is not necessary. Observe also that the sets that result from the operation of union tend to be relatively large, whereas those obtained through intersection are relatively small. You should formulate a more exact statement of this idea, using one of of the concepts introduced in Article 1.1. Finally, our previous example introduces the use of parentheses, as in the algebra of numbers, to set priorities when an expression contains more than one instance of a set theoretic operation. In view of this can you suggest how to apply the operation of intersection to three sets? union also? What would you expect to be the intersection of the preceding three sets A, B, and C? the union?

EXAMPLE 2   Let $D = \{2, 4, 6, 8, 10\}$, $E = (-5, 5)$, $F = [3, \infty)$, and $G = \emptyset$. Calculate $E \cap F$, $E \cup F$, $D \cap E$, $D \cup F$, and $D \cup G$. Also, using the sets A and C defined in Example 1, calculate $C \cap E$ and $A \cap D$.

Solution $E \cap F = [3, 5)$, whereas $E \cup F = (-5, \infty)$. Graphing along a number line is perhaps the easiest way of arriving at these answers. $D \cap E = \{2, 4\}$, since 2 and 4 are the only elements of D that are between -5 and 5. $D \cup F$ can perhaps be best expressed as $\{2\} \cup [3, \infty)$. (The other elements of D, besides 2, are already accounted for in F). What about $D \cup G$? What is the result of taking the union of a set with the empty set? The answer is either $D \cup \emptyset = D = (2, 4, 6, 8, 10\}$ or, $D \cup \emptyset = \{\emptyset, 2, 4, 6, 8, 10\}$. Which do you think is correct? (The answer is in Article 1.3.) Using a set defined in Example 1, we note that $C \cap E = \{-3, -1, 1, 3\}$. The numbers -5 and 5 are not in $C \cap E$, because they are not in E, an open interval. Finally, $A \cap D = \emptyset$. ☐

The intersection of A and D in Example 2 provides another justification for the existence of an empty set since A and D have no elements in common. Pairs of sets such as A and D, having no elements in common, are said to be *disjoint*. You should perform other calculations involving the sets in Examples 1 and 2, for instance, $B \cap F$. What about the intersection of the empty set with another set? In particular, what is $A \cap \emptyset$? Finally, does our calculation of $E \cap F$ and $E \cup F$ suggest any possible theorem about intervals? (See Article 5.2, Example 6 and Exercise 3.)

One reason that union and intersection are of value in mathematics is that, like the subject of set theory itself, they provide mathematicians with a convenient language for expressing solutions to problems.

EXAMPLE 3   (a)   Solve the inequalities $|2x + 3| \geq 5$ and $2x^2 + x - 28 > 0$. (b)   Find all real numbers that satisfy both inequalities in (a) simultaneously.

Solution   (a)   If $a \in \mathbf{R}$, then $|x| \geq a$ is equivalent to "either $x \leq -a$ or $x \geq a$. Hence $|2x + 3| \geq 5$ becomes "either $2x + 3 \leq -5$ or $2x + 3 \geq 5$," which simplifies to "either $x \leq -4$ or $x \geq 1$." The solution set is most conveniently expressed $(-\infty, -4] \cup [1, \infty)$. On the other hand, the quadratic inequality $2x^2 + x - 28 > 0$ is solved by all values of x to either the left of the smaller root or the right of the larger root of the corresponding quadratic equation, that is, by all values of x either less than -4 or greater than $\frac{7}{2}$. The solution set is $(-\infty, -4) \cup (\frac{7}{2}, \infty)$.

(b) We find the simultaneous solutions to the two inequalities by intersecting the two solution sets we got in (a). Graphing along a number line, we arrive at the set $(-\infty, -4) \cup (\frac{7}{2}, \infty)$. $\square$

In Article 1.3, as we develop the algebra of sets, we will discover theorems of set theory by which we may obtain the last answer in Example 3 systematically, avoiding graphing. Although union and intersection are binary operations, there is nothing to prevent the two sets to which they are applied from being the same set, so that an expression like $X \cap X$ or $X \cup X$ has meaning. For Examples 1 and 2, calculate $F \cap F$ and $B \cup B$. Does any general fact suggest itself?

COMPLEMENT

Our third operation, complement, is *unary* rather than binary; we obtain a resultant set from a <u>single</u> given set rather than from two such sets. The role of the universal set is so important in calculating complements that we mention it explicitly in the following definition.

DEFINITION 3

Let A be a subset of a universal set U. We define the **complement of A**, denoted A', by the rule $A' = \{x \in U \,|\, x \notin A\}$.

The complement of a set consists of all objects in the universe at hand that are <u>not</u> in the given set. Clearly the complement of A is very much dependent on the universal set, as well as on A itself. If $A = \{1\}$, then A' is one thing if $U = \mathbf{N}$, something quite different if $U = \mathbf{R}$, and something altogether different again (a singleton set in fact as opposed to an infinite set in the other two cases) if $U = \{1, 2\}$.

EXAMPLE 4 Letting $\mathbf{R}$ be the universal set, calculate the complement of the sets $A = [-1, 1]$, $B = (-\frac{1}{2}, 2]$, $C = (-\infty, 0]$, and $D = (0, \infty)$.

Solution A' consists of all real numbers that are not between -1 and 1 inclusive, that is, all numbers either less than -1 [i.e., in $(-\infty, -1)$] or greater than 1 [i.e., in $(1, \infty)$]. In conclusion, $A' = (-\infty, -1) \cup (1, \infty)$. Similarly, $B' = (-\infty, -\frac{1}{2}] \cup (2, \infty)$, $C' = (0, \infty) = D$, and $D' = (-\infty, 0] = C$. $\square$

What do the last two parts of Example 4 suggest about the complement of the complement of a set? Also, calculate $C \cup D$ and $C \cap D$.... Are any general facts suggested? Next, calculate $(A \cap B)'$. The use of parentheses indicates that you are to perform the operation of intersection first, then take the complement of the resulting set. Finally, calculate $A \cap B'$, where the lack of parentheses dictates that you first calculate the complement of B, and then intersect <u>that set</u> with A.

EXAMPLE 5   Let U be the set of all employees of a certain company. Let $A = \{x \in U \,|\, x$ is a male$\}$, $B = \{x \in U \,|\, x$ is 30 years old or less$\}$, $C = \{x \in U \,|\, x$ is paid \$20,000 per year or less$\}$. Describe the sets $A \cap C$, A', $A \cup B'$, and $C \cap B'$.

Solution $A \cap C = \{x \in U \,|\, x$ is a male *and* x is paid \$20,000 per year or less$\}$. We might paraphrase this by saying that $A \cap C$ consists of males who make \$20,000 per year or less. $A' = \{x \,|\, x$ is *not* a male$\} = \{x \,|\, x$ is a female$\}$. $A \cup B' = \{x \,|\, either\ x$ is a male or x is *not* 30 years old or less$\}$, that is, the set of all male employees together with all employees over 30. Finally, $C \cap B'$ is the set of all employees over 30 years old who are paid \$20,000 per year or less.   □

You should describe the sets $A \cap B'$, $(A \cap B)'$, $(A \cup B)'$, $A \cup A'$, and $C \cap C'$ in Example 5. See Exercise 12 for a mathematical example similar in nature to Example 5.

SET THEORETIC DIFFERENCE

In introducing the operation of complement, we noted that the complement of a set A is a relative concept, depending on the universal set as well as on A itself. However, for a fixed universal set U, the complement A' of A depends on A only. Our next operation on sets provides a true notion of "relative complement." *Set theoretic difference*, denoted $B - A$, is a binary operation that yields the complement of A relative to a set B.

DEFINITION   4
Let A and B be sets. We define the **difference** $B - A$ (read "B minus A") by the rule $B - A = \{x \,|\, x \in B$ and $x \notin A\}$.

The difference $B - A$ (also called the complement of A in B, or the complement of A relative to B) consists of all objects that <u>are</u> elements of B <u>and</u> <u>are not</u> elements of A. If $B = U$, then $B - A = U - A = A'$, the ordinary complement of A. Thus *complement* is a special case of *difference*. Note also that we need not know U in order to compute $B - A$.

EXAMPLE 6   Let $A = \{1, 3, 5, 7\}$, $B = \{1, 2, 4, 8, 16\}$, and $C = \{1, 2, 3, \ldots,$
100$\}$. Is 1 an element of $A - B$? Compute $A - B$, $B - A$, $B - C$, and
$A - C$.

Solution   Since $1 \in A$, there is a possibility that 1 could be in $A - B$. But
the fact that 1 is also an element of B rules this out; that is, $1 \notin A - B$.
In fact, to compute $A - B$, we simply remove from A any object that
is also in B. Hence $A - B = \{3, 5, 7\}$. Similarly, $B - A = \{2, 4, 8, 16\}$,
whereas $A - C = B - C = \varnothing$. $\square$

What general conclusions can be guessed from our calculation of $A - B$
and $B - A$ in Example 6? Do the results of calculating $A - C$ and $B - C$
suggest any possible general facts? Describe the sets $C - A$ and $C - B$?
Can you compute $A - B'$ from the information given?

Using the sets from Example 4, we note that $A - B = [-1, -\frac{1}{2}]$,
$B - A = (1, 2]$. Calculate also $A - C, C - D, C - B, A - \varnothing$, and $\varnothing - D$?
Are you willing to speculate on any further general properties of difference
based on these results?

SYMMETRIC DIFFERENCE

Very often in mathematics, once a certain body of material (e.g., definitions
and/or theorems) has been built up, the work becomes easier. New definitions can be formulated in terms of previous ones, rather than from first
principles, and proofs of theorems are frequently shorter and less laborious
once there are earlier theorems to justify or eliminate steps. The first example of this situation occurs now in the definition of our fifth operation on sets,
symmetric difference.

DEFINITION 5
Let A and B be sets. We define the **symmetric difference of A and B**, denoted $A \triangle B$, by the rule $A \triangle B = (A - B) \cup (B - A)$.

Note that we have not defined this operation using set-builder notation.
Rather, we have used a formula that employs previously defined set operations. This approach has advantages and disadvantages as compared to a
definition from first principles. Advantages include compactness and mathematical elegance, which make this type of definition more pleasing to experienced readers. The major disadvantage, however, affecting primarily
the less experienced, is that this type of definition usually requires some
analysis in order to be understood. In this case we must analyze carefully
the right-hand side of the equation, the *defining rule* for the operation.

To be in $A \triangle B$, an object must lie either in $A - B$ or $B - A$ (or both?
Which objects are in both $A - B$ and $B - A$?), that is, <u>either</u> in A but not

in B, or in B but not in A. Stated differently, elements of $A \triangle B$ are objects in one or the other of the sets A and B, but not in both.

EXAMPLE 7   Let $A = \{2, 4, 6, 8, 10\}$, $B = \{6, 8, 10, 12\}$, $C = \{1, 3, 5, 7, 9, 11\}$, and $D = \{4, 6, 8\}$. Calculate $A \triangle B$, $A \triangle C$, and $A \triangle D$.

Solution $A - B = \{2, 4\}$ and $B - A = \{12\}$, so that $(A - B) \cup (B - A) = A \triangle B = \{2, 4, 12\}$. Similarly, $A \triangle C = \{1, 2, \ldots, 11\}$ and $A \triangle D = \{2, 10\}$. You should calculate $B \triangle A$, $A \triangle (B \triangle C)$ and $(A \triangle B) \triangle C$. Are any possible general properties of the operation "symmetric difference" suggested by any of these examples?   □

EXAMPLE 8   Let $W = (-\infty, 3)$, $X = (-3, 5]$, and $Y = [4, \infty)$. Compute $W \triangle X$ and $W \triangle Y$.

Solution $W \triangle X = (-\infty, -3] \cup [3, 5]$ and $W \triangle Y = (-\infty, 3) \cup [4, \infty)$. You should calculate $X \triangle Y$.   □

ORDERED PAIRS AND THE CARTESIAN PRODUCT

The sixth and final operation on sets to be introduced in this article, cartesian product of sets, differs from the preceding five in a subtle but important respect. If U were the universal set for sets A and B, it would again be the universal set for $A \cap B$, $A \cup B$, A', $A - B$, and $A \triangle B$. Putting it differently, the elements of these sets are the same types of objects as those that constitute A and B themselves. This is not the case for $A \times B$, the cartesian product of A and B. The elements of $A \times B$ are *ordered pairs* of elements from A and B, and thus are not ordinarily members of the universal set for A and B.

Ordered pairs resemble notationally two-element sets but differ in two important respects. Represented by the symbol (a, b), the "ordered pair a comma b" differs from the set $\{a, b\}$ in that the *order* in which the elements are listed <u>makes a difference</u>. Specifically, the ordered pairs (a, b) and (b, a) are different, or unequal, unless $a = b$, based on Definition 6.

DEFINITION 6
Given ordered pairs (a, b) and (c, d), we say that these ordered pairs are **equal**, denoted $(a, b) = (c, d)$, if and only if $a = c$ and $b = d$.

Compare this definition with the criterion for equality of the sets $\{a, b\}$ and $\{c, d\}$ (Remark 2, Article 1.1), and note, for example, that $(2, 3) \neq (3, 2)$, whereas $\{2, 3\} = \{3, 2\}$. A second major distinction between ordered pairs and two-element sets is that the same element may be used twice in an ordered pair. That is, the expression (a, a) is a commonly used mathematical symbol, but $\{a, a\}$ is not (i.e., the latter is always expressed $\{a\}$.)

DEFINITION 7

Given sets A and B, we define the **cartesian product** $A \times B$ (read "A cross B," cartesian product is often called *cross product*) by the rule $A \times B = \{(a, b) | a \in A, b \in B\}$.

Thus $A \times B$ consists of all possible distinct ordered pairs whose first elements come from A and whose second elements come from B. An object x is an element of $A \times B$ if and only if there exist $a \in A$ and $b \in B$ such that $x = (a, b)$. Note that there is nothing in the definition to prevent A and B from being the same set.

EXAMPLE 9   Given $A = \{1, 2, 3\}$ and $B = \{w, x, y, z\}$, describe $A \times B$ by the roster method.

Solution $A \times B = \{(1, w), (1, x), (1, y), (1, z), (2, w), (2, x), (2, y), (2, z), (3, w),$ $(3, x), (3, y), (3, z)\}$. We have chosen to list these ordered pairs by first pairing the number 1 with each letter, then 2, then 3. We could have used some other approach, such as pairing each of the three numbers in A with w, then with x, y, and z, respectively. Any such approach is all right as long as all the ordered pairs are accounted for, since the order in which the ordered pairs in $A \times B$ are listed is, of course, inconsequential. Note that $(y, 2)$ is not an element of $A \times B$. You should be able to name a set closely related to $A \times B$ that contains the ordered pair $(y, 2)$, as well as list the elements of $A \times A$ and $B \times B$.   □

EXAMPLE 10   Describe $A \times B$ if $A = B = \mathbf{R}$. Describe geometrically the subset $I \times J$ of $\mathbf{R} \times \mathbf{R}$, where $I = [3, 7]$ and $J = (-2, 2)$.

Solution $\mathbf{R} \times \mathbf{R}$ is the set of all ordered pairs of real numbers, usually pictured by a two-dimensional graph, as shown in Figure 1.1a, with points in the plane corresponding to ordered pairs. These in turn are labeled

Figure 1.1   *(a) The x-y coordinate system; (b) $[3, 7] \times (-2, 2)$.*

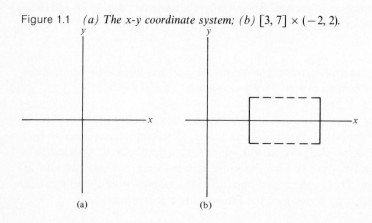

(a)   (b)

with reference to two perpendicular lines, the x axis and the y axis. $I \times J$ is the rectangle, open above and below, closed left and right, as illustrated in Figure 1.1*b*. $\square$

For other examples, suppose that $L = \{x \mid x \text{ is a student in Math 197}\}$ and $M = \{x \mid x \text{ is a possible final grade in a course}\} = \{A, B, C, D, E\}$. Can you describe generally what the set $L \times M$ looks like? In another vein, if $A = \{1, 2, 3\}$, can you describe $A \times \varnothing$? $\varnothing \times A$? What general results are suggested by this example? (See Fact 7 (49), Article 1.4.)

Like other operations on sets, cartesian products can be combined with other set operations to form expressions like $(A \cup B) \times C$. See Exercise 4 for other examples.

The cartesian product will be of particular importance in Chapters 7 and 8 where we study relations on sets, including equivalence relations and functions. It should be noted that a rigorous set theoretic definition of an ordered pair (omitted from the preceding informal discussion) is possible and may be found in Exercise 10, Article 4.1.

Finally, note that the use of $(\,,)$ as notation for ordered pairs, while also denoting open intervals, is an example of the ambiguity in mathematical notation alluded to earlier.

TOWARD MATHEMATICAL GENERALIZATION

Throughout this article and Article 1.1 you have been encouraged to speculate on possible general theorems of set theory as suggested by examples. For instance, you may have already conjectured that the union of two sets A and B is a superset of both A and B (between Examples 1 and 2), that the intersection of a set with its complement is the empty set (following Example 4), or that the intersection of two intervals is always an interval (following Example 2).

The mode of thinking we're trying to foster through our questions is the first half of a two-part process that is really the essence of mathematics! By looking at *particular situations*, the mathematician hopes to be able to formulate general conjectures that, if true, settle the question at hand about all other particular cases. The first step into the world of the mathematician is to form the intellectual habit of looking beyond the answer to the example at hand to possible general reasons for that answer. We will continue to discuss this first step, the formulation of conjectures, in Article 1.3 and will begin to pursue the second step, the construction of proofs that turn our conjectures into theorems in Chapter 4.

But for now we consider further the types of evidence on which mathematical conjectures might be based. We have already seen one type of such evidence, namely, computational solutions to particular problems. As further examples of this approach, the fact that $B \cap B = B$, which was discussed earlier for the particular set $B = \{1, 4, 7, 10, 13, 16\}$, should lead

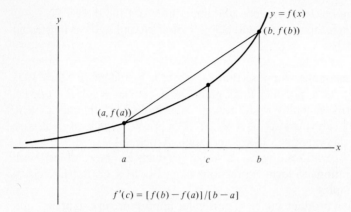

Figure 1.2 *Graphic interpretation of the mean value theorem:*
$f'(c) = [f(b) - f(a)]/[b - a]$.

to the conjecture that this relationship holds for any set B. In trigonometry the specific facts that $\sin (2\pi) = 0$, $\sin (4\pi) = 0$, and $\sin (-3\pi) = 0$ suggest a possible general theorem, namely, $\sin (k\pi) = 0$ for any integer k, which, upon being proved, encompasses an infinite number of particular cases. In elementary calculus the facts that $d/dx(x^2) = 2x$, $d/dx(x^3) = 3x^2$, and $d/dx(x^4) = 4x^3$, again suggest the possible formulation of a rule that includes these formulas and yields the answer for infinitely many similar differentiation problems.

Another type of evidence from which mathematical conjectures are frequently drawn is a *picture*. For example, the mean value theorem of calculus has a lengthy and complicated statement when expressed in words only, but becomes simple in concept when that statement is accompanied by a picture, as shown in Figure 1.2. In addition, many of the applied problems of calculus, such as "max-min" and "related rate" problems, have as a standard part of their approach the step "draw a picture of the physical situation described in the problem."

The kind of picture most frequently used to seek out theorems, or to test conjectures about possible theorems, in set theory is the *Venn diagram*.

VENN DIAGRAMS

Sets pictured by Venn diagrams appear as labeled circles, inside a rectangle that represents the universal set U. Most often, such diagrams will involve one, two or three circles, with various markings used to match regions in the diagram with sets formed, by employing the operations described earlier, from the sets represented by the circles. As one example, given two sets A and B, the set $A \cap B$ is represented by the shaded region of the diagram in Figure 1.3.

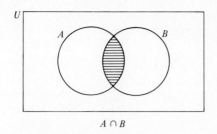

Figure 1.3   *Venn diagram representation of intersection.*

$$A \cap B$$

Some of the other four operations described earlier are pictured by the shaded regions of Venn diagrams in Figure 1.4. You should draw Venn diagrams to represent the sets $B - A$ and $A \triangle B$.

Venn diagrams become more complicated when used to represent sets constructed from more than two given sets and/or involving more than one

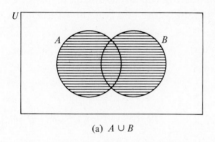

Figure 1.4   *(a) Union, (b) complement, and (c) difference.*

(a) $A \cup B$

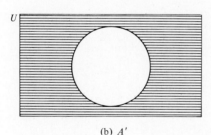

(b) A'

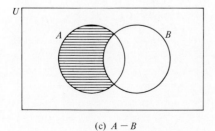

(c) $A - B$

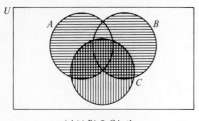

Figure 1.5   *A more complicated Venn diagram representation.*

$(A \cup B) \cap C$ is the crosshatched region

operation of set theory. For example, the set $(A \cup B) \cap C$ may be repre-sented by the doubly shaded region in the Venn diagram, Figure 1.5.

We will see in the next article how Venn diagrams can be useful for sug-gesting theorems of set theory; later we will encounter other interesting uses. In Article 1.5 they prove helpful for solving certain counting problems; in Article 3.5 we use them as an aid in analyzing the logical validity of certain kinds of arguments.

Exercises

In Exercises 1 through 4, let $U = \{1, 2, 3, \ldots, 9, 10\}$, $A = \{1, 7, 9\}$, $B = \{3, 5, 6, 9, 10\}$, and $C = \{2, 4, 8, 9\}$.

1. Calculate:

(a) $B \cup B$

(b) $C \cap C$

★(c) $A \cup A'$

(d) $B \cap B'$

(e) $(A \cup B) \cap A$

(f) $(B \cap C) \cup C$

(g) B'

(h) B''

(i) $A - A$

(j) $B - B'$

★(k) $A \triangle A$

★(l) $C \triangle C'$

2. Calculate:

(a) $A \cap C$

★(b) $(A \cap C)'$

(c) $A \cap C'$

★(d) $A' \cup C'$

(e) $C - B$

(f) $C \cap B'$

(g) $(A \cup B) \cup C$

(h) $A \cap (B \cap C)$

(i) $A \cup (B \cup C)$

(j) $(A \cap B) \cap C$

★(k) $(A \cup B) \cap C$

(l) $(A \cup C) \cap (B \cup C)$

(m) $(A \cup B) \cup (A \cup B')$

★(n) $(A \cap C) \cup (B \cap C)$

(o) $A \cup (C \cap A')$

(p) $(A \cap C) \cup (A \cap C')$

(q) $(B \cup C)'$

(r) $B' \cup C'$

3. Calculate:

(a) $(A \cap B \cap C)'$

(b) $A' \cup B' \cup C'$

★(c) $(A \cup C) - (A \cap C)$ ★(d) $A \triangle C$

(e) $B \triangle U$ (f) $A \triangle (B \triangle C)$

(g) $(A \triangle B) \triangle C$ (h) $C - (B - A)$

(i) $(C - B) - A$ ★(j) $(C - B) \cap (C - A)$

★(k) $C - (B \cup A)$ (l) $A \triangle (B \cup C)$

4. Calculate:

(a) $A \times C$ (b) $C \times B$

(c) $U \times B$ (d) $A \times U$

(e) $A \times B$ ★(f) $A \times (B \cup C)$

(g) $(A \times B) \cup (A \times C)$ (h) $B' \times C'$

(i) $(A \cap B) \times C$ (j) $(A \times C) \cap (B \times C)$

(k) $B \times (A - C)$ (l) $(B \times A) - (B \times C)$

5. Let $U = \{1, 2, 3, \ldots, 9, 10\}$, $A = \{2, 5, 7, 9\}$, $B = \{5, 7\}$, $C = \{2, 9\}$, and $D = \{1, 4, 6, 10\}$. Calculate:

(a) $(D - C) - B$ (b) $D - (C - B)$

(c) $A \triangle D$ (d) $A \cup D$

(e) $B \cup (A - B)$ (f) $A \cap (B \cup D')$

(g) $(A \cap B) \cup D'$ (h) $B \cup (C - B)$

(i) $A \triangle C$

6. Let $U = \mathbf{R}$, $A = [2, 9)$, $B = (0, 1]$, $C = [-1, 4]$. Each of the sets described here is an interval. Express each in interval notation:

★(a) $A \cap C$ (b) $A \cup C$

(c) $A \cap B$ (d) $A \cup B$

(e) $(A \cup B) - C$ ★(f) $A - C$

★(g) $C - A$ (h) $B \cap C$

(i) $B \cup C$ ★(j) $C - A'$

(k) $B - A$ (l) $B - C$

7. Let $U = \mathbf{R}$, $A = (-\infty, 6]$, $B = (-3, \infty)$, and $C = (-4, 1) \cup (3, 7)$. Calculate:

(a) $A \cap B$ (b) $A \cup B$

★(c) $A - B$ ★(d) $A \triangle B$

(e) $A \cap C$ (f) $B \cap C$

(g) $A \cup C'$ (h) $(A \cup C)'$

(i) $C - A$ (j) $A' \cap C'$

(k) $(A \cap B) \cap C$ ★(l) $(A \triangle B) \triangle C$

(m) $A \cap (B \triangle C)$ (n) $A \triangle (B \triangle C)$

(o) $(A \cap B) \triangle (A \cap C)$

8. Let $U = \mathbf{Z}$, $A = \{0, 5, 10, 15, \ldots\}$, $B = \{\ldots, -10, -5, 0\}$, $C = \{\ldots, -9, -6, -3, 0, 3, 6, 9, \ldots\}$, and $D = \{45, 90, 135, 180, \ldots\}$. Calculate:

(a) $A \cap B$ (b) $B \cap D$

★(c) $D \cap A'$ (d) $(A \cup B) \cap C$

(e) $(A \cap C) \cup (B \cap C)$ (f) $D - A$

(g) $[(A \cup B) \cap C] \cap D$ (h) $D \cap A$

★(i) $(D \cap A) \cup (D \cap A')$ (j) $D \cap C$

(k) $D \cap B'$ (l) $B \triangle D$

9. Given $U = \{1, 2, 3, 4\}$, $A = \{1, 3, 4\}$, $B = \{3\}$, $C = \{1, 2\}$, find all pairs of *disjoint* sets among the six sets A, A', B, B', C, C'.

10. The solution set to each of the following inequalities can be expressed as the union of intervals. Find them in each case:

(a) $|3x - 23| \geq 4$ ★(b) $2x^2 - 4x - 96 \geq 0$

(c) $(x - 5)/(5 - x) < 0$ (d) $|4x - 17| > 0$

★(e) $(3x^2 - 27)/[(x - 3)(x + 3)] > 0$

11. Solve simultaneously the pairs of inequalities:

★(a) $|x| \geq 1$ and $x^2 - 4 \leq 0$

(b) $|4x + 8| \leq 12$ and $x^2 + 6x + 8 > 0$

12. Let U be the set of all functions having $\mathbf{R}$ as domain and range a subset of $\mathbf{R}$. Let:

$A = \{f \mid f \text{ is continuous at each } x \in \mathbf{R}\}$

$B = \{f \mid f \text{ is differentiable at each } x \in \mathbf{R}\}$

$C = \{f \mid f'(x) = 2x + 3 \text{ for each } x \in \mathbf{R}\}$

$D = \{f \mid f \text{ is a quadratic polynomial}\}$

$E = \{f \mid f(0) = 0\}$

$F = \{f \mid f \text{ is a linear polynomial}\}$

(a) List all subset relationships between pairs of these six sets.
(b) List all pairs of disjoint sets among these six sets.
(c) Describe, as precisely as possible, the sets:

★(i) $C \cap E$	(ii) $A - B$	
(iii) $D \cap F$	★(iv) $A \cap D$	
(v) $A \cup D$	(vi) $C - E$	
(vii) $F - A$	(viii) $F \cap A'$	
(ix) $E \cap F$	(x) $B \cap E$	

13. (a) Consider the Venn diagram displayed in Figure 1.6*a*. Copy this diagram onto a separate piece of paper four times and shade the regions corresponding to the sets $A \cap B$, $A' \cap B$, $A \cap B'$, and $A' \cap B'$. [*Note:* A Venn diagram based on two sets (i.e., circles) divides the rectangle representing U into four regions, which can be represented by the preceding four expressions. These sets are *mutually disjoint*; that is, the intersection of any two of them is the empty set, and have the totality of U as their union.]
(b) Draw on a separate piece of paper a Venn diagram based on three sets, that is, three circles, as in Figure 1.6*b*. On this figure, shade the regions corresponding to the sets $A \cap B \cap C$, $A \cap B \cap C'$, $A' \cap B' \cap C$, and $A' \cap B' \cap C'$.
(c) In addition to the four regions shaded in (b), how many other nonoverlapping regions within U are induced by the three circles A, B, and C? Label each of those remaining regions in a manner consistent with the labeling of the four regions in (b).

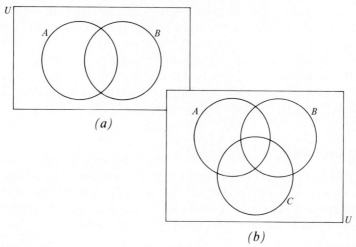

Figure 1.6

(d) How many regions (i.e., nonoverlapping subsets of U having all of U as their union) <u>should there be</u> in a Venn diagram based on <u>four</u> sets A, B, C, and D? Can you draw a diagram with four <u>circles</u> in which the expected number of regions actually occurs?

1.3 Algebraic Properties of Sets

WHY AN ALGEBRA OF SETS?

Like the rules of high school algebra [such as $(a + b)(a - b) = a^2 - b^2$ for any real numbers a and b], which are indispensable for solving applied problems such as "story problems," the rules of set theory are extraordinarily useful in dealing with any problem expressible in the language of sets. They are especially helpful in proving theorems and arise in proofs involving virtually every area of mathematics.

Many of the laws of set theory have a structure that enables us to simplify considerably the form of a set. Suppose, for instance, that a problem in advanced high school algebra (with $U = \mathbf{R}$) has a solution set of the form $(A \cap B) \cup (A' \cap B) \cup (A \cap B') \cup (A' \cap B')$, where $A = (-\infty, 4) \cup (7, \infty)$ and $B = [-2, 11]$. Calculating this set would be laborious if the problem is approached directly. But an identity of set theory tells us that any set of the preceding form equals U, the universal set, so that the solution set for the original problem equals $\mathbf{R}$. Another instance of the usefulness of the algebra of sets is suggested in the paragraph following Example 6, Article 1.2, where we asked whether $A - B'$ could be computed from the information given. The most accurate answer at that stage should have been "no," since a universal set must be specified if B', and thus $A - B'$, is to be computed.

In that example U was not specified, nor was it totally clear from the context what U should be ($\mathbf{R}$ and $\mathbf{Z}$ would both have been good guesses). But, by being familiar with set algebra and aware of the identity $A - B' = A \cap B$ of set theory, we can solve the problem with no further information.

Finally, the methods of proof we will study in Chapters 4 through 6, used initially in this text to prove theorems about the algebra of sets, apply to writing proofs in all other branches of mathematics.

ELEMENTARY PROPERTIES OF SETS

We begin now to formulate conjectures about general properties of sets. Using two devices described in Article 1.2, the computational results of specific examples and the evidence provided by pictures, we will attempt to discover reasonable candidates for theorems of set theory.

EXAMPLE 1   Let $U = \{1, 2, 3, \ldots, 9, 10\}$ and $A = \{1, 3, 5, 7, 9\}$. Compute $A \cup A'$, $A \cap A'$, $(A')'$, $A \cup A$, and $A \cap A$.

Solution   Since $A' = \{2, 4, 6, 8, 10\}$, then $A \cup A' = \{1, 2, 3, \ldots, 9, 10\} = U$, $A \cap A' = \emptyset$, $(A')' = \{2, 4, 6, 8, 10\}' = \{1, 3, 5, 7, 9\} = A$, and $A \cup A = \{1, 3, 5, 7, 9\} = A \cap A$. $\square$

You should repeat this example by using other subsets of U, such as $B = \{1, 2, 3\}$ and/or $C = \{3, 4, 6, 8\}$. Also, construct five Venn diagrams, corresponding to the five sets $A \cup A'$, $A \cap A'$, $(A')'$, $A \cup A$, and $A \cap A$, derived from A. Note that each diagram should contain only one circle, labeled A, inside the rectangle corresponding to U. After doing these exercises, you will probably agree with Conjecture 1.

CONJECTURE 1
Let X be any set with universal set U. Then:

(a) $X \cup X' = U$
(b) $X \cap X' = \emptyset$
(c) $X'' = X$
(d) $X \cup X = X$
(e) $X \cap X = X$

Let us caution that statements (a) through (e) do not assume the status of *theorem* until we provide a rigorous mathematical proof of each. Even with verification of specific examples and the evidence provided by pictures, the possibility exists of an example for which the conjectured statement is false. Later in this article we comment further on weaknesses of "proof" by Venn diagram.

COMMUTATIVITY AND ASSOCIATIVITY

EXAMPLE 2   Let $U = \{1, 2, 3, \ldots, 9, 10\}$, $A = \{2, 3, 5, 8\}$, $B = \{1, 2, 5, 6, 7, 10\}$, and $C = \{2, 3, 4, 9, 10\}$. Compute $(A \cap B) \cap C$ and $A \cap (B \cap C)$.

Solution   The significance of parentheses is the signal they give to perform the operation inside them first, then operate further with the result of that first computation. Thus, to compute $(A \cap B) \cap C$, we first compute $A \cap B = \{2, 5\}$, and then calculate the intersection of this result with $C = \{2, 3, 4, 9, 10\}$ to get $\{2\}$. On the other hand, $A \cap (B \cap C)$ is obtained by computing $B \cap C = \{2, 10\}$ and then intersecting this set with A to get $\{2\}$. In this particular example $A \cap (B \cap C) = \{2\} = (A \cap B) \cap C$. □

To test whether the equality of $A \cap (B \cap C)$ with $(A \cap B) \cap C$ for the three particular sets given in Example 2 was accidental (i.e., dependent on some special property of the given sets A, B, and C), or whether this equation might represent a candidate for a theorem (i.e., be true for any three sets), we construct two Venn diagrams as shown in Figure 1.7.

These two diagrams were drawn independently of each other and by two different procedures. In the first diagram we shaded horizontally the region corresponding to $B \cap C$ and then shaded circle A vertically; in the second diagram we shaded the $A \cap B$ region and circle C. Yet the crucial region in both pictures (i.e., the "crosshatched" region) is the same in both diagrams, namely, the region common to all three circles. These pictures support the case that the equality of Example 2 represents a general property.

You should be able to formulate further conjectures, based on the sets A, B, and C of Example 2, by computing the sets $A \cap B$, $B \cap A$, $B \cup C$, $C \cup B$, $A \cup (B \cup C)$, and $(A \cup B) \cup C$ and by constructing Venn diagrams corresponding to these sets. After carrying out these exercises, you should be ready to state Conjecture 2.

Figure 1.7   *Venn diagrams suggesting Conjecture 2(f).*

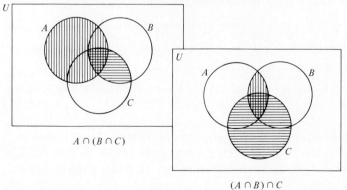

$A \cap (B \cap C)$

$(A \cap B) \cap C$

CONJECTURE 2

Let X, Y, and Z be any sets. Then:

(f) $X \cap (Y \cap Z) = (X \cap Y) \cap Z$ and $X \cup (Y \cup Z) = (X \cup Y) \cup Z$

(g) $X \cap Y = Y \cap X$ and $X \cup Y = Y \cup X$

Developing the analogy between the algebra of sets and the algebra of numbers, we are led to view the equations in (f), once they've been proved, as *associative* laws for intersection and union of sets and those in (g) as *commutative* laws for intersection and union. An associative law involves one binary operation and is the basis for our ability to apply such an operation to three or more sets, rather than just to two. Specifically, the law tells us to apply the operation to the objects two at a time, starting at either end of the expression; the result will be the same whether we work left to right or right to left. The upshot of the associative laws for union and intersection is that the union of three or more sets consists of all the objects in any of the sets, grouped together within one set, while the intersection of three or more sets consists of the objects common to all the sets. Commutativity says that, in computing unions and intersections of two sets, the *order* in which the two sets are listed is irrelevant.

DISTRIBUTIVITY

Distributivity, familiar as a property of the real numbers, has its analogy in set theory. Unlike commutativity and associativity, distributivity involves two operations at a time within one equation. Over the real numbers, the property that $a(b + c) = ab + ac$ for all $a, b, c \in \mathbf{R}$ is distributivity of multiplication over addition. By inquiring whether intersection distributes over union, we would be asking whether there is a general equivalent way of expressing $A \cap (B \cup C)$. Motivated by the associative law (in which a "shift" of parentheses leads to an identity), we could be tempted to conjecture (wrongly, we will soon see) that $A \cap (B \cup C) = (A \cap B) \cup C$ for any three sets A, B, and C. The following example explores this possibility.

EXAMPLE 3   With $U = \{1, 2, 3, \ldots, 9, 10\}$, let $A = \{2, 3, 5, 8\}$, $B = \{1, 2, 5, 6, 7, 10\}$, and $D = \{8\}$. Compute $(A \cap B) \cup D$ and $A \cap (B \cup D)$.

Solution $A \cap B = \{2, 5\}$ so that $(A \cap B) \cup D = \{2, 5, 8\}$, while $B \cup D = \{1, 2, 5, 6, 7, 8, 10\}$ so that $A \cap (B \cup D) = \{2, 5, 8\}$. In this example $(A \cap B) \cup D$ and $A \cap (B \cup D)$ are equal. $\square$

The result of Example 3 supports our conjecture. Do you think that $(X \cap Y) \cup Z = X \cap (Y \cup Z)$ holds for <u>any</u> three sets X, Y, and Z? Test this conjecture further by using the three sets A, B and C of Example 2. Also note the comparison of the Venn diagrams in Figure 1.8. In this case the regions in the two Venn diagrams <u>do not correspond</u>. This should

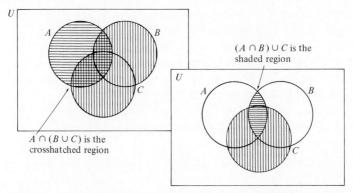

Figure 1.8 *Venn diagram suggesting the falsehood of the conjecture*
"$A \cap (B \cup C) = (A \cap B) \cup C$, *for any three sets A, B, and C.*"

confirm your results for the sets $(A \cap B) \cup C$ (= {2, 3, 4, 5, 9, 10}) and
$A \cap (B \cup C)$ (= {2, 3, 5}), calculated from Example 2.

Thus the conjecture of the preceding paragraph is <u>false</u>. This illustrates
the danger of believing a general conclusion too readily, based on only a
few examples, and especially, without seeing a proof. It also leaves us with
two problems:

1. Are there <u>valid</u> distributive laws of set theory?
2. Is there anything to be learned from exploring reasons why the two sets
    $(A \cap B) \cup D$ and $A \cap (B \cup D)$ <u>were equal</u> in Example 3?

We discuss (1) immediately while deferring consideration of (2) until Example 4.

We approach the distributive laws through an example from elementary
algebra. The problem is to solve the inequalities $x^2 - 6x - 7 < 0$ and
$|3x - 11| \geq 4$ simultaneously. Using elementary algebra, we solve the inequalities separately to get $(-1, 7)$, and $(-\infty, \frac{7}{3}] \cup [5, \infty)$ respectively, as
their solution sets. The simultaneous solutions are those real numbers that
are common to both solution sets, that is, the elements of the set $(-1, 7) \cap$
$\{(-\infty, \frac{7}{3}] \cup [5, \infty)\}$, a set having the form $A \cap (B \cup C)$. By graphing this
set along a number line, we obtain the result $(-1, \frac{7}{3}] \cup [5, 7)$, gotten geometrically by intersecting $(-1, 7)$ with the intervals $(-\infty, \frac{7}{3}]$ and $[5, \infty)$
and taking the union of the resulting sets. Put another way, the solution
set equals $\{(-1, 7) \cap (-\infty, \frac{7}{3}]\} \cup \{(-1, 7) \cap [5, \infty)\}$; that is, it equals
$(A \cap B) \cup (A \cap C)$.

The results of this example suggest the possibility that $A \cap (B \cup C) =$
$(A \cap B) \cup (A \cap C)$ is the distributive law we are seeking. This equation
resembles the distributive law for real numbers, $a \cdot (b + c) = a \cdot b + a \cdot c$, if
we substitute intersection for "times" and union for "plus," and so seems
like a plausible candidate on that basis as well.

To get further evidence, you should test this equation by using sets A, B, and C of Example 2 and also by drawing Venn diagrams. The results of this work should support (although of course not prove) the conjecture that this equation, which asserts that "intersection distributes over union," holds for all sets X, Y, and Z. Can you write an analogous equation representing the statement "union distributes over intersection?" Write this equation out, test it with sets A, B, and C of Example 2; then test it by drawing Venn diagrams. After doing all this, you should be ready for Conjecture 3.

CONJECTURE 3
Let X, Y, and Z be any sets. Then:

(h) $X \cap (Y \cup Z) = (X \cap Y) \cup (X \cap Z)$
(i) $X \cup (Y \cap Z) = (X \cup Y) \cap (X \cup Z)$

These equations, when proved, will be known as the *distributive laws* of set theory.

DE MORGAN'S LAWS

Thus far, we have not looked for any properties of sets that describe how complementation interacts with union and intersection. We might hope to find a property by which we could express the complement of the union $(X \cup Y)'$ of two sets X and Y in terms of the complements X' and Y' of the individual sets, and similarly for $(X \cap Y)'$. The "obvious" guesses are:

$$(X \cup Y)' = X' \cup Y' \quad \text{and} \quad (X \cap Y)' = X' \cap Y'$$

As in previous situations, you should test these equations with some examples. Compute $(X \cup Y)'$, $X' \cup Y'$, $(X \cap Y)'$, and $X' \cap Y'$ for the pairs of sets A and B of Example 2; do the same for sets A and C of the same example. Next, construct Venn diagrams corresponding to each of the four sets.

On the basis of your work, you should not only have rejected the preceding equations, but also should have discovered two replacement equations that seem, on the basis of this evidence, to be promising candidates for theorems of set theory:

CONJECTURE 4
Let X and Y be sets. Then:

(j) $(X \cup Y)' = X' \cap Y'$
(k) $(X \cap Y)' = X' \cup Y'$

These equations, when proved, will be referred to as *De Morgan's laws* of set theory.

THEOREMS INVOLVING A CONDITIONAL

As we progress in abstract mathematics, we find that the most interesting theorems (and many interesting theorems of set theory in particular) do not have so simple a form as those we have conjectured thus far. Instead of the form "for any pair of sets X and Y, some relationship involving X and Y is true," the more complex form "for every pair of sets X and Y, if relationship (P) involving X and Y is valid, then so is relationship (Q) involving the same two sets" occurs more often as we advance further into the subject. The logical structure of statements will be the topic of Chapters 2 and 3, and so we will not be too technical at this point. Rather, we will begin to explore this area by using examples and, especially, by recalling Question (2) from the discussion following Example 3, earlier in this article.

EXAMPLE 4   Explain why the sets A, B, and D of Example 3 satisfy the relationship $(A \cap B) \cup D = A \cap (B \cup D)$.

Discussion   In the paragraphs following Example 3 we found it to be false that $(X \cap Y) \cup Z = X \cap (Y \cup Z)$ for any three sets X, Y, and Z. Thus we are led to inquire under what circumstances the preceding equation will be valid, given that it is not always valid. We look for clues to this from sets A, B, and D of Example 3. The equation $(A \cap B) \cup D = A \cap (B \cup D)$ was valid for these three particular sets. What was so special about them? If we try to spot relationships (e.g., equality, subset, etc.) between pairs of these sets, we note that $D \subseteq A$ is the only such relationship. Perhaps the previous equation turned out to be valid because D was a subset of A. Putting it differently, we are now wondering whether we could find a subset X of A for which $(A \cap B) \cup X$ does not equal $A \cap (B \cup X)$. We can test this by trying subsets X of $\{2, 3, 5, 8\}$ other than $\{8\}$ (which has already been tested).

For instance, if $X = \{3, 5\}$, then $(A \cap B) \cup X = \{2, 5\} \cup \{3, 5\} = \{2, 3, 5\} = \{2, 3, 5, 8\} \cap \{1, 2, 3, 5, 6, 7, 10\} = A \cap (B \cup X)$. Or, if $X = \{2, 3, 8\}$, then $(A \cap B) \cup X = \{2, 5\} \cup \{2, 3, 8\} = \{2, 3, 5, 8\} = \{2, 3, 5, 8\} \cap \{1, 2, 3, 5, 6, 7, 8, 10\} = A \cap (B \cup X)$. In these two cases, in which X is a subset of A, the equation $(A \cap B) \cup X = A \cap (B \cup X)$, which is not generally true for any three sets, holds true. We could continue further, trying all possible subsets X of A and comparing $(A \cap B) \cup X$ with $A \cap (B \cup X)$. (Do you know how many such subsets there are? *Counting problems* such as this will be the subject of Article 1.5.) If we were to exhaust all these cases (try a few more for your own benefit, say, $X = \{3\}$ or $X = \{2, 8\}$), we would find that the equality of $(A \cap B) \cup X$ with $A \cap (B \cup X)$ always holds.

Suppose then we want to state this officially as a conjecture. What is an elegant way of saying that, for any sets A and B, there is no subset X of A for which $(A \cap B) \cup X$ does not equal $A \cap (B \cup X)$? In particular, we would like a formulation that avoids the double negative of the previous sentence. In essence, we are saying, for any sets A and B and for any subset X of A, the equation $(A \cap B) \cup X = A \cap (B \cup X)$ is valid. Stated differently, for any three sets A, B, and X, <u>if</u> $X \subseteq A$, <u>then</u> $(A \cap B) \cup X = A \cap (B \cup X)$.

We will prove in Chapter 5 that this is a theorem of set theory, the first we have seen involving an "if . . . then" statement. You should formulate other such statements in Exercises 3 through 6. For now, we record our tentative conclusion as Conjecture 5.   □

CONJECTURE 5.
Let X, Y, and Z be any sets:

(l)   If $Z \subseteq X$, then $(X \cap Y) \cup Z = X \cap (Y \cup Z)$

It is not so easy to illustrate Conjecture 5 by a Venn diagram as it was for earlier conjectures, due to the "if . . . then" form of the statement. Some scheme would have to be developed to represent the situation that X is a subset of Y. Even though this is possible (see Exercise 9), the information provided by Venn diagrams becomes less convincing as the statement of the conjecture becomes more complex. Thus results in set theory such as Conjecture 5 and those suggested in Exercises 3 through 6 highlight the need for rigorous techniques of mathematical proof. In particular, proof by Venn diagram is not accepted as a legitimate proof method. Nevertheless, Venn diagrams have been a helpful guide and we will continue to use them, when advantageous, for that purpose.

PROPERTIES OF THE EMPTY SET AND UNIVERSAL SETS

As suggested earlier, results involving the empty set can be particularly troublesome. Consider, for example, whether the following statements are true or false:

1. $\varnothing \cap \{\varnothing\} = \{\varnothing\}$
2. $\varnothing \cup \{\varnothing\} = \{\varnothing, \{\varnothing\}\}$
3. $\varnothing \in \mathscr{P}(\{\varnothing, \{\varnothing\}\})$

Most confusion about the empty set among beginning students of rigorous mathematics emanates from a misunderstanding of two facts: (1) *the empty set is a subset of every set* (including itself, i.e., $\varnothing \subseteq \varnothing$) and (2) *the empty set is not an element of itself* (i.e., $\varnothing \notin \varnothing$), and in fact the statement $x \in \varnothing$ is false for any object x.

In Exercise 7, Article 1.1, you were asked to discuss the pros and cons of the statement that $\varnothing \subseteq A$ for any set A. The fact that this statement is true depends on principles of logic that we will explore in Chapters 2 and 3. For now, you should accept the statement as true, but with an understanding of what the issues are, based on the following discussion, which is essentially an answer to the aforementioned Exercise 7.

Using Remark 3 of Article 1.1 (defining $X \subseteq A$ by "every element of X is also an element of A"), we could argue (fallaciously) that $\varnothing \nsubseteq \{1, 2\}$ (letting $A = \{1, 2\}$ for concreteness) because there are no elements in $\varnothing$ and thus no elements of $\varnothing$ that are also elements of $\{1, 2\}$. On the other hand, we could reason (correctly, it turns out) that, for a set X to fail to be a subset of A, there must be an element of X that is not an element of A. Since $X = \varnothing$ has no elements, this is impossible, so that $\varnothing$ cannot fail to be a subset of A; that is, $\varnothing \subseteq A$.

As for the second principle, we need only emphasize that, by definition, $\varnothing$ is the set containing no elements, so that $\varnothing \in \varnothing$ must be false. If it were true, then, for example, $\{2, 4, 6, 8, 10\} \cup \varnothing$ would equal $\{2, 4, 6, 8, 10, \varnothing\}$ rather than the correct $\{2, 4, 6, 8, 10\}$ (recall this question from Example 2, Article 1.2). Other important facts to note on this basis are that $\varnothing \neq \{\varnothing\}$ (the latter set has one element, the former has none) and $\varnothing \neq \{0\}$ (even though zero does equal the number of elements in $\varnothing$). Furthermore, whereas $\varnothing \in \varnothing$ is false, $\varnothing \in \{\varnothing\}$ is true. Think of $\varnothing$ as an empty box and $\{\varnothing\}$ as a box containing an empty box. The former is empty; the latter is not empty for it contains something, an empty box!

With these principles in mind, you should be able to convince yourself that the answers to the three questions posed at the start of this section are:

1. <u>False</u> (if $\varnothing$ were an element of $\varnothing$, it would be true)
2. <u>False</u> (since $\{\varnothing\} \notin \varnothing \cup \{\varnothing\}$)
3. <u>True</u> (since $\varnothing \subseteq X$ for any set X, then $\varnothing \in \mathscr{P}(X)$ for any set X)

We stated earlier that $\varnothing$ and U are at the "opposite ends of the spectrum." There are a number of senses in which this statement is accurate. One is that the two sets are complementary, that is, $\varnothing' = U$ and $U' = \varnothing$. Another is an extension of a fact we just discussed. Just as $\varnothing$ is a subset of any set, so is U a superset of any set (i.e., any set is a subset of U). Finally, the empty set equals the intersection of any set with its complement, whereas a universal set equals the union of any two such sets.

Exercises

1. Make a list of possible theorems of set theory suggested by the answers calculated in Exercises 1 through 5 of Article 1.2.

2. Let $U = \{1, 2, 3, \ldots, 9, 10\}$. Find specific subsets A, B, C, and/or X of U that contradict (i.e., disprove) the conjectures listed here. For any subsets A, B, C, and X of U:

(a) $A - (B - C) = (A - B) - C$ ★(b) $(A - B)' = A - B'$

(c) $A - (B' \cup C) = (A \cup B) - C$ (d) $A \triangle B = A \cup B$

(e) $B \cup (A - B) = A$

(f)   If $A \cap C \subseteq B \cap C$, then $A \subseteq B$

★(g)   If $X \subseteq A$, then $X \cup (A \cap B) = (X \cup A) \cap B$

(h)   If $A \times B = A \times C$, then $B = C$

Throughout Exercises 3 through 6, let $U = \{1, 2, 3, \ldots, 9, 10\}$. Part (a) of each exercise calls for some experimentation with specific subsets of U, similar to that required in Exercise 2.

3. (a)   Try to find a subsets A, B, and X of U with A and B distinct (i.e., $A \neq B$) such that $A \cup X = B \cup X$ and $A \cap X = B \cap X$. Do not try any more than five combinations of the three sets.

(b)   Suppose that three sets of the type described in (a) are impossible to find (i.e., do not exist). Can you formulate an elegant statement of a theorem asserting this fact? (*Note:* If $A = B$, then surely $A \cup X = B \cup X$ and $A \cap X = B \cap X$ for any set X).

4. ★(a)   Try to find subsets A, B, and X of U with A and B distinct, such that $A \cap X = B \cap X$ and $A \cap X' = B \cap X'$. Do not try any more than five combinations of the three sets.

★(b)   Suppose, as in Exercise 3(b), that three sets satisfying the description in (a) do not exist. Fomulate a well-stated theorem to this effect (noting that if $A = B$, then $A \cap X = B \cap X$ and $A \cap X' = B \cap X'$ for any set X).

5. (a)   Try to find subsets A, B, and Y of U, with A and B distinct and Y nonempty such that $A \times Y = B \times Y$. Do not try any more than five combinations of the three sets.

(b)   Suppose again that three sets of the type described in (a) do not exist. Formulate a theorem that states this fact.

6. (a)   Try to find subsets A and B of U such that either $A \subseteq B$ and $A \cap B' \neq \varnothing$ or $A \nsubseteq B$ and $A \cap B' = \varnothing$. Do not try more than five combinations of the two sets.

(b)   Formulate an elegantly stated theorem describing the situation that two sets of the type described in (a) do not exist.

7. (a)   The equation $a(b + c) = ab + ac$, with a, b, and c real numbers, is the statement that multiplication of real numbers distributes over addition:

(i)   Write an equation that states that addition distributes over multiplication.

(ii)   Is the equation you wrote for (i) true for all real numbers a, b, and c? (i.e., Does addition distribute over multiplication?) Give an example in support of your answer.

★(b)   Use the distributive law (h) of Conjecture 3 to calculate the simultaneous solutions to the inequalities in Example 3, Article 1.2. [*Hint:* Let $X = (-\infty, -4]$ $\cup [1, \infty)$, $Y = (-\infty, -4)$, and $Z = (\frac{7}{2}, \infty)$. The simultaneous solutions are the elements of the set $X \cap (Y \cup Z)$.]

8. Calculate the set of all real numbers that satisfy <u>at least one</u> of the following four pairs of inequalities simultaneously:

(a) $|x - \frac{3}{2}| > \frac{11}{2}$ and $x^2 - 9x - 22 > 0$

(b) $x^2 - 3x - 28 \leq 0$ and $x^2 - 9x - 22 \leq 0$

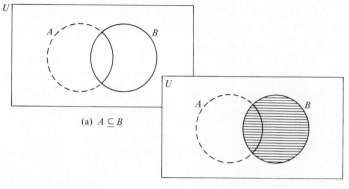

(a) $A \subseteq B$

(b) $A \cup B$ is the shaded region

Figure 1.9

(c) $x^2 - 3x - 28 > 0$ and $\left| x - \frac{9}{2} \right| \leq \frac{13}{2}$

(d) $\left| x - \frac{3}{2} \right| \leq \frac{11}{2}$ and $\left| x - \frac{9}{2} \right| > \frac{13}{2}$

9. One way of illustrating the relationship $A \subseteq B$ by Venn diagrams would be to sketch the diagram, as shown in Figure 1.9a, with the understanding that a region bounded by a "broken" curve is empty and so should never be "shaded in." Thus we represent $A \cup B$ in the preceding picture as shown in Figure 1.9b. Using this convention, illustrate the following theorems by Venn diagrams:

(a) If $X \subseteq B$, then $X \cup (A \cap B) = (X \cup A) \cap B$

(b) If $A \subseteq B$, then $A \cup B = B$ (c) If $A \subseteq B$, then $A \cap B = A$

(d) If $A \subseteq B$, then $B = A \cup (B - A)$ (e) If $A \subseteq B$, then $A \cap B' = \varnothing$

10. Letting $U = \{1, 2, 3, \ldots, 9, 10\}$, answer T or F for each of the following:

(a) $\{\varnothing\} \subseteq A$ for every set A (b) $\varnothing \in A$ for every set A

(c) $\varnothing \subseteq A$ for every set A (d) $\varnothing \in \mathscr{P}(A)$ for every set A

(e) $\varnothing \subseteq \mathscr{P}(A)$ for every set A ★(f) $\{\varnothing\} \subseteq \mathscr{P}(A)$ for every set A

(g) $\{\{\varnothing\}\} \subseteq \mathscr{P}(\varnothing)$ (h) $\{\varnothing\} \cup \varnothing = \{\varnothing\}$

(i) $\{\varnothing\} \cap \varnothing = \varnothing$ ★(j) $\varnothing \subseteq \mathscr{P}(U) - \varnothing$

(k) $\mathscr{P}(\{\varnothing\}) = \{\varnothing, \{\varnothing\}\}$ (l) $\{\varnothing\} \subseteq \{\{\varnothing, \{\varnothing\}, \{\{\varnothing\}\}\}\}$

1.4   Theorems of Set Theory

In this article we provide a lengthy list of selected theorems of set theory. The statement at this point that these results are "theorems," rather than only conjectures, represents our assertion that the statements are indeed true and our promise that we will be able to prove each of them once we address the topic of proof writing in Chapters 4 through 6. We list them at this stage primarily as a convenient reference for future work, and note that, until proofs are actually written, we must still regard these statements as "conjectures." You should already have conjectured, based on earlier exercises, a large number of potential theorems. See which of your conjectures are included in the following lists.

FACT 1

The following <u>basic laws of set equality or of subsets</u> can be proved to be theorems of set theory. For all sets X, Y, and Z in any universal set U:

1. $X = X$ (reflexive property of equality)
2. $X \subseteq X$ (reflexive property of the subset relation)
3. If $X = Y$, then $Y = X$ (symmetric property of equality)
4. $X = Y$ if and only if $X \subseteq Y$ and $Y \subseteq X$ (includes antisymmetric property of subset)
5. If $X = Y$ and $Y = Z$, then $X = Z$ (transitive property of equality)
6. If $X \subseteq Y$ and $Y \subseteq Z$, then $X \subseteq Z$ (transitive property of the subset relation)
7. $\varnothing \subseteq X$
8. $X \subseteq U$

FACT 2

The following <u>basic properties for union and intersection</u> can be proved to be theorems of set theory. For all sets X, Y, and Z in any universal set U:

9. $X \cup X = X$ (idempotent law for union)
10. $X \cap X = X$ (idempotent law for intersection)
11. $X \cup \varnothing = X$ (identity for union)
12. $X \cap U = X$ (identity for intersection)
13. $X \cap \varnothing = \varnothing$
14. $X \cup U = U$
15. $X \cup Y = Y \cup X$ (commutative law for union)
16. $X \cap Y = Y \cap X$ (commutative law for intersection)
17. $X \cup (Y \cup Z) = (X \cup Y) \cup Z$ (associative law for union)
18. $X \cap (Y \cap Z) = (X \cap Y) \cap Z$ (associative law for intersection)
19. $X \subseteq X \cup Y$
20. $X \cap Y \subseteq X$

FACT 3

The following <u>basic properties for set complement</u> can be proved to be theorems of set theory. For all sets X, Y, and Z in any universal set U:

21. $X'' = X$ (law of double complementation)
22. $X \cup X' = U$
23. $X \cap X' = \varnothing$
24. $U' = \varnothing$
25. $\varnothing' = U$

FACT 4

The following <u>distributive laws</u> can be proved to be theorems of set theory. For all sets X, Y, and Z in any universal set U:

26. $X \cup (Y \cap Z) = (X \cup Y) \cap (X \cup Z)$ (union over intersection)
27. $X \cap (Y \cup Z) = (X \cap Y) \cup (X \cap Z)$ (intersection over union)
28. $X \cap (Y \bigtriangleup Z) = (X \cap Y) \bigtriangleup (X \cap Z)$ (intersection over symmetric difference)

FACT 5

The following <u>basic properties of set difference</u> can be proved to be theorems of set theory. For all sets X, Y, and Z in any universal set U:

29. $X - Y = X \cap Y'$
30. $X - \varnothing = X$
31. $\varnothing - Y = \varnothing$
32. $X' - Y' = Y - X$
33. $(X - Y) - Z = (X - Z) - (Y - Z)$

FACT 6

The following <u>De Morgan's laws</u> can be proved to be theorems of set theory. For all sets X, Y, and Z in any universal set U:

34. $(X \cap Y)' = X' \cup Y'$
35. $(X \cup Y)' = X' \cap Y'$
36. $X - (Y \cup Z) = (X - Y) \cap (X - Z)$
37. $X - (Y \cap Z) = (X - Y) \cup (X - Z)$

FACT 7

The following <u>miscellaneous statements of equality or a subset relationship</u> can be proved to be theorems of set theory. For all sets X, Y, and Z in any universal set U:

38. $X = (X \cup Y) \cap (X \cup Y')$
39. $X = (X \cap Y) \cup (X \cap Y')$
40. $(X \cap Y) \cup (X' \cap Y) \cup (X \cap Y') \cup (X' \cap Y') = U$
41. $X \cup (Y - X) = X \cup Y$
42. $(X - Y)' = X' \cup Y$
43. $X \bigtriangleup Y = Y \bigtriangleup X$ (commutativity of symmetric difference)
44. $X \bigtriangleup (Y \bigtriangleup Z) = (X \bigtriangleup Y) \bigtriangleup Z$ (associativity of symmetric difference)
45. $X \bigtriangleup X = \varnothing$
46. $X \bigtriangleup U = X'$
47. $X \bigtriangleup \varnothing = X$
48. $X \bigtriangleup Y = (X \cup Y) - (X \cap Y)$
49. $Y \times \varnothing = \varnothing \times Z = \varnothing$
50. $(X \cup Y) \times Z = (X \times Z) \cup (Y \times Z)$
51. $(X \cap Y) \times Z = (X \times Z) \cap (Y \times Z)$
52. $(X - Y) \times Z = (X \times Z) - (Y \times Z)$

FACT 8

The following statements of equivalence, that is, involving "if and only if," can be proved to be theorems of set theory. For all sets X and Y in any universal set U:

53. $X \subseteq Y$ if and only if $Y' \subseteq X'$
54. $X \subseteq Y$ if and only if $X \cup Y = Y$
55. $X \subseteq Y$ if and only if $X \cap Y = X$
56. $X \subseteq Y$ if and only if $X - Y = \varnothing$
57. $X \subseteq Y$ if and only if $X \cap Y' = \varnothing$
58. $X \subseteq Y$ if and only if $X' \cup Y = U$

FACT 9

The following statements of implication, that is, involving "if . . . then," can be proved to be theorems of set theory. For all sets X, Y, and Z in any universal set U:

59. If $X \subseteq Y$ and $X \subseteq Z$, then $X \subseteq Y \cap Z$
60. If $X \subseteq Z$ and $Y \subseteq Z$, then $X \cup Y \subseteq Z$
61. If $X \subseteq Y$, then $Y = X \cup (Y - X)$
62. If $X \subseteq Z$, then $X \cup (Y \cap Z) = (X \cup Y) \cap Z$
63. If $X \cap Y = X \cap Z$ and $X \cup Y = X \cup Z$, then $Y = Z$
64. If $X \cap Y = X \cap Z$ and $X' \cap Y = X' \cap Z$, then $Y = Z$
65. If $X \cup Y = X \cup Z$ and $X' \cup Y = X' \cup Z$, then $Y = Z$
66. If $X \cap Y = \varnothing$, then $X \triangle Y = X \cup Y$
67. If $X \times Y = X \times Z$ and $X \neq \varnothing$, then $Y = Z$
68. If $X \times Y = Y \times X$, $X \neq \varnothing$, and $Y \neq \varnothing$, then $X = Y$
69. If $Y \times Z = \varnothing$, then $Y = \varnothing$ or $Z = \varnothing$

Exercise

Compare the list of possible theorems of set theory compiled in Exercise 1, Article 1.3, with the theorems stated in Article 1.4.

1.5 Counting Properties of Finite Sets (Optional)

At various stages of an introduction to advanced mathematics, it is important to be acquainted with both certain formulas for counting the number of elements in finite sets and methods of proof known as *counting arguments*. The latter are important, for example, in abstract algebra, with the proof of the famous theorem of Lagrange from group theory a case in point. The material in this article may be familiar to readers who have studied elementary probability.

We emphasize that the content of this article is restricted to finite sets. We will deal with the question of relative size of infinite sets under the heading "cardinality of sets" in Article 8.3.

REMARK 1   If S is a finite set, we use the symbol $n(S)$ to represent the **number of elements in S**, where $n(\varnothing) = 0$ and $n(S) = k$ (for $S \neq \varnothing$ and k a positive integer) if and only if k is the positive integer having the property that the elements in S can be matched, in a one-to-one fashion, with the positive integers $1, 2, \ldots ; k$.

It is common to describe a finite set F of unspecified elements by such notation as $F = \{x_1, x_2, \ldots, x_k\}$, where it is understood that the k elements are distinct so that $n(F) = k$.

FORMULA FOR $n(A \cup B)$

If A and B are sets, then their union contains all the elements from each of the two sets, combined into a single set. If A and B were disjoint, then clearly $n(A \cup B)$ would equal $n(A) + n(B)$. But if an object x is contained in both A and B, it will be counted doubly in the preceding formula, once as an element of A and once as an element of B, even though it represents a single element in $A \cup B$. To avoid this overcounting of members of $A \cup B$, we must subtract from $n(A) + n(B)$ the number of elements in $A \cap B$. Thus we arrive at Counting Formula 1.

COUNTING FORMULA 1
If A and B are finite sets, then $n(A \cup B) = n(A) + n(B) - n(A \cap B)$.

COROLLARY
If A and B are disjoint finite sets, then $n(A \cup B) = n(A) + n(B)$.

The latter result can be viewed as a corollary (i.e., consequence) of the first one, since if $A \cap B = \varnothing$, then $n(A \cap B) = n(\varnothing) = 0$. A rigorous approach to these results would require a proof of Formula 1 from some predetermined set of axioms and, in particular, a proof that does not use the result of the corollary. Our goal in this article is to provide an intuitive, rather than a rigorous development, with emphasis on uses of the formulas rather than on their rigorous derivation.

EXAMPLE 1   Thirty-six students are enrolled in either abstract algebra or advanced calculus. The enrollment in abstract algebra is 28, whereas advanced calculus has 24 students. How many students are enrolled in both these classes?

Solution   Let A be the set of students in advanced calculus, and B the set of students in abstract algebra. We wish to calculate $n(A \cap B)$, knowing that $n(A \cup B) = 36$, $n(A) = 24$, and $n(B) = 28$. By Counting Formula 1, $n(A \cap B) = n(A) + n(B) - n(A \cup B) = 24 + 28 - 36 = 16$.   □

In Exercise 4 we consider the problem of extending Formula 1 to the union of three sets, while in Exercise 3 we see an application of Venn diagrams to solving more complex problems of the type represented by Example 1.

FUNDAMENTAL COUNTING PRINCIPLE; $n(\mathscr{P}(A))$

Suppose, at registration for the fall term at a major university, a student must elect 1 course from among 12 humanities courses, 1 from among 5 physical science courses, 1 from 6 social science courses, and either Math 105 or Computer Science 100. How many ways are there for this student to select a slate of four courses?

This problem is typical of those whose solution is given by Counting Formula 2.

COUNTING FORMULA 2 (Fundamental Counting Principle).
If an activity can be carried out in exactly n_1 ways (n_1 a positive integer), and for each of these, a second activity can be carried out in n_2 ways, and for each of the first two a third activity can be carried out in n_3 ways, and so on, then the total number of ways of carrying out k such activities in sequence is the product $n_1 n_2 \cdots n_k$.

This principle is often illustrated by a *tree diagram*. In Figure 1.10 we use such a diagram to illustrate the choices of a student who must choose one of five physical science courses and one of two mathematical science courses. In this case $n_1 = 5$ and $n_2 = 2$; a representative tree diagram looks like the one in Figure 1.10.

The fundamental counting principle predicts that the student has a total of $n_1 n_2 = 5 \times 2 = 10$ possible choices; the prediction is confirmed by the tree diagram, where we label the physical science courses A, B, C, D, and E and the mathematical science courses X and Y.

Figure 1.10   *A tree diagram illustrating all possible choices in a practical problem.*

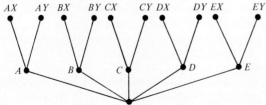

In the problem posed just before the statement of Counting Formula 2, we have $n_1 = 12$, $n_2 = 5$, $n_3 = 6$, $n_4 = 2$, and the total number of potential course elections is $12 \times 5 \times 6 \times 2 = 720$. Obviously, a tree diagram to depict this situation would require considerable space, time, and labor.

It should be noted that, in order to apply the fundamental principle, we must be able to assume that choices made at various stages of the sequence do not limit, or otherwise affect, the possibilities for choices at different stages. In real life this may not be the case. Our student at fall registration may find that 4 of the 12 humanities courses create a time conflict with the mathematics class. In such a case the assumptions of Counting Formula 2 do not apply so that, of course, the answer of 720 that it indicates is incorrect.

EXAMPLE 2   How many 5-letter "words" can be formed from the 26 letters of the alphabet, if there are no restrictions on the use of letters?

Solution   Since we may use letters without restrictions (in particular, the repeated use of a letter in the same word is <u>allowed</u>), we apply the fundamental counting principle with $k = 5$ and $n_1 = n_2 = n_3 = n_4 = n_5 = 26$. The total number of words is then 26^5.   □

EXAMPLE 3   How many 5-letter words can be formed from the vowels A, E, I, O, and U, if each vowel can be used exactly once in a word?

Solution   As in Example 2, $k = 5$, since we must perform five activities to form a word, namely, choose the first letter, then the second, and so on. But in this case $n_1 = 5$, $n_2 = 4$, $n_3 = 3$, $n_4 = 2$, and $n_5 = 1$. The reason is that once we have chosen the first letter, there are only four ways of choosing the second. Having chosen the first two letters, we have only three ways of choosing the third, and so on. Thus there is a total of only $5 \times 4 \times 3 \times 2 \times 1 = 120$ words in this case.   □

Examples 2 and 3 are representative of two classes of counting problems whose solutions, although a consequence of the fundamental counting principle, are of sufficient importance to warrant separate presentation.

COUNTING   FORMULA   3
The number of k-object arrangements that can be constructed from a set of n objects, if there are no restrictions on the number of uses of each of the n objects within an arrangement, is given by the formula n^k.

COUNTING   FORMULA   4
The number of n-object arrangements that can be constructed from a set of n objects, if each object can be used <u>only once</u> in each arrangement, is given by $n(n - 1)(n - 2) \cdots (3)(2)(1)$. Each such arrangement is called a **permutation** of the set of n objects.

The rationale behind Formula 3, as illustrated in Example 2, is that there are k activities to be performed and n ways of doing each of them, thus there is a total of "n multiplied by itself k times," or n^k possibilities.

The rationale behind Formula 4, illustrated in Example 3, is that n activities are to be carried out, with n ways of performing the first, $n - 1$ ways of performing the second, and so on. The problem described in Formula 4 is often called computing the *number of permutations of n things taken n at a time*, abbreviated $P(n, n)$. There is also a convenient shorthand notation for the quantity involved in Formula 4.

REMARK 2   If n is a positive integer, we denote by the term **n factorial**, symbolized by the notation $n!$, the quantity $(n)(n - 1)(n - 2) \cdots (3)(2)(1)$. Finally, we define $0! = 1$.

We may summarize the conclusion of Formula 4 by the equation $P(n, n) = n!$.

EXAMPLE 4   Consider the nine digits $1, 2, \ldots, 8, 9$. (a) How many nine-digit sequences can be built from these nine digits if no repeated uses of digits is allowed? (b) How many four-digit sequences, also with no repeats, are possible?

Solution   (a)   This solution follows directly from Counting Formula 4, letting $n = 9$. That is, $P(9, 9) = 9! = 362,880$.

(b)   For this problem we must return to the fundamental counting principle. There are nine ways of choosing the first digit, eight of choosing the second, seven of choosing the third, six of choosing the fourth, and we stop there. Thus there are a total of $9 \times 8 \times 7 \times 6 = 3024$ ways of forming such a sequence. Expressed in terms of factorial notation, the answer could be expressed as 9! divided by 5!.   □

The problem described in Example 4(b) is one of counting the *number of permutations of n objects* $(n = 9)$ *taken r at a time* $(r = 4)$, and is denoted $P(n, r)$. We may summarize the conclusion of Example 4(b) by the equation $P(n, r) = n!/(n - r)!, 0 \le r \le n$.

Counting formulas 3 and 4 are the basis of our ability to find counting formulas for three very important situations involving finite sets, namely:

(a)   If $n(A) = m_1$ and $n(B) = m_2$, what is $n(A \times B)$?
(b)   If $n(A) = m$, what is $n(\mathscr{P}(A))$?
(c)   If $n(A) = m$, what is the number of "k-element subsets" of A, where $0 \le k \le m$.

Discussion   (a) $A \times B$ consists of all ordered pairs of the form (a, b) where $a \in A$ and $b \in B$. Clearly there are m_1 ways of choosing the first entry in an ordered pair and, for each of these, there are m_2 ways of choosing

$$\underline{\quad\quad}\quad\underline{\quad\quad}\quad\underline{\quad\quad}\quad\text{-----------}\quad\underline{\quad\quad}\quad\underline{\quad\quad}$$

$a_1 \qquad\quad a_2 \qquad\quad a_3 \qquad\qquad\qquad\qquad\qquad a_{m-1} \qquad a_m$

Figure 1.11 *A device for representing pictorially the possible subsets of an m-element set.*

the second. By the fundamental counting principle there are $m_1 m_2$ ways of selecting a first entry, followed by a second. Thus $n(A \times B) = n(A)n(B)$.

(b) The calculation of $n(\mathscr{P}(A))$ involves our first clever (!) use of counting principles. We have a set A with m elements; we wish to count its subsets. How can we do this? We approach the problem by writing m blank spaces in a row, one space for each of the m objects in A, which we, in turn, represent by the symbols $a_1, a_2, \ldots, a_m$, as in Figure 1.11. Having done this, we represent a subset X of A by a string of m zeros and ones, where we write 1 in the kth place if $a_k \in X$ and 0 in the kth place if $a_k \notin X$. The string $100 \cdots 000$ thus represents the subset $\{a_1\}$; the string $111 \cdots 11$ represents A itself; the string $000 \cdots 00$ represents $\varnothing$. Clearly there is a one-to-one match-up between the subsets of A and the possible strings of m zeros and ones. (The details of this match-up constitute the technical part of the argument if a very formal approach is taken. We do not deal with these formalities here.) Thus we have shifted the original problem to one covered directly by Counting Formula 3, with $k = m$ and $n = 2$ (the two objects are the symbols 0 and 1). The answer, then, is $n^k = 2^m$.

Let us check this result with some familiar examples. If $A = \varnothing$, then $m = 0$, so we expect that $n(\mathscr{P}(A)) = 2^0 = 1$. Indeed, $\mathscr{P}(A) = \{\varnothing\}$ which has one element. If $A = \{\varnothing, \{\varnothing\}\}$, then $n(A) = 2$, so we expect $n(\mathscr{P}(A)) = 2^2 = 4$. In fact, $\mathscr{P}(A) = \{\varnothing, A, \{\varnothing\}, \{\{\varnothing\}\}\}$, so that theory again predicts the actual result! One final note: The power set of a finite set must be finite (recall Exercise 9(c), Article 1.1).

(c) The number of k-element subsets of an m-element set is often called the *number of combinations of m things taken k at a time*, abbreviated $C(m, k)$. We will arrive at a formula for $C(m, k)$, in terms of factorials, by using what we already know about permutations together with the fundamental counting principle. Suppose, for example, we wish to count the number of five-letter words that can be formed from the letters A, B, C, D, E, F, G, and H, with no repeated letters allowed. On the one hand, we know that there are $P(8, 5) = 8!/(8 - 5)! = 8!/3! = 8 \times 7 \times 6 \times 5 \times 4 = 6720$ such words. But we can also arrive at such a word by first choosing five letters in no particular order [in one of $C(8, 5)$ possible ways] and then counting the number of possible arrangements of those five letters [which is $P(5, 5) = 5! = 120$]. By the fundamental counting principle, the product $C(8, 5)$ times $P(5, 5)$ should be the number of words, namely, $P(8, 5) = 6720$. Hence the unknown $C(8, 5)$ must equal $P(8, 5)$ divided by $P(5, 5)$, or $8!/3!5!$. For a general m and

k $(0 \leq k \leq m)$, this becomes $C(m, k) = P(m, k)/P(k, k) = m!/(m - k)!k!$. This is the formula for the number of k-element subsets of an m-element set. Let us again try a few special cases. If $k = 0$, then $C(m, 0) = m!/m!0! = 1$. The empty set is, of course, the only zero-element subset of an m-element set! If $k = 1$, then $C(m, 1) = m!/(m - 1)!1! = m$. An m-element set has exactly m singleton subsets!

We summarize the results of the preceding discussion in Counting Formulas 5.

COUNTING FORMULAS 5
Let A and B be finite sets. Then:

(a) $n(A \times B) = n(A)n(B)$

(b)   If $n(A) = m$, then $n(\mathscr{P}(A)) = 2^m$.

(c)   If $n(A) = m$, then the number of k-element subsets of A $(0 \leq k \leq m)$ is given by $C(m, k) = m!/(m - k)!k!$.

EXAMPLE 5   Suppose $U = \{1, 2, 3, \ldots, 9, 10\}$. How many cases are covered by the statement of the associative law for union of sets, that is, $A \cup (B \cup C) = (A \cup B) \cup C$ for all subsets A, B, and C of U?

Solution.   The question is one of counting the number of ways of choosing three particular subsets of the ten-element universal set. By Counting Formula 5, part (b), there are $2^{10} = 1024$ ways of choosing the set A. Since repeated use of sets is clearly appropriate, there are again 2^{10} ways of selecting B and 2^{10} ways of taking a set C. By the fundamental counting principle, with $k = 3$ and $n_1 = n_2 = n_3 = 2^{10}$, there are $(2^{10})^3 = 2^{30} = (1024)^3$ cases of the associative law, for a universal set of ten elements. □

EXAMPLE 6   A student at registration for fall term must select 4 courses from a total of 25 available courses. How many choices of 4 courses does the student have?

Solution   This problem is a direct application of Formula 5(c), with $m = 25$ and $k = 4$. The total number of choices is $C(25, 4) = (25)!/(21)! \, 4! = 25 \times 23 \times 22 = 12,650$.   □

Compare the answer to Example 6 with the answer of 720 to the problem that immediately preceded Counting Formula 2. There is a relationship between the two problems. Can you explain why the answer to the second problem should be so much larger than the answer to the first?

There is much more that can be done with the theory of finite counting, including the theory of finite probability. Some additional information is contained in the exercises for this article. Our primary interest in counting, however, is that it serve as an aid in mathematical reasoning and especially in the writing of certain mathematical proofs. Another purpose is that the answer to certain counting problems can shed light on the value of generalization in mathematics. Example 5 showed that, even when the universal set is relatively small, the number of cases included by a well-known theorem of set theory is quite large. An abstract proof, of course, establishes the truth of the theorem in all these special cases and eliminates the need to count, or otherwise consider, the individual cases. See Exercises 9 and 11(c) for other similar examples.

If you are interested in further exposure to this branch of mathematics, you should refer to texts in areas such as probability and combinatorial mathematics.

Exercises

1. Find $n(A)$ where $A =$

(a) $\{1, 3, 4, 7\} \cup \{4, 6, 7, 8, 9, 12\}$

(b) $\{\ldots, -4, -2, 0, 2, 4\} \cap \{1, 2, 3, 4, \ldots\}$

(c) $\varnothing$ (d) $\{\varnothing\}$

(e) $\varnothing \cup \{1, 2, 3\}$ (f) $\varnothing \cap \{1, 2, 3\}$

(g) $\{\varnothing\} \cup \{1, 2, 3\}$ (h) $\{\varnothing, \{\varnothing\}\}$

★(i) $\{\{\varnothing, \{\varnothing\}\}\}$ (j) $\{\{1, 2, 3\}, \{4, 5, 6, 7, 8, 9, 10\}\}$

(k) $\{1, 2, 3\} - \{1, 2, 3, 4\}$ (l) $\mathscr{P}(\{\varnothing, \{\varnothing\}\})$

★(m) $\mathscr{P}(\{1, 2, 3, 4, 5\})$ ★(n) $\mathscr{P}(\{\{1, 2, 3, 4, 5\}\})$

(o) $\{2, 3, 4, 5, \ldots\}'$ where $U = \mathbf{N}$ ★(p) $\{1, 2, 3, 4\} \triangle \{3, 4, 5, 6\}$

(q) $\{1, 2, 3\} \times \{1, 2, 3, 4\}$

2. The faculty of 34 at a local college has invested its retirement contributions in either the stock fund or the money market fund. There are 22 with money in the stock fund and 27 with money in the money market fund. How many have invested a portion of their money in both funds?

3. An inspection of 63 automobiles available for sale at a local dealership revealed that 41 had air conditioning, 31 had cruise control, and 37 had tilt wheel. Also, 27 have both air conditioning and cruise control, 18 have cruise control and tilt wheel, whereas 30 have air conditioning and tilt wheel. Finally, 18 have all three options. How many of the cars have none of the options? (*Hint:* Construct a Venn diagram based on three circles. Insert numbers into as many of the eight regions induced by the three circles as the preceding data provide for.)

4. Find a formula for $n(A \cup B \cup C)$, analogous to the formula (Counting Formula 1) for $n(A \cup B)$. [*Hint:* Review the reasoning used to justify the formula for $n(A \cup B)$. Your answer should involve $n(A)$, $n(B)$, $n(C)$, and n(various intersections of these sets).]

5. (a)   How many committees, with at least one member, can be formed from a club with eight members?

★(b)   How many three-person committees can be formed from the club in part (a)? five-person committees?

(c)   How many ways are there of selecting a president, vice-president, and secretary from the club in part (a)?

6. (a)   How many 5-card poker hands can be dealt from a deck of 52 cards?

★(b)   If five cards are dealt consecutively from a standard deck, how many ways are there to deal first an ace, second a seven, third an eight, fourth a ten, and fifth a face card?

(c)   How many 13-card bridge hands can be dealt from a deck of 52 cards?

7. (a)   How many sets of ten answers to ten questions on a true-false test are possible?

(b)   How many ways are there to respond to eight questions on a multiple-choice test if each question has four choices?

(c)   How many ways are there to match the first ten letters of the alphabet with the integers 1 through 10 on a column-matching test?

8. (a)   How many pairs of names consisting of a female name followed by a male name can be formed from a list of eight female and five male names?

(b)   How many automobile license plates can your state issue, using its current format for such plates?

9. Suppose $U = \{1, 2, 3, \ldots, 9, 10\}$. How many particular cases are encompassed by the theorems:

(a) $A \cap (B \cup C) = (A \cap B) \cup (A \cap C)$ for all subsets A, B, and C of U?

★(b) $A = (A \cap B) \cup (A \cap B')$ for all subsets A, B of U?

10. Numbers of the form $C(n, k) = n!/k!(n - k)!$ $(0 \le k \le n)$ are of considerable importance. In particular, the alternative notation $\binom{n}{k}$, called the **binomial coefficient** of n over k (or else simply **n choose k**), is used to denote this quantity (the name comes from the binomial theorem whose statement involves binomial coefficients).

(a)   Let $n = 10$ and $k = 0, 3, 4, 6, 7, 10$, and verify for these cases the formulas:

(i) $$\binom{n}{k} = \binom{n}{n - k} \qquad (0 \le k \le n)$$

(ii) $$\binom{n}{0} = \binom{n}{n} = 1$$

(iii) $$\binom{n}{1} = \binom{n}{n - 1} = n$$

(iv) $$\binom{n + 1}{k} = \binom{n}{k} + \binom{n}{k - 1}$$

(b)   Formula (i) of part (a) suggests that, for example, the number of three-element subsets of an eight-element set equals the number of five-element subsets of that set. Describe a general way of constructing a "one-to-one match-up" between the k-element subsets of an n-element set and the $(n - k)$-element subsets of that set?

11. (a)   Find a formula relating 2^n to the binomial coefficients of the form $\binom{n}{k}$, $k = 0, 1, 2, \ldots, n$, where $n \in \mathbf{N}$. [*Hint:* Keep in mind that 2^n is the total number of subsets of an n-element set, whereas $\binom{n}{k}$ gives the number of k-element subsets of that set, for each $k = 0, 1, 2, \ldots, n$.]

(b)   Verify your formula from part (a) of this exercise for the case $n = 10$.

Figure 1.12

*	a	b	c
a			
b			
c			

(a)

*	a	b	c
a		c	
b			
c			

(b)

(c)   Let $U = \{1, 2, 3, \ldots, 9, 10\}$. Use the formula from part (a) of this exercise to calculate the number of specific cases encompassed by Conjecture 5, Article 1.3. If $X \subseteq Y$, then $(Y \cap Z) \cup X = Y \cap (Z \cup X)$.

12. Suppose we wish to construct a *multiplication table*, as in Figure 1.12*a*, based on a three-element set $S = \{a, b, c\}$. We define the "product" $x * y$ of two elements in S by entering a symbol in the box corresponding to the row of x and the column of y. Thus Figure 1.12*b* indicates that $a * b = c$. Assuming that only the symbols a, b, and c may be used to fill each of the empty boxes in Figure 1.12*b*:

★*(a)*   How many possible ways are there to construct such a table?

★*(b)*   How many such tables can be constructed if $*$ must be "commutative"; that is, if $x * y = y * x$ for all elements $x, y \in S$?

(c)   How many tables are possible if none of the symbols a, b, and c can be used more than once in any row?

(d)   How many tables are possible if no symbol can be used more than once in any row and once in any column?

Logic, Part I:
The Propositional Calculus
CHAPTER 2

Consider the sentence "Mathematics is a complicated subject, and in order to study mathematics, we must accept the fact that many mathematical concepts cannot be formulated in a simple manner." In addition to expressing ideas that are true (a reason students of junior-senior level mathematics must be well grounded in logic), this sentence provides an example of the object that is central to the study of logic, the *statement*, and, in particular, the *compound statement*.

Statements, or declarative sentences, are basic to all human communication, and are not specific to mathematics. But there are few areas of endeavor in which precise command over the structure of statements is as critical as it is in mathematics (the law might be one example). Mathematics is full of subtleties, of fine distinctions and complicated formulations. Take, for example, the epsilon-delta definition of the limit of a function: If f is defined on an open interval containing a real number a, and if L is a real number, then we say

$L = \lim_{x \to a} f(x)$ if and only if, for every $\varepsilon > 0$, there exists $\delta > 0$
such that whenever $0 < |x - a| < \delta$, then $|f(x) - L| < \varepsilon$

This definition is of crucial importance in mathematical analysis. But even though most students are exposed to it early in their first calculus course, few come to appreciate its meaning until much later, and many never do.

Why is this definition perceived as formidable? Why, for instance, would it be beyond most calculus students to describe, in terms of epsilons and deltas, what it means for L not to equal $\lim f(x)$ as x tends to a? [Can you, at this point, write a positive statement corresponding to $L \neq \lim_{x \to a} f(x)$? If not, you will find a detailed consideration of this problem in Article 4.3.] One reason is that this definition contains three instances of *quantifiers*, that is, the phrases "for every" and "there exists." Another reason is that a major part of the definition is a *conditional*, that is, a statement of the form "if . . . then." The heavy use of quantifiers and the use of *connectives* (such as "and," "or," and "if . . . then") are part of the normal vocabulary of mathematicans, but these are not nearly so prevalent in everyday usage. Facility with this mode of expression, then, doesn't come naturally; it must be acquired.

Fortunately, this ability is more science than art. Gaining it is not strictly a matter of experience and intuition, although both help. There are specific rules for dealing with compound statements, which fall under the heading of the *propositional calculus* and the *predicate calculus*. The former is about compound statements (e.g., "either $2 \neq 3$ or $2 + 3 = 4$") and connectives, and will be studied in this chapter. The latter studies *open sentences*, or *predicates* (sentences containing an unknown, as in "$|x^2 - 16| < 4$" or "f is a continuous function") and the modification of such expressions with various combinations of the two quantifiers described earlier. This is the subject of Chapter 3. Many of the theorems of logic presented in these two chapters are the basis of theorem-proving strategies in mathematics we use throughout the remainder of the text. We will take specific note of such strategies as they arise in these two chapters. Then, in Chapter 4 we will focus on several immediate applications of principles of logic, as we begin our emphasis on the writing of proofs.

Historically, the development of symbolic logic traces back primarily to the work of the nineteenth-century British mathematician George Boole, after whom *Boolean algebra*, an important branch of symbolic logic, is named.

2.1   Basic Concepts of the Propositional Calculus

Consider the assertions "$\sin 2\pi = 1$" and "the function $f(x) = \sin x$ is periodic." From trigonometry, we know that the first is false, whereas the second is true. But what about sentences such as "$\sin 2\pi = 1$ *and* the sine function is periodic" or "*if* $\sin 2\pi = 1$, *then* the function $f(x) = \sin x$ is periodic"? The truth or falsehood of these *compound* sentences, it turns out, depends on the truth or falsehood of their component simple sentences and on characteristics of the connective involved in the compound sentence. In this article we begin to study the precise nature of this dependence.

STATEMENTS OR PROPOSITIONS

DEFINITION 1
A **statement**, or **proposition**, is a declarative sentence that is either true or false, but is not both true and false.

The designation T(true) or F(false), one and only one of which is assignable to any given statement, is called the *truth value* of that statement.

EXAMPLE 1   The following are statements:

(a)   The moon is made of green cheese.
(b) $(e^\pi)^2 = e^{2\pi}$.
(c)   6 is a prime number.
(d)   February 5, 1992 falls on a Wednesday.
(e)   The millionth digit in the decimal expansion of $\sqrt{2}$ is 6.

Discussion   Statements (a) and (c) are clearly false (i.e., have truth value F), whereas (b) is true. The truth values of statements (d) and (e) are not so evident, but are determinable; item (d), for instance, is true. In connection with (e), it is important to understand that we need not know specifically whether or not a statement is true in order to label it a statement. It is only in recent years, with the advent of high-speed computers, that it has become practical to find the answer to such questions.   □

EXAMPLE 2   The following are not statements:

(a)   Is $(e^\pi)^2$ equal to $e^{2\pi}$?
(b)   If only every day could be like this one!
(c)   Every google is an aardling.
(d) $2 + 3i$ is less than $5 + 3i$.
(e) $x > 5$.
(f)   This proposition is false.

Discussion   Items (a) and (b) fail to be statements, because they are interrogative and exclamatory sentences, respectively, rather than declarative. Item (c) fails, since some of its words are not really words, but rather, nonsense collections of letters. Item (d) fails for the same reason as (c), but in a more subtle and purely mathematical way. We will see in Chapter 9 that there is no notion of "less than" or "greater than" between pairs of complex numbers, so a statement that one is less than another is meaningless.

Item (e) is an important example. It is not a statement, but rather, it is an open sentence or predicate, the topic of the next chapter. It is neither true nor false since it contains a variable, essentially an "empty place" in the sentence. A predicate becomes either true or false, and thus a statement, when we either quantify it or substitute a specific object for its variable. A less clearcut example related to item (e) is a sentence such as $x(x + 4) = x^2 + 4x$. Strictly speaking, this sentence is a predicate. Yet, because it is true for any possible substitution of a real number for x, it is common practice to say "$x(x + 4) = x^2 + 4x$" when we mean "for every x, $x(x + 4) = x^2 + 4x$," and treat the former as a (true) statement. You should adopt the strict point of view whenever this issue arises in the exercises for this article.

Item (f) may remind you of Exercise 10, Article 1.1, since it involves a paradox. At first glance, it may appear to be a statement. But if it's true, then it must be false (Why?), and if it's false, it must be true. In other words, if it's either true or false, then it must be both true and false; but this violates the definition of "statement." □

Another situation worth mentioning in connection with Example 2 is sentences whose truth or falsehood depends on the time at which they are uttered. In the strictest sense, a sentence like "today is Monday" might be regarded not to be a statement, because "today" is a variable (like x in the inequality $x > 7$). The same can be said for "it is raining," and "the current Speaker of the U.S. House of Representatives is a Democrat." But often in practice, when such sentences are used in everyday discourse, there is a great deal of unspoken, but solidly understood, background material (involving implicitly either substitution or quantification) that renders the sentence clearly true or false, and thus "a statement when used in context." Therefore when you say "it is sunny outside," you are usually saying something that, in that specific time and place, can be confirmed or refuted. It is interesting to note that this problem doesn't arise in sentences with purely mathematical content; perhaps this can be regarded as a manifestation of the timelessness of mathematics.

COMPOUND STATEMENTS AND LOGICAL CONNECTIVES

All the statements in Example 1 were *simple* statements not composed in any way of other statements. The propositional calculus is about *compound* statements consisting of two or more component statements, joined by one or more *logical connectives*.

The propositional calculus is to statements what ordinary algebra is to numbers. In algebra we use variables x, y, z, etc., to represent numbers; in the propositional calculus we use letters in lower case, such as p, q, and r to represent statements. In algebra we have operations such as "plus" and "times" that allow us to combine numbers to get a new number; in the propositional calculus we have logical connectives, represented by symbols such as $\vee$, $\wedge$, and $\rightarrow$, by which we can combine statements to get a new statement. Thus if p and q are statements, then $p \vee q$ and $q \rightarrow p$, for instance, will also be statements, compound statements in fact. It is important to realize that the truth value of a compound statement will depend on the *truth values* of its component statements only (in a manner prescribed by the connective involved) and not on the compound statements themselves. Thus to know whether a statement of the form $p \wedge q$ is true, we need only know the <u>truth values</u> of p and q, and not p and q themselves. Clearly then, the connectives are crucial. We deal in this article with the five most common logical connectives, "and," "or," "not," "if . . . then," and "if and only if." We define each connective by specifying when a compound statement involving it is true. We begin with negation, conjunction, and disjunction.

NEGATION, CONJUNCTION, AND DISJUNCTION

DEFINITION 2

Given statements p and q, we define three statements formed from p and q.

(a) The **negation** (or **denial**) of p, denoted $\sim p$ and read "not p," is true precisely when p is false.

(b) The **conjunction** of p and q, denoted $p \wedge q$ and read "p and q," is true precisely when p and q are both true.

(c) The **disjunction** (or **alternation**) of p and q, denoted $p \vee q$ and read "p or q," is true when one or the other or both of the statements p and q is (or are) true.

If p represents the statement "5 is a prime number" (true) and q the statement "5 times 9 equals 46" (false), then the statement $\sim p$ (5 is <u>not</u> a prime number) is false, the statement $\sim q$ (5 times 9 does not equal 46) is true, and $p \wedge q$ is false (since q is false), but $p \vee q$ is true (since p is true).

Although our definition of "and" corresponds to its normal usage in English, the same is not true of "or." Everyday usage of or is "one or the other, but not both" (exclusive alternation). The alternation we've defined, often called the *mathematical or*, is inclusive, corresponding to "and/or" in English.

When dealing with expressions such as $\sim p$, $p \wedge q$, and $p \vee \sim q$, in a case where p and q are variables representing unknown statements with unknown truth values, we refer to these expressions as *statement forms*. A statement form becomes a statement when a specific statement is substituted each of its unknowns (the latter sometimes referred to as *components*). As it stands, a statement form is neither true nor false; indeed, our immediate interest is to determine under what truth conditions a given statement form is true and when it is false. The most convenient device for illustrating the truth values of a compound statement form under the various possible truth conditions is the *truth table*. We construct truth tables for the three previously defined connectives in Figure 2.1.

These truth tables may well be thought of as the definitions of the connectives "not," "and," "or." Note that each *row* of a truth table specifies a particular combination of truth values of the component(s); hence the number of rows equals the number of possible combinations of those truth values (see Exercise 2). We see tables with two and four rows in Figure 2.1; another situation occurs in the following example.

p	$\sim p$
T	F
F	T

p	q	$p \wedge q$
T	T	T
T	F	F
F	T	F
F	F	F

p	q	$p \vee q$
T	T	T
T	F	T
F	T	T
F	F	F

(a)   (b)   (c)

Figure 2.1 *Truth tables for negation, conjunction, and disjunction.*

EXAMPLE 3   Determine under what truth conditions the statement form for the compound statement "Either $\int_{-\pi}^{\pi} \sin x \, dx \neq 0$ and $d/dx(2^x) = x2^{x-1}$ or $\int_{-\pi}^{\pi} \sin x \, dx = 0$ and $\ln 6 = (\ln 2)(\ln 3)$" is true. Is the statement itself true or false?

Solution   Let p represent the statement "$\int_{-\pi}^{\pi} \sin x \, dx = 0$," so that "$\int_{-\pi}^{\pi} \sin x \, dx \neq 0$" corresponds to $\sim p$. Let q symbolize "$d/dx(2^x) = x2^{x-1}$" and let r denote "$\ln 6 = (\ln 2)(\ln 3)$." The main connective in the given compound statement is "either . . . or." The two statements joined by this disjunction are themselves compound, each involving the connective "and." Specifically, the latter two statements, in symbols, have the form $\sim p \wedge q$ and $p \wedge r$. To signify that $\vee$ is the main connective, we use (as in the algebra of numbers) parentheses around the expressions $\sim p \wedge q$ and $p \wedge r$, arriving finally at $(\sim p \wedge q) \vee (p \wedge r)$ as the symbolic form of the given statement.

We must next construct a truth table for this statement form. The first three columns should be headed by p, q, and r, whereas the last column (farthest to the right) has at its head the statement form $(\sim p \wedge q) \vee (p \wedge r)$ itself. Intermediate columns need to be provided for any compound statement forms that occur as components of the final statement form, in this case $\sim p$, $\sim p \wedge q$, and $p \wedge r$. The number of rows is the number of possible truth combinations of the component statement forms p, q, and r. Based on Exercise 2, our table should have eight rows; based on the number of column headings we've noted, it requires seven columns, as shown in Figure 2.2.

Note that the truth values in column 5 were obtained with reference to columns 2 and 4 (linked by conjunction); column 7 resulted from columns 5 and 6 (linked by disjunction). Finally, notice that the statement form is true in four of the eight cases, namely, those in which either p and r are both true (rows 1 and 2), or p is false and q is true (rows 3 and 7). Only one of the eight cases, of course, corresponds to the situation of our original example, namely, row 6 (Why?). The original compound statement in this example is false. □

p	q	r	$\sim p$	$\sim p \wedge q$	$p \wedge r$	$(\sim p \wedge q) \vee (p \wedge r)$
T	T	T	F	F	T	T
T	F	T	F	F	T	T
F	T	T	T	T	F	T
F	F	T	T	F	F	F
T	T	F	F	F	F	F
T	F	F	F	F	F	**F**
F	T	F	T	T	F	T
F	F	F	T	F	F	F

Figure 2.2   *The statement form* $(\sim p \wedge q) \vee (p \wedge r)$ *is true in some cases, false in others.*

Exercises

1. Which of the following are statements? (In some cases the best answer may be "a statement only if a specific context is understood."):

(a) $4 + 3 = 7$.

★(c)   All men are mortal.

(e)   What a surprise!

(g) $\sin^2 x + \cos^2 x = 1$.

★(i)   Today is not Friday.

★(k) $x^2 + 6x + 9 = (x + 3)^2$.

(m)   The day after Tuesday is Wednesday.

(n)   This book has a red cover.

(o)   Is there any real-valued function of a real variable that is continuous everywhere and differentiable nowhere?

(p)   If yesterday was Wednesday, then today is Thursday.

(q)   The baseball world series champions are in the American League.

(r)   The Baltimore Orioles are in the American League.

(s)   The president of the United States is a Republican.

(b) $5 - 7 > 0$.

(d)   What day is today?

(f) $\sin^2(3\pi/2) + \cos^2(3\pi/2)$.

(h) $\sin^2(0) + \cos^2(0) < 1$.

(j) $x^2 + 6x + 9 = 0$.

(l) f is continuous at a.

2. (a)   Set up an explicit one-to-one matching between the rows of a truth table for a statement form in n variables, say, $p_1, p_2, \ldots, p_n$, and the set of all subsets of the set $\{p_1, p_2, \ldots, p_n\}$.

(b)   On the basis of (a) and Counting Formula 5(b), Article 1.5, how many distinct rows are there in a truth table for a statement form in n variables?

3. Construct a truth table for each of the following statement forms:

(a) $\sim (p \vee \sim p)$

(c) $\sim (p \vee q)$

(b) $p \wedge \sim p$

(d) $\sim p \vee \sim q$

(e) $(p \vee q) \wedge r$

(f) $(p \wedge r) \vee (q \wedge r)$

(g) $\sim(p \wedge q \wedge r)$

(h) $\sim p \vee \sim q \vee \sim r$

(i) $(p \wedge q) \vee (\sim p \wedge q) \vee (p \wedge \sim q) \vee (\sim p \wedge \sim q)$

(j) $p \,\underline{\vee}\, q$, where $\underline{\vee}$ represents exclusive alternation, that is, "p or q but not both."

4. Determine whether each of the following statements is true or false, based on the truth or falsehood of the component simple statements. (*Note:* Unlike what was done in Example 3, you need not construct complete truth tables. You should, however, express each statement in symbolic form, as we did in the first paragraph of the solution to Example 3.)

(a) It is not the case that 5 is not an odd integer.

(b) Either the derivative of a linear function is its slope or the moon is made of green cheese.

(c) $e = \lim_{x \to \infty} (1 + 1/x)^x$ and $1/e = \lim_{x \to \infty} (1 - 1/x)^x$

★(d) The sum of two even integers is even and it is not the case that the product of two odd integers is odd.

(e) Either $2 \neq 5$ and the sine function is an even function or it is not the case that every real number has a multiplicative inverse, that is, reciprocal.

★(f) It is not the case that April, September, and Wednesday are names of months.

★(g) April is not the name of a month, and September is not the name of a month, and Wednesday is not the name of a month.

(h) Either April, September, or Wednesday is not the name of a month.

(i) It is not the case that either April, September, or Wednesday is the name of a month.

(j) It is not the case that either April and September are not names of a month or Wednesday is the name of a month.

2.2   Tautology, Equivalence, the Conditional, and Biconditional

The compound statement form $(\sim p \wedge q) \vee (p \wedge r)$ of Example 3, Article 2.1, turned out to be true under some truth conditions and false under others. We occasionally refer to such a statement form as a *contingency*. Statement forms that are <u>always</u> true or <u>always</u> false are of particular importance.

DEFINITION 1

A statement form that is true under all possible truth conditions for its components is called a **tautology**. A statement form that is false under all possible truth conditions for its components is called a **contradiction**.

EXAMPLE 1   Show that the statement forms $p \vee \sim p$ and $p \wedge \sim p$ are, respectively, a tautology and a contradiction.

Solution   We demonstrate this by means of truth tables. Since only one unknown is involved in each statement form, our table will require only two rows. For the sake of compactness, we use a single table for

p	$\sim p$	$p \wedge \sim p$	$p \vee \sim p$
T	F	F	T
F	T	F	T

Figure 2.3   *The statement form $p \wedge \sim p$ is always false, whereas $p \vee \sim p$ is always true.*

both statement forms. Column 3 of the table in Figure 2.3 consists entirely of F's and column 4 solely of T's, as claimed. □

Can you think of any other examples of tautologies or contradictions by using the three connectives $\sim$, $\vee$, and $\wedge$ available to us so far? (*Hint*: One occurred in Exercise 3, Article 2.1.) Another possible idea is that we can always generate a contradiction if we know a tautology, by negating that tautology, and vice versa. What new examples are suggested by this comment?

A large part of our study of statement forms concerns relationships among various forms. One such important relationship is given by the next definition.

DEFINITION 2
Two compound statement forms that have the same truth values as each other under all possible truth conditions for their components are said to be **logically equivalent**.

EXAMPLE 2   Show that the statement forms $\sim(p \vee q)$ and $\sim p \wedge \sim q$ are logically equivalent.

Solution   We do this by constructing a truth table of four rows and seven columns, as shown in Figure 2.4, noting that the entries in the columns headed by $\sim p \wedge \sim q$ and $\sim(p \vee q)$ are identical. □

Figure 2.4   *The statement forms $\sim p \wedge \sim q$ and $\sim(p \vee q)$ have the same truth values as each other, under all possible truth conditions.*

p	q	$p \vee q$	$\sim p$	$\sim q$	$\sim p \wedge \sim q$	$\sim(p \vee q)$
T	T	T	F	F	F	F
T	F	T	F	T	F	F
F	T	T	T	F	F	F
F	F	F	T	T	T	T

A consequence of Example 2 is that, if one person claims

$$\{-1, 0\} \cap \{0, 1\} \neq \{0\} \quad \text{and} \quad (-1, 0) \cap (0, 1) \neq \emptyset$$

and if another claims

It is not the case that either $\{-1, 0\} \cap \{0, 1\} = \{0\}$ or $(-1, 0) \cap (0, 1) = \emptyset$

they are both saying the same thing; thus they are either both right or both wrong. The first statement has the form $\sim p \wedge \sim q$, whereas the second is structured $\sim (p \vee q)$ (What is p? What is q?), two statement forms that we have seen in Example 2 to be logically equivalent or *the same* in a logical sense. Note that both are wrong in their claims since p and q are both true (row 1 of the table in Figure 2.4).

The main role in mathematics of logical equivalence lies in the idea, implied in the previous paragraph, that two logically equivalent statement forms can be thought of as "the same," from the point of view of logic, and so are interchangeable. Thus if we must prove a statement whose form is p, and find it easier to prove q, where q is logically equivalent to p, then we may prove p by proving q. We will see numerous applications of this principle later in the text.

Can you give other examples of logically equivalent statement forms using only three connectives $\sim$, $\vee$, and $\wedge$? Think about this question; then see Exercise 3, Article 2.1, and Theorem 1, Article 2.3.

THE CONDITIONAL AND BICONDITIONAL

Very few statements with significant mathematical content that are easily understandable can be formulated by using the connectives and, or, and not alone (see, however, Exercises 10 and 11, Article 2.3). As noted earlier in this chapter, most theorems have the form "if . . . then" or "if and only if," while every definition, by nature, admits an "if and only if" formulation. Thus we are led to Definition 3.

DEFINITION 3
Given statements p and q, we define:

(a)   The statement **p implies q**, denoted $p \rightarrow q$, also read "if p, then q," is true except in the case where p is true and q is false. Such a statement is called a **conditional**; the component statements p and q are called the **premise** and **conclusion**, respectively.

(b)   The statement **p if and only if q**, denoted $p \leftrightarrow q$, also written "p iff q," is true precisely in the cases where p and q are both true or p and q are both false. Such a statement is called a **biconditional**.

The truth tables for these two connectives are given in Figure 2.5.

p	q	$p \rightarrow q$	$p \leftrightarrow q$
T	T	T	T
T	F	F	F
F	T	T	F
F	F	T	T

Figure 2.5   *Truth tables for the conditional and biconditional.*

Examples of conditionals include:

1.   If I finish my work, I go out on the town.
2.   If $2 + 2 = 5$, then $\{0, 1\} \subseteq (0, 1)$.
3.   If $2 + 2 = 4$, then 5 is not a prime number.

Examples of biconditionals include:

4.   3 is odd if and only if 4 is even.   (true)
5. $7 + 6 = 14$ if and only if 7 times 6 equals 41.   (true)
6.   A triangle has three sides if and only if a hexagon has   (false)
     seven sides.

Students generally find the conditional to be the least intuitive of all the connectives. One reason is that normal usage of "if ... then" presupposes a causal connection between the premise and the conclusion, as in (1). Sentences such as (2) and (3) seem somehow unnatural, perhaps not even worthy of being regarded as statements. But in applications of the propositional calculus to mathematics, it is crucial that $p \rightarrow q$ be a statement whenever p and q are (with no regard for any "cause and effect" relationship) with its truth or falsehood totally a function of the (possibly independent) truth values of p and q. Thus we consider (2) to be true (since its premise is false, the truth value of the conclusion doesn't matter) and (3) to be false.

Another problem many students encounter with the truth table defining the conditional lies in row 3. Why do we regard $p \rightarrow q$ as true when p is false and q is true? Consider sentence (1). Most people would (justifiably) regard this statement as <u>true</u> if, on a given evening, "I finished my work and went out" (row 1) or if "I did not finish my work and didn't go out" (row 4), and <u>false</u> (i.e., I lied) if "I finished my work and stayed home" (row 2). But what if "I don't finish and still go out"? Given the imprecision with which language is used in everyday life, many would comment that (1) is a false statement. Looking at what this statement <u>actually says</u>, and not at any hidden meaning that is often read into such a statement, is this a fair comment? Not at all! The statement deals only with "what

I would do if I finished my work" and made no commitment otherwise; surely it cannot be labeled "false" in this case. Since it must have a truth value, the only reasonable value is true. There are other good arguments for the suitability of "F → T is T." One is found in Exercise 9, Article 2.3, another in Example 3, Article 3.2.

One final remark along this line is related to row 4 of the table defining the biconditional. When we assert that a statement such as (5) is true, we are in no way asserting that either of its component statements is necessarily true, only that the entire "if and only if" statement is true. A similar remark could be made in reference to row 4 of the table defining the conditional. The truth of a statement such as (2) does not mean that the conclusion ("$\{0, 1\} \subseteq (0, 1)$" in this case) is necessarily true. Indeed, the <u>conclusion</u> is false in this particular example!

You may have noticed earlier that none of the conditional statements (1 through 3) seems similar to the conditionals in mathematical theorems. What is missing in these examples? Statements such as "if n is odd, then $n + 1$ is even" or "if f is differentiable at 2, then f is continuous at 2" or "$x^2 - 5x + 6 = 0$ if and only if $x = 2$ or $x = 3$" are what we mainly have in mind when thinking of "if . . . then" theorems or "if and only if" theorems. Note, however, that the component sentences in these examples (e.g., "n is odd," "f is continuous at 2") are not statements, but rather, open sentences. Also, implicit in each of these "if . . . then" sentences is an unwritten "for every," that is, a quantifier. A nonmathematical example is the sentence, "If today is Monday, then tomorrow is Tuesday." In this statement, which happens to be true, the words "today" and "tomorrow" are both variables. In Chapter 3, where we study open sentences and quantifiers, you will see the "if . . . then" and "iff" connectives used in their most natural and mathematically useful setting. For now, you should focus on mastering certain mechanical properties of the connectives.

Exercises

1. Four binary connectives $\wedge$, $\vee$, $\rightarrow$, and $\leftrightarrow$ have been defined, each by means of a truth table with four rows. Show that there are exactly 16 possible definitions of binary connectives [recall Exercise 12(a), Article 1.5].

2. Construct a truth table for each of the following statement forms. Label each a tautology, contradiction, or contingency?

(a) $(p \wedge q) \rightarrow p$

(b) $p \rightarrow (p \vee q)$

(c) $(p \vee q) \rightarrow (p \wedge q)$

(d) $p \leftrightarrow \sim p$

(e) $p \rightarrow [\sim p \rightarrow (q \wedge \sim q)]$

(f) $(p \rightarrow q) \vee (q \rightarrow p)$

(g) $(p \rightarrow r) \rightarrow [(p \rightarrow q) \wedge (q \rightarrow r)]$

(h) $[(p \wedge q) \rightarrow r] \rightarrow (p \rightarrow r)$

(i) $\{[(p \wedge q) \rightarrow r] \rightarrow (p \rightarrow r)\} \leftrightarrow (p \rightarrow q)$

(j) $[(p \rightarrow q) \wedge (q \rightarrow r) \wedge (s \rightarrow r)] \rightarrow (\sim p \rightarrow \sim s)$

3. Let *p* represent the statement "I pass the test." Let *q* symbolize "I pass the course." Let *r* stand for "I make the dean's list."

(a)   Express as a statement in English:

(i)	$p \vee \sim q$	*(ii)*	$(p \to q) \wedge (q \to r)$
(iii)	$\sim p \to \sim q$	★*(iv)*	$q \wedge \sim r$
(v)	$q \to p$	★*(vi)*	$q \to r$
(vii)	$\sim p \to \sim r$	*(viii)*	$(p \to r) \wedge (r \to p)$
(ix)	$\sim p \wedge q$		

(b)   Express symbolically:

  (i)   Passing the test will put me on the dean's list.
★*(ii)*   Either I pass the course or I don't make the dean's list.
  (iii)   If I don't pass the course, I don't make the dean's list.
★*(iv)*   In order to pass the course, I must pass the test.
  (v)   I passed the course, but I didn't make the dean's list.
  (vi)   Passing the test is tantamount to passing the course.

4. Determine whether each of the following statements is true or false, based on the truth or falsehood of the component simple statements: (As in Exercise 4, Article 2.1, first express each statement in symbolic form.)

  (a)   If 5 is not an odd integer, then 8 is prime.
  (b)   If $e = \lim_{x \to \infty} (1 + 1/x)^x$, then $\ln e = 1$.
★*(c)*   If either $2 \neq 5$ or $4 + 5 = 9$, then $5^2 \neq 25$.
  (d)   If the moon is made of green cheese, then the derivative of a linear function does not equal its slope.
  (e)   The sine function is even if and only if the cosine function is odd.
★*(f)*   If $\int_{-\pi}^{\pi} \sin x \, dx = 0$ and $d/dx(2^x) \neq x2^{x-1}$, then $\ln 6 = (\ln 2)(\ln 3)$.
  (g) $\int_{-\pi}^{\pi} \sin x \, dx = 0$ if and only if either $d/dx(2x^x) = x2^{x-1}$ or $\ln 6 = (\ln 2)(\ln 3)$.
★*(h)*   If $\int_{-\pi}^{\pi} \sin x \, dx = 0$, then $\ln 6 = (\ln 2)(\ln 3)$ implies that $d/dx(2^x) = x2^{x-1}$.

2.3   Theorems of the Propositional Calculus

The theorems of the propositional calculus are the tautologies. In an informal approach such as the one we use "proofs" of theorems are the truth tables by which a statement form is seen to be a tautology. The tautologies of primary interest for mathematics are those whose main connective is either the biconditional or the conditional, that is, the *equivalences* and the *implications*.

If *p* and *q* are compound statement forms, then the statement form $p \leftrightarrow q$ is a tautology if and only if *p* and *q* have the same truth values under all possible truth conditions; that is, if and only if *p* and *q* are logically equivalent. Thus we refer to any tautology having the biconditional as its main connective as an *equivalence*. We begin our study of theorems of the propositional calculus by focusing on important equivalences. Several important results of this type are suggested in the following example.

p	q	$\sim p$	$\sim q$	$p \to q$	$q \to p$	$\sim p \to \sim q$	$\sim q \to \sim p$
T	T	F	F	T	T	T	T
T	F	F	T	F	T	T	F
F	T	T	F	T	F	F	T
F	F	T	T	T	T	T	T

Figure 2.6   *Truth tables for the original, converse, inverse, and contrapositive of a conditional $p \to q$.*

EXAMPLE 1   Find pairs of equivalent statement forms among $p \to q$, $q \to p$, $\sim q \to \sim p$, and $\sim p \to \sim q$.

Solution   We can most efficiently deal with this problem by constructing a single truth table, as illustrated in Figure 2.6. A comparison of columns (5) through (8) shows that $p \to q$ and $\sim q \to \sim p$ are logically equivalent, as are $q \to p$ and $\sim p \to \sim q$. □

DEFINITION 1
If $p \to q$ is a conditional, then the corresponding conditional $\sim q \to \sim p$ is called its **contrapositive**, $q \to p$ is called its **converse**, and $\sim p \to \sim q$ is called its **inverse**.

The final outcome of Example 1 is that any conditional is equivalent to its contrapositive, but not to its converse and inverse. The converse and inverse of a given conditional, however, are equivalent to each other. [Why? What is the relationship between $q \to p$ and $\sim p \to \sim q$? See Exercise 4(b).] The theorem of the propositional calculus suggested by Example 1 is: The statement form $(p \to q) \leftrightarrow (\sim q \to \sim p)$ is a tautology. The fact that $p \to q$ is not equivalent to its converse $q \to p$ means that the statement form $(p \to q) \leftrightarrow (q \to p)$ is not a tautology. This means that a statement of the form $p \to q$ can be true, even when the corresponding statement $q \to p$ is false. Can you give some examples from your mathematical experience of this situation?

In the next example we encounter two more important equivalences; the statement form $p \leftrightarrow q$ is equivalent to $(p \to q) \wedge (q \to p)$ and the form $p \to (q \vee r)$ is equivalent to $(p \wedge \sim q) \to r$.

EXAMPLE 2   Show that the following biconditionals are tautologies:

(a) $(p \leftrightarrow q) \leftrightarrow [(p \to q) \wedge (q \to p)]$
(b) $[p \to (q \vee r)] \leftrightarrow [(p \wedge \sim q) \to r]$

Solution   We construct truth tables as shown in Figures 2.7a and 2.7b:

(a)

p	q	$p \to q$	$q \to p$	$(p \to q) \wedge (q \to p)$	$p \leftrightarrow q$	$\leftrightarrow$
T	T	T	T	T	T	T
T	F	F	T	F	F	T
F	T	T	F	F	F	T
F	F	T	T	T	T	T

(b)

p	q	r	$q \vee r$	$p \to (q \vee r)$	$\sim q$	$p \wedge \sim q$	$(p \wedge \sim q) \to r$	$\leftrightarrow$
T	T	T	T	T	F	F	T	T
T	F	T	T	T	T	T	T	T
F	T	T	T	T	F	F	T	T
F	F	T	T	T	T	F	T	T
T	T	F	T	T	F	F	T	T
T	F	F	F	F	T	T	F	T
F	T	F	T	T	F	F	T	T
F	F	F	F	T	T	F	T	T

Figure 2.7   *Truth table proofs of two important equivalences.*

In both examples the conclusion that the given biconditional statement is a tautology follows from the column of T's at the right of both tables. In Figure 2.7a we obtain the values in the final column by linking the fifth and sixth columns by the connective ↔. In Figure 2.7b we make the same final step, linking columns 5 and 8.   □

MATHEMATICAL SIGNIFICANCE OF EQUIVALENCES

Tautologies involving the biconditional as main connective (i.e., logical equivalences) have an important bearing on theorem-proving in mathematics. The connection is: A mathematical statement having a given logical form may be proved by proving any corresponding statement whose form is logically equivalent to that of the original. Examples 1 and 2 provide some specific illustrations of how this principle may be applied. Example 2(b), for instance, indicates that if we must prove a theorem whose conclusion has the form "either q or r" (with hypothesis p), we may do so by assuming q false (i.e., assuming $\sim q$ is true) and trying to deduce r from the expanded hypothesis $p \wedge \sim q$. A practical application of this principle is the theorem about real numbers "if $xy = 0$, then $x = 0$ or $y = 0$." We can approach the proof of this result by assuming that $x \neq 0$ (so that we now have <u>two</u> hypotheses to work with, $xy = 0$ *and* $x \neq 0$) and attempting to conclude that y must equal zero (the full proof is found in Article 6.2).

The other two equivalences in Examples 1 and 2 are of even greater importance for theorem-proving. The tautology in 2(a) says that we may divide an "if and only if" proof into two parts, namely, "if p, then q" and "if q, then p," and carry out the proof by proving each of these two parts separately. This is the approach most often taken to prove a theorem whose statement involves the biconditional (Examples 9 and 10, Article 4.1, illustrate another approach to proving such theorems). The tautology in Example 1 is the basis of proof by *contrapositive*, a form of *indirect proof*. Instead of proving directly that q follows from p, we may instead proceed by assuming the conclusion q to be false and trying to show that it follows that p must be false.

In summary, many logical equivalences correspond to possible strategies for approaching proofs of mathematical theorems. We will look in detail at several such methods of proof, as well as a wealth of specific proofs, in Chapters 4 through 6. But for now, the important idea that you should be beginning to sense is: The rules of the propositional calculus, a part of logic, are crucial to mainstream mathematics!

Equivalents to the negation of the five connectives. Earlier we suggested a method of proof, proof by contrapositive, that involves assuming the negation of a desired conclusion. Suppose we wish to use this approach to prove a result whose conclusion is itself a compound statement form, say $p \wedge q$ or $p \rightarrow q$. In the latter case, for instance, we would have to begin the proof by stating "suppose the conclusion $p \rightarrow q$ is false." At this point, before we could effectively <u>use</u> that assumption, we would need to know some statement involving p and q that is thereby <u>true</u>. Thus it would clearly be of value to have at our disposal "positive" statement forms (i.e., statement forms in which negation is not the main connective) equivalent to the negation of each of the five connectives, that is, equivalent to $\sim(\sim p)$, $\sim(p \wedge q)$, $\sim(p \vee q)$, $\sim(p \rightarrow q)$, and $\sim(p \leftrightarrow q)$. In Theorem 1 we will give a list of tautologies of the propositional calculus whose main connective is the biconditional (i.e., equivalences); parts (b) through (f) of this theorem give equivalents to the negation of each of the five connectives.

Part (b) of Theorem 1 asserts that the negation of the negation of a statement is the statement itself. Parts (c) and (d) state that the negation of

conjunction involves disjunction (and the negation of the original component statements), and vice versa. Like the two analogous theorems of
set theory [Fact 6, (34)(35), Article 1.4], these are known as De Morgan's
laws. To get a feeling for (e), ask yourself what must happen (i.e., What
statement is true?) in order for the promise "if you pass this test, you will
pass the course" to be a lie, that is, a false statement. As for (f), we can
convince ourselves of its reasonableness by combining the first tautology
in Example 2 with parts (c) and (e) of Theorem 1. Here is an alternative
approach to understanding (f). Suppose your teacher had promised "you
will pass the course if and only if you pass this test." What possibilities
could have occurred if you conclude, after the fact, that the instructor did
not keep the promise?

EXAMPLE 3   Write a positive statement equivalent to the negation of "If
rainfall is light, then the crop is disappointing and grain prices rise."

Solution   This statement has the form $p \to (q \wedge r)$. By Theorem 1(e), its
negation has the form $p \wedge [\sim(q \wedge r)]$ which, by (c) of Theorem 1, is equivalent to $p \wedge (\sim q \vee \sim r)$. This statement form may be interpreted in this
example as "rainfall is light and (yet) either the crop is not disappointing
or grain prices are not rising."   □

Selected equivalences of the propositional calculus. The proof of each part
of the following theorem consists of a truth table. Since the process of constructing truth tables has been demonstrated earlier and is laborious, there
is little to be gained from proving all parts of this theorem. A compromise
is suggested in Exercise 2(a).

THEOREM 1
The following statement forms, each having the biconditional as main connective, are all tautologies (and thus equivalences):

(a) $p \leftrightarrow p$ (reflexive property of
                                                                    equivalence)

(b) $p \leftrightarrow \sim(\sim p)$ (negation of negation)

(c) $\sim(p \wedge q) \leftrightarrow \sim p \vee \sim q$ (negation of conjunction;
                                                                    De Morgan's law)

(d) $\sim(p \vee q) \leftrightarrow \sim p \wedge \sim q$ (negation of disjunction;
                                                                    De Morgan's law)

(e) $\sim(p \to q) \leftrightarrow p \wedge \sim q$ (negation of conditional)

(f) $\sim(p \leftrightarrow q) \leftrightarrow (p \wedge \sim q) \vee (\sim p \wedge q)$ (negation of biconditional)

(g) $(p \vee q) \leftrightarrow (q \vee p)$ (commutativity of disjunction)

(h) $(p \wedge q) \leftrightarrow (q \wedge p)$ (commutativity of conjunction)

(i) $(p \vee q) \vee r \leftrightarrow p \vee (q \vee r)$ (associativity of disjunction)

(j) $(p \wedge q) \wedge r \leftrightarrow p \wedge (q \wedge r)$ (associativity of conjunction)

(k) $p \vee (q \wedge r) \leftrightarrow (p \vee q) \wedge (p \vee r)$ (disjunction distributes over
                                                                    conjunction)

(l) $p \land (q \lor r) \leftrightarrow (p \land q) \lor (p \land r)$ (conjunction distributes over disjunction)

(m) $(p \leftrightarrow q) \leftrightarrow [(p \to q) \land (q \to p)]$ (biconditional law; strategy in an iff proof)

(n) $(p \to q) \leftrightarrow (\sim q \to \sim p)$ (equivalence of contrapositive)

(o) $(p \to q) \leftrightarrow \sim p \lor q$

(p) $[p \to (q \lor r)] \leftrightarrow [(p \land \sim q) \to r]$ (strategy for deriving conclusion $q \lor r$)

(q) $[(p \lor q) \to r] \leftrightarrow [(p \to r) \land (q \to r)]$ (strategy for using hypothesis $p \lor q$)

(r) $[p \to (q \land r)] \leftrightarrow [(p \to q) \land (p \to r)]$ (strategy for deriving conclusion $q \land r$)

(s) $[(p \land q) \to r] \leftrightarrow [(p \land \sim r) \to \sim q]$ (indirect approach to using hypothesis $p \land q$)

(t) $[(p \land q) \to r] \leftrightarrow [(p \to r) \lor (q \to r)]$ (strategy for using hypothesis $p \land q$)

(u) $[(p \land q) \to r] \leftrightarrow [p \to (q \to r)]$

(v) $(p \leftrightarrow q) \leftrightarrow (\sim q \leftrightarrow \sim p)$

IMPORTANT IMPLICATIONS

If p and q are statement forms such that the conditional $p \to q$ is a tautology, we say that this conditional statement is an *implication* and that *p logically implies q*. Because this situation means that q is true under all truth conditions for which p is true (i.e., the truth of p "forces" q to be true), we say that p is a *stronger* statement form than q, or that q is *weaker* than p in this case.

Note the relationship between implication and equivalence. Part (m) of Theorem 1 indicates that if p and q are equivalent, then each implies the other. On the other hand, if it is known only that p implies q, the possibility that p and q are equivalent is left open. In fact, the latter is true if and only if q implies p. The relationship between implication and equivalence is described in another way in (n) of Theorem 2; equivalence is stronger than (mere) implication.

EXAMPLE 4 Show that $p \land q$ is a stronger statement form than p, which is, in turn, stronger than $p \lor q$.

Solution We need only show that both the conditionals $(p \land q) \to p$ and $p \to (p \lor q)$ are tautologies. This conclusion should have been reached in Exercises 2(a, b), Article 2.2. □

EXAMPLE 5 Show that $p \land (p \to q)$ is a stronger statement form than q.

Solution This means simply that the conditional $[p \land (p \to q)] \to q$ is a tautology, as may be verified easily by constructing a truth table. □

The tautology in Example 5, known as *modus ponens*, is a particularly important principle of logic, and is actually the cornerstone of the relevance of the implication connective to mathematical theorem-proving. We can conclude the truth of a desired proposition q if we can derive q as a logical consequence of some statement p, where p in turn is known to be true. Perhaps, in a particular problem, we may wish to prove q and find that q can be proved as a consequence of p, where p is some well-known theorem. In such a case we say that q is a *corollary* to p. On the other hand, we may wish to prove q where it is evident that q follows from a statement p, where the truth of p, however, is not known. In such a case the burden of proof shifts from proving q directly to trying somehow to prove p. A statement p in this context (assuming it can be proved) is often referred to as a *lemma*. In such proofs phrasing like "in order to prove q, it is clearly sufficient to prove p, where p is the statement . . ." is common.

In Theorem 2 we provide a list of selected implications of the propositional calculus. These statements can be verified on a selective basis [see Exercise 2(b)] by using truth tables.

THEOREM 2
The following statement forms, each having the conditional as main connective, are all tautologies (and hence are implications):

(a)	$p \to p$	(reflexive property of implication)
(b)	$[(p \to q) \wedge (q \to r)] \to (p \to r)$	(law of syllogism; transitive property of implication)
(c)	$(p \wedge q) \to p$	(law of simplification)
(d)	$p \to (p \vee q)$	(law of addition)
(e)	$[p \wedge (p \to q)] \to q$	(law of detachment; *modus ponens*)
(f)	$[(p \to q) \wedge \sim q] \to \sim p$	(indirect proof; proof by contrapositive; *modus tollens*)
(g)	$[\sim p \to (q \wedge \sim q)] \to p$	(indirect proof; proof by contradiction; *reductio ad absurdum*)
(h)	$(p \leftrightarrow q) \to (q \leftrightarrow p)$	(symmetric property of equivalence)
(i)	$[(p \leftrightarrow q) \wedge (q \leftrightarrow r)] \to (p \leftrightarrow r)$	(transitive property of equivalence)
(j)	$(p \to r) \to [(p \wedge q) \to r]$	
(k)	$[(p \vee q) \wedge \sim p] \to q$	(law of disjunction; *modus tollendo ponens*)
(l)	$\sim p \to (p \to q)$	
(m)	$q \to (p \to q)$	
(n)	$(p \leftrightarrow q) \to (p \to q)$	

In addition to the implications stated in Theorem 2, each equivalence in Theorem 1 yields a new tautology if the biconditional connective is replaced by the conditional in either direction (because of part (n) of Theorem 2, which asserts formally that the biconditional is stronger than the conditional). Furthermore, precisely three of the conditional statement forms in Theorem 2 can be strengthened to biconditionals, that is, remain true if the arrow is replaced by a double arrow. Can you determine which ones? (See Exercise 3.)

MATHEMATICAL SIGNIFICANCE OF TAUTOLOGIES INVOLVING THE CONDITIONAL

The significance of implication statements for mathematical theorem-proving was discussed before Theorem 2, in connection with *modus ponens*. Let us see, however, how this reasoning applies to actual problems from mathematics, with specific reference to tautologies from Theorem 2.

Suppose, for example, we wish to prove that if a function f is differentiable at a, then $\lim_{x \to a} f(x)$ exists. Suppose, furthermore, that we have at our disposal the well-known theorem of elementary calculus, "if f is differentiable at a, then f is continuous at a," as well as the definition "f is continuous at a if and only if $\lim_{x \to a} f(x)$ exists <u>and</u> equals $f(a)$." Since f is differentiable at a implies f is continuous at a by the known theorem (denote by $p \to q$), and since f is continuous at a implies $\lim_{x \to a} f(x)$ exists (denote by $q \to r$), we may draw the desired conclusion (which has the form $p \to r$) by (b) of Theorem 2.

As a second example, consider the famous proof that $\sqrt{2}$ is irrational (a detailed discussion of this proof is given in Article 6.2). The proof proceeds by assuming that $\sqrt{2}$ is rational (denote by $\sim p$) and deducing from this a logical contradiction of the form $q \wedge \sim q$. Part (g) of Theorem 2 indicates that whenever we can deduce a contradiction from the negation of a statement the statement itself must be true.

Finally, consider (j) of Theorem 2. Suppose we wish to derive a conclusion r from hypotheses p and q. Suppose we are able to derive r from hypothesis p alone, that is, write a proof that makes no use of hypothesis q. By (j), if we can do this, our desired theorem is thereby also proved (see Exercise 7).

The approach suggested in the previous paragraph is a logically valid method of proof, but it calls for a word of warning. Perhaps we are able to prove a theorem without using all the hypotheses given. If we can, then by (j), we have <u>improved upon</u> the result we were asked to derive; that is, we have proved a stronger statement than the one requested. But ordinarily, theorems posed to students at the junior-senior level require all the hypotheses given and cannot be proved (i.e., aren't true) if a hypothesis is omitted. Failure to use one of the hypotheses in a proof is often a telltale sign that the proof is in error. Always check your proofs to see that you have used all the hypotheses; if you haven't, investigate further! One additional related note: Many unsolved problems in research mathematics today involve "strengthening" known theorems, that is, removing some hypothesis that, up to now, has been used in every known derivation of the conclusion of the theorem.

ENGLISH-LANGUAGE TRANSLATIONS OF THE CONDITIONAL AND BICONDITIONAL CONNECTIVES

As seen already, certain uses of the propositional calculus require that we translate sentences expressed in English into precise symbolic form. Since there are many ways of expressing an idea in English, the following list of translations may prove helpful.

REMARK 1   The following three lists provide translations between English sentences and symbolic representation of those sentences.

1. $p \to q$ may be interpreted in any of the following ways:

   (a)   If p, then q (q if p)
   (b) p implies q (q is implied by p)
   (c)   Whenever p, then q (q whenever p)
   (d) p is stronger than q (q is weaker than p)
   (e) q unless $\sim p$ ($\sim p$ unless q)
   (f)   If not q, then not p (p only if q)
   (g)   Not q implies not p (not p is implied by not q)
   (h) p is sufficient for q ($\sim q$ is sufficient for $\sim p$)
   (i) q is necessary for p ($\sim p$ is necessary for $\sim q$)
   (j)   Either not p or q.

2. $p \leftrightarrow q$ may be interpreted as:

   (a) p is equivalent to q
   (b) p if and only if q
   (c) p is necessary and sufficient for q
   (d) p implies q and q implies p
   (e)   If p, then q and if q, then p

3. The following miscellaneous correspondences are also valid:

Sentence	*Symbolic translation*
(a) p or q or both	$p \vee q$
(b) p or q, but not both	$\sim(p \leftrightarrow q)$
(c) p, but not q	$p \wedge \sim q$
(d) p unless q	$\sim q \to p$

You should convince yourself of the reasonableness of these various translations and representations, in particular, noting explicitly the role of various equivalences from Theorem 1 as justification for the translation (Exercise 8).

Exercises

1. *(a)* In Exercise 3, Article 2.2, find any examples of pairs of statement forms [in (a)] or statements [in (b)] that are either equivalent to or negations of each other.

(b)   In Exercise 4, Article 2.2, write the negation of each statement, using parts (b) through (f) of Theorem 1 to avoid having negation as the main connective. Write the converse of all except (e) and (g).

2. *(a)*   Prove, by using a truth table, five of the equivalences listed in Theorem 1. More specifically, choose one from (c) through (f), one from (g) through (1), one from (m) through (o), and two from (p) through (t).

(b)   Verify, by using a truth table, three of the implications in Theorem 2, choosing (g) and (j) and one from among (b), (i), and (k).

3. Determine which three of the implications in Theorem 2 are reversible, that is, have a converse that is also a tautology (recall remarks from the paragraph immediately following Theorem 2).

4. *(a)*   Write the converse, contrapositive, and inverse of each of the following conditionals. (Your final answer in each case should not use the "not" connective to modify a compound statement form. Use (b) through (f) of Theorem 1 to simplify any such expressions that occur.)

★*(i)* $(p \land q) \to r$
(ii) $p \to (q \to p)$
(iii) $(p \leftrightarrow q) \to (p \to q)$

(b)   Fill in each of the blanks with one of the words *original, converse, contrapositive,* or *inverse.*

(i)   The converse of the converse of $p \to q$ is the _____ of $p \to q$.
(ii)   The inverse of the contrapositive of $p \to q$ is the _____ of $p \to q$.
★*(iii)*   The contrapositive of the converse of $p \to q$ is the _____ of $p \to q$.
(iv)   The converse of the inverse of $p \to q$ is the _____ of $p \to q$.
(v)   The inverse of the converse of $p \to q$ is the _____ of $p \to q$.
(vi)   The original of the converse of $p \to q$ is the _____ of $p \to q$.
★*(vii)*   The contrapositive of the contrapositive of $p \to q$ is the _____ of $p \to q$.

(c)   Give a concise description of the pattern emerging from the answers in (b), governing the effect of two successive applications of the operations *original, contrapositive, converse,* and *inverse* to a given statement form $p \to q$.

(d)   Write the converse, inverse, contrapositive, and negation of the statements:

(i)   If the economy improves, then I get a better job.
★*(ii)*   If $2 < 4$ and $5 + 5 = 10$, then $\sin (\pi/3) = \frac{1}{2}$.
(iii)   If I finish my work, I play golf unless it rains.
(iv)   If f differentiable implies f is continuous, then f is continuous.
(v)   If f is defined at a, then the existence of $\lim_{x \to a} f(x)$ implies f is continuous at a.
(vi)   If $(F, +, \cdot)$ is a field, then $(F, +)$ and $(F - \{0\}, \cdot)$ are both abelian groups.

5. Let p, q, and r represent statements defined as follows:

p: lines x and y lie in the same plane.

q: lines x and y are parallel.

r: lines x and y have no points in common.

Express symbolically as compound statement forms in the letters p, q, and r.

(a)   If x and y are parallel, then they have no points in common.

★*(b)*   Lines x and y intersect unless they are parallel.

(c)   Lines x and y have no points in common, but they are not parallel.

(d)   The statement "lines x and y are parallel" is stronger than the statement "lines x and y have no points in common."

★*(e)*   In order for x and y having no points in common to imply that x and y are parallel, it is necessary that x and y lie in the same plane.

(f)   Whenever x and y are parallel, then x and y lie in the same plane.

(g)   Lines x and y intersect unless they are parallel or don't lie in the same plane.

(h)   Either x and y are parallel or x and y have points in common, but not both.

6. According to (v) of Theorem 1, two statement forms are equivalent if and only if their negations are equivalent. Use this fact, together with the other parts of Theorem 1 [except (q) and (u)] to argue the equivalence of the statement forms:

(a) $(p \vee q) \rightarrow r$ and $(p \rightarrow r) \wedge (q \rightarrow r)$ [(q) of Theorem 1]

(b) $(p \wedge q) \rightarrow r$ and $p \rightarrow (q \rightarrow r)$ [(u) of Theorem 1]

7. *(a)*   Give three examples of well-known corollaries to the mean value theorem of elementary calculus.

(b)   In each of parts (a′) through (g′), one of the given compound statements p or q is formally stronger than the other; in fact, either $p \rightarrow q$ or $q \rightarrow p$ is an instance of a tautology.

(i)   Determine which of the two is stronger in each case.

(ii)   Based on your previous mathematical experience, label each of the following 14 statements as true or false [when each is preceded by the appropriate number of occurrences of the universal quantifier *for every*. For example, both sentences in (d′) should be preceded by *for every f and for every a*].

(iii)   Check that your answers in (ii) are consistent with your conclusions in (i).

★*(a′)* p: If $0 < |x - a| < \beta$, then $x \neq a$ and $a - \beta < x < a + \beta$.

   q: If $0 < |x - a| < \beta$, then $a - \beta < x < a + \beta$.

★*(b′)* p: If a, b, and x are real numbers such that $ax = bx$, then $a = b$.

   q: If a, b, and x are real numbers such that $ax = bx$ and $x \neq 0$, then $a = b$.

(c′) p: If f has a relative maximum at a and f is differentiable at a, then $f'(a) = 0$.

   q: If f has relative maximum at a, then $f'(a) = 0$.

(d′) p: If f is differentiable at a, then f is continuous at a.

   q: If f is differentiable at a and f has a relative maximum at a, then f is continuous at a.

(e′) p: If f is defined at a and $\lim_{x \to a} f(x)$ exists and equals $f(a)$, then f is continuous at a.

   q: If f is defined at a and $\lim_{x \to a} f(x)$ exists, then f is continuous at a.

(f′) p: If a, b, and p are integers, if p is prime, and p divides the product ab of a and b, then either p divides a or p divides b.

q: If a, b, and p are integers and if p divides ab, then either p divides a or p divides b.

(g') [Some abstract algebra background is necessary to be able to answer (ii).]
  p: If a finite group G is cyclic, then G is abelian.
  q: If a group G (finite or infinite) is cyclic, then G is abelian.

8. (a) For each of the following parts of Remark 1, determine which tautology or tautologies from Theorem 1 or Theorem 2 provide justification.

  (i)   1(e)   (ii)   1(f)
  (iii) 1(j)   (iv)   2(d)
  (v)   3(b)

(b) Give a specific nonmathematical example to show that the tautology $(p \to q) \leftrightarrow (\sim p \vee q)$ (part (o) of Theorem 1) is intuitively reasonable.

9. The law of syllogism, which states that $[(p \to q) \wedge (q \to r)] \to (p \to r)$ is a tautology, is important in logic and represents a common form of an argument in ordinary discourse. Consider three possible alternative definitions for "conditionals," denoted $\to_i^*$ for $i = 1, 2, 3$, defined by the table in Figure 2.8. The first two rows in each case, of course, seem reasonable and agree with the corresponding rows of the definition of the "honest" conditional. The last two rows may seem arbitrary, but actually represent all other possible definitions of a "conditional" connective. Show that the law of syllogism fails for all three of these possible definitions.

10. (a) Prove that the compound statement forms $p \vee q$, $p \to q$, and $p \leftrightarrow q$ are each logically equivalent to statement forms in p and q involving the connectives *not* and *and* only. [*Hint:* See parts (c), (o), and (m) of Theorem 1.]
(b) Based on your answers to (a), express each of the following compound statement forms in terms of $\sim$ and $\wedge$ only:

  (i) $p \to (q \vee r)$ ★(ii) $p \to (q \to r)$
  (iii) $(p \to q) \to r$ (iv) $(p \vee q) \vee r$
  (v) $p \vee (q \vee r)$

11. The main thrust of Exercise 10 is that the five connectives $\vee$, $\wedge$, $\sim$, $\to$, and $\leftrightarrow$ are not all needed for the propositional calculus. Any statement form that can be expressed in terms of any of these five connectives has an equivalent representation

Figure 2.8   *Three possible, but incorrect,*
definitions of the conditional connective. The law
of syllogism fails to be a tautology if $\to$ is defined
in any of these three ways.

p	q	$p \to_1^* q$	$p \to_2^* q$	$p \to_3^* q$
T	T	T	T	T
T	F	F	F	F
F	T	F	T	F
F	F	F	F	T

p	q	p/q
T	T	F
T	F	T
F	T	T
F	F	T

Figure 2.9   *Truth table defining the Sheffer stroke.*

involving $\wedge$ and $\sim$ only. [Note, however, from your answers to Exercise 10(b) that expressions using $\wedge$ and $\sim$ only are lengthier and more complicated in form than equivalent expressions in which all five connectives may be used.)] Because of this, we say that the pair of connectives $\wedge$ and $\sim$ is **adequate** for the propositional calculus. A kind of question that is of interest to logicians (although of no practical application in mainstream undergraduate mathematics) is whether there is, among the 16 possible binary connectives [recall Exercise 2(b), Article 2.1] any single connective that is adequate. The answer is "yes," as the following exercises demonstrate:

We define the connective /, called the *Sheffer stroke*, by the table in Figure 2.9.

(a)   Show that $(p/p) \leftrightarrow \sim p$ is a tautology.

(b)   Show that $(p/q)/(q/p) \leftrightarrow p \wedge q$ is a tautology.

(c)   Combine the results of Exercises 10(a) and 11(a, b) to find expressions involving the Sheffer stroke only that are equivalent to $p \vee q, p \to q$, and $p \leftrightarrow q$. Conclude from this that any statement form involving any of the five connectives of the propositional calculus has an equivalent representation that uses the Sheffer stroke only. [Note, however, that as in Exercise 10(b) the cost of this economy in number of connectives is the necessity for much lengthier, more complicated, and far less meaningful expressions.]

2.4   Analysis of Arguments for Logical Validity, Part 1 (Optional)

An interesting and useful application of the propositional calculus is the analysis of certain kinds of arguments for logical validity. An argument consists of a series of "given" statements, whose conjunction constitutes the *premise* of the argument (the individual statements comprising the premise may each be called a *partial premise*) and a *conclusion*.

DEFINITION 1
An argument consisting of the premise $p_1 \wedge p_2 \wedge \cdots \wedge p_n$ and a conclusion q is said to be a **valid argument** if and only if the statement form $(p_1 \wedge p_2 \wedge \cdots \wedge p_n) \to q$ is a tautology.

The requirement of Definition 1 is that the conclusion be true in all cases in which each of the partial premises is true; that is, the conjunction of the partial premises must logically imply the conclusion. Stated differently, the truth of the conclusion must "follow from" the assumed truth of all the premises, in order for an argument to be valid. In particular, the conclusion of an argument need not be true in order for an argument to be valid (see Exercise 5). The following example illustrates a rather standard format in which premise and conclusion of an argument are presented.

EXAMPLE 1   Test the validity of the argument

$$p$$
$$p \to q$$
$$\sim q \vee r$$

Therefore r

Solution   The statement forms above the horizontal line are the partial premises, whereas the one below the line is the conclusion. The issue is whether the conditional $[p \wedge (p \to q) \wedge (\sim q \vee r)] \to r$ is a tautology. You should verify, by using truth table, that the answer is "yes," so that the given argument is logically valid.   □

In Examples 3 and 4 we discuss a method of avoiding the need to construct a truth table in order to determine whether the conditional arising from an argument is actually an implication. In the next example we deal with an argument involving specific statements in which we must first assign a letter to each simple statement involved and then represent symbolically each of the partial premises and the conclusion. As a rule, the premise ends and the conclusion begins with a word like "therefore," or "hence," or "thus."

EXAMPLE 2   Express symbolically and analyze for validity the argument "If interest rates fall, the economy improves. If the economy improves, unemployment drops. In order for incumbents to win reelection, it is necessary that unemployment drop. Hence a sufficient condition for incumbents to win reelection is that interest rates fall."

Solution   First, we must symbolize each simple statement involved in the argument. We do this by

p: interest rates fall

q: the economy improves

r: unemployment drops

s: incumbents are reelected

The partial premises, then, have the form $p \to q$, $q \to r$, and $s \to r$ [recall, e.g., from Remark 1, part 1(i), Article 2.3, that "r is necessary for s" translates to $s \to r$]. The conclusion has the form $p \to s$. Hence the argument, in symbolic form, looks like

$$p \rightarrow q$$
$$q \rightarrow r$$
$$\underline{s \rightarrow r}$$

Therefore $\quad p \rightarrow s$

Proceeding by either constructing a truth table or using the method de-scribed in Examples 3 and 4, we conclude that this argument is not logi-cally valid. $\square$

The tautologies $[p \wedge (p \rightarrow q)] \rightarrow q$ *(modus ponens)*, $[(p \rightarrow q) \wedge (q \rightarrow r)] \rightarrow$ $(p \rightarrow r)$ (transitivity of implication), and $[p \rightarrow (q \rightarrow r)] \leftrightarrow [(p \wedge q) \rightarrow r]$, provide a method of concluding validity of an argument (or suspecting non-validity) that allows us to avoid writing cumbersome truth tables repeatedly. *Modus ponens* indicates that we can conclude q whenever we have p and $p \rightarrow q$. Transitivity of implication says that we can replace two hypotheses of the form $(p \rightarrow q)$ and $(q \rightarrow r)$ by the single hypothesis $(p \rightarrow r)$, if this is to our advantage. The third implication says that if our conclusion has the form $q \rightarrow r$, we may add q to the list of partial premises and deduce r, rather that $q \rightarrow r$, from this expanded list. Finally, recall the significance of logical equivalence: A statement form may be replaced by any equivalent statement form. We illustrate the method in Example 3.

EXAMPLE 3   Analyze the argument from Example 1 without using a truth table.

Solution   The question is whether we can validly deduce r from the assumed truth of each of the three partial premises p, $p \rightarrow q$, and $\sim q \vee r$. We re-call first the equivalence $(\sim q \vee r) \leftrightarrow (q \rightarrow r)$ [Theorem 1(o), Article 2.3]. Thus our premise becomes $p \wedge (p \rightarrow q) \wedge (q \rightarrow r)$. From $p \wedge (p \rightarrow q)$, we may conclude q, by *modus ponens*. From q and $q \rightarrow r$, we may conclude r, again by *modus ponens*, as desired. We conclude from this analysis that r does follow logically from the premise, so that the argument is indeed valid. $\square$

An argument of the form $[(p \rightarrow q) \wedge (q \rightarrow r) \wedge (r \rightarrow s)] \rightarrow (p \rightarrow s)$ can be analyzed as follows. The question is whether we can derive s from p, given the three hypotheses. Add p to the list of partial premises and ask instead whether we can derive s from this expanded list. From $p \wedge (p \rightarrow q)$, we get q. From q and $q \rightarrow r$, we get r. From $r \wedge (r \rightarrow s)$, we get s, as desired.

EXAMPLE 4   Analyze the argument in Example 2, without constructing a complete truth table.

Solution   The question is whether we can derive s from p, given hypotheses $p \rightarrow q$, $q \rightarrow r$, and $s \rightarrow r$. First, add p to the list of hypotheses. The question now shifts to whether we can derive s from this expanded list. Well, from p and $p \to q$, we get q. From q and $q \to r$, we get r. Now we are left with r and $s \to r$. At this point, the chain of reasoning grinds to a halt. We have no means of concluding s from $r \wedge (s \to r)$ (check if you wish that $[r \wedge (s \to r)] \to s$ is not a tautology). Hence we are <u>led to doubt</u> the validity of the argument. To <u>prove</u> that nonvalidity, we must come up with a combination of truth values for which the conditional in question is false. This we can also do without resorting to a complete table.

We reason as follows: We wish to find truth values for p, q, r, and s such that the conjunction $(p \to q) \wedge (q \to r) \wedge (s \to r)$ of the partial premises is true while the conclusion $p \to s$ is false. Clearly p must be true and s must be false in order for $p \to s$ to be false. In that case if $p \to q$ is to be true, then q must be true. But then r must be true in order for $q \to r$ to be true. Note that if s is false and r is true, the final partial premise $s \to r$ is true. Hence we have found a combination of truth values, namely, TTTF for p, q, r, and s, respectively, for which the premise of the argument is true while the conclusion is false. This proves conclusively the nonvalidity of the argument. $\square$

You will probably enjoy the exercises that follow much more if you employ the approach of Examples 3 and 4, rather than the boring and mechanical truth table approach. Also, you should use throughout these exercises the "strict mathematical" translation into symbols, given in Remark 1, Article 2.3, for such expressions as "unless," "only if," and "necessary."

Exercises

Analyze these arguments for logical validity:

1. Good weather is necessary for a successful garden. The garden is successful. Therefore the weather was good.

2. If today is Monday, then tomorrow is Tuesday. But today is not Monday. Therefore tomorrow is not Tuesday.

3. Either today is Monday or today is Tuesday. But today is not Monday. Therefore today is Tuesday.

★4. I will lose my job unless Smith is retained. He will be fired only if you recommend it. Therefore I will keep my job if you do not recommend his firing.

5. If $5 + 7 = 12$, then $6 > 8$. If $5 + 7 = 7 + 5$, then $5 + 7 = 12$. But $5 + 7 = 7 + 5$. Therefore we may conclude $6 > 8$. (*Hint:* Recall the discussion immediately following Definition 1.)

6. If the dollar is strong, then exports decrease. Unemployment will rise unless the decrease in exports is halted. A drop in interest rates is necessary to weaken the dollar. Hence a drop in interest rates is sufficient to cause unemployment to fall.

7. If I study all night for the abstract algebra examination, I will be tired. If I'm not energetic, I will not do the assignment for Fourier analysis. Therefore in order both to pass the exam and do the assignment, it is necessary that I not study all night.

★8. Given that $p \rightarrow q$ is a tautology, in order for $q \rightarrow p$ to be a tautology, it is necessary and sufficient that $p \leftrightarrow q$ be a tautology. We know that $p \rightarrow q$ is a tautology and that $p \leftrightarrow q$ is not a tautology. Hence $q \rightarrow p$ is not a tautology.

9. If Dawson did not meet James last night, then either Dawson is the murderer or James was out of town. If Dawson was not the murderer, then James did not meet Dawson last night and the murder took place in the hotel. If the murder took place in the hotel, then either Dawson was the murderer or James was out of town. But Dawson met James last night and James was not out of town. Therefore Dawson was the murderer.

Logic, Part II: The Predicate Calculus

CHAPTER 3

There are many kinds of statements that we wish to make in mathematics (and in everyday life) that cannot be symbolized and logically analyzed solely in terms of the propositional calculus. In addition to the <u>external</u> complexity introduced by the need to link statements by using connectives, there is an <u>internal</u> complexity in statements containing words such as "all," "every," and "some," which requires logical analysis beyond that afforded by the propositional calculus. Such an analysis is the subject of the *predicate calculus*, the topic of this chapter.

The following example demonstrates the difficulties that can arise if only the propositional calculus is available to analyze statements.

EXAMPLE 1   Let P and Q be sets, let p represent the statement "x is an element of P" and q the statement "x is an element of Q." Analyze, in terms of the propositional calculus, the statement $(p \rightarrow q) \vee (q \rightarrow p)$.

Discussion   Perhaps the best place to begin the analysis is with the truth table for the statement form $(p \rightarrow q) \vee (q \rightarrow p)$. Before reading further, you should construct that table. The results may be somewhat surprising, for this statement form is a tautology (all possible tautologies were not exhausted in Chapter 2!). Hence, in particular, if we make the indicated substitutions for p and q, the statement form $p \rightarrow q$ becomes "$x \in P$ implies $x \in Q$," while $q \rightarrow p$ is "$x \in Q$ implies $x \in P$." The disjunction then says "($x \in P$ implies $x \in Q$) or ($x \in Q$ implies $x \in P$)" and is true, since any statement of the form $(p \rightarrow q) \vee (q \rightarrow p)$ is true under all possible truth conditions. But "$x \in P$ implies $x \in Q$ <u>or</u> $x \in Q$ implies $x \in P$" seems to be saying "either *P* is a subset of *Q* or *Q* is a subset of *P*," which would appear, thereby, always to be a true statement. But experience indicates that this is not the case [see, in particular, Example 3(b), Article 1.1]. Our analysis apparently has led to a contradiction.

The resolution to the paradox presented in Example 1 lies in the fact that the two sentences symbolized earlier by *p* and *q* are not statements, but rather, are *open sentences* or *predicates*, and furthermore, sentences such as "*P* is a subset of *Q*" have an internal structure requiring the use of *quantifiers* (i.e., the expressions "for every" and "there exists") for logical accuracy. In particular, one of the theorems of the predicate calculus to be studied in this chapter provides the specific fact that will enable us to resolve the paradox. We will return to this question following Theorem 2 and Example 3, Article 3.3.

Since most definitions and theorems in mathematics employ terms such as "every" and "some" as well as the familiar "and," "or," and "if . . . then," most applications of logic to mathematics involve principles of both the propositional calculus and predicate calculus, applied together in a single setting. Armed with an understanding of the main tautologies of the propositional calculus and main theorems of the predicate calculus, students who have also developed a working knowledge of their combined use (the subject of Chapters 4, 5, and 6) will be well prepared for the rigors of junior-senior level mathematics and beyond!

3.1   Basic Concepts of the Predicate Calculus

Expressions such as "she is a doctor," "$x^2 - 3x - 40 = 0$," and "$A \cap (B \cup C) = (A \cap B) \cup (A \cap C)$," known as *predicates*, or *propositional functions* (also known as *open sentences*), are the building blocks of the predicate calculus. A **predicate** is a declarative sentence containing one or more *variables*, or *unknowns*. As the preceding examples indicate, an unknown may be a mathematical symbol, representing a number, a set, or some other mathematical quantity. Additionally, it could be a pronoun, such as "he" or "it," or for that matter, any other word with a variable meaning, like "yesterday" or "tomorrow." A predicate is not a statement, since a predicate is neither true nor false. On the other hand, predicates are closely related to statements, and our notation for them (e.g., $p(x)$ or $q(x, y)$, where *x* and *y* are unknowns) reflects that fact. In particular, there are two standard procedures by which a predicate can be converted into a statement. These procedures are *substitution* and *quantification*.

SUBSTITUTION, DOMAIN OF DISCOURSE, AND TRUTH SET

The sentence $p(x)$: $x > 4$ is an example of a predicate; in fact, it is a predicate *in one variable*. If the number 5 is substituted for *x*, the predicate becomes a statement $p(5)$: $5 > 4$ which happens to be true. If 2 is substituted for x, we get $p(2)$: $2 > 4$, a false statement, but a statement nonetheless. The predicate $q(x, y)$: $\tan x = \tan y$, an example of a propositional function in two variables, becomes a true statement when we substitute, for instance, $\pi/4$ for x and $9\pi/4$ for y.

Not all substitutions of specific objects for variables make a predicate into a statement. For one thing, if we substitute $\pi/4$ for x in $q(x, y)$, but do not substitute for y, the resulting sentence $q(\pi/4, y)$: $\tan \pi/4 = \tan y$ is still an open sentence, neither true nor false as it stands. In fact, $p(y) = q(\pi/4, y)$ is a propositional function in the single variable y. Thus, if we wish to convert a predicate into a statement by substitution, we must take care to substitute for each of the unknowns.

A second problem is that if we, for example, substitute the complex number $2 + 3i$ for x into the predicate $p(x)$, we are left with a nonsense expression $2 + 3i > 4$. The same problem would occur (even more glaringly) if we substituted an object other than a number, such as "John Smith" for x. The message of these examples is one we saw in Chapter 1, in the context of sets. Associated with each predicate $p(x)$, there must be a universal set U of objects that may be substituted for the variable. For the preceding $p(x)$, the set $\mathbf{R}$ of all real numbers would be a reasonable possibility for U, whereas $\mathbf{R} \times \mathbf{R}$ could be the universal set for $q(x, y)$. The set U, often referred to as the *domain of discourse* in the context of the predicate calculus, is sometimes named explicitly and sometimes must be surmised, as was the case with the concept of universal set in set theory.

For each open sentence $p(x)$, with associated domain of discourse U, the subset P of U defined by $P = \{x \in U \,|\, p(x)$ is a true statement$\}$, henceforth described simply by $\{x \,|\, p(x)\}$, is called the **truth set** of $p(x)$. As examples, if $U = \mathbf{R}$, the truth set of $p(x)$: $x > 4$ is the interval $(4, \infty)$, whereas the subset $\{(x, y) \in \mathbf{R} \times \mathbf{R} \,|\, x \in$ domain $(\tan)$ and $y = x + n\pi$ for some integer $n\}$ is the truth set of $q(x, y)$: $\tan x = \tan y$. As a matter of convention, we will adopt the notation that truth sets of general predicates $p(x)$, $q(x, y)$, $r(x, y, z)$ are denoted by the corresponding uppercase letters P, Q, R, and the like.

We can use the idea of truth set to extend many of the concepts of the propositional calculus to the predicate calculus. One example is provided in the following definition.

DEFINITION 1

We say that two propositional functions $p(x)$ and $q(x)$ (over a common domain of discourse U) are **logically equivalent over U** if and only if they have the same truth sets; that is, $P = Q$.

Two predicates $p(x)$ and $q(x)$ may be equivalent over one domain of discourse and nonequivalent over another. For example, $p(x, y)$: $x^2 = y^2$ and $q(x, y)$: $x = y$ are equivalent over $U_1 = \mathbf{R}^+ \times \mathbf{R}^+$, where $\mathbf{R}^+$ represents the set of positive real numbers but are not equivalent over $\mathbf{R} \times \mathbf{R}$. Just as every propositional function determines a truth set, so is every set P the truth set of some propositional function, namely, the open sentence "$x \in P$." If P is the truth set of a propositional function $p(x)$, then $p(x)$ is logically equivalent (over its domain U) to the open sentence "$x \in P$."

We can also use the "truth set" concept to extend the applicability of the five logical connectives defined in Chapter 2 from propositions to propositional functions. As one example, given propositional functions $p(x)$ and $q(x)$ over a common domain U, what meaning should we attach to the expression $p(x) \vee q(x)$? Having familiarity with the "or" connective from the propositional calculus, we read such an expression as "either $p(x)$ or $q(x)$." The expression contains a single variable x; it seems reasonable to treat this "compound predicate" just as we would any predicate in one variable. On that basis its truth set should consist of all objects a in U such that the compound proposition $p(a) \vee q(a)$ is true. According to Definition 2(c), Article 2.1, this means that an object a should be in the truth set of the predicate $p(x) \vee q(x)$ if and only if either the proposition $p(a)$ is true or the proposition $q(a)$ is true (or possibly both). Similar criteria could be applied to the compound predicates $p(x) \wedge q(x)$ and $\sim p(x)$. An object a should be in the truth set of $p(x) \wedge q(x)$ if and only if $p(a)$ and $q(a)$ are both true statements; an object a should be in the truth set of $\sim p(x)$ if and only if the proposition $p(a)$ is false.

EXAMPLE 1   Let $U = \{1, 2, 3, \ldots, 10\}$. Let predicates $p(x)$, $q(x)$, and $r(x)$ be defined over U by $p(x)$: x is odd, $q(x)$: $3 \leq x < 8$, $r(x)$: x is the square of an integer. Use the criteria outlined previously to describe the truth sets of the compound predicates $\sim p(x)$, $p(x) \vee q(x)$, and $q(x) \wedge r(x)$.

Solution   According to our criteria, an element a of U is in the truth set of $\sim p(x)$ if and only if $p(a)$ is false; that is, a is not odd, or, a is even. Thus the truth set of $\sim p(x)$ is $\{2, 4, 6, 8, 10\}$. An integer a, between 1 and 10 inclusive, is in the truth set of $p(x) \vee q(x)$ if and only if either $p(a)$ is true or $q(a)$ is true; that is, either a is odd or $3 \leq a < 8$. The truth set of $p(x) \vee q(x)$ therefore equals $\{1, 3, 4, 5, 6, 7, 9\}$. Finally, an element a of U is in the truth set of $q(x) \wedge r(x)$ if and only if $q(a)$ and $r(a)$ are both true; the truth set in this case equals $\{4\}$.   □

The results of Example 1 suggest an important connection between the truth set of a compound predicate and the truth sets of its component predicates. This connection highlights, at the same time, important connections between the algebra of logic and the algebra of sets, and more specifically, correspondences between the logical connectives *and*, *or*, and *not*, and the set operations *intersection union*, and *complement*, respectively. In particular, in Example 1, we had $P = \{1, 3, 5, 7, 9\}$, $Q = \{3, 4, 5, 6, 7\}$, and $R = \{1, 4, 9\}$. Note that:

1.   The truth set of $\sim p(x)$ equals $\{2, 4, 6, 8, 10\} = \{1, 3, 5, 7, 9\}' = P'$.

2. The truth set of $p(x) \lor q(x)$ equals $\{1, 3, 4, 5, 6, 7, 9\} = \{1, 3, 5, 7, 9\} \cup \{3, 4, 5, 6, 7\} = P \cup Q$.
3. The truth set of $q(x) \land r(x)$ equals $\{4\} = \{3, 4, 5, 6, 7\} \cap \{1, 4, 9\} = Q \cap R$.

These observations set the pattern for our formal approach to compound predicates:

DEFINITION 2

Let $p(x)$ and $q(x)$ be propositional functions over a domain of discourse U, with truth sets P and Q, respectively. We define the truth set of

(a) $\sim p(x)$, **not** $p(x)$, to be P'
(b) $p(x) \lor q(x)$, $p(x)$ **or** $q(x)$, to be $P \cup Q$
(c) $p(x) \land q(x)$, $p(x)$ **and** $q(x)$, to be $P \cap Q$

It is not so immediately evident how to define the truth sets of $p(x) \rightarrow q(x)$ and $p(x) \leftrightarrow q(x)$, but consider the following. Suppose that $p(x)$ and $q(x)$ are propositional functions such that the proposition $p(a) \leftrightarrow q(a)$ is a <u>tautology</u> for every specific substitution of an element a from U for the variable x. For example, $p(x)$ might be $r(x) \lor s(x)$, while $q(x)$ might be $s(x) \lor r(x)$ [recall that $(r \lor s) \leftrightarrow (s \lor r)$ is a tautology]. We would certainly expect $p(x)$ and $q(x)$ to be logically equivalent (i.e., $P = Q$) <u>over any</u> domain of discourse. With this in mind, we recall from Article 2.3 that $(p \rightarrow q) \leftrightarrow (\sim p \lor q)$ and $(p \leftrightarrow q) \leftrightarrow [(\sim p \lor q) \land (p \lor \sim q)]$ are tautologies, leading to the next definition.

DEFINITION 3

Given $p(x)$ and $q(x)$ as in Definition 2, we define the truth set of

(d) $p(x) \rightarrow q(x)$, **if** $p(x)$, **then** $q(x)$, to be $P' \cup Q$
(e) $p(x) \leftrightarrow q(x)$, $p(x)$ **if and only if** $q(x)$, to be $(P' \cup Q) \cap (P \cup Q')$

It may be instructive here to test the reasonableness of Definitions 2 and 3 (relative to the definitions of the connectives in Articles 2.1 and 2.2) by looking at some specific open sentences. As one instance, it should be that, if a is a specific element of U, and $p(a) \rightarrow q(a)$ is a <u>true</u> statement (by the truth tabular definition of Article 2.2), then $a \in P' \cup Q$, the set we have just designated as the truth set of $p(x) \rightarrow q(x)$. On the other hand, if $p(a) \rightarrow q(a)$ is false, then a should lie outside $P' \cup Q$. The following example illustrates this correspondence.

EXAMPLE 2   Let $U = \mathbf{R}$ and define propositional functions in one variable, $p(x)$ and $q(x)$, by $p(x)$: $|x| \leq 1$ and $q(x)$: $|x - 1| < 1$. Use Definitions 2 and 3 to calculate the truth sets of $p(x) \land q(x)$ and $p(x) \rightarrow q(x)$. Use specific examples to check that these results are consistent with the truth tabular definitions of the connectives $\land$ and $\rightarrow$ from Chapter 2.

Solution   We first calculate P and Q and express them in interval notation. The absolute value inequality $|x| \leq 1$ is equivalent to the two inequalities $-1 \leq x \leq 1$ so that $P = [-1, 1]$, whereas $|x - 1| < 1$ may be expressed $-1 < x - 1 < 1$, so that $0 < x < 2$ and $Q = (0, 2)$. By Definition 2(iii), the truth set of $p(x) \wedge q(x)$ is $P \cap Q = (0, 1]$. By Definition 3(d), the truth set of $p(x) \rightarrow q(x)$ is $P' \cup Q = (-\infty, -1) \cup (0, \infty)$.

Let us now test the reasonableness of these results. We consider first $p(x) \wedge q(x)$. Let $a = 0$. Since $0 \notin (0, 1] = P \cap Q$, we expect that $p(0) \wedge q(0)$ is false. This is so since $q(0)$ is false (i.e., $x = 0$ does not satisfy the inequality $|x - 1| < 1$). Check for yourself that $a = -5$ and $a = 2$ result in a truth value of "false" for $p(a) \wedge q(a)$. On the other hand, if we let $a = \frac{1}{2}$, both $p(\frac{1}{2})$ and $q(\frac{1}{2})$ are true (Why?) so that $p(\frac{1}{2}) \wedge q(\frac{1}{2})$ is true (Why?). This is no surprise since $\frac{1}{2} \in (0, 1]$, the truth set of $p(x) \wedge q(x)$. Try $a = 1$ as another example.

Next, we consider $p(x) \rightarrow q(x)$ a more difficult case for our intuition to handle. We proceed mechanically, however. Let $a = -1$; since $-1 \notin (-\infty, -1) \cup (0, \infty)$, we expect that $p(-1) \rightarrow q(-1)$ should be false. This is indeed the case, since $-1 \in [-1, 1] = P$ [the truth set of $p(x)$] so that $p(-1)$ is true, whereas $q(-1)$ is false [since $-1 \notin (0, 2) = Q$]. Recall that T $\rightarrow$ F is the only case in the truth table for $\rightarrow$ which yields the truth value F. On the other hand, if we let $a = 3$, we find that $p(3) \rightarrow q(3)$ is true since $p(3)$ is false ($3 \notin P = [-1, 1]$) and $q(3)$ is false [$3 \notin Q = (0, 2)$]. This result is consistent with our calculation of the truth set of $p(x) \rightarrow q(x)$ since $3 \in (-\infty, -1) \cup (0, \infty) = P' \cup Q$. Try $a = \frac{1}{2}$, $a = \frac{3}{2}$, and $a = -\frac{1}{2}$ for yourself. In each case, before determining the truth value of $p(a) \rightarrow q(a)$ directly, make a prediction based on our calculation of the truth set.   □

As we conclude this article, let us briefly discuss the logical direction of material in this chapter. Our main goals here are the "theorems of the predicate calculus" in Articles 3 and 4, especially Theorems 1 and 2, Article 3.3, and Theorems 1 and 3, Article 3.4. These are crucially important principles of reasoning. Any serious student of mathematics at the junior-senior level must have at least general familiarity with them, although a detailed understanding is preferable.

For a text at this level, formal proofs of theorems of the predicate calculus are omitted. But although we present these theorems without formal proof, we do not present them in a vacuum. Specifically, through development of the notion of truth set in this article and in Article 3.2, we will be able to justify a number of theorems of the predicate calculus by means of corresponding theorems of set theory. The latter, of course, have not been formally proved, but, based on the "intuitive feel" for sets acquired in Chapter 1, you should be easily able to recognize them as true. A danger in this approach is that we may seem to be using "circular" reasoning, since in later chapters we will use principles of logic to prove theorems of set theory. You should understand, then, that our approach is to accept theorems of the predicate calculus without proof. The pairing of unproved theorems of set theory with theorems of logic in Articles 3.3 and 3.4 should not be viewed as an attempt to prove the latter, but only as confirmation of their plausibility.

Exercises

In Exercises 1 through 4, let $U = \{1, 2, 3, \ldots, 9, 10\}$. Let propositional functions $p(x)$, $q(x)$, $r(x)$, and $s(x)$ be defined on U by $p(x)$: $x \leq 3$, $q(x)$: $x \leq 7$, $r(x)$: $x > 3$, and $s(x)$: $x \not> 3$.

1. Use the roster method to describe the truth sets P, Q, R, and S explicitly.

2. Use Definitions 2 and 3 to find the truth sets of the following compound propositional functions:

(a) $\sim s(x)$ (b) $p(x) \vee q(x)$

(c) $p(x) \wedge q(x)$ (d) $p(x) \vee r(x)$

(e) $p(x) \wedge r(x)$ (f) $q(x) \vee r(x)$

★(g) $q(x) \wedge r(x)$ (h) $\sim p(x) \wedge \sim q(x)$

(i) $\sim p(x) \vee \sim q(x)$ (j) $p(x) \vee \sim s(x)$

★(k) $p(x) \rightarrow q(x)$ ★(l) $p(x) \wedge \sim q(x)$

(m) $q(x) \rightarrow p(x)$ (n) $q(x) \wedge \sim p(x)$

(o) $\sim q(x) \rightarrow \sim p(x)$ (p) $q(x) \leftrightarrow r(x)$

(q) $\sim q(x) \leftrightarrow \sim r(x)$ (r) $p(x) \leftrightarrow s(x)$

★(s) $(r(x) \rightarrow q(x)) \vee (q(x) \rightarrow r(x))$

3. (a)   What would you expect to be the truth set of each of the following compound open sentences:

(i) $p(x) \vee \sim p(x)$ (ii) $r(x) \rightarrow r(x)$

(iii) $q(x) \wedge \sim q(x)$ (iv) $(p(x) \rightarrow q(x)) \leftrightarrow (\sim q(x) \rightarrow \sim p(x))$

(v) $[(p(x) \vee q(x)) \wedge r(x)] \leftrightarrow [(p(x) \wedge r(x)) \vee (q(x) \wedge r(x))]$?

(b)   Compute each of these truth sets directly from Definitions 2 and 3 [relative to the specific predicates $p(x)$, $q(x)$, $r(x)$, and $s(x)$ given before Exercise 1] and compare the results with your expectations from (a).

4. (a)   Calculate the truth sets of the following compound open sentences:

★(i) $\sim(r(x) \wedge q(x))$ and $\sim r(x) \vee \sim q(x)$

(ii) $\sim(r(x) \vee q(x))$ and $\sim r(x) \wedge \sim q(x)$

(iii) $\sim(\sim r(x))$ and $r(x)$

(iv) $\sim(r(x) \rightarrow q(x))$ and $r(x) \wedge \sim q(x)$

(v) $\sim(r(x) \leftrightarrow q(x))$ and $(r(x) \wedge \sim q(x)) \vee (q(x) \wedge \sim r(x))$

(b)   What do the results in (a) suggest about the negation of the five connectives in the context of propositional functions, compared to that of propositions, our context in Article 2.3?

3.2 Quantification

It may have seemed surprising at the outset of Article 3.1 when we stated that the equation $A \cap (B \cup C) = (A \cap B) \cup (A \cap C)$ is an open sentence rather than a statement. After all, we went to considerable trouble in Chapter 1 (recall Example 3, ff., Article 1.3) to convince ourselves, short of a rigorous proof, that this equation is valid. So why then isn't it (strictly speaking) a statement? The answer is that the statement discussed in Chapter 1 involves more than just the preceding equation. The law asserting that intersection distributes over union states that <u>for every set A</u>, <u>for every set B</u>, and <u>for every set C</u>, the equation $A \cap (B \cup C) = (A \cap B) \cup (A \cap C)$ is valid. The expressions preceding the equation in the previous sentence are examples of the *universal quantifier* "for every," denoted by the symbol $\forall$. The symbolized statement corresponding to the distributive law we discussed in Chapter 1 is

$$(\forall A)(\forall B)(\forall C)\left[A \cap (B \cup C) = (A \cap B) \cup (A \cap C)\right]$$

The universal quantifier is one of two quantifiers of the predicate calculus. The other is the *existential quantifier* "there exists," denoted by the symbol $\exists$. A simple example of a statement involving the existential quantifier is $(\exists x)(5x - 3 = 0)$, $U = \mathbf{R}$, a true assertion that the linear equation $5x - 3 = 0$ has a real solution.

We now give a formal definition of the two quantifiers for the case of open sentences in one variable. In this article and the next we will concentrate on the one-variable case. Quantification of propositional functions in more than one variable will be considered in Article 3.4.

DEFINITION 1

If $p(x)$ is a propositional function with variables x and domain of discourse U, then:

(a) The sentence **for all x, $p(x)$**, symbolized **$(\forall x)(p(x))$**, is a proposition that is true if and only if the truth set P of $p(x)$ equals U.

(b) The sentence **there exists x, $p(x)$**, symbolized **$(\exists x)(p(x))$**, is a proposition that is true if and only if the truth set P of $p(x)$ is nonempty.

Certain features of Definition 1 deserve amplification. First, it is important to understand that an expression $(\forall x)(p(x))$ or $(\exists x)(p(x))$ is a proposition and not a propositional function, even though it involves a variable. Unlike a propositional function, its truth value does not depend on the variable x, but only on the propositional function $p(x)$ and the domain of discourse U. We might think of the variable x in a quantified predicate as a "dummy variable," analogous to the role played by x in the definite integral $\int_a^b f(x)\,dx$. Just as the name of the dummy variable makes no difference in a definite integral [so that $\int_0^1 (x^2 + x)\,dx = \int_0^1 (y^2 + y)\,dy$, e.g.], so the name of the dummy variable is of no consequence in a quantified predicate [so that, e.g., $(\forall x)(x^2 \geq 0)$ and $(\forall y)(y^2 \geq 0)$ are the same statement].

Second, notice that the statement $(\forall x)(p(x))$ is true precisely when the statement $p(a)$ is true <u>for every</u> possible substitution of a specific object a from the domain of discourse U, whereas $(\exists x)(p(x))$ is true precisely when $p(a)$ is true <u>for at least one</u> substitution of an object a from U. Third, note that in translating a symbolized statement $(\exists x)(p(x))$ into English, we must insert the words "such that" or some equivalent formulation (e.g., "for which") before the translation of $p(x)$. Finally, we note that definitions pertaining to situations in which quantified variables are restricted to certain subsets of the universal set U are presented in Exercise 7, Article 3.3.

EXAMPLE 1   Let $U = \mathbf{R}$. Then:

(a) $(\exists x)(x^2 = 4)$ is true, whereas $(\forall x)(x^2 = 4)$ is false. This is so because the truth set of the open sentence $p(x)$: $x^2 = 4$ is $P = \{-2, 2\}$ which is, on the one hand, nonempty, but on the other, fails to equal U.

(b) $(\forall x)(x^2 \geq 0)$ is true, as is $(\exists x)(x^2 \geq 0)$. (Why?)

(c) $(\forall x)(x^2 = -5)$ and $(\exists x)(x^2 = -5)$ are both false, since the truth set of the predicate "$x^2 = -5$" is $\varnothing$ and $U = \mathbf{R} \neq \varnothing$.

(d)   Can you produce an open sentence $p(x)$, with $U = \mathbf{R}$, for which $(\forall x)(p(x))$ is true, while $(\exists x)(p(x))$ is false? If not, and if no such predicate exists, what possible theorem of the predicate calculus is suggested? [See Theorem 2(c), Article 3.3.] Can you think of a circumstance, involving a different choice of U, that might allow $(\forall x)(p(x))$ to be true, while $(\exists x)(p(x))$ is false? [See Exercise 8(b), Article 3.3.]

ENGLISH TRANSLATIONS OF STATEMENTS INVOLVING QUANTIFIERS

There are many possible English translations of quantified predicates. Since you will on occasion need to write a given English sentence in symbolic form, it is important to become familiar with these translations, some of which involve the phrases "for every" and "there exists" only implicitly (we say that such a statement involves a *hidden quantifier*). Consider the predicate $x^2 = 4$ of part (a) of Example 1. Read literally, $(\forall x)(x^2 = 4)$ says "for every x, x squared equals four." This, however, can also be expressed "for all real numbers x, $x^2 = 4$," or "every (each) real number x has 4 as its square." Note that, in this last translation, we do not explicitly say "for every" and do not use any dummy variable. Similarly, $(\exists x)(x^2 = 4)$, which we read literally "there exists x such that $x^2 = 4$," can also be expressed "there exists a real number x <u>for which</u> $x^2 = 4$" or "there exists a number x <u>whose</u> square is 4," or finally, "<u>some</u> real number has 4 as its square." The existential quantifier is hidden in the last translation. The main point of these examples is that you learn to associate the universal quantifier with the words "every," "each," and "all," and the existential quantifier with the word "some," and with sequences of words such as "there exists . . . such that" or "there exists . . . for which."

The problem of appropriate English translation of quantified predicates becomes more difficult when dealing with compound predicates.

EXAMPLE 2   Let $U = \mathbf{Z}$. Let propositional functions p, q, r, and s be defined over $\mathbf{Z}$ by

$p(n)$: n is even, $P = \{\ldots, -4, -2, 0, 2, 4, \ldots\}$

$q(n)$: n is odd, $Q = \{\ldots, -5, -3, -1, 1, 3, 5, \ldots\}$

$r(n)$: n is divisible by 4, $R = \{\ldots, -8, -4, 0, 4, 8, \ldots\}$

$s(n)$: n is divisible by 3, $S = \{\ldots, -6, -3, 0, 3, 6, 9, \ldots\}$

Analyze some compound predicates involving these open sentences.

Discussion   (a) $(\forall n)(\sim p(n))$ is the statement that "every integer is not even" (false since $P' \neq U$), whereas $\sim[(\forall n)(p(n))]$ is the statement "it is not the case that every integer is even" (true since $(\forall n)(p(n))$ is false). The symbolized statement $(\exists n)(\sim p(n))$ says that "some integers are not even" (true since $P' \neq \varnothing$). What is the translation of $\sim[(\exists n)(p(n))]$? Is this statement true or false? Do you see any connections among these four statements?

(b) $(\exists n)(r(n) \wedge s(n))$ is the statement that some integers are divisible by 4 <u>and</u> by 3 (true since $R \cap S = \{\ldots, -12, 0, 12, 24, 36, \ldots\} \neq \varnothing$), also intepretable as "some multiples of 4 are divisible by 3" or "some multiples of 3 are divisible by 4." On the other hand, $(\exists n)(p(n) \wedge q(n))$ ("some even integers are odd") is false since $P \cap Q = \varnothing$, but $(\exists n)(p(n)) \wedge (\exists n)(q(n))$ ("some integers are even and some integers are odd") is true, because $(\exists n)(p(n))$ is true ($P \neq \varnothing$) and $(\exists n)(q(n))$ is true ($Q \neq \varnothing$).

(c)   By (b), $(\exists n)(r(n) \wedge p(n))$ symbolizes "some multiples of 4 are even." How would we symbolize the (intuitively true) statement "every multiple of 4 is even"? We might consider $(\forall n)(r(n) \wedge (p(n))$. But this translates to "every integer is divisible by 4 and is even," clearly a false statement. What we want to express is that an integer is even, <u>if</u> it is a multiple of 4. "If" suggests the conditional; let us try $(\forall n)(r(n) \rightarrow p(n))$. This translates literally to "for every integer n, if n is a multiple of 4, then n is even," which seems to carry the same meaning as "every multiple of 4 is even." Another test for possible equivalence is whether $(\forall n)(r(n) \rightarrow p(n))$ is true, since we know intuitively that "every multiple of 4 is even" is true. Let us try some substitutions for n; suppose $n = 8$. Since $r(8)$ and $p(8)$ are both true, so is $r(8) \rightarrow p(8)$. If $n = 2$, then $r(2)$ is false, $p(2)$ is true, and so $r(2) \rightarrow p(2)$ is true. If $n = 3$, then $r(3)$ and $p(3)$ are both false, thus, again, $r(3) \rightarrow p(3)$ is true. What case would make $r(n) \rightarrow p(n)$ false? We would need a substitution for n that makes $r(n)$ true (n is a multiple of 4), whereas $p(n)$ is false (n is not even). Does any such integer exist? Common sense tells us that there is none; that is, $r(n) \rightarrow p(n)$ is true in all cases that can actually occur. For this reason, $(\forall n)(r(n) \rightarrow p(n))$ is true, in correspondence with the intuitively evident truth of "every multiple of 4 is even." For another approach to the truth of $(\forall n)(r(n) \rightarrow p(n))$, calculate the truth set $R' \cup P$ of the predicate $r(n) \rightarrow p(n)$. $\square$

The most important conclusion to be drawn from Example 2 [specifically, part (c)] is that a statement such as "all men are mortal" is symbolized logically by the universal quantifier with an implication connective. Letting $p(x)$ represent "x is a man" and $q(x)$ stand for "x is mortal," the expression $(\forall x)(p(x) \rightarrow q(x))$ corresponds to "every man is mortal." This fact is important because many theorems in mathematics have this form, for example, "every differentiable function is continuous," "every cyclic group is abelian," (from group theory, a branch of abstract algebra) and "every function continuous on a closed and bounded interval attains a maximum on that interval."

A second, and almost equally important, conclusion from Example 2 is that a statement such as "some men are mortal" is symbolized by the existential quantifier and conjunction, specifically by $(\exists x)(p(x) \wedge q(x))$. Note that "some men are not mortal" is represented by $(\exists x)(p(x) \wedge \sim q(x))$. Can you spot any relationship between the statements "all men are mortal" and "some men are not mortal"? We will discuss one in the next article (see Example 3, Article 3.3).

Another important message of Example 2 [recall part (b)] is that expressions such as $(\forall x)(h(x) \vee k(x))$ and $(\forall x)(h(x)) \vee (\forall x)(k(x))$ represent different statements. First, their English translations are different. Second, the role of the connective $\vee$ in each is different. Namely, $\vee$ is a connective between propositions in $(\forall x)(h(x)) \vee (\forall x)(k(x))$. The truth of this compound statement depends on the truth of the individual statements $(\forall x)(h(x))$ and $(\forall x)(k(x))$ in accordance with the truth tabular definition of $\vee$ in Article 2.1. In the statement $(\forall x)(h(x) \vee k(x))$, $\vee$ is a connective between propositional functions, as defined in Definition 2(b), Article 3.1. We must look at the truth set $H \cup K$ of $h(x) \vee k(x)$ (and ask whether it equals U) to determine whether this quantified compound predicate is true. A third, and most crucial, difference between $(\forall x)(h(x) \vee k(x))$ and $(\forall x)(h(x)) \vee (\forall x)(k(x))$ is that, in some cases, it is possible for a statement of one form to be true, whereas the corresponding statement of the other form is false. Can you find predicates $h(x)$ and $k(x)$ such that one of $(\forall x)(h(x) \vee k(x))$ and $(\forall x)(h(x)) \vee (\forall x)(k(x))$ is true, whereas the other is false? [see Exercise 3(e) and (f)]. Does it seem to you that the truth of one of these two statements forces the other to be true? Your answer to both questions should be "yes." Before going on to the next article, try to decide which of the two preceding statement forms is "stronger" than the other.

EXAMPLE 3 Examples involving quantifiers can shed further light on the definition of the conditional connective $\rightarrow$. Consider the statement "every square is a rectangle," where $U =$ the set of all quadrilaterals in a given plane. This statement is evidently true, and may be symbolized $(\forall x)(s(x) \rightarrow r(x))$, where $s(x)$ represents "x is a square" and $r(x)$ stands for "x is a rectangle." If $(\forall x)(s(x) \rightarrow r(x))$ is true, as our intuition dictates, the conditional $s(q) \rightarrow r(q)$ must be true <u>for every substitution</u> of a specific quadrilateral q for the variable x. Note, however, that q_1, q_2, and q_3 are possible substitutions, where:

Name	*Physical model*	*Description*	$s(q)$	$r(q)$
q_1		q_1 is a square and a rectangle	T	T
q_2		q_2 is a rectangle but not a square	F	T
q_3		q_3 is neither a rectangle nor a square.	F	F

Hence if $(\forall x)(s(x) \rightarrow r(x))$ is a true statement, the truth tabular definition of $s(x) \rightarrow r(x)$ must be such that $s(q) \rightarrow r(q)$ is true in all preceding cases (which it is!). The fourth case, where $s(q)$ is T and $r(q)$ is F, cannot occur, since a physical model would have to be a square which is not a rectangle. The fact that $s(q) \rightarrow r(q)$ would be false in such a situation (by the truth tabular definition of $\rightarrow$) has no bearing on the truth of $(\forall x)(s(x) \rightarrow r(x))$ precisely because this situation can never occur. $\square$

Exercises

1. Let U be the set of all problems on a comprehensive list of problems in science. Define four predicates over U by:

$p(x)$: x is a mathematics problem.

$q(x)$: x is difficult.   (according to some well-defined criterion)

$r(x)$: x is easy.   (according to some well-defined criterion)

$s(x)$: x is unsolvable.

Translate into an English sentence each of the following statement forms:

(a) $(\forall x)(p(x))$ (b) $(\forall x)(\sim s(x))$
(c) $(\exists x)(q(x))$ ★(d) $(\forall x)(r(x) \rightarrow \sim s(x))$
(e) $(\forall x)(q(x) \vee r(x))$ (f) $(\forall x)[p(x) \rightarrow (r(x) \vee s(x))]$
(g) $(\forall x)(s(x) \rightarrow p(x))$ (h) $(\exists x)(\sim q(x) \wedge \sim r(x))$
★(i) $(\exists x)(s(x) \wedge \sim p(x))$ (j) $(\exists x)(r(x) \wedge s(x))$
(k) $\sim[(\forall x)(\sim r(x) \vee \sim s(x))]$ (l) $(\forall x)(q(x) \leftrightarrow \sim r(x))$
(m) $(\forall x)[p(x) \rightarrow (q(x) \leftrightarrow \sim r(x))]$

2. Let U be the set of all human beings living in the year 1987. Define three predicates over U by:

   $p(x)$: x is young.

   $q(x)$: x is male.

   $r(x)$: x is an athlete.

Express symbolically each of the statements:

(a)   All athletes are young.   (b)   Some athletes are not young.
★(c)   Not all young people are athletes.   (d)   No young people are athletes.
(e)   All young people are not athletes.
(f)   Some young people are not athletes
(g)   Some athletes are young males.   (h)   All young males are athletes.
★(i)   All athletes are young females.
(j)   Some athletes are male and are not young.
(k)   Some young males are not athletes.
(l)   All athletes are either female or are young.

Throughout Exercises 3 through 8, let $U = \mathbf{Z}$, the set of all integers, and consider pairs $h(x)$ and $k(x)$ of open sentences over $\mathbf{Z}$ given by:

(i) $h(x)$: x is even $k(x)$: x is odd
(ii) $h(x)$: x is an integral multiple of 4 $k(x)$: x is a multiple of 7
(iii) $h(x)$: $x^2 \geq 0$ $k(x)$: $-1 \leq \sin x \leq 1$
(iv) $h(x)$: $x^2 \leq 0$ $k(x)$: $|\sin x| > 1$
(v) $h(x)$: $x^2 \geq 0$ $k(x)$: x is odd
(vi) $h(x)$: $x > 0$ $k(x)$: $x < 0$

3. For <u>each</u> of the preceding pairs (i) through (vi), use Definition 1 in combination with Definition 2, Article 3.1 [parts (b) and (c)] to label either true or false each of the following statement forms. [*Suggestion:* First describe the truth sets H and K for each of the six pairs. Then set up an 8×6 matrix with (a) through (h) as row labels, (i) through (vi) as column headings, and T's and F's as entries.]

(a) $(\forall x)(h(x) \wedge k(x))$ (b) $(\forall x)(h(x)) \wedge (\forall x)(k(x))$
★(c) $(\exists x)(h(x) \wedge k(x))$ ★(d) $(\exists x)(h(x)) \wedge (\exists x)(k(x))$
(e) $(\forall x)(h(x)) \vee (\forall x)(k(x))$ (f) $(\forall x)(h(x) \vee k(x))$
(g) $(\exists x)(h(x)) \vee (\exists x)(k(x))$ (h) $(\exists x)(h(x) \vee k(x))$

4. In each of parts (a) through (h) of Exercise 3, translate the six symbolized statement forms into English sentences corresponding to each of (i) through (vi). In each case (a total of 48), compare your answer of true or false in Exercise 3 with your intuitive judgment of truth or falsehood of your English translation.

5. Use your true–false answers from Exercise 3 to compare certain pairs of statement forms from that exercise, namely:

(A)   (a) with (b)   (compare the first two rows of the matrix from Exercise 3)

(B)   (c) with (d)

(C)   (e) with (f)

(D)   (g) with (h)

Are any general conclusions suggested by these comparisons? (*Note:* This exercise, along with Exercise 8, anticipates Theorems 1 and 2 of the next article.)

6. In (i) through (iv) (of the list of pairs of open sentences preceding Exercise 3), use Definition 1, in combination with Definition 2, Article 3.1 [part (a)] to label either true or false each of the following statement forms. (As in Exercise 3, set up a matrix of T's and F's, this time of shape 4×4.)

(a) $(\forall x)(\sim h(x))$ (b) $\sim[(\forall x)(h(x))]$
(c) $(\exists x)(\sim h(x))$ (d) $\sim[(\exists x)(h(x))]$

7. In parts (a) through (d) of Exercise 6, translate the four symbolized forms into English sentences corresponding to each of (i) through (iv). In each case (a total of 16), compare your answer of true or false in Exercise 6 with your intuitive judgment of the truth or falsehood of your English translation.

8. Use your true-false answers from Exercise 6 for each of the four cases (i) through (iv), to compare pairs of the statement forms (a) through (d) in Exercise 6. Are any general conclusions suggested by these comparisons?

9. Recall, from Definition 1, Article 3.1, that propositional functions $p(x)$ and $q(x)$ are equivalent over a common domain U if and only if $P = Q$.

★(a)   Write a quantified compound predicate involving arbitrary predicates $p(x)$ and $q(x)$ that should, intuitively, be a true statement precisely when $p(x)$ and $q(x)$ are equivalent.

★(b)   Write an equation involving the truth sets P and Q that must be satisfied if the quantified statement you wrote in (a) is true.

★(c)   Use the result of (b), together with Definition 1, Article 3.1, to state a possible theorem of set theory suggested by the equivalence ("precisely when") implied in (a).

10. Analogous to Definition 1, Article 3.1, we say, given propositional functions $p(x)$ and $q(x)$ over a common domain U, that $p(x)$ *implies* $q(x)$ if and only if $P \subseteq Q$.

(a)   Write a quantified compound predicate involving $p(x)$ and $q(x)$ that should, intuitively, be a true statement precisely when $p(x)$ implies $q(x)$.

(b)   Write an equation involving the truth sets P and Q that must be satisfied if the quantified statement you wrote in (a) is true.

(c)   Use the result of (b), together with Definition 1, to state a possible theorem of set theory suggested by the equivalence implied in (a).

11. In the following list, (a) through (i), of propositional functions over the domain of discourse $U = \mathbf{R}$, find all instances of pairs that are either equivalent or in which one implies the other:

★(a) $p(x)$: $|x| \le 1$ ★(b) $q(x)$: $-4 < x < 4$

(c) $r(x)$: $x^2 < 25$ ★(d) $s(x)$: $|x - 4| < 1$
★(e) $t(x)$: $3 < x < 5$ (f) $u(x)$: $|x| \leq 0$
(g) $v(x)$: $x^2 \leq 1$ (h) $w(x)$: $(x \geq 0) \wedge (x \leq 0)$
(i) $y(x)$: $0 < |x| < 2$

3.3   Theorems About Predicates in One Variable

After doing the preceding exercises, you may be thinking of possible general relationships, involving equivalence or implication, that might exist between various quantified compound predicates. Some were hinted at rather directly in the exercises (e.g., Exercises 5 and 8). Example 1 presents another approach to one of the pairs of statements you might have compared in Exercise 8.

EXAMPLE 1   Describe in terms of truth sets the conditions under which the quantified compound predicates $(\forall x)(\sim p(x))$ and $\sim[(\exists x)(p(x))]$ are true.

Solution   By Definition 2(a), Article 3.1, the truth set of $\sim p(x)$ is P'. By Definition 1(a), Article 3.2, the universally quantified statement $(\forall x)(\sim p(x))$ is true if and only if $P' = U$. On the other hand, by Definition 2(a), Article 2.1, $\sim[(\exists x)(p(x))]$ is true if and only if $(\exists x)(p(x))$ is false. This in turn [by Definition 1(b), Article 3.2] is the case if and only if it is false that $P \neq \varnothing$, that is, if and only if the statement $P = \varnothing$ is true.   □

Example 1 indicates that a statement of the form "for every x, not $p(x)$" is true precisely when $P' = U$, while the corresponding statement "it is not the case that there exists x for which $p(x)$" is true precisely when $P = \varnothing$. Looking at these two conditions about truth sets, we see intuitively that they are logically equivalent, that is, either both true or both false (i.e., $P' = U$ if and only if $P \neq \varnothing$). Accepting this unproved statement about sets as true (recall the remarks in the last several paragraphs of Article 3.1), we must conclude, by transitivity of the biconditional, that $(\forall x)(\sim p(x))$ and $\sim[(\exists x)(p(x))]$ are logically equivalent statements for any propositional function $p(x)$. This means that, for a given predicate $p(x)$, either both are true or both are false. This conclusion is consistent with results you should have gotten in Exercises 6 and 8, Article 3.2.

Several other theorems of the predicate calculus, involving equivalence between pairs of quantified propositional functions of one variable, can be arrived at in a similar manner. In Theorem 1 we list beside each statement about quantified predicates a corresponding assertion about truth sets. Note, in each case, that the latter statement about sets, although unproved as yet, is intuitively believable. For further evidence to support the conclusions of Theorem 1, review your answers to Exercises 3(a, b, g, h) and 6, Article 3.2.

THEOREM 1 (Equivalences Involving Compound Predicates in One Variable)
Let $p(x)$ and $q(x)$ be predicates over a domain of discourse U with truth sets P and Q. Then:

Statement about quantified predicates	*Corresponding statement about truth sets*
(a) $\sim[(\forall x)(p(x))] \leftrightarrow (\exists x)(\sim p(x))$	(a′) $P = U$ is false $\leftrightarrow P' \neq \varnothing$
(b) $\sim[(\exists x)(p(x))] \leftrightarrow (\forall x)(\sim p(x))$	(b′) $P \neq \varnothing$ is false $\leftrightarrow P' = U$
(c) $(\forall x)(p(x) \wedge q(x)) \leftrightarrow (\forall x)(p(x)) \wedge (\forall x)(q(x))$	
	(c′) $P \cap Q = U \leftrightarrow P = U$ and $Q = U$
(d) $(\exists x)(p(x) \vee q(x)) \leftrightarrow (\exists x)(p(x)) \vee (\exists x)(q(x))$	
	(d′) $P \cup Q \neq \varnothing \leftrightarrow P \neq \varnothing$ or $Q \neq \varnothing$

Next, we apply the approach of Example 1 to another of the pairs of quantified predicates from Exercise 3 [parts (e) and (f)], Article 3.2.

EXAMPLE 2   Describe in terms of truth sets the conditions under which the quantified predicates $(\forall x)(h(x)) \vee (\forall x)(k(x))$ and $(\forall x)(h(x) \vee k(x))$ are true.

Solution   By Definition 2(b), the truth set of $h(x) \vee k(x)$ is $H \cup K$. By Definition 4(a), the universally quantified statement $(\forall x)(h(x) \vee k(x))$ is true if and only if $H \cup K = U$. On the other hand, by Definition 2(b), Article 2.1, $(\forall x)(h(x)) \vee (\forall x)(k(x))$ is true if and only if either $(\forall x)(h(x))$ is true, which means $H = U$, or $(\forall x)(k(x))$ is true; that is, $K = U$. We conclude that $(\forall x)(h(x)) \vee (\forall x)(k(x))$ is true if and only if either $H = U$ or $K = U$. $\square$

Let us now compare the two conditions about sets arrived at in Example 2. Intuitively, it is clear that if either $H = U$ or $K = U$, then $H \cup K = U$. What about the converse? Do we need either $H = U$ or $K = U$ in order to have $H \cup K = U$? The example $U = \mathbf{R}$, $H = \mathbf{Q}$, and $K = \mathbf{Q}'$ shows that the answer is "no." In this case the implication between the two statements from set theory goes in one direction only. Using transitivity of implication [Theorem 2(b), Article 2.3], we conclude that $(\forall x)(h(x)) \vee (\forall x)(k(x))$ implies $(\forall x)(h(x) \vee k(x))$, by the argument

$$(\forall x)(h(x)) \vee (\forall x)(k(x)) \text{ is true} \leftrightarrow (H = U) \vee (K = U)$$
$$\rightarrow H \cup K = U$$
$$\leftrightarrow (\forall x)(h(x) \vee k(x)) \text{ is true}$$

As in the discussion following Example 1, this argument is based on the assumption of a theorem from set theory that we have not, as yet, proved. Thus it does not constitute a proof of the logical principle in question, but only an argument that this principle is reasonable.

Our assertion that $(\forall x)(h(x)) \vee (\forall x)(k(x))$ implies $(\forall x)(h(x) \vee k(x))$ means that, for given predicates $h(x)$ and $k(x)$, the truth of the first statement implies (or forces) that of the second. There are various other ways of expressing this idea. The second statement cannot be false for predicates $h(x)$ and $k(x)$ for which the first statement is true, or the second cannot be false unless the first is false. Recalling language introduced in Article 2.3, we say also that the first statement form is *stronger* than the second. We express this idea in symbols by

$$[(\forall x)(h(x)) \vee (\forall x)(k(x))] \rightarrow [(\forall x)(h(x) \vee k(x))]$$

This conclusion is consistent with answers you should have gotten in Exercises 3(e, f) and 5, Article 3.2. Several other theorems of the predicate calculus, involving implication between pairs of quantified propositional functions in one variable, can be arrived at in a similar manner. We state Theorem 2 in a format analogous to that of Theorem 1.

THEOREM   2 (Implications Involving Quantified Predicates in One Variable) Let $p(x)$ and $q(x)$ be predicates over a domain of discourse U with truth sets P and Q. In (c) we assume further that U is nonempty, while in (d) and (e), we assume that a is a specific element of U. Then:

Statement about quantified predicates		Corresponding statement about truth sets	
Stronger	Weaker	Stronger	Weaker
(a) $(\forall x)(p(x)) \vee (\forall x)(q(x)) \rightarrow (\forall x)(p(x) \vee q(x))$			
		(a′) $P = U$ or $Q = U \rightarrow P \cup Q = U$	
(b) $(\exists x)(p(x) \wedge q(x)) \rightarrow (\exists x)(p(x)) \wedge (\exists x)(q(x))$			
		(b′) $P \cap Q \neq \varnothing \rightarrow P \neq \varnothing$ and $Q \neq \varnothing$	
(c) $(\forall x)(p(x)) \rightarrow (\exists x)(p(x))$			
		(c′) $P = U \rightarrow P \neq \varnothing$	
(d) $(\forall x)(p(x)) \rightarrow p(a)$ (d′)		$P = U \rightarrow a \in P$	
(e) $p(a) \rightarrow (\exists x)(p(x))$			
		(e′) $a \in P \rightarrow P \neq \varnothing$	

The converse of each of the statements in Theorem 2 is false; that is, specific propositional functions $p(x)$ and $q(x)$ can be found for which the weaker statement form is true, whereas the corresponding stronger one is false. Recall, for example, Article 3.2, Exercise 3, part (iv)(c, d), and part (i)(e, f).

Theorems 1 and 2 can be used, together with previous results, to establish other results of the predicate calculus.

EXAMPLE 3   Find a statement equivalent to the logical negation of $(\forall x)(p(x) \rightarrow q(x))$, in which "negation" is not a main connective.

Solution   According to (a) of Theorem 1, $\sim [(\forall x)(p(x) \rightarrow q(x))]$ is equivalent to $(\exists x)[\sim(p(x) \rightarrow q(x))]$. By Exercise 4(a), Article 3.1, the compound predicate $\sim(p(x) \to q(x))$ is equivalent to (i.e., has the same truth set as) $p(x) \wedge \sim q(x)$. Hence we have

$$\sim[(\forall x)(p(x) \to q(x))] \leftrightarrow (\exists x)[\sim(p(x) \to q(x))]$$
$$\leftrightarrow (\exists x)(p(x) \wedge \sim q(x))$$

where the latter is the desired form. If $p(x)$ represents "x is a man" and $q(x)$ stands for "x is mortal," this equivalence indicates that "some men are not mortal" is equivalent to the negation of "all men are mortal."

More generally, the negation of any statement of the form "every X is a Y" can be expressed in the form "some X's are not Y's." This logical principle has important implications for theorem-proving. Suppose we wish to use proof by contrapositive [recall Theorem 1(n), Article 2.3] to prove a theorem whose conclusion is "every X is a Y." We would begin by assuming the negation of that conclusion, that is, "there exists an X that is not a Y." Another application of the principle occurs whenever we doubt the truth of a conjecture "every X is a Y" and wish to prove it false. How can we do this? The answer is: by showing that there exists an X that is not a Y.

We conclude this article by returning to the paradox outlined in the introduction to this chapter. Theorem 2 provides the means to resolve it. Why is it not the case, for any two sets P and Q, that either $P \subseteq Q$ or $Q \subseteq P$ when, for any x, the statement $[(x \in P) \to (x \in Q)] \vee [(x \in Q) \to (x \in P)]$ is true? The answer is that "$P \subseteq Q$ or $Q \subseteq P$" is symbolized in the predicate calculus by $(\forall x)((x \in P) \to (x \in Q)) \vee (\forall x)((x \in Q) \to (x \in P))$. As seen in Theorem 2(a), a statement of this form can be false even when the corresponding statement $(\forall x)[((x \in P) \to (x \in Q)) \vee ((x \in Q) \to (x \in P))]$ is true. Such is the case in this example.

Exercises

1. Express the logical negation of each of the following statements by a sentence beginning with "all" or "some," as appropriate:

(a)   All young women are athletes.
(b)   No young men are athletes.
★*(c)*   Some women are young athletes.
(d)   All athletes are either young or are men.
(e)   Some athletes are young men.
(f)   If all athletes are young men, then no women are athletes.
★*(g)*   Either all athletes are young women or some men are athletes.

2. *(a)*   In parts (a) through (e) of Theorem 2, give examples different from those in Exercise 3, Article 3.2, of propositional functions, $p(x)$ and $q(x)$ over a domain U, for which the weaker statement form is true while the stronger one is false.
   (b)   Is it possible to find such examples if we interchange the words "weaker" and "stronger" in (a)?

(c)   The statement form $(\forall x)(p(x) \vee q(x))$ from Theorem 2(a) asserts, when true, that for every substitution of an object a from a universal set U, either statement $p(a)$ or statement $q(a)$ is true. Express in your own words the "extra" condition that must hold if the stronger statement form $(\forall x)(p(x)) \vee (\forall x)(q(x))$ is also to be true.

(d)   The statement form $(\exists x)(p(x)) \wedge (\exists x)(q(x))$ from Theorem 2(b) asserts, when true, that there is some substitution of an object a from U such that $p(a)$ is true and there is some substitution of an object b from U such that $q(b)$ is true. What extra condition must hold in order that the stronger statement form $(\exists x)(p(x) \wedge q(x))$ also be true?

3. (a)   Give an example of propositional functions $p(x)$ and $q(x)$ over a nonempty domain U for which $(\forall x)(p(x) \vee q(x))$ is true and $(\forall x)(p(x)) \vee (\forall x)(q(x))$ is false, whereas $(\exists x)(p(x) \wedge q(x))$ and $(\exists x)(p(x)) \wedge (\exists x)(q(x))$ both have the same truth value. (*Note:* This combination did not occur in any of the examples (i) through (vi) of Exercise 3, Article 3.2.)

(b)   Is it possible to find $p(x)$ and $q(x)$ in part (a) so that $(\exists x)(p(x) \wedge q(x))$ and $(\exists x)(p(x)) \wedge (\exists x)(q(x))$ are both false?

4. In Example 3 the negation of $(\forall x)(p(x) \to q(x))$ was expressed in the equivalent form $(\exists x)(p(x) \wedge \sim q(x))$. Note that the "not" connective does not occur as a "main connective"; that is, it does not modify any compound proposition or compound predicate in the latter form. Use a similar approach to express the negation of each of the following statement forms in a form in which "not" does not appear as a main connective:

(a) $(\forall x)(\sim p(x))$ (b) $(\exists x)(\sim p(x))$
★(c) $(\forall x)(p(x) \vee q(x))$ (d) $(\exists x)(p(x) \vee q(x))$
(e) $(\forall x)(p(x) \wedge q(x))$ (f) $(\exists x)(p(x) \wedge q(x))$
(g) $(\exists x)(p(x) \to q(x))$ ★(h) $(\forall x)(p(x) \leftrightarrow q(x))$
(i) $(\exists x)(p(x) \leftrightarrow q(x))$

5. Express the negation of each of the following statement forms in a form that does not employ the connective "not" as a main connective:

(a) $(\forall x)(p(x) \vee \sim p(x))$ (b) $(\exists x)(p(x) \wedge q(x) \wedge r(x))$
★(c) $(\forall x)(p(x) \to (q(x) \vee r(x)))$ (d) $(\forall x)(p(x) \to (q(x) \to p(x)))$
(e) $(\forall x)((q(x) \wedge \sim r(x)) \leftrightarrow p(x))$

6. In each of (a) through (e), describe precisely what must be proved in order to disprove the given (false) statement:

(a)   For every function f (with domain and range both equal to **R**), if $f'(0) = 0$, then f has a relative maximum or minimum at $x = 0$.

(b)   For every square matrix A, if A is upper triangular, then A is diagonal.

(c)   For every curve C in $\mathbf{R} \times \mathbf{R}$, if C is symmetric with respect to the x-axis, then C is symmetric with respect to the origin.

★(d)   For every function f, if f has a relative maximum or minimum at $x = 0$, then $f'(0) = 0$.

(e)   For every function f, if f is defined at $x = 0$ and if both $\lim_{x \to 0^-} f(x)$ and $\lim_{x \to 0^+} f(x)$ exist, then f is continuous at $x = 0$.

(f)   For every group G, if G is abelian, then G is cyclic.

(g)   For every subset S of a metric space X, S is compact if and only if S is closed and bounded.

[*Note:* The concepts in (b) are from elementary linear algebra, (f) is from abstract algebra, whereas (g) would be encountered in advanced calculus or elementary topology. You need not be familiar with these definitions in order to answer the questions.]

7. Frequently, in mathematics, we wish to restrict a quantified variable to a portion (i.e., subset A) of the domain of discourse U. A familiar example is the epsilon-delta definition of limit, in which epsilon and delta are both taken to be positive real numbers. We <u>define</u> $(\forall x \in A)(p(x))$ and $(\exists x \in A)(p(x))$ by the rules:

$$(\forall x \in A)(p(x)) \leftrightarrow (\forall x)((x \in A) \to p(x))$$

$$(\exists x \in A))(p(x)) \leftrightarrow (\exists x)((x \in A) \wedge (p(x)))$$

(a) Prove that $\sim[(\forall x \in A)(p(x))] \leftrightarrow (\exists x \in A)(\sim p(x))$.
(b) Prove that $\sim[(\exists x \in A)(p(x))] \leftrightarrow (\forall x \in A)(\sim p(x))$.

8. (Continuation of 7) *(a)* Consider the special case $A = U$ of the two definitions in Exercise 7. Explain why $(\forall x \in U)(p(x))$ is equivalent to $(\forall x)(p(x))$ and why $(\exists x \in U)(p(x))$ is equivalent to $(\exists x)(p(x))$.
(b) Consider the (even more) special case $A = U = \emptyset$ in part (a). Explain why $(\forall x)(p(x))$ is true whereas $(\exists x)(p(x))$ is false in this case. [*Note:* Theorem 2(c) precludes this possibility in the case of a <u>nonempty</u> universal set.]

9. Frequently, in mathematics, we wish to assert not only that there exists an object with a certain property (existence), but that there exists <u>only one</u> such object (uniqueness). We define the statement "there exists a unique x such that $p(x)$," denoted $(\exists!\, x)(p(x))$ by

$$(\exists!x)(p(x)) \leftrightarrow [(\exists x)(p(x))] \wedge [(\forall x)(\forall y)((p(x) \wedge p(y)) \to (x = y))].$$

Thus a proof of "unique existence" consists of an existence proof [often by producing a specific object satisfying $p(x)$] and a uniqueness proof. The latter is often approached by assuming that two objects both satisfy $p(x)$ and then showing that those two objects are actually the same object. Or, if existence of a specific object b, for which $p(b)$ is true, has been proved first, then uniqueness may be proved by showing that any x satisfying $p(x)$ equals this b. Let $U = \mathbf{R}$ and prove:

(a) $(\exists!x)(7x - 5 = 0)$
★(b) $(\exists!x)(x^2 + 8x + 16 = 0)$
(c) $(\exists!x)(x - 5 = \sqrt{(x + 7)}$
(d) $\sim[(\exists!x)((x^2 - 1)^{1/4} = 1)]$
(e) $(\exists!x > 0)(x^2 - 5x - 36 = 0)$
(f) $\sim[(\exists!x)(x^2 - 5x - 36 = 0)]$

10. (Continuation of 9) Given a subset A of a universal set U, we define *a complement B of A* to be any subset B of U satisfying the equations $A \cup B = U$ and $A \cap B = \emptyset$. Describe precisely what must be proved in order to show that "any set has a unique complement." (You will be asked to <u>prove</u> this theorem in Article 6.3.)

11. In each of (a) through (d), give an informal argument to support the stated theorem of the predicate calculus. Let $p(x)$ and $q(x)$ be predicates over a domain of discourse U and let r be a proposition. Then:

(a) $[(\forall x)(p(x) \to q(x))] \to [((\forall x)(p(x)) \to (\forall x)(q(x)))]$
(b) $(\forall x)(r \vee q(x)) \leftrightarrow r \vee (\forall x)(q(x))$
(c) $(\exists x)(r \wedge q(x)) \leftrightarrow r \wedge (\exists x)(q(x))$
(d) $[(\forall x)(p(x) \to r)] \to [((\forall x)(p(x)) \to r]$

[*Hints:* In (a) and (d), look at the logical negation of both sides, recalling that p is stronger than q if and only if $\sim q$ is stronger than $\sim p$[by Theorem 1(n), Article 2.3]. In (b) and (c), consider what each statement means with respect to the proposition r and the truth set Q of $q(x)$.]

12. Recall from Theorem 1(t), Article 2.3, that $[(p \wedge q) \to r] \leftrightarrow [(p \to r) \vee (q \to r)]$ is a tautology. Let U equal the set of all real valued functions of a real variable. Let propositional functions in the variable f, $p(f)$, $q(f)$, and $r(f)$ be defined by:

$p(f)$: f has a relative maximum at $x = 0$

$q(f)$: f is differentiable at $x = 0$

$r(f)$: $f'(0) = 0$

With these substitutions, the left side of the preceding tautology seems to say "functions that have a relative maximum at $x = 0$ and are differentiable at $x = 0$ have derivative zero at $x = 0$" (which is <u>true</u>). The right side would appear to represent "<u>either</u> functions that have a relative maximum at 0 have derivative zero at $x = 0$ <u>or</u> functions that are differentiable at 0 have derivative zero at $x = 0$." Both of these are false so that their disjunction is <u>false</u>. Resolve this apparent contradiction.

3.4 Quantification of Propositional Functions in Several Variables

Expressions such as "ℓ_1 is perpendicular to ℓ_2" (U = the set of all lines in a given plane), "$x \le y$" or "$x + y = z$" ($U = \mathbf{R}$), and "$f = g \circ h$" (U = the set of all real-valued functions of a real variable), are examples of propositional functions in two or more variables. If we denote "$x + y = z$" by the symbol $p(x, y, z)$, then $p(5, -3, 2)$ is a true statement and $p(4, 0, 5)$ is false. On the other hand, $p(5, y, z)$ and $(\exists x)(p(x, y, z))$ are not statements, but rather, they are propositional functions in two variables, whereas $p(5, y, 7)$ is a propositional function in the single variable y. Each of the last three expressions, of course, is neither true nor false as it stands.

Assuming that a set U_i constitutes the domain of discourse for the ith of the n variables of a propositional function $p(x_1, x_2, \ldots, x_n)$, the cartesian product $U_1 \times U_2 \times \cdots \times U_n$ is the domain of discourse for p. In particular, if U is a common domain for all n variables, then $U^n = U \times U \times \cdots \times U$ (n times) is the domain of p, so that the truth set of any such predicate is a subset of U^n.

There is a greater variety of ways to make a propositional function into a statement, for functions of several variables, than was the case for functions of a single variable. We may, of course, substitute for each of the variables. But then again, we might substitute for all variables except one and modify the remaining "one variable predicate" with a quantifier. Letting $p(x, y, z)$ stand for the equation $x + y = z$ and letting $r(y) = p(5, y, 7)$, we find that the quantified predicate $(\exists y)(r(y))$ or $(\exists y)(p(5, y, 7))$ is the (true) assertion that the equation $5 + y = 7$ has a real solution. Here is another example of this situation.

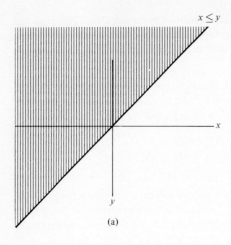

(a)

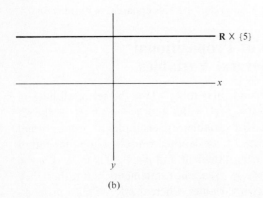

(b)

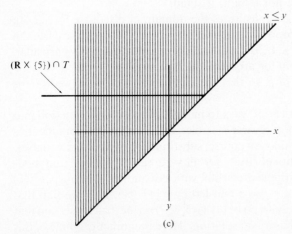

(c)

Figure 3.1   *Graphs pertaining to Example 1.*

EXAMPLE 1   Let $t(x, y)$ represent the inequality $x \leq y$ with domain of discourse $\mathbf{R} \times \mathbf{R}$. Describe the truth set of $q(x) = t(x, 5)$. Determine whether $(\forall x)(q(x))$ and $(\exists x)(q(x))$ are true or false.

Solution   We can best describe the various truth sets by graphing. The truth set of $t(x, y)$, call it T, is described in Figure 3.1a. Note that $T \subseteq \mathbf{R} \times \mathbf{R}$. The truth set of $q(x)$: $x \leq 5$ is necessarily a subset of $\mathbf{R} \times \{5\}$, since the value of y has been fixed at 5. In other words, the set $\mathbf{R} \times \{5\}$, better known as the horizontal line with equation $y = 5$, is the domain of discourse for $q(x)$ [see Figure 3.1b]. The truth set is that portion of $\mathbf{R} \times \{5\}$ that is also in T [see Figure 3.1c], namely, the set $\{(x, y) \mid x \leq y, y = 5\} = (\mathbf{R} \times \{5\}) \cap T$. Since this truth set is nonempty [(3,5) is an element, e.g.], then $(\exists x)(q(x))$ is true. Since it does not equal all of $\mathbf{R} \times \{5\}$ [e.g., $(7, 5) \in \mathbf{R} \times \{5\}$, but is not in T and so is not in the truth set of $q(x)$], then $(\forall x)(q(x))$ is false.   □

MIXED QUANTIFIERS

Another possibility for converting $p(x, y, z)$: $x + y = z$ into a proposition is to quantify all the variables, as in the statements $(\forall x)(\forall y)(\forall z)p(x, y, z)$, a false statement, and $(\exists x)(\exists y)(\exists z)p(x, y, z)$, which is true. You should have no difficulty in recognizing the meaning of these statements; the first says that the given equation is true for any three real numbers, the second states that it is true at least once, that is, for some three real numbers.

The meaning may not be so obvious if we write $(\forall x)(\exists y)(\forall z)p(x, y, z)$ or $(\exists x)(\exists y)(\forall z)p(x, y, z)$; these are examples of *mixed quantifiers* and are in general much more difficult to interpret than our first two examples. One difficulty comes in trying simply to formulate such symbolized statements into meaningful English sentences. Three keys to this are: (1) Insert "such that" or "having the property that" after any occurrence of $\exists$ that is followed directly by $\forall$ or by the predicate. (2) Insert "and" between any two occurrences of the same quantifier. (3) Whenever $(\exists y)$ follows $(\forall x)$, read "to every x, there corresponds at least one y" rather than "for every x, there exists a y." We will explore in detail the reasons for the latter interpretation after Theorem 1. Thus we read $(\forall x)(\exists y)(\forall z)p(x, y, z)$ as "to every x, there corresponds at least one y such that, for every z, $p(x, y, z)$." The more complicated expression $(\exists v)(\exists w)(\forall x)(\forall y)(\exists z)p(v, w, x, y, z)$ is read "there exist v and w having the property that, to every x and y, there corresponds at least one z such that $p(v, w, x, y, z)$."

It is in dealing with mixed quantifiers that the true nature of multiple quantification, namely, a series of single quantifications, becomes both apparent and important.

EXAMPLE 2   Given a propositional function $p(x, y)$, describe graphically conditions for the truth of $(\forall x)(\exists y)(p(x, y))$ and $(\exists y)(\forall x)(p(x, y))$.

Solution   Let $U_1 \times U_2$ be the domain of discourse for $p(x, y)$, and let $P \subseteq U_1 \times U_2$ be the truth set of $p(x, y)$. Let us first examine $(\forall x)(\exists y)(p(x, y))$. Let $r(x)$ represent the one-variable propositional function $(\exists y)(p(x, y))$. Then an element $u_1 \in U_1$ is in the truth set of $r(x)$ if and only if $(u_1, y) \in P$; that is, $p(u_1, y)$ is true, <u>for some</u> $y \in U_2$. Graphically, this means that the set P must meet, or have nonempty intersection with, the "vertical line" $x = u_1$. The assertion $(\forall x)(r(x))$, or $(\forall x)(\exists y)(p(x, y))$, therefore means that P must *meet every vertical line.*

On the other hand, to analyze $(\exists y)(\forall x)(p(x, y))$, let $s(y)$ stand for one-variable propositional function $(\forall x)(p(x, y))$. An element $u_2 \in U_2$ is in the truth set of $s(y)$ if and only if $(x, u_2) \in P$, that is, $p(x, u_2)$ is true, <u>for every</u> $x \in U_1$. Graphically, this means that the set P must <u>contain</u> the "horizontal line" $y = u_2$ as a subset. The assertion $(\exists y)(s(y))$ or $(\exists y)(\forall x)(p(x, y))$ therefore means that the truth set P of $p(x, y)$ *must contain some horizontal line.* □

Suppose now that $p(x, y)$ is the inequality of Example 1. Then Figure 3.1a shows that $(\forall x)(\exists y)(x \leq y)$ is true; the "upper-triangular" region T clearly meets every vertical line. But $(\exists y)(\forall x)(x \leq y)$ is false, because there is no horizontal line entirely contained in T.

This example shows that $(\forall x)(\exists y)(p(x, y))$ can be true while $(\exists y)(\forall x)(p(x, y))$ is false. But what if $(\exists y)(\forall x)(p(x, y))$ is true? Then P contains some "horizontal line" $y = u_2$ (i.e., $U_1 \times \{u_2\} \subseteq P$). Consider an arbitrary "vertical line" $x = u_1$. This line must intersect P in at least one point, namely (u_1, u_2) [i.e., $(u_1, u_2) \in (\{u_1\} \times U_2) \cap P$] so that the statement $(\forall x)(\exists y)(p(x, y))$ must also be true.

Our conclusion from this discussion is expressed in the following theorem.

THEOREM   1
For any propositional function $p(x, y)$ in two variables,

$$(\exists y)(\forall x)(p(x, y)) \to (\forall x)(\exists y)(p(x, y))$$

Thus any statement of the form $(\exists y)(\forall x)(p(x, y))$ is <u>stronger than</u> the corresponding statement $(\forall x)(\exists y)(p(x, y))$. A familiar example of the first form is the true assertion $(\exists x)(\forall y)(x + y = y)$, $U = \mathbf{R}$, that an *additive identity* (i.e., zero) exists for $\mathbf{R}$. Note that, as Theorem 1 promises, the statement $(\forall y)(\exists x)(x + y = y)$ is also true, where we may take $x = 0$ to correspond to any given y. On the other hand, the proposition $(\forall x)(\exists y)(x + y = 0)$ over $\mathbf{R}$, which states that every real number has an *additive inverse*, or *negative*, has its corresponding proposition $(\exists y)(\forall x)(x + y = 0)$ false. For clearly there does not exist a single value of y that is the additive inverse of every x.

A statement $(\forall x)(\exists y)(p(x, y))$, when true, asserts that, for any given x, there is at least one <u>corresponding</u> y such that $p(x, y)$ is true. As a rule, the

y whose existence is being asserted, although not necessarily being uniquely determined by x, depends on x, as in the preceding example, where the additive inverse of $x = 6$ is $y = -6$, the inverse of $x = -7$ is $y = 7$, if $x = \pi$, then $y = -\pi$, and so on. If, in addition to $(\forall x)(\exists y)(p(x, y))$, the stronger statement $(\exists y)(\forall x)(p(x, y))$ is also true [which may or not be the case, for a given predicate $p(x, y)$], then this y does not depend on x; the object whose existence is being asserted need not vary as x varies. Stated differently, there is at least one specific value of y ($y = 0$ in the case of our "additive identity" example) that makes $p(x, y)$ true for every x.

An understanding of the difference, and the logical relationship, between the mixed quantifiers $(\forall x)(\exists y)$ and $(\exists y)(\forall x)$ is crucial to much theoretical work in upper-level undergraduate mathematics and is absolutely basic at the graduate level. A special effort should be made to understand Theorem 1, the examples of the previous two paragraphs, and this final example.

EXAMPLE 3   Let U be the collection of all finite subsets, including $\emptyset$, of the set $\mathbf{N}$ of all positive integers. Define a propositional function s on $U \times U$ by $s(X, Y): X \subseteq Y$. Analyze the four statements:

(a) $(\forall X)(\exists Y)(s(X, Y))$
(b) $(\forall Y)(\exists X)(s(X, Y))$
(c) $(\exists Y)(\forall X)(s(X, Y))$
(d) $(\exists X)(\forall Y)(s(X, Y))$

Discussion   Statement (a) says that, for every set X in the collection U (of finite subsets of $\mathbf{N}$), there corresponds some set Y in U that contains X as a subset. Let us try some examples:

Given $X = \{1, 2, 3\}$, we could let $Y = \{1, 2, 3, 4\}$.

Given $X = \{1, 2, \ldots, 49, 50\}$, we could let $Y = \{1, 2, \ldots, 85, 86\}$. For that matter, we could let $Y = X$, since every set is a subset of itself.

Given $X = \{2; \ldots; 999,999; 1,000,000\}$, we may let $Y = \{2; \ldots; 2,000,000\}$. Short of a formal proof, we seem to have good reason to believe, from these examples, that statement (a) is true.

Statement (b) says that, to any set Y in U, there corresponds at least one set X in U that is a subset of Y. As in the previous paragraph, given $Y = \{1; 2; 3; \ldots; 1,000,000\}$, we may let $X = \{1; 2; 3; \ldots; 999,999\}$. If $Y = \{1; 2; \ldots; 50,000\}$, we may let $X = \{1; 2; \ldots; 10,000\}$. Or, if $Y = \{1, 2, 3, 4\}$, we may let $X = \{1\}$. Note that, as in the previous paragraph, these choices of sets X, corresponding to a given set Y, are by no means unique. In fact, see the discussion of (d), which follows, for an entirely different approach.

The relationship between statements (c) and (a) is that discussed in Theorem 1. Statement (c) is stronger than (a), a true statement, so that

(c) may be either true or false. What does (c) assert? It says that there is some set Y in U that contains every set X in U as a subset. Is there a single finite subset of $\mathbf{N}$ that contains all finite subsets of $\mathbf{N}$? You are correct if your intuition tells you "no."

Statement (d) is related to (b) as (c) was related to (a). Again, since (b) was true, (d) may be either true or false. We must now ask whether there exists a single finite subset of $\mathbf{N}$ that is a subset of every finite subset of $\mathbf{N}$. Our answers in part (b) did not settle this question; for each given Y, we gave back a corresponding X that changed as Y changed. Was there some single subset X we could have given back in response to every given Y? Yes! The empty set $\varnothing$ fulfills this role. Unlike (c), statement (d) is true.

To summarize, (a) and (b) are both true but differ from each other in a significant respect. Since (c) is false, the Y corresponding to a given X in (a) *must depend on* (or *vary with*) *that* X. *There is no single* Y *that works for every given* X. On the other hand, since (d) is true, then the X corresponding to a given Y in (b) need not depend on Y. There exists a specific set X, namely, $X = \varnothing$, that is a subset of every $Y \in U$. $\square$

Theorem 1 has a *generalization*; here is a brief and informal description. If p is a propositional function of more than two variables, say, $p = p(w, x, y, z)$, then Theorem 1 enables us to conclude (by an argument we omit) that a statement such as $(\forall w)(\exists x)(\forall y)(\forall z)p(w, x, y, z)$ is stronger than the corresponding statement $(\forall w)(\forall y)(\exists x)(\forall z)p(w, x, y, z)$. Note that the statements are identical except that $(\exists x)$ precedes $(\forall y)$ in the first statement, whereas $(\forall y)$ precedes $(\exists x)$ in the second. In the first statement, x depends on w only; in the second, x depends on both w and y. Other examples of this sort are found in Exercise 6, while an important application of this principle to mathematical analysis is contained in Exercise 7, Article 4.3.

An analysis similar to that preceding Theorem 1 would convince us of the following less difficult properties, which we summarize in the next theorem.

THEOREM 2

Let $p(x, y)$ be any propositional function in two variables. Then:

(a) $(\forall x)(\forall y)p(x, y) \leftrightarrow (\forall y)(\forall x)p(x, y)$

(b) $(\exists x)(\exists y)p(x, y) \leftrightarrow (\exists y)(\exists x)p(x, y)$

(c) $(\forall x)(\forall y)p(x, y) \rightarrow (\exists x)(\exists y)p(x, y)$, provided that each domain U_1 and U_2 is nonempty.

Theorem 2 generalizes to any finite number of variables. Parts (a) and (b) say essentially that if only one quantifier is involved in a statement, the order of quantification is of no consequence (unlike the situation with mixed quantifiers). Part (c) generalizes (c) of Theorem 2, Article 3.3.

NEGATION OF PROPOSITIONAL FUNCTIONS IN SEVERAL VARIABLES

In parts (a) and (b) of Theorem 1, Article 3.3, we saw how to formulate a positive statement of the negation of universally and existentially quantified predicates in one variable. We now extend this to propositional functions of two variables; in particular, we look at propositions involving mixed quantifiers.

EXAMPLE 4 Formulate a positive statement of the negation of $(\forall x)(\exists y)p(x, y)$.

Solution We must find a quantified predicate equivalent to $\sim[(\forall x)(\exists y)p(x, y)]$ in which negation is not a main connective. Let $s(x)$ represent $(\exists y)p(x, y)$. Then $\sim[(\forall x)(\exists y)p(x, y)]$ is the same as $\sim[(\forall x)(s(x))]$ which, by Theorem 1(a), Article 3.3, is equivalent to $(\exists x)(\sim s(x))$. But $\sim s(x)$ in turn is $\sim[(\exists y)p(x, y)]$ which, by Theorem 1(b), Article 3.3, is equivalent, for fixed x, to $(\forall y)(\sim p(x, y))$. Hence our original statement $\sim[(\forall x)(\exists y)p(x, y)]$ is equivalent to $(\exists x)(\forall y)(\sim p(x, y))$. □

Example 4 indicates that a statement of the form $(\forall x)(\exists y)p(x, y)$ is negated by changing $\forall$ to $\exists$, $\exists$ to $\forall$, and negating the predicate $p(x, y)$. It is left to you [Exercise 5(c)] to provide an argument, similar to that given in Example 4, showing that the same process is used to negate $(\exists x)(\forall y)p(x, y)$. We summarize these facts and deal, for the record, with negations of nonmixed quantifiers as well in the next theorem:

THEOREM 3

For any propositional function $p(x, y)$ in two variables:

(a) $\sim[(\forall x)(\exists y)p(x, y)] \leftrightarrow (\exists x)(\forall y)(\sim p(x, y))$

(b) $\sim[(\exists x)(\forall y)p(x, y)] \leftrightarrow (\forall x)(\exists y)(\sim p(x, y))$

(c) $\sim[(\forall x)(\forall y)p(x, y)] \leftrightarrow (\exists x)(\exists y)(\sim p(x, y))$

(d) $\sim[(\exists x)(\exists y)p(x, y)] \leftrightarrow (\forall x)(\forall y)(\sim p(x, y))$

Like Theorem 2, Theorem 3 generalizes to propositional functions in any finite number of variables. To negate a statement involving the predicate $p(x_1, x_2, \ldots, x_n)$, preceded by n quantifiers, we use the guiding rule:

Change each universal quantifier $\forall$ to $\exists$, change each existential quantifier $\exists$ to $\forall$, and negate the predicate.

EXAMPLE 5 Express the negation of $(\forall w)(\exists x)(\exists y)(\forall z)p(w, x, y, z)$ in a form that does not have negation as a main connective.

Solution By the preceding principle, $\sim[(\forall w)(\exists x)(\exists y)(\forall z)p(w, x, y, z)]$ is equivalent to $(\exists w)(\forall x)(\forall y)(\exists z)(\sim p(w, x, y, z))$. □

Exercises

1. Given a propositional function $p(w, x, y, z)$ over a domain of discourse, $U = U_1 \times U_2 \times U_3 \times U_4$, let a_i be a specific element of U_i for each $i = 1, 2, 3, 4$. Identify each of the following as either a "proposition" or a "propositional function in n variables." In the latter, determine n.

(a) $p(a_1, a_2, a_3, a_4)$

★(b) $(\forall w)p(w, a_2, a_3, a_4)$

(c) $(\forall w)p(w, x, y, z)$

(d) $p(a_1, x, a_3, z)$

(e) $(\forall w)(\forall x)(\forall y)p(w, x, y, a_4)$

★(f) $(\forall w)(\exists z)p(w, x, y, z)$

(g) $(\forall w)(\exists x)(\exists y)(\forall z)p(w, x, y, z)$

(h) $(\exists y)(\forall z)p(w, a_2, y, z)$

2. Translate into an English sentence each of the following symbolized statements involving an arbitrary predicate $p(x, y)$ or $p(x, y, z)$:

(a) $(\forall x)(\exists y)p(x, y)$

(b) $(\exists x)(\forall y)p(x, y)$

(c) $(\forall x)(\exists y)(\exists z)p(x, y, z)$

(d) $(\forall x)(\exists y)(\forall z)p(x, y, z)$

★(e) $(\exists x)(\forall y)(\forall z)p(x, y, z)$

(f) $(\forall x)(\forall y)(\exists z)p(x, y, z)$

(g) $(\exists x)(\exists y)(\forall z)p(x, y, z)$

(h) $(\exists z)(\forall y)(\exists x)p(x, y, z)$

3. Write a symbolized statement equivalent to the negation of each of parts (a) through *(h)* of Exercise 2, in which the negation connective does not occur as a main connective (i.e., the negation connective should modify the predicate only).

4. Let U be the set of all people living in the year 1987. Define a propositional function f in two variables over U (i.e., the domain of f equals $U \times U$) by $f(x, y)$: x is a friend of y. Translate into a good English sentence.

(a) $(\forall x)(\forall y)(f(x, y))$

(b) $(\exists x)(\exists y)(\sim f(x, y))$

★(c) $(\forall x)(\exists y)(f(x, y) \wedge \sim f(y, x))$

(d) $(\exists x)(\forall y)(f(x, y))$

(e) $(\exists y)(\forall x)(f(x, y))$

(f) $(\forall x)(\exists y)(f(x, y))$

★(g) $(\forall x)(f(x, x))$

(h) $(\forall x)(\exists y)(\forall z)(f(y, z) \rightarrow f(x, z))$

5. (Continuation of 4) *(a)* Express in symbols the negation of each of parts (a) through (h) of Exercise 4. (As usual, do not use "not" as a main connective in your final answer to any part).

(b) Translate each of your symbolized statements in (a) into a good English sentence. Compare each of these translations with its corresponding translation in Exercise 4.

(c) Write an argument similar to that given in Example 4 to justify (b) of Theorem 3.

6. *(a)* A statement of the form $(\forall x)(\exists y)p(x, y)$ asserts, when true, that to every x there corresponds at least one y for which $p(x, y)$ is true. Express in your own words the "extra" property that must hold if the stronger (by Theorem 1) statement $(\exists y)(\forall x)p(x, y)$ is also to be true.

(b) In each of parts (i) through (v), use the remark preceding Theorem 2 to determine which of the two given symbolized statements is stronger:

(i) $(\forall x)(\forall y)(\exists z)p(x, y, z)$ and $(\forall x)(\exists z)(\forall y)p(x, y, z)$

(ii) $(\forall x)(\exists y)(\exists z)p(x, y, z)$ and $(\exists y)(\forall x)(\exists z)p(x, y, z)$

(iii) $(\exists x)(\exists y)(\forall z)p(x, y, z)$ and $(\exists x)(\forall z)(\exists y)p(x, y, z)$

(iv) $(\forall w)(\exists x)(\exists y)(\forall z)p(w, x, y, z)$ and $(\forall w)(\forall z)(\exists x)(\exists y)p(w, x, y, z)$

(v) $(\exists z)(\forall x)(\forall y)(\forall w)p(w, x, y, z)$ and $(\forall w)(\forall x)(\forall y)(\exists z)p(w, x, y, z)$

(c) In parts (ii) through (v) of (b), indicate, for each existentially quantified variable, all possible dependencies on universally quantified variables (e.g., in the first part of (i), z may depend on both x and y, whereas in the second part of (i) z may depend only on x. Note that you should find fewer dependencies in statements judged stronger in part (b) than in corresponding weaker statements).

7. Let $U = \mathbf{Z}$, the set of all integers. Given two elements $m, n \in \mathbf{Z}$, we say that m *divides* n if and only if there exists $p \in \mathbf{Z}$ such that $n = mp$. Define a propositional function d on $\mathbf{Z} \times \mathbf{Z}$ by $d(m, n)$: m divides n.

(a) Translate each of the following symbolized statements into a good English sentence. Label each as either true or false:

(i)	$d(5, 7)$		(ii)	$d(4, 16)$
(iii)	$d(16, 4)$		(iv)	$d(1, 7)$
★(v)	$d(-8, 0)$		(vi)	$d(7, -7)$
(vii)	$d(-7, 7)$		(viii)	$(\forall m)d(m, m)$
(ix)	$(\forall n)d(1, n)$		(x)	$(\forall m)d(m, 0)$

★(xi) $(\forall m)(\forall n)[d(m, n) \to d(n, m)]$

(xii) $(\forall m)(\forall n)(\forall p)[(d(m, n) \wedge d(n, p)) \to d(m, p)]$

(xiii) $(\forall m)(\forall n)[(d(m, n) \wedge d(n, m)) \to m = n]$

(b) Suppose we now let $U = \mathbf{N}$, the set of all <u>positive</u> integers. We wish to consider the four statements $(\forall m)(\exists n)d(m, n)$, $(\exists n)(\forall m)d(m, n)$, $(\forall n)(\exists m)d(m, n)$, and $(\exists m)(\forall n)d(m, n)$.

(i) The statement $(\forall m)(\exists n)d(m, n)$ is true. In particular, for each of the following given values of m, give back a corresponding value of n for which $d(m, n)$ is true:

(A)	$m = 2$	$n =$ _____ ?
(B)	$m = 4$	$n =$ _____ ?
(C)	$m = 16$	$n =$ _____ ?
(D)	$m = 464$	$n =$ _____ ?
(E)	$m = 1,000,000$	$n =$ _____ ?

(ii) Do you think that the statement $(\exists n)(\forall m)d(m, n)$ is true? Explain the connection between this question and your answers to (i).

(iii) The statement $(\forall n)(\exists m)d(m, n)$ is true. In particular, for each of the following given values of n, give back a corresponding value of m for which $d(m, n)$ is true:

(A)	$n = 2$	$m =$ _____ ?
(B)	$n = 4$	$m =$ _____ ?
(C)	$n = 16$	$m =$ _____ ?
(D)	$n = 464$	$m =$ _____ ?
(E)	$n = 1,000,000$	$m =$ _____ ?

(iv) Do you think that the statement $(\exists m)(\forall n)d(m, n)$ is true? Explain the connection between this question and your answers in (iii).

(c) Reconsider part (ii) of (b) if we let $U = \mathbf{Z}$, rather than $U = \mathbf{N}$.

8. (Continuation of Exercises 7 and 8, Article 3.3) Let us consider again the matter of the restriction of a quantified variable to a subset of the domain of discourse U. Let $p(x, y)$ be a predicate with domain $U_1 \times U_2$, and let $A \subseteq U_1$ and $B \subseteq U_2$.

Then we define

$$(\forall x \in A)(\exists y \in B)p(x, y) \quad \text{by} \quad (\forall x)[(x \in A) \rightarrow (\exists y)((y \in B) \land p(x, y))]$$

$$\text{and} \quad (\exists x \in A)(\forall y \in B)p(x, y) \quad \text{by} \quad (\exists x)[(x \in A) \land (\forall y)((y \in B) \rightarrow p(x, y))]$$

(a) Prove that $\sim[(\forall x \in A)(\exists y \in B)p(x, y)] \leftrightarrow (\exists x \in A)(\forall y \in B)(\sim p(x, y))$.

(b) Prove that $\sim[(\exists x \in A)(\forall y \in B)p(x, y)] \leftrightarrow (\forall x \in A)(\exists y \in B)(\sim p(x, y))$. *Note:* Parts (a) and (b) generalize, respectively, parts (a) and (b) of Theorem 3. It is interesting to know that Theorem 1 generalizes also, namely

$$(\exists x \in A)(\forall y \in B)p(x, y) \rightarrow (\forall y \in B)(\exists x \in A)p(x, y)$$

9. Translate each of the following symbolized statements into an English sentence, where $U = \mathbf{R}$. Label each true or false:

(a) $(\forall x)(\exists y)(xy = x)$

$\star$(b) $(\exists x)(\forall y)(xy = x)$

(c) $(\forall x)(\exists y)(xy = 1)$

(d) $(\forall x \neq 0)(\exists y)(xy = 1)$

(e) $(\exists y)(\forall x \neq 0)(xy = 1)$

(f) $(\forall x)(\exists m \in \mathbf{N})(m > x)$

$\star$(g) $(\forall \mu > 0)(\exists n \in \mathbf{N})((1/n) < \mu)$

(h) $(\forall x)(\exists n \in \mathbf{N})(n \leq |x| < n + 1)$

(i) $(\forall x)(\exists! n \in \mathbf{N})(n \leq |x| < n + 1)$

10. Express in symbolic form each of the following English sentences, where we let $U = \mathbf{R}$ and recall that $\mathbf{Z}$ = set of all integers, $\mathbf{Q}$ = set of all rational numbers. In each case, decide also whether the statement is true or false:

$\star$(a) There is a smallest real number.

(b) There is no smallest real number.

(c) There is an irrational number between any two reals.

$\star$(d) There is a rational number between any two irrationals.

(e) Every real number lies between two consecutive integers.

(f) Every positive real number has a positive square root.

(g) There exists a smallest rational number whose square is greater than 2.

11. Suppose $p(x, y, z)$ and $q(x, y)$ are propositional functions where each variable comes from a common nonempty domain of discourse U. One of the statement forms

$$(\forall x)(\forall y)(\forall z)[p(x, y, z) \rightarrow q(x, y)] \quad \text{and} \quad (\forall x)(\forall y)[((\forall z)p(x, y, z)) \rightarrow q(x, y)]$$

is stronger than the other. Determine which is stronger by taking the negation of both propositions and recalling the equivalence $(p \rightarrow q) \leftrightarrow (\sim q \rightarrow \sim p)$. [*Note:* This exercise generalizes part (d) of Exercise 11, Article 3.3. This result is related to Exercise 4(b, c, d), Article 5.3.]

3.5 Analysis of Arguments for Logical Validity, Part II (Optional)

In this article we consider methods of analyzing for logical validity arguments whose partial premises and conclusion have any of the forms:

1. All p's are q's.

2. Some p's are q's.

3. No p's are q's.
4. Some p's are not q's.

As seen earlier in this chapter, statements of each of these four types may be recast, in terms of either formal logical symbolism or statements about the truth sets involved. We may summarize the situation as follows:

Logical symbolism	*Corresponding statement(s) about truth sets*
1. $(\forall x)(p(x) \rightarrow q(x))$	1. $P \cap Q' = \emptyset$ <u>or</u>, equivalently, $P \subseteq Q$.
2. $(\exists x)(p(x) \wedge q(x))$	2. $P \cap Q \neq \emptyset$.
3. $(\forall x)(p(x) \rightarrow \sim q(x))$	3. $P \cap Q = \emptyset$ <u>or</u>, equivalently, $P \subseteq Q'$.
4. $(\exists x)(p(x) \wedge \sim q(x))$	4. $P \cap Q' \neq \emptyset$.

Let us consider some examples.

EXAMPLE 1   Analyze for logical validity the argument, "all dinosaurs are cold-blooded animals. All cold-blooded animals are vegetarians. Therefore all dinosaurs are vegetarians."

Solution   Denote by $d(x)$, $c(x)$, and $v(x)$, respectively, the predicates, "x is a dinosaur," "x is a cold-blooded animal," and "x is a vegetarian," with D, C, and V representing the respective truth sets. Our argument can then be symbolized:

$$(\forall x)(d(x) \rightarrow c(x)) \qquad (\text{or } D \subseteq C)$$
$$\underline{(\forall x)(c(x) \rightarrow v((x)) \qquad (\text{or } C \subseteq V)}$$
therefore $\quad (\forall x)(d(x) \rightarrow v(x)) \qquad (\text{or } D \subseteq V)$

The validity or nonvalidity of the argument in this case "boils down" to the truth or falsehood of the theorem from set theory, "if D is a subset of C and C is a subset of V, then D is a subset of V, (for any three sets D, C, and V)" [recall (6) of Fact 1, Article 1.4]. Assuming the truth of this statement, the argument is seen to be valid. □

The situation in Example 1 can also be represented on a Venn diagram, as shown in Figure 3.2. With three or fewer predicates involved in an argument, Venn diagrams can be a useful tool in deciding validity.

EXAMPLE 2   Analyze the argument, "all violence is crime. Some violence is necessary. Therefore some crime is necessary."

Solution   Denote the three predicates involved in this argument by $v(x)$, $c(x)$, and $n(x)$, with truth sets V, C, and N (refer to the solution to Example 1 for guidance in writing out these predicates in detail). The argument

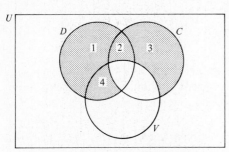

Figure 3.2   *Venn diagram representation of Example 1. We symbolize the fact that a portion of a circle is necessarily empty, due to the given premises, by the dotted design within the region. Portions 1 and 4 are empty since D is a subset of C. Since C is a subset of V, then 2 and 3 are empty. Since 1 and 2 are empty, we may conclude D is a subset of V, so that the argument is valid.*

may then be represented:

$$(\forall x)(v(x) \to c(x)) \qquad (\text{or } V \subseteq C)$$
$$(\exists x)(v(x) \wedge n(x)) \qquad (\text{or } V \cap N \neq \varnothing)$$
therefore $(\exists x)(c(x) \wedge n(x)) \qquad (\text{or } C \cap N \neq \varnothing)$

A fairly convincing Venn diagram presentation may be given, as shown in Figure 3.3. Taking a more rigorous approach, we may argue first that there exists x such that $x \in V$ and $x \in N$. Since this x is an element of V, and since V is a subset of C, then $x \in C$. Since $x \in C$ and $x \in N$, then $x \in C \cap N$, so that $C \cap N \neq \varnothing$, the conclusion of the argument. Since the conclusion is thereby seen to follow from the premise, the argument may be deemed valid. $\square$

EXAMPLE 3   Analyze the argument, "all professors are logical. Some men are logical. Some professors are overweight. Therefore either some men are overweight or some professors are men."

Solution   Proceeding as in Examples 1 and 2, we may symbolize this argument in terms of truth sets:

$$P \subseteq L$$
$$M \cap L \neq \varnothing$$
$$P \cap O \neq \varnothing$$
therefore $(M \cap O \neq \varnothing) \vee (P \cap M \neq \varnothing)$

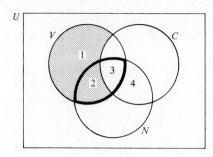

Figure 3.3 *The argument in Example 2, represented by the Venn diagram. Let us agree that a region contained inside a darkened circular arc is necessarily non-empty. The union of regions 2 and 3 is nonempty, whereas 2 is empty. Hence 3 is nonempty, so that the union of 3 and 4 is necessarily nonempty. This is the conclusion of the argument, which is thereby valid.*

Recalling the tautology $[p \rightarrow (q \vee r)] \leftrightarrow [(p \wedge \sim q) \rightarrow r]$ [Theorem 1(p), Article 2.3], we note first that we may add the equation $M \cap O = \varnothing$ to our list of hypotheses and try to deduce the conclusion $P \cap M \neq \varnothing$ from the expanded list. Several approaches similar to that taken in Example 2 may be tried in an attempt to draw this conclusion. After noting that all these approaches fail, we will not be surprised to find that an example such as $P = \{1, 2\}$, $L = \{1, 2, 3, 4\}$, $M = \{4, 5, 6\}$, and $O = \{2, 3\}$ can be found to show that the conclusion <u>does not need</u> to follow from the premise, that is, the argument is invalid. □

Exercises

Analyze these arguments for logical validity:

1. All men are mortal. Socrates is a man. Therefore Socrates is mortal.

2. Some students are athletes. Some athletes fail courses. Therefore some students fail courses.

★3. All good citizens register to vote. Some registered voters do community service. No lazy people do community service. Therefore some good citizens are not lazy.

4. All statesmen are politicians. Some statesmen are wise. Some politicians are dishonest. Therefore either no politicians are wise or no wise people are dishonest.

5. All pessimists are unhappy. Some happy people are healthy. Therefore some healthy people are not pessimists.

6. All bigots are intolerant. Some fanatics are bigots. All fanatics hate the truth. Therefore every lover of truth is tolerant.

★7. All fields are rings. Some rings are integral domains. Some integral domains are not fields. Therefore some rings are not fields.

8. All monotonic functions are one to one. Some monotonic functions are increasing. All increasing functions have inverses. Therefore all monotonic functions have inverses.

9. An argument can be valid without the conclusion's being true. If the premise is true, the argument is valid if and only if the conclusion is true. Hence a sufficient condition for an argument to be valid is that the premise and conclusion both be false.

Elementary
Applications
of Logic
CHAPTER 4

In this chapter, we begin to apply the principles of logic developed in Chapters 2 and 3. In Article 4.1 for the first time we look at *mathematical proofs*, limiting our consideration at this stage to proofs of elementary properties of sets. In Article 4.2 we introduce the notion of an *infinite collection of sets* and analyze basic properties of such collections. In Article 4.3 we examine in detail the *epsilon-delta definition of limit*.

4.1 Applications of Logic to Set Theory—Some Proofs

We now take a somewhat more formal approach to the theory of sets, introduced informally in Chapter 1. In particular, we begin here to apply the principles of logic developed in Chapters 2 and 3 to the problem of constructing proofs of theorems in set theory.

Recall our informal definitions of set equality and set inclusion from Article 1.1 (Remarks 2 and 3). Two sets are *equal* if and only if they have precisely the same elements. Set A is a *subset* of set B if and only if every element of A is also an element of B. Using connectives and quantifiers, we can now restate these definitions in a more formal way. The precision we gain from this added formality will enable us to deal with some questions that were not fully resolved in the informal context of Chapter 1 (e.g., Example 1).

DEFINITION 1
Let A and B be sets:

(a) We say that **A equals B** (denoted $A = B$) if and only if the statement $(\forall x)((x \in A) \leftrightarrow (x \in B))$ is true.
(b) We say that **A is a subset of B** ($A \subseteq B$) if and only if the statement $(\forall x)((x \in A) \rightarrow (x \in B))$ is true.

PROVING SET INCLUSION

EXAMPLE 1   Prove that $\varnothing \subseteq A$ for any set A [Fact 1 (7), Article 1.4].

Solution   Let A be an arbitrary set. By definition, $\varnothing \subseteq A$ has the meaning $(\forall x)[(x \in \varnothing) \rightarrow (x \in A)]$. But the predicate $x \in \varnothing$ is false for any object x, so that the conditional $(x \in \varnothing) \rightarrow (x \in A)$ is true for any x, regardless of the truth value of the predicate $x \in A$. Hence the statement $(\forall x)[(x \in \varnothing) \rightarrow (x \in A)]$ is true, so that $\varnothing \subseteq A$ is true, as claimed.   □

EXAMPLE 2   Prove that $A \subseteq A$ for any set A [Fact 1 (2), Article 1.4].

Solution   Let A be an arbitrary set. By definition, $A \subseteq A$ has the meaning $(\forall x)[(x \in A) \rightarrow (x \in A)]$. But the predicate $(x \in A) \rightarrow (x \in A)$ has the form $p \rightarrow p$ for any substitution of a particular object for x and so is true for any such substitution, since $p \rightarrow p$ is a tautology [Theorem 2(a), Article 2.3]. Hence the statement $(\forall x)[(x \in A) \rightarrow (x \in A)]$ is true, as is (consequently) the statement $A \subseteq A$.   □

EXAMPLE 3   Prove that, for any sets A and B, $A = B$ if and only if $A \subseteq B$ and $B \subseteq A$ [Fact 1(4), Article 1.4].

Solution   The definition of $A = B$ is $(\forall x)[(x \in A) \leftrightarrow (x \in B)]$, whereas $A \subseteq B$ is defined by $(\forall x)[(x \in A) \rightarrow (x \in B)]$. Therefore our theorem asserts that $(\forall x)[(x \in A) \leftrightarrow (x \in B)]$ is logically equivalent to the conjunction $(\forall x)[(x \in A) \rightarrow (x \in B)] \wedge (\forall x)[(x \in B) \rightarrow (x \in A)]$. Using the tautology $(p \leftrightarrow q) \leftrightarrow [(p \rightarrow q) \wedge (q \rightarrow p)]$ [Theorem 1(m), Article 2.3], and the theorem $(\forall x)(p(x) \wedge q(x)) \leftrightarrow (\forall x)(p(x)) \wedge (\forall x)(q(x))$ of the predicate calculus [Theorem 1(c), Article 3.3], we observe $(\forall x)[(x \in A) \leftrightarrow (x \in B)]$

$\leftrightarrow (\forall x)[((x \in A) \rightarrow (x \in B)) \wedge ((x \in B) \rightarrow (x \in A))]$

$\leftrightarrow (\forall x)[(x \in A) \rightarrow (x \in B)] \wedge (\forall x)[(x \in B) \rightarrow (x \in A)]$, as desired.   □

Each of the results in Examples 1 through 3 is an important foundational result in set theory. Each can be paraphrased in a form that is perhaps more easily remembered than the formal statement. The first states "the empty set is a subset of every set," the second is "every set is a subset of itself," while the third has the meaning "two sets are equal if and only if each is a subset of the other."

The proofs we have given in Examples 1 through 3 make explicit reference to logical principles from Chapters 2 and 3. In actual practice, the style of proof writing that mathematicians use in proving less basic results about set inclusion and equality is not quite so formal. As one becomes more experienced in writing proofs, the underlying logical principles are used in a (hopefully correct, but) less explicit manner. The point of departure toward writing such proofs is a method of proof so widely applicable that its importance cannot be stressed strongly enough. It might be called the "elementhood" method, the "choose" method, or the "pick-a-point" method. Whatever it's called, the principle sets forth:

> The direct way to prove that a set A is a subset of a set B is to start by letting a symbol x represent an arbitrary element of A. This element, though generic (i.e., not a specifically identified or named element of A), is to remain fixed throughout the proof. The proof is carried out by deducing, through methods depending on the specifics of the problem at hand, that this x must be an element of B.

The proofs in Examples 4 and 5, below, constitute our introduction to this method.

Using the notation of Chapters 2 and 3, we can reformulate the definitions of the operations intersection, union, complement, and difference in terms of the logical connectives and quantifiers. This is the object of Exercise 1. Some proofs of elementary theorems of set theory are now direct consequences of corresponding theorems of the propositional calculus.

EXAMPLE 4   Prove that, for any sets A and B, $A \cap B \subseteq A$ and $A \subseteq A \cup B$ [Fact 2, (20), (19), Article 1.4].

Solution   To prove that $A \cap B \subseteq A$ by the elementhood method, we begin by letting x be an arbitrary element of $A \cap B$. We must prove that this x is an element of A. Now since $x \in A \cap B$, then $x \in A$ and $x \in B$. Hence $x \in A$, as desired, where we note that the last step makes implicit use of the tautology $(p \wedge q) \to p$ [Theorem 2(c), Article 2.3].

To prove that $A \subseteq A \cup B$, let $x \in A$ be given. We must prove that $x \in A \cup B$; that is, either $x \in A$ or $x \in B$. Since $x \in A$, the latter statement follows directly. (What tautology is being used in passing from the assumption "$x \in A$" to the conclusion "either $x \in A$ or $x \in B$"?) □

EXAMPLE 5   Prove that, for any sets A and B, $A \subseteq (A \cup B) \cap (A \cup B')$.

Solution   Let x be an arbitrary element of A. In order to prove that $x \in (A \cup B) \cap (A \cup B')$, we must prove that $x \in A \cup B$ and $x \in A \cup B'$. Since $x \in A$, then $x \in A \cup B$, by Example 4. The same result implies that $x \in A \cup B'$ as well. Thus $x \in (A \cup B) \cap (A \cup B')$, as desired.

In Article 5.1, Exercise 4, you are to prove that, in fact, $A = (A \cup B) \cap (A \cup B')$ for any two sets A and B. □

Beginning students often complain that the choose method doesn't seem adequate to prove that every element of A is an element of B. After all, we appear to be starting the proof by picking only one element of A. Such an objection overlooks the power of universal quantification and, especially, the fact that the "chosen x" is arbitrarily chosen. For those of you who remain unconvinced, however, let us consider another way to justify the choose method as a means of verifying the definition of $A \subseteq B$. Suppose we show, as in the proofs in Examples 4 and 5, that if x is an arbitrarily chosen element of A, then x must lie in B. Then we have shown that there is no x in A that does not lie in B, in symbols $\sim[(\exists x)((x \in A) \wedge (x \notin B))]$. But this is logically equivalent, by Theorem 1(b), Article 3.3, to $(\forall x)[\sim((x \in A) \wedge (x \notin B))]$, which is equivalent to $(\forall x)[(x \in A) \to (x \in B)]$ [cf., Theorem 1(e), Article 2.3], the latter being the definition of "A is a subset of B."

As the structure of theorems to be proved becomes more complex, so do their proofs, as other techniques must be incorporated, along with the basic elementhood approach.

EXAMPLE 6   Prove that $A \cap (B \cup C) \subseteq (A \cap B) \cup C$, where A, B, and C are arbitrary sets.

Solution   Let $x \in A \cap (B \cup C)$. To prove that $x \in (A \cap B) \cup C$, we must prove that either $x \in A \cap B$ or $x \in C$. Suppose $x \notin C$. We claim this additional assumption forces the conclusion $x \in A \cap B$. To show that $x \in A \cap B$, we must prove that $x \in A$ and $x \in B$. Now, by hypothesis, $x \in A$ and $x \in B \cup C$. Since $x \in A$ is true by assumption, only $x \in B$ remains to be proved. Since $x \in B \cup C$, then either $x \in B$ or $x \in C$. Since $x \notin C$, then $x \in B$, as desired.   □

Note the approach we took (starting with "suppose $x \notin C$") to deduce a conclusion whose logical form is $q \vee r$. You will recall the tautology $[p \to (q \vee r)] \leftrightarrow [(p \wedge \sim q) \to r]$, discussed in Article 2.3 [Theorem 1(p)]. To prove that "one or the other" of two conclusions is true, we may take the approach of *assuming the negation of one of them* and, *on that basis*, trying to prove the other. We will discuss this technique in more detail in Article 6.2. Notice also that the argument in the last two sentences of the proof was based on a tautology. Can you identify it? (If not, see the last sentence of the solution to Example 13.)

EXAMPLE 7   Prove that, for any sets A, B, and C, if $A \subseteq B$ and $B \subseteq C$, then $A \subseteq C$.

Solution   To prove $A \subseteq C$, we must verify $(\forall x)[(x \in A) \to (x \in C)]$, based on the hypotheses $A \subseteq B$ and $B \subseteq C$. We proceed by letting x be an arbitrary element of A. We must show that $x \in C$. We may argue as follows: Since $x \in A$ and $A \subseteq B$, then $x \in B$. Since $x \in B$ and $B \subseteq C$, then $x \in C$, our desired conclusion.   □

In addition to its basic structure, involving the choose method, the other important aspect of the proof in Example 7 is the conclusion "$x \in B$" from the statements "$x \in A$" and "$A \subseteq B$." The validity of this step follows ultimately from the logical principle *modus ponens*, $[p \wedge (p \to q)] \to q$ [Theorem 2(e), Article 2.3]. Given that $x \in A$ is true and that the statement $(\forall y)[(y \in A) \to (y \in B)]$ is true, from which we may conclude that the statement $(x \in A) \to (x \in B)$ is true for the given x, we have $(x \in A) \wedge ((x \in A) \to (x \in B))$, and hence, by *modus ponens*, the conclusion $x \in B$.

One final remark on Example 7: This is the first theorem we've proved in which a conclusion of set containment (i.e., $A \subseteq C$) is preceded by some hypotheses (namely, $A \subseteq B$ and $B \subseteq C$). An important rule of procedure in setting up a proof in such a situation is at the start of the proof to focus on the desired conclusion, rather than on the hypotheses. The starting point of our proof was to pick an arbitrary element of A, with the stated hope of proving that it is also an element of C. The motivation for beginning the proof in this manner was solely the form of the conclusion of the theorem. The hypotheses are brought into play only in the course of the proof. This principle will be discussed and demonstrated in much more detail in Article 5.2.

PROVING SET EQUALITY

Combining the elementhood method of proving set inclusion with the result of Example 3, we see that a basic way to approach a proof of set equality is to prove *mutual inclusion*. This procedure involves two distinct proofs, one proof of containment in each direction.

EXAMPLE 8   Assuming the theorem "for all real numbers x and y, if $xy = 0$, then $x = 0$ or $y = 0$," prove that the set $A = \{5, -7\}$ equals the set $B = \{x \in \mathbf{R} \mid x^2 + 2x - 35 = 0\}$.

Solution   To prove $A = B$, we prove mutual inclusion; that is, we prove $A \subseteq B$ and $B \subseteq A$. We approach each of these proofs, in turn, by the choose method.

(a)   To prove $A \subseteq B$, let $a \in A$ be given. To prove $a \in B$, we must prove that a is a real number satisfying $a^2 + 2a - 35 = 0$. Now since $a \in A$, then either $a = 5$ or $a = -7$. If $a = 5$, then $a \in \mathbf{R}$ and $a^2 + 2a - 35 = (5)^2 + (2)(5) - 35 = 25 + 10 - 35 = 0$, as required. On the other hand, if $a = -7$, then again $a \in \mathbf{R}$ and $a^2 + 2a - 35 = (-7)^2 + (2)(-7) - 35 = 0$. In either case we have $a \in B$, as desired.

(b)   Conversely, to prove $B \subseteq A$, suppose $x \in B$, so that x is a real number satisfying $x^2 + 2x - 35 = 0$. But then, $0 = x^2 + 2x - 35 = (x - 5)(x + 7)$ so that, by the assumed theorem, either $x = 5$ or $x = -7$. Thus $x \in \{5, 7\} = A$, as desired.   □

In part (a) of the proof in Example 8 we used the technique of *division of an argument into cases*. We will elaborate on this important proof writing technique in Article 5.3.

EXAMPLE 9   Given sets A and B, prove that $A \cap B = A$ if and only if $A \subseteq B$.

Solution   Using the tautology, $(p \leftrightarrow q) \leftrightarrow [(p \rightarrow q) \wedge (q \rightarrow p)]$ [Theorem 1(m), Article 2.3], we approach this proof, as we will most proofs of "iff" statements, by splitting the proof of a biconditional into two separate proofs of conditionals. That is, we will prove:

1.   If $A \cap B = A$, then $A \subseteq B$.
2.   If $A \subseteq B$, then $A \cap B = A$.

Note that (2), in turn, is a proof of set equality that will, in its own right, require a proof of containment each of two directions.

Proof of (1):   To prove $A \subseteq B$, let $x \in A$ be given. We must prove $x \in B$. Since $x \in A$ and $A = A \cap B$, then $x \in A \cap B$. Since $A \cap B \subseteq B$, by Example 4, we conclude $x \in B$, as desired.

Proof of (2):   To prove $A \cap B = A$, we must prove that $A \cap B \subseteq A$ and $A \subseteq A \cap B$. The first of these was proved earlier, in Example 4, so we are left with only $A \subseteq A \cap B$ to be derived from the hypothesis $A \subseteq B$. To prove $A \subseteq A \cap B$, let $x \in A$. To show $x \in A \cap B$, we must prove $x \in A$ and $x \in B$. Since we already know $x \in A$, this amounts to proving $x \in B$. But since $x \in A$ and $A \subseteq B$, we have $x \in B$, completing the proof. $\square$

Sometimes the proof of an iff statement can be carried through by using a string of valid biconditional statements, thereby eliminating the need to write two distinct proofs, as we did in Example 9. An example of this type of proof follows.

EXAMPLE 10   Prove that, for any sets A, B, and C, $A \cap (B \cup C) = (A \cap B) \cup (A \cap C)$ [Fact 4(27), Article 1.4—"intersection distributes over union"].

Solution   Rather than proving mutual inclusion, we note that, for any object x, we have:

$$x \in A \cap (B \cup C) \leftrightarrow (x \in A) \wedge (x \in B \cup C)$$
$$\leftrightarrow (x \in A) \wedge [(x \in B) \vee (x \in C)]$$
$$\leftrightarrow [(x \in A) \wedge (x \in B)] \vee [(x \in A) \wedge (x \in C)]$$
$$\leftrightarrow (x \in A \cap B) \vee (x \in A \cap C)$$
$$\leftrightarrow x \in (A \cap B) \cup (A \cap C)$$

The third step uses the tautology $p \wedge (q \vee r) \leftrightarrow (p \wedge q) \vee (p \wedge r)$. Supply justifications for the remaining steps. $\square$

PROOFS INVOLVING THE EMPTY SET

Among the proofs we have seen thus far, the only one for which the choose method cannot be employed, and that therefore depends entirely on the logical structure of the formal definition of $A \subseteq B$, is the proof that the empty set is a subset of any set (Example 1). Surely, we cannot begin a proof that $\emptyset \subseteq A$ by writing "let $x \in \emptyset$." Other theorems from Article 1.4 whose statement involves $\emptyset$ may require something other than a direct "containment" or "mutual inclusion" approach as well. In the next example we consider problems that arise when we must prove that a given set is empty (i.e., equals the empty set $\emptyset$).

EXAMPLE 11 Prove that, for any set A, $A \cap A' = \emptyset$ [Fact 3(23), Article 1.4].

Solution Seemingly, the straightforward way to approach a proof that a set X equals $\emptyset$ is by mutual inclusion, that is, try to prove that $\emptyset \subseteq X$ and $X \subseteq \emptyset$. But in any such proof the first of these is automatically true (recall Example 1) and so does not need to be proved again. As for the second part, can we attack the problem by beginning "Let $x \in X$. We will prove $x \in \emptyset$. . . ."? Obviously, the latter conclusion can never be proved, so that this approach will not work. Instead, we use another special method of proof, *proof by contradiction* (which will be elaborated on in Article 6.2). To prove that a set X equals $\emptyset$, we begin by supposing that $x \in X$ (so that we are effectively assuming that X is nonempty) and showing that this supposition leads to a contradiction. In the case at hand, suppose that $x \in A \cap A'$. Then $x \in A$ and $x \in A'$ so that $x \in A$ and $x \notin A$. Since the latter statement has logical form $p \wedge \sim p$ (a contradiction), the supposition must be false and the desired theorem thereby true. $\square$

EXAMPLE 12 Prove that, for any sets A and B, if $A \subseteq B$, then $A \cap B' = \emptyset$ [Fact 8(57), Article 1.4].

Solution Assume $A \subseteq B$. Proceeding as in Example 11, let $x \in A \cap B'$. Our goal is to reach a contradiction. Since $x \in A \cap B'$, then the statement $(\exists x)[(x \in A) \wedge (x \in B')]$ is true, as is the equivalent statement $(\exists x)[(x \in A) \wedge (x \notin B)]$. But the latter statement is the logical negation of $(\forall x)[(x \in A) \rightarrow (x \in B)]$, which happens to be the definition of $A \subseteq B$. Hence our assumption "$x \in A \cap B'$" contradicts the hypothesis $A \subseteq B$, so we must conclude $A \cap B' = \emptyset$, as desired. $\square$

Other proofs involving $\emptyset$, even for theorems not making an assertion that a given set is empty, can be difficult to write out, and so must be approached carefully.

EXAMPLE 13 Prove that, for any set X, $X \cup \emptyset = X$ [Fact 2(11), Article 1.4].

Solution We will prove that $X \subseteq X \cup \emptyset$ and $X \cup \emptyset \subseteq X$. For the first one, we note that $X \subseteq X \cup Y$ is known to be true for any two sets X and Y (recall Example 4). In particular, if $Y = \emptyset$, we have $X \subseteq X \cup \emptyset$.

On the other hand, suppose $x \in X \cup \varnothing$; we must prove $x \in X$. Now, by our supposition, either $x \in X$ or $x \in \varnothing$. But $x \in \varnothing$ is false, so we may conclude $x \in X$, as desired. {*Note:* We have implicitly used the tautology $[(p \vee q) \wedge \sim p] \rightarrow q$, Theorem 2(k), Article 2.3, in the preceding sentence. The tautologies of the propositional calculus are of vital importance for writing proofs in mathematics!} □

The technique used in the first part of the proof of Example 13 (letting $Y = \varnothing$ in the known theorem $X \subseteq X \cup Y$ to conclude $X \subseteq X \cup \varnothing$) is called *specialization*, which we will focus on in Article 5.3.

The point was made earlier that we cannot employ the choose approach ("let $x \in \varnothing$") to prove $\varnothing \subseteq A$. The perceptive reader may have thought of the following objection to a number of the proofs presented in this article. In Example 4, for instance, we began the proof that $A \cap B \subseteq A$ with the step "let $x \in A \cap B$." But what if $A \cap B = \varnothing$? The argument given does not apply in this case; we cannot choose an element from $\varnothing$. More generally, whenever we prove a set X is a subset of a set Y by using the choose method, the argument applies only to the case "X nonempty." Again what if X is empty? The answer to this dilemma is an implicit "division into cases" [recall Example 8(a)] with the two cases (1) X nonempty and (2) X empty. In case (1) the proof proceeds by using the choose method, as in all our earlier examples. In case (2) the desired result follows directly from the result in Example 1, with no further proof required. As stated previously, this division into cases is "implicit." That is, since the case "X empty" is trivially true whenever we prove $X \subseteq Y$, we do not normally make explicit reference to it when proving set containment.

The proofs in the exercises that follow may not be enjoyable. For very elementary, and seemingly obvious, theorems in mathematics, it is sometimes difficult, or frustrating, to try to write a proof, since there often appears to be little or nothing to say. Two remarks may alleviate this problem somewhat: (1) We will give hints, for many of the exercises, of how you should proceed or to what example(s) you should refer. In this connection we note that a key step in proving many "obvious" theorems of set theory, such as Exercise 5, is identifying explicitly the relevant tautology, as we did in Examples 4, 6, 10, and 13, among others. (2) We promise more interesting (and less vacuous) proofs of theorems in set theory, as well as in other areas of undergraduate mathematics, in Chapter 5.

Exercises

We assume as axioms throughout these exercises that $x \in U$ for any object x (U being a universal set) and that $U \neq \varnothing$.

1. Formulate definitions of $A \cap B$, $A \cup B$, A', and $A - B$ using set-builder notation and the logical connectives introduced in Chapters 2 and 3.

2. Proceed as in Examples 6 and 7 to show that, for any three sets X, Y, and Z

★(a) If $X \subseteq Y$ and $X \subseteq Z$, then $X \subseteq Y \cap Z$

(b) If $X \subseteq Z$ and $Y \subseteq Z$, then $X \cup Y \subseteq Z$. [*Note:* For (b), see the remarks following Example 8 about division of an argument into cases.]

3. Proceed as in Example 9 to show that, for any two sets A and B, $A \subseteq B$ if and only if $A \cup B = B$. (Again, keep in mind the possibility of division of an argument into cases.)

4. Proceed as in Example 11 to show that, for any set X, $X \cap \emptyset = \emptyset$.

5. Follow the approach of Example 10 to prove that, for any sets A, B, and C:

(a) $A - B = A \cap B'$

(b) $A \cap B = B \cap A$

(c) $A \cup B = B \cup A$

(d) $A \cap (B \cap C) = (A \cap B) \cap C$

(e) $A \cup (B \cup C) = (A \cup B) \cup C$

(f) $A \cup (B \cap C) = (A \cup B) \cap (A \cup C)$

(g) $(A \cap B)' = A' \cup B'$

(h) $(A \cup B)' = A' \cap B'$

6. Follow the approach of Examples 1 through 3 (relying directly on logical principles) to prove that

(a) For any set A:

(i) $A \subseteq U$

(ii) $A = A$

(iii) $A = A''$

(iv) $A \cup A = A$

(v) $A \cap A = A$

(b) (i) $\emptyset' = U$ [*Hint:* Use (i) of (a) for one part of this argument.]

(ii) $U' = \emptyset$

7. (a) Prove that if A and B are any sets such that $A \subseteq B$, then $B' \subseteq A'$. (*Hint:* Start by letting $x \in B'$ and suppose the opposite of what you need to conclude. Reread the solution to Example 12.)

★(b) Use (a), together with the fact that $A = A''$ for any set A, to prove the converse of (a); that is, given sets A and B, if $B' \subseteq A'$, then $A \subseteq B$.

(c) Use the results in (a) and (b), together with the result of Example 3, to show that if A and B are any two sets, then $A = B$ if and only if $A' = B'$.

8. (a) Prove that, for any sets A and B, if $A \subseteq B$, then $A' \cup B = U$. [*Hint:* One approach is to use the result of Example 12, one of De Morgan's laws, and the fact that $\emptyset' = U$.]

(b) Prove that, for any set A, $A \cup A' = U$. [*Hint:* Use (a).]

9. Prove that, for any sets A and B:

★(a) $A \cap B = U$ if and only if $A = U$ and $B = U$

(b) $A \cup B \neq \emptyset$ if and only if either $A \neq \emptyset$ or $B \neq \emptyset$

(c) If $A = U$ or $B = U$, then $A \cup B = U$

(d) If $A \cap B \neq \emptyset$, then $A \neq \emptyset$ and $B \neq \emptyset$ (*Note:* Check the connection between the statements in Exercise 9 and various parts of Theorems 1 and 2, Article 3.3.)

10. As suggested in Article 1.2, a set theoretic definition of the "ordered pair" concept exists. We may define (a, b) to be the set $\{\{a\}, \{a, b\}\}$, where a and b are any objects.

Using this definition, prove:

(a) $(a, b) = (c, d)$ if and only if $a = c$ and $b = d$
(b) $(a, b) = (b, a)$ if and only if $a = b$

11. (Critique and complete.) Beginning with this exercise and continuing in Chapter 5, exercises will occasionally appear under this heading. Each will consist of three or more parts. Parts (a) and (b) will contain complete "proofs" of theorems, one correct and in good form, the other having deficiencies. You are to identify the faulty argument and rewrite it correctly. Each of the remaining parts will contain the first several steps of a possible proof of a theorem. You should either complete the proof, based on the suggested steps, or else judge the approach inappropriate and write a correct proof using a different approach:

(a) THEOREM If M and N are sets, then $M \cap (N \cup M') \subseteq M \cap N$.

"Proof" Let $x \in M \cap (N \cup M')$. To prove $x \in M \cap N$, we must prove $x \in M$ and $x \in N$. Since $x \in M \cap (N \cup M')$, then $x \in M$ and $x \in N \cup M'$ so that $x \in M$. Since $x \in N \cup M'$, then either $x \in N$ or $x \in M'$. But we know already that $x \in M$ so that $x \notin M'$. Hence $x \in N$, as desired.

(b) THEOREM If $A = \{x \in \mathbf{N} \mid 2x^4 - 5x^3 - 4x^2 + 3x = 0\}$ and $B = \{3\}$, then $A = B$.

"Proof" Since $2(3)^4 - 5(3)^3 - 4(3)^2 + 3(3) = 162 - 135 - 36 + 9 = 0$, so that 3 satisfies the equation defining A, we conclude $A = B$, as desired.

(c) THEOREM If A, B, and C are sets with $A \subseteq B$, then $A \cap C \subseteq B \cap C$.

Start of "Proof" Let x be an arbitrary element of A....

(d) THEOREM If X and Y are sets, then $Y \subseteq X \cup (Y \cap X')$.

Start of "Proof" Let $w \in Y$. We must prove that either $w \in X$ or $w \in Y \cap X'$. Suppose $w \notin X$....

(e) THEOREM If A and B are sets, then $A \cap (B - A) = \emptyset$.

Start of "Proof" We use a mutual inclusion approach. To prove $A \cap (B - A) \subseteq \emptyset$, let x be an arbitrary element of $A \cap (B - A)$. We must prove $x \in \emptyset$....

4.2   Infinite Unions and Intersections

One of the nice applications of the language of quantifiers to set theory is in the definition of union and intersection of infinite collections, or families, of sets. In particular, we consider in this article collections of sets *indexed* by the set $\mathbf{N}$ of all positive integers.

DEFINITION 1
The collection of sets $\mathscr{A} = \{A_1, A_2, A_3, \ldots\} = \{A_i \mid i \in \mathbf{N}\}$, containing a set A_i corresponding to each positive integer i (where some universal set U contains each set A_i in the collection) is called a **family** (or **collection**) of sets indexed by the set $\mathbf{N}$ of all positive integers. A positive integer i used to label a set A_i in the collection is called an **index**.

The collection $\mathscr{A}$ is also sometimes denoted $\{A_i\}_{i \in \mathbf{N}}$ or $\{A_i | i = 1, 2, 3, \ldots\}$.

EXAMPLE 1   (a)   Let $A_i = \{i\}$ for each $i = 1, 2, 3, \ldots$.   Then $\mathscr{A} = \{A_i | i \in \mathbf{N}\} = \{\{1\}, \{2\}, \{3\}, \ldots\}$ is a collection of singleton sets. Note that if positive integers i and j are two distinct indices, then $A_i \cap A_j = \varnothing$. For this reason we say that this family of sets is **pairwise disjoint** (or **mutually disjoint**).

   (b)   Let $B_i = \{1, 2, 3, \ldots, i\}$ for each $i = 1, 2, 3, \ldots$, so that $\mathscr{B} = \{\{1\}, \{1, 2\}, \{1, 2, 3\}, \ldots\}$. In this example, for any two indices i and j, $i < j$ implies $B_i \subseteq B_j$. For this reason $\mathscr{B}$ is called an **increasing** family of sets.

   (c)   Let $C_i = [i, \infty)$ for each $i = 1, 2, 3, \ldots$, so that $\mathscr{C} = \{C_i | i \in \mathbf{N}\}$ is a family of closed, unbounded intervals satisfying the condition $i < j$ implies $C_i \supseteq C_j$. Any family of sets indexed by $\mathbf{N}$ possessing this property is called a **decreasing** family of sets. In particular, a collection of intervals satisfying this property is called a **family of nested intervals**.

   (d)   Let $D_i = [0, 1 - (1/i)]$ for each $i = 1, 2, 3, \ldots$.   Then each set D_i in the collection $\mathscr{D} = \{D_i\}_{i \in \mathbf{N}}$ is a closed and bounded interval. Which of the properties defined in (a), (b), and (c) does $\mathscr{D}$ possess?

The reader should easily grasp the meaning of expressions such as $A_1 \cup A_2 \cup \cdots \cup A_n$. [Calculate this expression in (a) of Example 1] and $B_1 \cap B_2 \cap \cdots \cap B_m$. [What does this set equal in (b) of Example 1?] We use the notation $\bigcup_{i=1}^{n} A_i$ and $\bigcap_{j=1}^{m} B_j$, respectively, as shorthand representation of the preceding two sets. This notation is also suggestive of the next definition, in which we generalize union and intersection to certain types of infinite collections of sets.

DEFINITION 2

Let $\mathscr{A} = \{A_i | i = 1, 2, 3, \ldots\}$ be a collection of sets indexed by **N**. We define:

(a)   The **union of the collection** $\mathscr{A}$, denoted $\bigcup_{i=1}^{\infty} A_i$ (also denoted $\bigcup_{i \in \mathbf{N}} A_i$ and $\bigcup \{A_i | A_i \in \mathscr{A}\}$) to be the set $\{x | x \in A_i \text{ for some } i \in \mathbf{N}\} = \{x | \exists i \in \mathbf{N} \text{ such that } x \in A_i\}$

(b)   The **intersection of the collection** $\mathscr{A}$, denoted $\bigcap_{i=1}^{\infty} A_i$ (also denoted $\bigcap_{i \in \mathbf{N}} A_i$ and $\bigcap \{A_i | A_i \in \mathscr{A}\}$) to be the set $\{x | x \in A_i \text{ for every } i \in \mathbf{N}\} = \{x | x \in A_i \; \forall i \in \mathbf{N}\}$.

If $\mathscr{A}$ is a collection of sets $A_1, A_2, A_3, \ldots$, with U as universal set, then both $\bigcup_{i=1}^{\infty} A_i$ and $\bigcap_{i=1}^{\infty} A_i$ are sets and both have U as universal set. The former consists of all the elements in any of the sets A_i, grouped together into one set, whereas the latter consists only of those objects common to all the sets A_i. Note also that the letter i, in this context, is a dummy variable (recall the discussion following Definition 1, Article 3.2).

EXAMPLE 2   Consider the collection of intervals $\mathscr{J} = \{J_n | n \in \mathbf{N}\}$, where each $J_n = [1/n, 2]$. Calculate $\bigcap_{n=1}^{\infty} J_n$ and $\bigcup_{n=1}^{\infty} J_n$.

Solution   First, note that the collection $\mathscr{J}$ is an increasing family of intervals, since if $i < j$, then $1/j < 1/i$ so that $[1/i, 2] \subseteq [1/j, 2]$, and thus $J_i \subseteq J_j$.

Now, to calculate $\bigcap_{n=1}^{\infty} J_n$, we must ask which real numbers are common to all of the intervals J_n. Surely, each such number is contained in $J_1 = [1, 2]$ and J_1, in turn, is a subset of every other set in the collection (since the collection is increasing). Hence we reason that $\bigcap_{n=1}^{\infty} J_n = J_1$ [note Exercise 5(a)].

On the other hand, to find $\bigcup_{n=1}^{\infty} J_n$, we must ask which real numbers are in at least one of the sets J_n. Note the pattern $J_1 = [1, 2], J_1 \cup J_2 = [\frac{1}{2}, 2], J_1 \cup J_2 \cup J_3 = [\frac{1}{3}, 2]$, and so on. Note especially that the right-hand end point of each such interval is fixed at 2, so that we need worry only about the left-hand end point. It is intuitively clear (although hard to prove rigorously) that every positive real number less than or equal to 2 will eventually fall into one of the intervals J_n. Also, clearly no negative number is in any of the J_n's. Thus the desired union equals either $(0, 2]$ or $[0, 2]$. Will zero eventually fall into an interval J_n for some sufficiently large n? The answer is "no!" Since $0 < 1/n$ for any positive integer n, no matter how large, then $0 \notin [1/n, 2]$ for any positive integer n. We conclude that $\bigcup_{n=1}^{\infty} J_n = (0, 2]$. $\square$

The theoretical property needed to justify the "hard to prove" statement in Example 2 is the so-called *Archimedean property* of the set $\mathbf{N}$ of all positive integers. This property (in one of its many forms) states that, to any positive real number μ, no matter how small, there corresponds a positive integer n such that $1/n < \mu$. This property is, among other things, the basis of the important fact that the infinite sequence $\{1/n\}$ converges to zero in the real number system. We will encounter the Archimedean property again in Chapters 9 and 10.

As Example 2 suggests, infinite unions and intersections behave differently from finite unions and intersections in a variety of ways. Intuitive expectations should be adjusted carefully to correspond to these differences. Some cases in point are provided in Exercise 6.

One general property of infinite collections of sets, whose proof is assigned as Exercise 5(a), was hinted at in the solution to Example 2. Proofs of other general properties of infinite collections of sets constitute Exercises 4, 5, and 7. The general approach to these proofs is outlined in the preceding article. You should keep in mind especially the "choose" approach to proving inclusion and the "mutual inclusion" approach to proving equality of sets.

EXAMPLE 3   Prove that if $\{A_k | k = 1, 2, 3, \ldots\}$ is a decreasing collection of sets, then $\bigcup_{k=1}^{\infty} A_k \subseteq A_1$.

Solution   Let $x \in \bigcup_{k=1}^{\infty} A_k$, so that $x \in A_j$ for some positive integer j. We must prove $x \in A_1$. Clearly either $j = 1$ or $j > 1$. If $j = 1$, then $x \in A_j = A_1$, so $x \in A_1$, as desired. If $j > 1$, then $A_j \subseteq A_1$ (by the definition of "decreasing family") so that $x \in A_j \subseteq A_1$ and $x \in A_1$, again as desired. In either case we have the desired conclusion $x \in A_1$, so that our theorem is proved. $\square$

In Article 8.3 we will study *cardinality of sets*, a means of distinguishing the "relative size" of infinite sets. At that point we will consider so-called *arbitrary collections of sets*, that is, families of sets indexed by any set, not necessarily **N**. In that context we will come to recognize the kinds of collections we have studied in this article as *countably infinite collections of sets*.

Exercises

1. Find $\bigcup_{k=1}^{\infty} A_k$ and $\bigcap_{k=1}^{\infty} A_k$ for each of the collections of sets $\{A_k | k = 1, 2, 3, \ldots\}$ that follow:

(a) $A_k = \{-k\}$ ★(b) $A_k = \{1, 2, 3, \ldots, k\}$
★(c) $A_k = \{k, k + 1, k + 2, \ldots\}$ (d) $A_k = \{k, k + 1, k + 2, \ldots, 2k\}$
(e) $A_k = (0, 1/k)$ (f) $A_k = [0, 1/k]$
(g) $A_k = (-1/k, 1/k)$ (h) $A_k = [0, 1 + 1/k)$
(i) $A_k = [10/(k + 1), 10]$ ★(j) $A_k = (-\infty, k]$
★(k) $A_k = (-\infty, -k)$ (l) $A_k = (0, k - 1)$
(m) $A_k = [1/(k + 2), (k + 1)/(k + 2)]$
(n) $A_k = [0, 1/(k + 2)] \cup [(k + 1)/(k + 2), 1]$

2. Label each of the collections in Exercise 1 as either increasing, decreasing, mutually disjoint, or none of the above.

3. Give examples other than those in the text or in Exercise 1 of collections of sets $\{A_k | k = 1, 2, 3, \ldots\}$ that are:

(a)   Increasing (b)   Decreasing
(c)   Mutually disjoint (d)   None of the above

4. Suppose that $\{A_k | k = 1, 2, 3, \ldots\}$ is an infinite collection of sets from a universal set U, B is a subset of U, and n is an arbitrary positive integer. Prove that:

(a) $A_n \subseteq \bigcup_{k=1}^{\infty} A_k$ [Recall Theorem 2(e), Article 3.3.]

(b) $\bigcap_{k=1}^{\infty} A_k \subseteq A_n$ [Recall Theorem 2(d), Article 3.3.]

(c) $(\bigcap_{k=1}^{\infty} A_k)' = \bigcup_{k=1}^{\infty} A_k'$ [Generalized De Morgan's law; see Theorem 1(a), Article 3.3.]

(d) $(\bigcup_{k=1}^{\infty} A_k)' = \bigcap_{k=1}^{\infty} A_k'$ [See Theorem 1(b), Article 3.3.]

(e) $(\bigcup_{k=1}^{\infty} A_k) \cap B = \bigcup_{k=1}^{\infty} (A_k \cap B)$ [Generalized distributivity; recall
Exercise 11(c), Article 3.3.]

(f) $(\bigcap_{k=1}^{\infty} A_k) \cup B = \bigcap_{k=1}^{\infty} (A_k \cup B)$ [Recall Exercise 11(b), Article 3.3.]

5. (a) Prove that if $\{A_k | k = 1, 2, 3, \ldots\}$ is an increasing family of sets, then
$(\bigcap_{k=1}^{\infty} A_k) = A_1$. (Recall Example 2.)

★(b) Prove that if $\{A_k | k = 1, 2, 3, \ldots\}$ is a decreasing family of sets, then
$(\bigcup_{k=1}^{\infty} A_k) = A_1$.

(c) Prove that if $\{A_k | k = 1, 2, 3, \ldots\}$ is a mutually disjoint family of sets, then
$\bigcap_{k=1}^{\infty} A_k = \varnothing$.

(d) Prove or disprove: $\{A_k | k = 1, 2, 3, \ldots\}$ is a mutually disjoint family of sets
if and only if $\bigcap_{k=1}^{\infty} A_k = \varnothing$.

(e) Prove or disprove: If $\{A_k | k = 1, 2, 3, \ldots\}$ is a family of sets, then for any pair
of positive integers m and n:

★(i) If $m < n$, then $(\bigcap_{k=m}^{\infty} A_k) \subseteq (\bigcap_{k=n}^{\infty} A_k)$

(ii) If $m < n$, then $(\bigcup_{k=m}^{\infty} A_k) \subseteq (\bigcup_{k=n}^{\infty} A_k)$

6. Let $\{A_k | k = 1, 2, 3, \ldots\}$ be a collection of subsets of $U = \mathbf{R}$:

★(a) Suppose <u>each</u> A_k is an open and bounded interval, that is, of the form (a, b).
Is it possible for $\bigcap_{k=1}^{\infty} A_k$ to be an interval of another form? (Recall Definition
3, Article 1.1.)

(b) Suppose each A_k is a closed and bounded interval, that is, of the form $[a, b]$.
Is it possible for $\bigcup_{k=1}^{\infty} A_k$ to be an interval of another form?

(c) Suppose $\bigcap_{k=1}^{\infty} A_k = \varnothing$. Must there exist some positive integer n such that
$\bigcap_{k=1}^{n} A_k = \varnothing$?

(d) Suppose $\bigcup_{k=1}^{\infty} A_k = U$. Need it be true that $U = \bigcup_{k=1}^{n} A_k$ for some positive
integer n?

7. Let $\{A_k | k = 1, 2, 3, \ldots\}$ be a family of subsets of a universal set U. According to
Exercise 4(a), the set $\bigcup_{k=1}^{\infty} A_k$ <u>contains</u> each set in this family as a subset, whereas
by Exercise 4(b), the set $\bigcap_{k=1}^{\infty} A_k$ <u>is contained in</u> each set in the family.

(a) Prove that $\bigcup_{k=1}^{\infty} A_k$ is the *smallest* subset of U having the property described
above. Specifically, prove that if B is any subset of U having the property that
$A_k \subseteq B$ for each $k = 1, 2, 3, \ldots$, then $\bigcup_{k=1}^{\infty} A_k \subseteq B$. (For this reason it is often
said that $\bigcup_{k=1}^{\infty} A_k$ is the *least upper bound* of the given family of sets.)

★(b) Prove that $\bigcap_{k=1}^{\infty} A_k$ is the *largest* subset of U having the property described
above. Specifically, prove that if C is any subset of U having the property that
$C \subseteq A_k$ for each $k = 1, 2, 3, \ldots$, then $C \subseteq \bigcap_{k=1}^{\infty} A_k$. (For this reason it is often
said that $\bigcap_{k=1}^{\infty} A_k$ is the *greatest lower bound* of the family $\{A_k | k = 1, 2, 3, \ldots\}$.)

4.3 The Limit Concept (Optional)

In the introduction to Chapter 2 we noted that the limit concept, especially
the epsilon-delta definition of limits, is one of the most difficult ideas for
most students of elementary calculus. At the same time, however, we suggested that a thorough grounding in logic, especially quantification, could

remove much of that difficulty. We will now "deliver" on that promise. In this article, with the introduction to logic completed, we return to the limit concept with three specific goals: (1) We review and attempt to put into perspective a number of basic facts about limits (including the definition and basic properties of continuity) through a number of examples that illustrate the three basic categories into which every limit problem falls. (2) We attempt to help you to appreciate the geometric meaning of the epsilon-delta definition. A major tool in this endeavor is a close analysis of the logical negation of that definition. Principles of the predicate calculus, in turn, are indispensable for formulating that logical negation. (3) We attempt, by means of the material in this article, to pave the way for the writing of epsilon-delta proofs, a topic pursued further in Article 6.1.

REVIEW

In most elementary calculus classes the emphasis in the treatment of limits is placed on a "working knowledge" of the concept; given a function $y = f(x)$ and a point $x = a$, it is hoped that students can learn to use intuition, information from the graph of the function, and certain "rules of thumb" to determine the value of $\lim_{x \to a} f(x)$. Seldom are students expected, at that level, to bring the epsilon-delta definition of limit explicitly into play in solving a problem about limits. Before focusing on that definition, let us review, first, the basic rules of thumb by which students are generally expected to handle limit problems. This, in turn, is best done by a description of the three categories of answer to a limit problem, namely:

Type I: $\lim_{x \to a} f(x)$ exists and equals $f(a)$.

Type II: $\lim_{x \to a} f(x)$ exists but does not equal $f(a)$.

Type III: $\lim_{x \to a} f(x)$ does not exist.

Note that these categories are, in a logical sense, mutually exclusive and exhaustive; that is, every problem of the form "find $\lim_{x \to a} f(x)$" falls into exactly one of these three types.

Type 1. The easiest situation to deal with (and the situation most commonly seen initially in an elementary calculus class) in a limit problem is "$\lim_{x \to a} f(x)$ exists and equals the value of f at a." If a limit problem is in this category, we solve it simply by plugging the specific value $x = a$ into the defining rule for $f(x)$. If $\lim_{x \to a} f(x) = f(a)$, we say that f is *continuous at a*. The intuitive interpretation of "continuity at a" is that there is no "hole" in the graph at a, nor is there a "break" in the graph in the "immediate vicinity" of a. We will soon see that this intuitive description, although useful, oversimplifies and can mislead.

Many of the most familiar functions lead always to the Type I limit scenario and thus cause little difficulty in the context of limit problems. In particular, polynomial functions are continuous everywhere and rational functions are continuous everywhere except at those values of a that make their denominator zero. Also, familiar transcendental functions such as e^x, ln x, sin x, and cos x are continuous wherever defined. Other, less conventional, examples are:

$$f(x) = \begin{cases} 2x + 1, & x \geq 0 \\ x - 1, & x < 0 \end{cases},$$ which is continuous everywhere except at $x = 0$.

$$g(x) = \begin{cases} 2x, & x \geq 0 \\ x, & x < 0 \end{cases},$$ which is continuous everywhere, even at $x = 0$.

$$h(x) = \begin{cases} 1, & x \text{ rational} \\ -1, & x \text{ irrational} \end{cases},$$ which is continuous nowhere.

$$k(x) = \begin{cases} x, & x \text{ rational} \\ 0, & x \text{ irrational} \end{cases},$$ which is continuous at one point only namely, $x = 0$.

Continuity of a function f at a point a requires three things: (1) a must be in the domain of f, often stated f is *defined at a* or $f(a)$ *exists*. (2) $\lim_{x \to a} f(x)$ must exist. (3) The number $\lim_{x \to a} f(x)$ must be the same as the number $f(a)$. We will discuss the reasons for the noncontinuity of functions such as the preceding f, h, and k, at some or all points of their domain, after our introduction to categories II and III.

Type II. Under this category, we consider the possibility that $\lim_{x \to a} f(x)$ might exist, but have a value other than $f(a)$. Within this category $f(a)$ itself may or may not be defined. This is probably the category on which most students have the most tenuous hold, after their first exposure to limits, so we will look at it carefully.

Graphically, this situation is characterized by an otherwise continuous curve with a point missing at $x = a$. In this situation f is said to have a *removable discontinuity* at a. The name is apt; we could "remove" the discontinuity simply by redefining f at one point, or graphically, by plugging the hole in the curve. We now give examples to illustrate the two possibilities (1) $f(a)$ exists and (2) f is not defined at a.

(a)   A typical example for which $\lim_{x \to a} f(x)$ and $f(a)$ both exist, but are not equal, is a function defined by two rules, one rule for $x = a$ and another for all other values of x; that is, $x \neq a$. For example, the function

$$f(x) = \begin{cases} 5x - 3, & x \neq 2 \\ 8, & x = 2 \end{cases}$$

is not continuous at $x = 2$, even though $\lim_{x \to 2} f(x)$ exists (*Note:* This limit equals 7. When graphing this function, notice that the limit as x approaches 2 is the y component of the "missing point.") and even though $f(2)$ is defined [namely, $f(2) = 8$]. The problem is that the two values, 7 and 8, are different; this f has a removable discontinuity at $x = 2$. An important missing link in this discussion, and a question you should be thinking about, is "Why, according to the epsilon-delta definition of limit, does the preceding limit equal 7?" A careful analysis of the epsilon-delta definition, soon to come, provides the answer.

(b) A typical example for which $\lim_{x \to a} f(x)$ exists, while $f(a)$ does not exist, is a function defined by a rule such as

$$f(x) = (x^2 - 36)/(x - 6)$$

which collapses to $0/0$, and is left undefined, at $x = 6$. For all values of x except 6, $f(x)$ equals $x + 6$. In fact, $\lim_{x \to 6} (x^2 - 36)/(x - 6) = \lim_{x \to 6} x + 6 = 12$. [Again, when graphing this function, note that the limit is the y component of the "missing point" $(6, 12)$]. Thus the limit exists even though $f(6)$ is undefined. Again, we have a removable discontinuity, this time at $x = 6$.

This category of limit problem is particularly important because, every time we use the definition $f'(a) = \lim_{x \to a} (f(x) - f(a))/(x - a)$ of the *derivative*, we must deal with a limit of this type. Review how to compute $d/dx(x^3)$ and $d/dx(x^4 + x^2)$ from the definition of derivative.

Type III. Under this category, we consider situations in which $\lim_{x \to a} f(x)$ does not exist. Once again, f may or may not be defined at a. This category may be divided into three subcases:

1. One-sided (i.e., left- and right-hand) limits exist, but are different. For example, if

$$f(x) = \begin{cases} 1, & x \geq 0 \\ -1, & x < 0 \end{cases}$$

we have $\lim_{x \to 0^-} f(x) = -1 \neq 1 = \lim_{x \to 0^+} f(x)$. Thus $\lim_{x \to 0} f(x)$ does not exist. (*Note:* an important theorem, which you should recall from calculus, states that $\lim_{x \to a} f(x)$ exists if and only if $\lim_{x \to a^-} f(x)$ and $\lim_{x \to a^+} f(x)$ both exist and are equal.]

2. Infinite limits at $x = a$ (i.e., the line $x = a$ is a vertical asymptote to the curve). This occurs especially in a rational function in which the denominator tends to zero as $x \to a$ while the numerator approaches some nonzero quantity. This fact will be proved in Article 6.2, when we consider indirect proofs (see Exercise 16, Article 6.2.).

3. The one-sided limits are not infinite, but they do not exist as finite real numbers either. This is the strangest case, since it must involve rather wild fluctuations in the function. An example of this is $f(x) = \sin(1/x)$, $x \neq 0$. In any interval $(0, \mu)$ this function "bounces up and down" between $y = -1$ and $y = 1$ infinitely many times, no matter how small we choose the positive real number μ.

THE EPSILON-DELTA DEFINITION AND
ITS RELATIONSHIP TO TYPES I, II, AND III

By definition

$$L = \lim_{x \to a} f(x)$$ if and only if, for every $\varepsilon > 0$, there exists $\delta > 0$ such that whenever $0 < |x - a| < \delta$, then $|f(x) - L| < \varepsilon$

In this definition we assume that f is defined in an open interval containing a. The logical complexity of this definition is considerable. In particular, for a fixed value of a, this expression is a compound propositional function in three variables, ε, δ, and x, involving the connective $\to$, the most difficult connective from the point of view of intuition. Furthermore, the quantification of the three variables is mixed quantification, again, the most difficult case intuitively. Not surprisingly, this rigorous definition was formulated (by the German mathematician Karl Weierstrass) a full two hundred years after the intuitive idea of limit had been used by both Newton and Leibniz in their independent invention of the derivative concept, and thereby the calculus itself, around 1675. Even after understanding the geometric significance of the inequalities $0 < |x - a| < \delta$ and $|f(x) - L| < \varepsilon$ [the former determining the "interval minus one point" $(a - \delta, a + \delta) - \{a\}$, along the x axis, the latter the interval $(L - \varepsilon, L + \varepsilon)$ along the y axis], we still have difficulty in seeing the connection between the epsilon-delta definition and the results obtained in actual calculations of specific limits. See Figure 4.1,

Figure 4.1   *Epsilon and delta bands.*

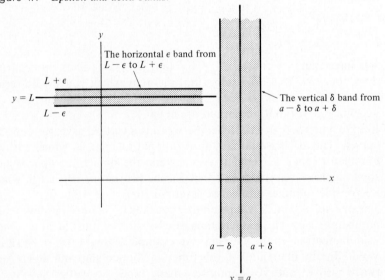

which pictures the vertical "δ band" about the line $x = a$, and the horizontal "ε band" about the line $y = L$, determined by these inequalities, respectively.

Frequently in mathematics, a good way to get the meaning of definition—to figure out what it says—is to consider what it doesn't say, and more particularly, write out carefully its logical negation (this in addition to knowing at least one example that satisfies the definition and one that does not. At any level of mathematics, no matter how abstract, you should never be satisfied with your level of understanding of a definition unless you are familiar with at least one specific example that satisfies, and one that doesn't satisfy, that definition, assuming, of course, that such examples exist.). This is the case for the epsilon-delta definition of limit. Before proceeding, you should review the general rule for negating multiply quantified predicates (Theorem 3 and Example 5, Article 3.4) and attempt to write out the epsilon-delta formulation of the statement $L \neq \lim_{x \to a} f(x)$.

EXAMPLE 1 Characterize the statement $L \neq \lim_{x \to a} f(x)$ in terms of epsilon and delta.

Solution The rule for negating any quantified predicate is, "change each $\forall$ to $\exists$, each $\exists$ to $\forall$, and negate the predicate." In view of this rule, and recalling from Chapter 2 the tautology $\sim(p \to q) \leftrightarrow p \wedge \sim q$, we see that $L \neq \lim_{x \to a} f(x)$ is expressed as

$$(\exists \varepsilon > 0)(\forall \delta > 0)(\exists x)[(0 < |x - a| < \delta) \wedge (|f(x) - L| \geq \varepsilon)]. \quad \square$$

There are two reasons for expecting that the characterization of $L \neq \lim_{x \to a} f(x)$, given in Example 1, might be easier to grasp than its negation (i.e., than the original epsilon-delta definition of limit). One is that the string of quantifiers in this statement begins with the quantifier $\exists$ rather than $\forall$, thus lending greater concreteness when the definition is applied. Second, the connective $\wedge$ replaces the connective $\to$ in the negated definition; most readers probably concluded, in the course of Chapter 2, that $\wedge$ is, on an intuitive basis, an easier connective to work with than $\to$.

Let us now examine the geometric meaning of the negation of the definition of limit in several examples. Throughout these examples, we will pay particular attention to the relationship between the graph of f, in the "immediate vicinity" of $x = a$, and possibilities for a value of ε that can be chosen to prove that $L \neq \lim_{x \to a} f(x)$.

EXAMPLE 2 Consider the function $f(x) = \begin{cases} 2x + 1, & x \geq 0 \\ x - 1, & x < 0 \end{cases}$. Use an epsilon-delta argument to prove that $1 \neq \lim_{x \to 0} f(x)$. Then prove that $-1 \neq \lim_{x \to 0} f(x)$ and $0 \neq \lim_{x \to 0} f(x)$. Finally, indicate how to generalize these arguments to prove formally that $\lim_{x \to 0} f(x)$ does not exist.

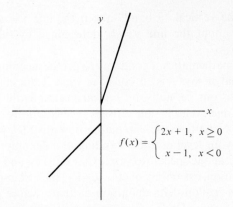

$$f(x) = \begin{cases} 2x + 1, & x \geq 0 \\ x - 1, & x < 0 \end{cases}$$

Figure 4.2   *The graph of y = f(x) in Example 2.*

Solution   It is intuitively clear that $\lim_{x \to 0} f(x)$ should not exist, since the graph of f(see Figure 4.2) has a break in the immediate vicinity of $x = 0$; but how can we argue this formally in terms of epsilon and delta? Let us try first to show that $L = 1$ does not satisfy the definition of limit, or more precisely, does satisfy the negation of that definition.

We must show that there exists (i.e., we must produce) a positive ε, giving rise to a horizontal "ε band" $\{(x, y) | x \in \mathbf{R}, 1 - \varepsilon < y < 1 + \varepsilon\}$ about the line $y = 1$ (see Figure 4.3) such that, for any δ, no matter how small, there can always be found a value of x that is within δ of $a = 0$, but whose functional value $f(x)$ does not lie in the given horizontal band; that is, $f(x)$ is not within ε of 1. Let us try $\varepsilon = 1$, so that we are specifying the horizontal ε band $\{(x, y) | x \in \mathbf{R}$ and $0 < y < 2\}$. Let an arbitrary

Figure 4.3   *A value of ε has been chosen small enough so that the entire portion of the curve to the left of $x = 0$ lies outside the resulting ε-band.*

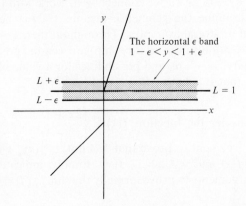

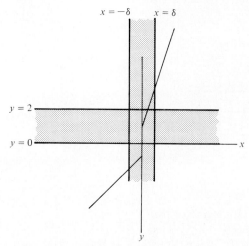

$x = -\delta$ $x = \delta$

$y = 2$

$y = 0$

x

y

Figure 4.4   *A graphic indication that*
$1 \neq \lim_{x \to 0} f(x)$. *If* $-\delta < x < 0$, *then* $f(x)$ *does
not fall between 0 and 2, no matter how small we
choose* δ.

positive δ be given as shown in Figure 4.4. Now, can we find a value
of x between $0 - \delta$ and $0 + \delta$ (along the x axis) for which $f(x)$ is <u>not
between</u> 0 and 2 (along the y axis)? We can indeed! Simply choose any x
between $-\delta$ and 0, that is, any x in the <u>left half</u> of the interval $(-\delta, \delta)$,
and note that $f(x)$ equals $x - 1$, which is less than -1, and hence is not
between 0 and 2.

Note that the key to the preceding argument was the choice of ε <u>small
enough</u> so that, within any vertical δ band about the line $x = 0$, no
matter how narrow, at least part of the graph of f, inside that vertical
band, does not lie inside the horizontal ε band surrounding the line
$y = 1$ ($y = L$ in general). What values of ε, other than $\varepsilon = 1$, would have
been permissible? Surely, any positive ε less than a value that is known
to "work," as $\varepsilon = 1$ does in the preceding argument, will also work.
(Think about this statement for a moment and make sure you under-
stand it.) So the question is <u>how large</u> a value of ε will permit us to use
successfully the preceding argument. Could we, for instance, let $\varepsilon = \frac{5}{2}$,
giving rise to an ε band of width 5 about the line $y = 1$? See Figure 4.5.
Again, let an arbitrary positive δ be chosen. Examine the picture in this
case; it is clear from the picture that if δ is reasonably small, say, $\frac{1}{2}$,
we cannot find a value of x within δ of $x = 0$ for which $f(x)$ lies outside
the given ε band. So $\varepsilon = 1$ works, whereas $\varepsilon = \frac{5}{2}$ is too large. Where is
the dividing line between values of epsilon that work and those that
don't? Geometric sense tells us that it is $\varepsilon = 2$, the vertical distance
between the proposed limit ($L = 1$ in this case) and the part of the graph

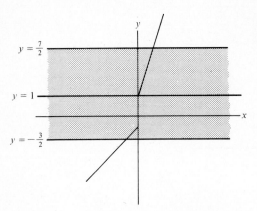

Figure 4.5   *Not just any ε can be used in a proof that*
$L \neq \lim_{x \to a} f(x)$. *The ε band* $(\varepsilon = \frac{5}{2}) - \frac{3}{2} < y < \frac{7}{2}$ *is too*
wide to be useful in proving $1 \neq \lim f(x)$ *as x tends to 0.*
If $\delta = \frac{1}{2}$, *then every x within δ of x = 0 has its*
corresponding f(x) between $-\frac{3}{2}$ *and* $\frac{7}{2}$, *that is, within the*
given ε band.

whose *y* values do not all "lie close to" *L* (the part of the graph of *f* to
the left of $x = 0$ in this case). Thus, in the argument that $1 \neq \lim_{x \to 0} f(x)$,
given in the previous paragraph, we could have used as our ε any specific
positive number less than or equal to 2, rather than $\varepsilon = 1$, with the
same argument working.

We next consider how that argument would have to be modified in
order to show that $-1 \neq \lim_{x \to 0} f(x)$. Again, we could start by specifying $\varepsilon = 1$ (or ε equals any other specific positive number less than or
equal to 2). This time, for an arbitrarily chosen positive δ, we can find
values of *x* to the right of $x = 0$ whose functional value $f(x) = 2x + 1$,
being greater than 1, is certainly not within distance $\varepsilon = 1$ of the proposed limit $L = -1$. Hence this value of *L* fails to be a limit as *x*
approaches 0.

$L = 0$, being halfway between the two separate pieces of the graph,
might be thought to serve as $\lim_{x \to 0} f(x)$. How can we use an epsilon-
delta argument to discredit this idea? We must specify a value of ε; can
we still use any value as large as 2? See Figure 4.6. The answer is "no!"
Since the vertical distance from $L = 0$ to the part of the graph on either
side of $x = 0$ is 1, we must start with a specific ε less than or equal to
1, say, $\varepsilon = \frac{1}{2}$. You should try to complete the argument that, for any
positive δ, no matter how small, there can always be found a value of
x within δ of $x = 0$, whose corresponding $f(x)$ is not within a distance
$\varepsilon = \frac{1}{2}$ of $L = 0$. Also, determine the largest value of ε that can be used
to prove that $L \neq \lim_{x \to 0} f(x)$, where $L = \frac{2}{3}$, $L = 3$, $L = -5$.

Finally, if ambitious, you may want to consider the problem of arguing that $L \neq \lim_{x \to 0} f(x)$, where *L* is an arbitrary number along the *y*

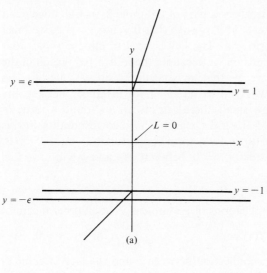

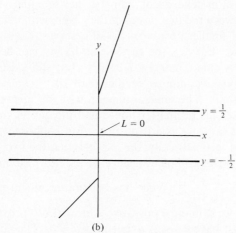

Figure 4.6   *We can prove* $0 \neq \lim_{x \to 0} f(x)$, *but the specific value of* ε *we use in the proof may not exceed 1. (a) Any* $\varepsilon > 1$ *is too large to be useful in proving* $0 \neq \lim f(x)$ *as x tends to 0; (b)* $\varepsilon = \frac{1}{2}$ *does the job.*

axis. This, of course, means that the proposed limit <u>does not exist</u>, as our intuition had indicated from the start. In approaching this problem, you should separate the problem into three cases $L \leq -1$, $-1 < L < 1$, and $L \geq 1$ (see Exercise 3(b)).   □

EXAMPLE 3   Let $f(x) = \begin{cases} 2x + a, & x \geq 0 \\ x - a, & x < 0 \end{cases}$, where a is a fixed positive real number. Argue that $0 \neq \lim_{x \to 0} f(x)$.

Solution   This problem generalizes a part of Example 2, in which we dealt with the particular case $a = 1$. To prove that $0 \neq \lim_{x \to 0} f(x)$, we must start by specifying a positive ε. The key is how to choose this ε; that choice quite clearly depends on a. Recalling the fourth paragraph of the solution to Example 2, we see that any specific positive value of ε less than or equal to a will work. If we let $\varepsilon = a$, for instance, then for any positive δ, no matter how small, there can always be found a value of x within δ of 0, measured along the x axis, whose corresponding $f(x)$ is a distance greater than ε (or a) away from 0, measured along the y axis. In fact, any x on either side of $x = 0$, between $-\delta$ and δ will have this property. □

Let us consider some implications of Example 3. The number 0 cannot serve as $\lim_{x \to 0} f(x)$, where $f(x) = \begin{cases} 2x + a, & x \geq 0 \\ x - a, & x < 0 \end{cases}$, for any $a > 0$. Furthermore, there is a specific connection between a and the largest value of ε that will work in the epsilon-delta proof, namely, they're equal. If $a = \frac{1}{2}$, we have a "gap" of 1 between the two pieces of the graph, with 0 halfway between, and $\varepsilon = \frac{1}{2}$ (or any smaller positive value of ε) serves to show that $0 \neq \lim_{x \to 0} f(x)$ in this case. If $a = \frac{1}{4}$, the gap is $\frac{1}{2}$ and $\varepsilon = \frac{1}{4}$ can be used. If $a = 10^{-5}$, the gap is very small, namely, 2×10^{-5}, but still exists, and $\varepsilon = 10^{-5}$ (or any specific positive number smaller than 10^{-5}) can be used to prove that 0 is not the limit. The same argument, with $\varepsilon = a$, works no matter how small a is, and thus no matter how small the gap is between the two pieces of the curve, as long as a is positive. But suppose we now let $a = 0$? We observe that, geometrically, the gap between the two pieces of the curve has now been closed completely, since we are now dealing with the function $g(x) = \begin{cases} 2x, & x \geq 0 \\ x, & x < 0 \end{cases}$. What has become of our argument that $0 \neq \lim_{x \to 0} g(x)$? Can we still find a positive ε that works to prove this? As seen previously, we must have $0 < \varepsilon \leq a$, but now $a = 0$. The largest ε we could use has been shrunk down to zero; that is, no positive ε can be found to prove that $0 \neq \lim_{x \to 0} g(x)$. What we are saying can be symbolized, in general (remember that $a = 0$ and $L = 0$ in our current example):

$$\sim \{(\exists \varepsilon > 0)(\forall \delta > 0)(\exists x)[(0 < |x - a| < \delta) \wedge (|g(x) - L| \geq \varepsilon)]\}$$

Geometrically, we know that $\lim_{x \to 0} g(x)$ exists and equals zero in this example, since there is no longer any break in the curve in the immediate vicinity of $x = 0$. This corresponds to the fact that the preceding symbolized statement is logically equivalent to

$$(\forall \varepsilon > 0)(\exists \delta > 0)(\forall x)[(0 < |x - a| < \delta) \rightarrow (|g(x) - L| < \varepsilon)]$$

where the latter is precisely the definition of $\lim_{x \to a} g(x) = L$.

Variations of the arguments used in Examples 2 and 3 are needed to prove that limits do not exist in other cases, as in Example 4.

EXAMPLE 4 Use an epsilon-delta argument to show that $1 \neq \lim_{x \to 0} h(x)$, where $h(x) = \begin{Bmatrix} 1, & x \text{ rational} \\ -1, & x \text{ irrational} \end{Bmatrix}$.

Solution Note first from Figure 4.7 that the graph of h consists of parts of the two horizontal lines $y = 1$ and $y = -1$, each line, however, having infinitely many "missing points." The two pieces of the graph of this function near $x = 0$ have a gap of 2 separating them. Thus, to prove $1 \neq \lim_{x \to 0} h(x)$, we may let $\varepsilon = \frac{3}{2}$ (we could in fact choose any specific value of ε less than or equal to 2), thus determining a horizontal ε band about the line $y = 1$, extending from $-\frac{1}{2}$ to $\frac{5}{2}$, measured along the y axis. Let $\delta > 0$ be arbitrary. Can we find x between $-\delta$ and δ whose corresponding $f(x)$ is <u>not between</u> $-\frac{1}{2}$ and $\frac{5}{2}$? Yes! Simply let x be an irrational number between $-\delta$ and δ (*Note:* It can be proved that there is an irrational number between any two reals). Then $f(x) = -1 \notin (-\frac{1}{2}, \frac{5}{2})$. $\square$

An argument similar to the preceding one can be used to show that $\lim_{x \to 0} h(x)$ does not exist and, more generally, that $\lim_{x \to a} h(x)$ does not exist for any real number a.

As indicated earlier, we will not focus on epsilon-delta proofs that $L = \lim_{x \to a} f(x)$ until Article 6.1, but a few words about them now may be appropriate. This type of proof differs from the "negative" epsilon-delta arguments we've seen in Examples 2, 3, and 4 in that we may not specify a

Figure 4.7 *Graph pertaining to Example 4.*
The function $h(x) = \begin{cases} 1, & x \text{ rational} \\ -1, & x \text{ irrational} \end{cases}$
cannot really be graphed. Its graph consists of parts of two parallel lines, each with infinitely many missing points. Every vertical line $x = k$ meets either the upper portion (k rational) or the lower portion (k irrational), but not both.

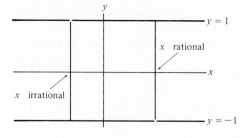

particular ε anywhere in such a proof. We must begin by letting an arbitrary positive ε be given. This ε, although arbitrary (i.e., not a specifically named number, like $\frac{1}{2}$ or $\pi/3$) is fixed at the start and used throughout the remainder of the proof. Our job in writing the proof is to determine a positive number δ, in terms of the given ε, such that every x within distance δ of a, other than a itself, has its corresponding $f(x)$ lying within ε of L. In doing this, we are determining geometrically the comparative width between a given ε band, about the line $y = L$ and a corresponding δ band about the line $x = a$, for which the definition of limit is satisfied. Of particular importance is the fact that δ depends on ε; typically, δ might be taken to equal ε, or $\varepsilon/2$, or the smaller of 1 and $\varepsilon/3$. Dependence of this type, a consequence of the logical structure of the definition of limit, in which $\exists$ follows $\forall$, was highlighted in Article 3.4.

An interesting application of this reasoning is in arguing that $\lim_{x \to 0} k(x) = 0 = k(0)$, where $k(x) = \begin{cases} x, & x \text{ rational} \\ 0, & x \text{ irrational} \end{cases}$, so that k is continuous at zero. Since k is continuous at no other point, k provides us with an example in which continuity at a point fails to correspond to our intuitive notion of "no break in the graph in the immediate vicinity of $x = a$."

FURTHER REMARKS ON THE TYPE II CASE

To conclude this article, we recall the question raised in considering Type II limit problems. How does the epsilon-delta definition of limit yield the rule of thumb that the "y component of the missing point" serves as $\lim_{x \to a} f(x)$ for a function such as $f(x) = \begin{cases} 2x + 5, & x \neq 3 \\ 2, & x = 3 \end{cases}$? Note that this rule of thumb yields the conclusion that $\lim_{x \to 3} f(x) = \lim_{x \to 3} 2x + 5 = 11$, even though $f(3) = 2$. Hence f is not continuous at 3, in spite of the fact that $f(3)$ is defined and $\lim_{x \to 3} f(x)$ exists.

At the same time as we raise this question, let us ask another question about the structure of the epsilon-delta definition. Why does the definition contain the two inequalities $0 < |x - a| < \delta$ rather than just the single inequality $|x - a| < \delta$? It turns out that the two questions are related to each other and to a statement about which you have probably heard or read concerning limits, namely, "the value of $\lim_{x \to a} f(x)$ is in no way influenced by the ★value of f at a, but is instead completely determined by the values of $f(x)$, for x in the immediate vicinity of a."

Why are we really dealing here with three pieces of the same puzzle? Let us begin with the second piece, the epsilon-delta definition itself. Suppose the definition of limit were formulated

$$L = \lim_{x \to a} f(x) \Leftrightarrow (\forall \varepsilon > 0)(\exists \delta > 0)(\forall x)[(|x - a| < \delta) \to (|f(x) - L| < \varepsilon)].$$

What then would be the situation in the limit problem we proposed earlier? In particular, would we still have $\lim_{x\to 3} f(x) = 11$, according to this "definition"? Here is the reason we <u>would not</u>! Let ε be any positive real number less than or equal to 9 (note that 9 is the gap between $y = 2$ and $y = 11$). Then, no matter how small we choose δ, the particular value $x = 3$ of x satisfies $|x - 3| < \delta$, since $|3 - 3| = 0 < \delta$, while at the same time $|f(x) - L| = |f(3) - L| = |2 - 11| = 9 \geq \varepsilon$. This shows that $L = 11$ <u>fails to satisfy</u> this (incorrect) version of the definition.

The correct epsilon-delta definition of limit requires, in order for L to equal $\lim_{x\to a} f(x)$, that we be able to make all corresponding values of $f(x)$ (other than $f(a)$ itself if it exists) <u>as close as we please</u> to L, that is, within distance ε of L, by considering only values of x <u>sufficiently close</u> to a, that is, within δ of a (but again, <u>not equal</u> to a). If we omit the parenthetical parts of the preceding sentence, the example of the previous paragraph shows that limit problems we have designated "Type II" would instead be of Type III, since no value of L could satisfy the epsilon-delta definition. Indeed, if we allow the value of f <u>at a</u> to influence the value of $\lim_{x\to a} f(x)$, by using the preceding incorrect "definition" of limit, we are not only doing away with the category of "Type II limit" (the most important category because of its role in the definition of derivative), but are simultaneously removing much of the subtlety that makes the limit concept interesting.

Finally, why does the correct epsilon-delta definition of limit yield the rule of thumb that "L = the y component of the missing point" in a Type II example? If our characterization of the "$0 < |x - a|$" part of the definition as mandating that the value of $f(a)$ is irrelevant to the value of L is accepted, then the following is evident. Suppose g is a function continuous at each point of some open interval I containing a. Further suppose

$$f(x) = \begin{cases} g(x), & \text{if } x \in I, \ x \neq a \\ \text{either undefined or not equal to } g(a), & \text{if } x = a \end{cases}. \quad \text{By definition of}$$

continuity at a, $\lim_{x\to a} g(x) = g(a)$. It stands to reason that, since f agrees with g everywhere except at a, and since $\lim_{x\to a} f(x)$ is completely determined by the values of $f(x)$ at points x close to a, and not at all by $f(a)$, then $\lim_{x\to a} f(x)$ should equal $\lim_{x\to a} g(x)$; that is, should equal $g(a)$. But $g(a)$ is precisely the "missing point" in the graph of f as shown in Figure 4.8.

EXAMPLE 5   Compute $\lim_{x\to 3} \left[(x^2 - 5x + 6)/(x - 3) \right]$

Solution $f(x) = \left[(x^2 - 5x + 6)/(x - 3) \right]$ is undefined at $x = 3$, but if $x \neq 3$, then $f(x) = \left[(x^2 - 5x + 6)/(x - 3) \right] = x - 2$, where we denote the latter function by $g(x)$. Now g, being a linear polynomial function, is continuous everywhere, in particular, $\lim_{x\to 3} g(x) = g(3) = 3 - 2 = 1$. Since f agrees with g everywhere except at $a = 3$, so that the graph of f is simply a line with the point $(3, 1)$ missing, then $\lim_{x\to 3} f(x) = \lim_{x\to 3} g(x) = 1$.

□

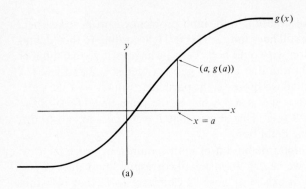

(a)

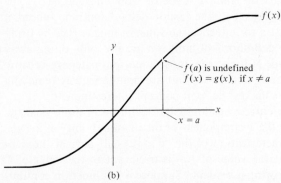

(b)

Figure 4.8   *The graphs of f and g are identical,
except for their values at x = a. In such a
situation, g(a) = lim f(x) as x tends to a.*

Exercises

1. For each of the following limit problems:

(a)   Evaluate $\lim_{x \to a} f(x)$ or conclude that it doesn't exist.
(b)   Categorize each as Type I, II or III, and decide whether f is continuous at a.

(i) $\lim_{x \to 3} (-4x^3 + 5x + 7)$ (ii) $\lim_{x \to -7} (x + 7)/(x - 2)$
(iii) $\lim_{x \to 3} (x^2 + 4x + 3)/(x + 3)$ (iv) $\lim_{x \to 3} (x^2 - 2x - 3)/(x - 3)$
(v) $\lim_{x \to 3} (x^2 - 2x + 3)/(x - 3)$ (vi) $\lim_{h \to 0} [(4 + h)^2 - 16]/h$
(vii) $\lim_{x \to 4} (\sqrt{x} - 2)/(x - 4)$ ★(viii) $\lim_{x \to 3} [(1/x) - (\frac{1}{3})]/(x - 3)$
(ix) $\lim_{x \to 2/\pi} \sin(1/x)$

2. Evaluate $\lim_{x \to a} f(x)$ or determine that it doesn't exist for:

★(a) $f(x) = \begin{cases} 2x - 5, & x \geq 3 \\ x^2, & x < 3 \end{cases}$ at $a = 3$

★(b) $f(x) = \begin{cases} 2x - 5, & x \neq 3 \\ 9, & x = 3 \end{cases}$ at $a = 3$

(c) $f(x) = (x^3 - 8)/(x - 2)$ at $a = 2$

(d) $f(x) = \begin{cases} \sin x, & x \text{ rational} \\ 0, & x \text{ irrational} \end{cases}$ at $a = 0$

(e) $f(x) = \begin{cases} \sin x, & x \text{ rational} \\ 0, & x \text{ irrational} \end{cases}$ at $a = \pi/2$

3. (a)   Give an epsilon-delta argument that $L \neq \lim_{x \to a} f(x)$ for each of the following functions. In each case, indicate the largest value (if any) of ε that could be used in such a proof:

(i) $f(x) = \begin{cases} 1, & x \geq 5 \\ 0, & x < 5 \end{cases}$ $L = 1, a = 5$

(ii) $f(x) = \begin{cases} 1, & x \text{ rational} \\ 0, & x \text{ irrational} \end{cases}$ $L = \frac{1}{2}, a = 5$

★(iii) $f(x) = \begin{cases} 5x + B, & x > 0 \\ 2x - B, & x \leq 0 \end{cases}$ $L = 0, a = 0$, where $B > 0$

(iv) $f(x) = \begin{cases} x, & x \text{ rational} \\ 0, & x \text{ irrational} \end{cases}$ $L = 1, a = 1$

(v) $f(x) = |1/x|,$ $L = 1, a = 0$

(b)   Argue that, for any real number L, $L \neq \lim_{x \to a} f(x)$, where $f(x)$ is the function given in Example 2. (See especially the last paragraph of the solution to Example 2.)

4. Let f be a function defined on the interval $[a, a + r)$ for some $r > 0$. A real number L^+ is said to be a *right-hand limit* of $f(x)$, as x approaches a, denoted $L^+ = \lim_{x \to a^+} f(x)$, if and only if $(\forall \varepsilon > 0)(\exists \delta > 0)(\forall x)[(a < x < a + \delta) \to (|f(x) - L^+| < \varepsilon)]$. Left-hand limit L^- of f at a is defined analogously; write out this definition. It is a theorem, to be proved in Article 6.1 (see Exercise 19), that $\lim_{x \to a} f(x)$ exists if and only if $\lim_{x \to a^+} f(x)$ and $\lim_{x \to a^-} f(x)$ both exist and are equal. Evaluate both the right- and left-hand limit as x tends to a for each of the following functions:

(a) $f(x) = \begin{cases} 5x + B, & x > 0 \\ 2x - B, & x \leq 0 \end{cases}$, $a = 0$, where $B > 0$

(b) $f(x) = [x]$, the greatest integer less than or equal to x, $a = 1$

(c) $f(x) = \begin{cases} 2x + 7, & x < 3 \\ x^2 + 4, & x \geq 3 \end{cases}$, $a = 3$

★(d) $f(x) = \tan x,$ $a = \pi/2$

(e) $f(x) = \begin{cases} x, & x \text{ rational} \\ 2, & x \text{ irrational} \end{cases}$, $a = 2$

5. ★*(a)*   Give an epsilon-delta argument that $\lim_{x \to 0^+} \sin(1/x) \neq 0$.

(b)   How might an argument given in (a) have to be altered to prove that $\lim_{x \to 0^+} (\frac{1}{10}) \sin(1/x) \neq 0$? $\lim_{x \to 0^+} (\frac{1}{100}) \sin(1/x) \neq 0$?

(c)   Do you think that the kind of argument given in (a) and (b) could be used to prove that $\lim_{x \to 0^+} (x \sin(1/x)) \neq 0$? Do you think that this one-sided limit exists? If so, what do you think is its value? (See Exercise 13(c), Article 6.1.)

6. Let f be a function defined on the interval $[a, a + r)$ for some $r > 0$. We say that f is *right-continuous*, or *continuous from the right* at a if and only if $\lim_{x \to a^+} f(x) = f(a)$.

(a)   Give an analogous definition of *left-continuous* at a.

(b)   Give examples of functions $f(x)$, $g(x)$ such that:

    (i) f is continuous from the right, but not the left, at $x = 6$.

    (ii) g is continuous from the left, but not the right, at $x = 3$.

(c)   Suppose that $\lim_{x \to a} f(x)$ exists, but does not equal $f(a)$ (i.e., f is Type II at a). Is it possible for f to be continuous from either the left or the right at a?

(d)   Using the theorem stated in Exercise 4, state and prove a theorem that relates right and left continuity of f at a to ordinary continuity of f at a.

7. A function f is said to be *continuous on an open interval I* if and only if f is continuous at each point of I. In terms of epsilons and deltas, f is continuous on I if and only if

$$(\forall a \in I)(\forall \varepsilon > 0)(\exists \delta > 0)(\forall x \in I)[|x - a| < \delta) \to (|f(x) - f(a)| < \varepsilon)]$$

On the other hand, a function f is said to be *uniformly continuous* on I if and only if

$$(\forall \varepsilon > 0)(\exists \delta > 0)(\forall a \in I)(\forall x \in I)[(|x - a| < \delta) \to (|f(x) - f(a)| < \varepsilon)]$$

(a)   Explain, in terms of theorems of the predicate calculus, why <u>uniform continuity</u> on I is a stronger property than <u>continuity</u> on I. That is, why is it true that, for any function f, if f is uniformly continuous on I, then f is continuous on I?

We can give many examples of functions that are uniformly continuous on various intervals, for instance, $f(x) = Mx + B$ is uniformly continuous over any interval, $g(x) = x^2$ is uniformly continuous on $(0, 2)$, while $h(x) = 1/x$ is uniformly continuous on $[1, \infty)$. On the other hand, there are functions that are continuous, but not uniformly continuous, on certain intervals [i.e., the converse of the result in (a) is false]. For example, $f(x) = x^2$ is not <u>uniformly</u> continuous on $(0, \infty)$ and $h(x) = 1/x$ is not <u>uniformly</u> continuous on $(0, 1)$, even though both functions are continuous on those intervals.

(b)   Suppose we are writing proofs, by using epsilons and deltas, that $f(x) = x^2$ is continuous on the intervals $(0, 2)$ and $(0, \infty)$. Note that f is uniformly continuous in the first case, but not in the second. Describe the qualitative difference in the choice of δ, given a positive ε, between these two cases. (Recall Example 3 and Exercises 6 and 7, Article 3.4.)

8. Let f be defined on some open interval (a, ∞) and let L be a real number. We say $L = \lim_{x \to \infty} f(x)$ iff $(\forall \varepsilon > 0)(\exists N > 0)(\forall x)[(x > N) \to (|f(x) - L| < \varepsilon)]$. Geometrically, this means that any ε band about the horizontal line $y = L$, no matter how narrow, contains every point on the graph of f for values of x to the right of some number (namely, N). Note that, from the logical structure of the definition, N

depends on ε; specifically, the smaller ε is chosen, the larger will be corresponding values of N that can be chosen.

(a) In the case where the graph of f is a continuous curve, what is the relationship between the line $y = L$ and the graph of f, when $\lim_{x \to \infty} f(x) = L$?

(b) Evaluate these limits (*Hint:* Let $x = 1/t$, simplify, and let $t \to 0$):
   (i) $\lim_{x \to \infty} (x - 3)/(x + 4)$
   ★ (ii) $\lim_{x \to \infty} (x + 6)/(x^2 - 10)$
   ★ (iii) $\lim_{x \to \infty} (x^2 - 2x + 3)/(2x^2 + 5x - 3)$
   (iv) $\lim_{x \to \infty} (x^2 - 6x - 7)/(x + 2)$

(c) Write a formal definition of $\lim_{x \to -\infty} f(x) = L$.

(d) ★ (i) Write a formal definition of $\lim_{x \to a} f(x) = \infty$.
   (ii) In a case where f is continuous in an open interval containing a, but not at a itself, and $\lim_{x \to a} f(x) = \infty$, what is the relationship between the graph of f and the line $x = a$?

Methods of Mathematical Proof, Part I: Elementary Methods
CHAPTER 5

As undergraduate students of mathematics pass through the sophomore to the junior level, a major change in their mathematical career occurs with the seemingly sudden emphasis on the need to understand and, especially, to write proofs. Indeed, the most common refrain heard by instructors of undergraduates in courses such as abstract algebra, advanced calculus, number theory, and linear algebra, is "I understand the material, but I can't do the proofs."

From one point of view, it is not surprising that students find proof writing difficult. After all, mathematicians themselves spend a lifetime absorbed in the attempt to discover and prove theorems, a pursuit involving the combination of expertise (sometimes genius), effort, and occasional luck, which is the basis of all scientific discovery. For these professionals, a major part of the challenge, and of the beauty of mathematics itself, emanates from what is at the core of the difficulty that most undergraduate students experience. Namely, there is no formula for writing proofs; writing even simple proofs involves a certain degree of creativity as well as uncertainty at the outset of where the process will lead. Furthermore, there is generally no unique correct answer to a problem calling for writing a proof. For an undergraduate student, then, an assignment that involves writing a proof is bound to produce anxiety, in contrast with the security most feel when working, say, to differentiate a function or find the inverse of a matrix.

But a case can be made that students should not view proof writing to be so difficult as many do. For one thing, undergraduate students are, for the most part, spared the difficulty that both haunts and delights research mathematicians, namely, lack of certainty whether the result they are trying to prove is actually true. Furthermore, proofs that students are asked to write at the sophomore-senior level are usually not "hard," from the point of view of their mathematical content. Finally, and most relevant to our work in this chapter, there are a number of underlying principles and techniques involving proof writing per se that experienced mathematicians take for granted. Proof writing can never be reduced to a mechanical process, but considerable anxiety and uncertainty can be eliminated from the process—indeed, much of the "mystique" can be removed from the entire activity of proof writing—if students are exposed to these principles and techniques explicitly and systematically.

After some probing, students who utter the complaint at the end of the first paragraph will often remark, "I just don't know where to begin." There is more validity to this complaint than sometimes meets the eye, for many elementary proofs are essentially completed once the proper starting point has been found, once what has to be proved is carefully written down. This step usually involves the careful interpretation of a definition. This is the point at which problems can occur, even for students who were expert at writing proofs in plane geometry and in deriving trigonometric identities. A major difficulty in writing proofs at the postcalculus level is that, at this level, the logical structure of many of the definitions encountered becomes rather complicated. As examples, to prove that a function f is *increasing* on a interval I, we must show "for every pair of numbers $a, b \in I, a < b$ implies $f(a) < f(b)$," a statement involving both the universal quantifier and implication arrow. To prove that an integer m *divides* an integer n, we must prove that there exists an integer p such that $n = mp$, a statement involving the existential quantifier. To verify the definition of limit in a particular case, we need to work with the epsilon-delta definition, involving three uses of quantifiers (two universal and one existential), and one use of the implication connective. Different proofs require different starting points, a different "setting up" according to the logical structure of the conclusion to be derived. In particular, as soon as either an existential quantifier or an implication arrow occurs in a definition involved in a desired conclusion, the proof will involve a setting up different from anything encountered in plane geometry or trigonometry, or in writing the few proofs that might be required in elementary and intermediate calculus.

In this chapter we will deal systematically with various techniques of proof, categorized largely according to different possibilities for logical structure of definitions. Since it is fruitless to discuss such techniques in a vacuum, we will illustrate each category of proof by considering specific mathematical problems, involving concepts that either should be familiar

to, or can quickly be grasped by, students at the sophomore level of undergraduate mathematics.

5.1   Conclusions Involving ∀, but Not ∃ or →. Proof by Transitivity

In this article we focus on proofs of the most elementary type from a logical, or structural, point of view. Generally, theorems whose conclusion
involves neither the existential quantifier nor implication arrow are proved
by methods familiar to students with a strong high school mathematics
background. Since these methods continue to be useful at every level of
mathematics, their proper application in the context of sophomore-junior
level university mathematics is an appropriate starting point for our study
of theorem-proving techniques.

Most students of mathematics are first exposed to proof writing in the
plane geometry, intermediate algebra, and trigonometry courses that pre-
cede the introduction to calculus. Here are typical proofs from each of the
three courses.

EXAMPLE 1 (Plane Geometry)   *Hypothesis: BC* and *AD* are straight lines,
AB = *DC, O* bisects *BC*, angle *B* = 90°, angle *C* = 90°. *Conclusion: AO* =
DO. Plan: Prove that *AO* and *DO* are corresponding parts of congruent
triangles. See Figure 5.1.

Solution

Statements		*Authorities*	
In $\triangle ABO$ and $\triangle DCO$;			
1.	$AB = BC$	1.	By hypothesis
2.	O bisects BC	2.	By hypothesis
3.	Therefore $BO = CO$	3.	Definition of bisector
4.	Angle $B = 90°$, angle $C = 90°$	4.	By hypothesis
5.	Therefore angle B = angle C	5.	Axiom "two quantities equal to the same quantity are equal to each other."
6.	Therefore $\triangle ABO$ is congruent to $\triangle DCO$	6.	SAS (two sides, included angle)
7.	AO and DO are corresponding sides of triangles $\triangle ABO$ and $\triangle DCO$	7.	AO and DO lie opposite equal angles.
8.	Therefore $AO = DO$	8.	Corresponding sides of congruent triangles are equal. □

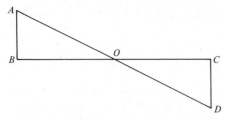

Figure 5.1 *Triangles ABO and DCO, from Example 1, can be proved to be congruent.*

It is generally through plane geometry that students are introduced to mathematics as a deductive science. In that subject we begin with a set of *axioms*, general statements about relationships in plane geometry that are assumed true, and build from these a collection of *theorems*. Theorems are deduced by means of a *proof*, a series of statements, each of whose validity is based on an axiom or a previously proved theorem. In constructing plane geometry proofs, we gain an appreciation of the critical importance of the question, "What facts am I allowed to use in this proof?" This question continues to be important in higher level college mathematics and seldom, at that level, is the issue ever again as clearcut as it was in high school geometry, since the latter is a self-contained and generally very tightly constructed system. Often, when proofs are assigned in an upper-level mathematics course, it is a fair question to ask of the instructor whether a particular theorem or approach (perhaps from a previous course) may be assumed and used in your proof.

EXAMPLE 2 (Intermediate Algebra)   Use the associative and commutative laws of multiplication to prove that $(ab)(cd) = [(dc)a]b$ for any real numbers a, b, c, and d.

Solution   Assume that a, b, c, and d are real numbers. We note that:

$$(ab)(cd) = (ab)(dc)$$ (since $cd = dc$, by commutativity, and by the basic principle, "equals multiplied by equals yield equals")

$$= (dc)(ab)$$ (again, by commutativity, applied to the real numbers ab and dc)

$$= [(dc)a]b$$ (by associativity, applied to the real numbers (dc), a, and b)   □

Usually in proofs such as the one in Example 2 students are introduced to a very basic, but crucial, idea: *We cannot prove a general theorem (e.g., one involving universal quantification over an infinite universal set, such as the real numbers) by giving a particular example, or by trying to enumerate all cases.* Note also the form of the proof given in Example 2. To prove that two quantities, say, A and Z, are equal, we have provided a string of equations:

$$A = B = C = \cdots = Z$$

beginning with A and ending with Z. This form of proof, which we refer to as a *proof by transitivity*, is the most elegant and desirable form in which a conclusion whose statement involves $\forall$, but not $\exists$ or $\rightarrow$, can be written. We give examples later of proofs by transitivity of conclusions asserting the relationships $=$ and $\leq$ between real numbers, and $=$ and $\subseteq$ between pairs of sets.

EXAMPLE 3 (Trigonometry)   Derive the identity

$(\cos 2x - \sin^2 x)/\sin 2x = \frac{1}{2}\cot x - \tan x,$

for any real number x, not of the form $x = n\pi/2$, where n is an integer. Use double angle formulas for sine and cosine and the definitions of cot and tan, in terms of sin and cos.

Solution   Let x be a real number, not of the form $x = n\pi/2$, where n is an integer. Then

$$\begin{aligned}
(\cos 2x - \sin^2 x)/\sin 2x &= [(\cos^2 x - \sin^2 x) - \sin^2 x]/\sin 2x \\
&= [(\cos^2 x - 2\sin^2 x)]/\sin 2x \\
&= [(\cos^2 x - 2\sin^2 x)]/2\sin x \cos x \\
&= ((\cos x/2\sin x)) - (\sin x/\cos x) \\
&= \tfrac{1}{2}\cot x - \tan x. \quad \square
\end{aligned}$$

In this proof, studied at a more advanced level of high school mathematics than the proof in Example 2, we have altered the approach taken in Example 2 by not stating explicitly a justification for each step. This is common in proof writing past the elementary level. We note at the same time, however, that the proof has been carefully laid out, with each line representing a step that is clearly intelligible to those who are reasonably well-informed. If specific reasons for individual steps are not supplied in a proof (as is customary), then the writer of a proof must use good judgment in providing a fair amount of detail; with too few steps, it might not be possible to follow the reasoning. Also, it is often appropriate to state explicitly the justification for a step that is either especially important or particularly tricky to understand.

On the other hand, we could have inserted into the proof of Example 3 (between lines 3 and 4) an additional line containing the expression

$[(\cos^2 x)/(2\sin x \cos x)] - [(2\sin^2 x)/(2\sin x \cos x)]$

but chose not to do so. Surely most readers can follow the progression from line 3 to line 4 in the form given; with too many steps, the proof becomes cluttered and boring. There is no universally correct answer; what constitutes a proof that is both informative and pleasing to read is largely a matter of individual judgment and taste, both of which generally improve with experience in writing proofs.

Thus far, in this article, we have focused on how a proof is to be presented. But knowing how to present a proof is of little value without being able to discover it—to find a path linking A to Z—in the first place. The next example highlights this issue.

EXAMPLE 4   Prove that $(1 + \sin x)/\cot^2 x = \sin x/(\csc x - 1)$, for all values of x where both quantities are defined.

Solution   Note first that the statement to be proved involves the universal quantifier ("for all") but no existential quantifier or implication arrow. Consequently, we wish to write a proof by transitivity, as we did in Examples 2 and 3. Since both expressions are rather complex, however, it is probably not easy to find a direct route from the expression on the left to that on the right. In such a situation the best procedure is to try to change the form of both expressions, in the hope of reducing (or expanding) both to a common third expression. Taking this approach, and assuming that x is a real number for which both quantities we're working with are defined, we find that

$$(1 + \sin x)/\cot^2 x = (1 + \sin x)(\tan^2 x)$$
$$= (1 + \sin x)(\sin^2 x/\cos^2 x)$$
$$= (\sin^2 x)(1 + \sin x)/(\cos^2 x)$$

whereas

$$\sin x/(\csc x - 1) = \sin x/((1/\sin x) - 1)$$
$$= \sin x/((1 - \sin x)/\sin x)$$
$$= \sin^2 x/(1 - \sin x)$$
$$= (\sin^2 x)(1 + \sin x)/(1 - \sin x)(1 + \sin x)$$
$$= (\sin^2 x)(1 + \sin x)/(1 - \sin^2 x)$$
$$= (\sin^2 x)(1 + \sin x)/(\cos^2 x)$$

At this point we have essentially solved the problem, but the question remains how to present the proof. The easiest way, from the point of view of the writer, is to append to the previous arguments the conclusion

$$(1 + \sin x)/\cot^2 x = (\sin^2 x)(1 + \sin x)/(\cos^2 x)$$
$$= \sin x/(\csc x - 1)$$

whenever these expressions are all defined, so that the desired equality is proved. The best way to present the proof, however, is to combine the two strings of equations into a single string, that is, to write a proof by transitivity. The string should begin with $(1 + \sin x)/\cot^2 x$, end with $\sin x/(\csc x - 1)$, and involve the quantity $(\sin^2 x)(1 + \sin x)/(\cos^2 x)$ at an intermediate step. It is left to you, in Exercise 2(b), to write out such a presentation of this proof (see the solution to Example 6, for further guidance).

Here is a form of presentation of the preceding proof that you <u>should not use</u>.

$$(1 + \sin x)/\cot^2 x = \sin x/(\csc x - 1)$$

$$(1 + \sin x)(\tan^2 x) = \sin x/((1/\sin x) - 1)$$

$$(1 + \sin x)(\sin^2 x/\cos^2 x) = \sin^2 x/(1 - \sin x)$$

$$(\sin^2 x)(1 + \sin x)/(\cos^2 x) = (\sin^2 x)(1 + \sin x)/(1 - \sin x)(1 + \sin x)$$

$$(\sin^2 x)(1 + \sin x)/(\cos^2 x) = (\sin^2 x)(1 + \sin x)/(\cos^2 x)$$

In this illustration we have given a series of steps that starts with the equation to be derived (thus effectively <u>assuming</u> that which is to be proved) and ends with a tautology, namely, a statement that a quantity equals itself. This is a logically incorrect presentation of the proof, even though all the correct trigonometric relationships are there. □

Some proofs of equality <u>in set theory</u> can be carried out by a transitivity argument, using results proved in Article 4.1 by the choose method.

EXAMPLE 5   Prove that $X - (Y \cap Z) = (X - Y) \cup (X - Z)$ for any three subsets X, Y, and Z of a universal set U.

Solution   Let X, Y, and Z be arbitrary subsets of U. Then

$$\begin{aligned}
X - (Y \cap Z) &= X \cap (Y \cap Z)' \\
&= X \cap (Y' \cup Z') \\
&= (X \cap Y') \cup (X \cap Z') \\
&= (X - Y) \cup (X - Z)
\end{aligned}$$

Supply the justification for each of these equations. Each step depends on a result derived in Article 4.1. □

The next example is also from set theory and has a solution similar in approach to the solution to Example 4. Due to the complex form both quantities involved, we take the approach of converting each to a common third quantity.

EXAMPLE 6   Prove that intersection distributes over symmetric difference, that is, for any three sets A, B, and C in a universal set U, $A \cap (B \bigtriangleup C) = (A \cap B) \bigtriangleup (A \cap C)$.

Solution   Before attempting a general proof of an unfamiliar theorem, you should always test the truth of the statement with at least one example. You should compute both these quantities for $U = \mathbf{Z}$, $A = \{2, 4, 5, 7\}$, $B = \{4, 7, 11, 15\}$, and $C = \{7, 15, 23, 26\}$. Drawing relevant pictures, in this case Venn diagrams, can also be helpful. As to the proof, note first that

$$A \cap (B \bigtriangleup C) = A \cap [(B \cap C') \cup (B' \cap C)]$$
$$= (A \cap B \cap C') \cup (A \cap B' \cap C)$$

whereas

$$(A \cap B) \bigtriangleup (A \cap C) = [(A \cap B) \cap (A \cap C)'] \cup [(A \cap B)' \cap (A \cap C)]$$
$$= [(A \cap B) \cap (A' \cup C')] \cup [(A' \cup B') \cap (A \cap C)]$$
$$= [(A \cap B \cap A') \cup (A \cap B \cap C')] \cup [(A' \cap A \cap C) \cup (B' \cap A \cap C)]$$
$$= [\varnothing \cup (A \cap B \cap C')] \cup [\varnothing \cup (B' \cap A \cap C)]$$
$$= (A \cap B \cap C') \cup (A \cap B' \cap C)$$

Again, you should supply justifications for the preceding steps.

Having changed the form of both involved quantities to a common third quantity, we have essentially solved the problem, but there remains the matter of how to present the proof. The proof may be presented correctly in one of two ways. Most conveniently, we may simply append to the two derivations, given earlier, the statement that both given quantities equal $(A \cap B \cap C') \cup (A \cap B' \cap C)$, and so equal each other. Or else, more desirable from the point of view of someone with experience (such as an instructor), the proof might be written in the form of a proof by transitivity, as in

$$(A \cap B) \bigtriangleup (A \cap C) = [(A \cap B) \cap (A \cap C)'] \cup [(A \cap B)' \cap (A \cap C)]$$
$$= [(A \cap B) \cap (A' \cup C')] \cup [(A' \cup B') \cap (A \cap C)]$$
$$= [(A \cap B \cap A') \cup (A \cap B \cap C')] \cup [(A' \cap A \cap C) \cup (B' \cap A \cap C)]$$
$$= [\varnothing \cup (A \cap B \cap C')] \cup [\varnothing \cup (B' \cap A \cap C)]$$
$$= (A \cap B \cap C') \cup (A \cap B' \cap C)$$
$$= A \cap [(B \cap C') \cup (B' \cap C)]$$
$$= A \cap (B \bigtriangleup C) \quad \square$$

A proof by transitivity may also be appropriate for a theorem asserting an <u>inequality</u> between numbers or a subset relationship between sets, as in these examples.

EXAMPLE 7   Suppose it is known that $|x + y| \le |x| + |y|$ for all real numbers x and y [see Exercise 8(a)]. Prove that $|x - z| \le |x - y| + |y - z|$ for all real numbers x, y, and z.

Solution   Let x, y, and z be given.   Then

$$|x - z| = |x + (-y + y) - z|$$
$$= |(x - y) + (y - z)|$$
$$\leq |x - y| + |y - z|, \text{ as desired.} \quad \square$$

EXAMPLE 8   Assume the theorem, for any sets A, X, and Y, if $X \subseteq Y$, then $A \cap X \subseteq A \cap Y$. Use this fact, along with an appropriate distributive property, to prove that, for any three sets A, B, and C,

$$A \cap (B \cup C) \subseteq (A \cap B) \cup C$$

Solution   Let A, B, and C be given sets.   Then

$$(A \cap B) \cup C = (A \cup C) \cap (B \cup C) \qquad \text{(by distributivity)}$$
$$\supseteq A \cap (B \cup C)$$

where the latter step follows from the fact that $A \subseteq A \cup C$ and the theorem assumed in the statement of the example. $\square$

In the discussion following Example 2 we noted a common pitfall, namely, trying to prove a universally quantified statement by giving a specific example or by enumerating cases. As with all general rules, the principle of proving statements by a deductive general argument can be carried too far, being applied where it shouldn't be. In particular, suppose we wish to dis-prove the assertion that subtraction of real numbers is associative; that is, $a - (b - c) = (a - b) - c$ for all real numbers a, b, and c. A common, but logically incorrect approach, is to argue

$$a - (b - c) = (a - b) - (-c)$$
$$= (a - b) + c$$
$$\neq (a - b) - c$$

But recall from Article 3.3 that the negation of a statement $(\forall x)(p(x))$ is $(\exists x)(\sim p(x))$. That is, to disprove a universally quantified statement, we must prove that the predicate in question is false for some substitution for x. Generally, this is best done by producing a specific object a from U for which $p(a)$ is false; such a specific object is called a *counterexample* to the statement $(\forall x)(p(x))$. This is a situation in which proof (or actually disproof) by example is not only permissible, but is in fact the correct approach. We reemphasize: *to establish that a universally quantified predicate is false, display a counterexample!*

In the preceding situation we may, for instance, let $a = 7$, $b = 4$, and $c = 2$. Then $a - (b - c) = 7 - (4 - 2) = 7 - 2 = 5$ and $(a - b) - c = (7 - 4) - 2 = 3 - 2 = 1$. Since $5 \neq 1$, our goal is accomplished.

There is one other situation in which proof by example(s) or by enumerating cases may be a viable approach to theorem-proving. If the domain of discourse for a universally quantified predicate happens to be finite, it may be possible, if not practical, to prove the theorem by enumerating all the cases. We proved theorems of the propositional calculus in this manner in Chapter 2. A truth table merely enumerates all the possible truth combinations (2^n corresponding to n letters) for the simple statements that comprise a given compound statement form. Recall, in this connection, Exercises 9 and 11(c), Article 1.5. We deal with another example of this type in Exercise 16.

As we conclude this article and you begin the exercises, there are two general principles to keep in mind: (1) It is essential in doing any proof, especially proofs by transitivity, to have a clear picture of what has come before—that is, what axioms, previously proved theorems, or any facts that are taken to be "known," are available for use in the proof. (2) It is important to approach theorem-proving in an active way: Always have pen and paper in front of you. Don't waste time staring at the book; write things down instead. In particular, write down the desired conclusion and the hypothesis (if any) and write a list of any definitions and known relationships that may be relevant. Don't be discouraged if your first approach doesn't work; be flexible and willing to try a number of approaches.

If the logical structure of the conclusion to be derived is more complex than we have considered thus far, you will still be faced with the question, "How do I go about starting this proof?" Read on, for forthcoming articles will deal directly with this question, in a variety of situations.

Exercises

1. Throughout this exercise, make use of the associative and commutative laws for addition and multiplication of real numbers, as well as the law of distributivity of multiplication over addition. Write explicitly the justification for each step. Prove that:

(a) $(a + b)^2 = a^2 + 2ab + b^2$ $\quad$ $\forall a, b \in \mathbf{R}$
(b) $(a + b)(a - b) = a^2 - b^2$ $\quad$ $\forall a, b \in \mathbf{R}$
(c) $[a + (b + c)] + d = a + [b + (c + d)]$ $\quad$ $\forall a, b, c, d \in \mathbf{R}$
(d) $a(bc) = c(ba)$ $\quad$ $\forall a, b, c \in \mathbf{R}$
(e) $(ab + ad) + (cb + cd) = (a + c)(b + d)$ $\quad$ $\forall a, b, c, d \in \mathbf{R}$
(f) $a(b + c + d) = ab + ac + ad$ $\quad$ $\forall a, b, c, d \in \mathbf{R}$

2. *(a)* Use elementary trigonometric identities (e.g., double angle formulas, definition of tan x in terms of sin x and cos x, etc.) to verify these trigonometric identities:

★*(i)* $\cos^4 x - \sin^4 x = \cos 2x$ $\quad$ $\forall x \in \mathbf{R}$
(ii) $4 \sin^3 x \cos x = \sin 2x - \sin 2x \cos x$ $\quad$ $\forall x \in \mathbf{R}$
(iii) $\sec x - \sin x \tan x = \cos x$ $\quad$ $\forall x \in \mathbf{R}$ such that $\cos x \neq 0$
(iv) $(\tan x - 1)/(\tan x + 1) = (1 - \cot x)/(1 + \cot x)$ $\quad$ $\forall x \in \mathbf{R}$ $\quad$ such $\quad$ that $\sin x \neq 0$ and $\cos x \neq 0$.

(b) Write out a complete proof by transitivity for the identity of Example 4.

Throughout Exercises 3 through 6, let all sets involved be subsets of a universal set U. Use properties of sets proved in Article 4.1 and an argument by transitivity in each case.

3. Prove that for any sets A and B

(a) $A - \emptyset = A$ (b) $\emptyset - A = \emptyset$

(c) $A \triangle \emptyset$ $\star$(d) $A \triangle U = A'$

(e) $A \triangle A = \emptyset$

(f) If $B = \emptyset$, then $A = (A \cap B') \cup (A' \cap B)$

(g) If $B = A$, then $U = (A' \cup B) \cap (A \cup B')$. [*Note:* The converses of the results in (f) and (g) are also true; see Example 8 and Exercise 1(h), Article 6.2, respectively.]

4. Prove that for any sets A and B:

(a) $A = (A \cup B) \cap (A \cup B')$

(b) $A = (A \cap B) \cup (A \cap B')$

(c) $(A \cap B) \cup (A' \cap B) \cup (A \cap B') \cup (A' \cap B') = U$

(d) $(A \cup B) \cap (A' \cup B) \cap (A \cup B') \cap (A' \cup B') = \emptyset$

(e) $A \triangle B = B \triangle A$

5. *(a)* Prove that, for any sets A, B, and C:

(i) $A - (B \cup C) = (A - B) \cap (A - C)$

$\star$(ii) $(A \cup B) - C = (A - C) \cup (B - C)$

(iii) $(A - B) - C = (A - C) - (B - C)$

(b) Prove that, for any sets A, B, C, and D:

(i) $A \cap (B \cup C \cup D) = (A \cap B) \cup (A \cap C) \cup (A \cap D)$

(ii) $A \cup (B \cap C \cap D) = (A \cup B) \cap (A \cup C) \cap (A \cup D)$. (*Hint:* Use associativity. These results generalize distributivity to "distributivity across three sets." In Article 5.4, on mathematical induction, we will see how to prove "distributivity across any finite number of sets.")

6. Prove that for any set A and for any collection $\{B_i \mid i = 1, 2, \ldots\}$ of sets indexed by **N** (recall Exercise 4, Article 4.2):

(a) $A - \left(\bigcap_{i=1}^{\infty} B_i \right) = \bigcup_{i=1}^{\infty} (A - B_i)$ (b) $\left(\bigcup_{i=1}^{\infty} B_i \right) - A = \bigcup_{i=1}^{\infty} (B_i - A)$

7. Use the definition of $\binom{n}{k}$ from Article 1.5, together with the facts that $(n + 1)! = (n + 1)n!$ (for all $n \in$ **N**) and $0! = 1$, to show that whenever each expression is defined, the given equation must hold:

$\star$(a) $\binom{n+1}{k} = \binom{n}{k-1} + \binom{n}{k}$

(b) $\binom{n}{k+1} = [(n - k)/(k + 1)]\binom{n}{k}$

(c) $\binom{n}{m}\binom{m}{k} = \binom{n}{k}\binom{n-k}{m-k}$ (*Suggestion:* Try some specific substitutions before attempting the proof.)

8. The *absolute value* of a real number x, denoted $|x|$, is defined by the rule

$$|x| = \begin{cases} x, & x \geq 0 \\ -x, & x < 0 \end{cases}$$

It follows directly from the definition that $-|x| \leq x \leq |x|$ for all $x \in$ **R**. From this it can be proved that for any real number x and positive real number a, $|x| \le a$ if and only if $-a \le x \le a$.

(a)   Use these facts to conclude that $|x + y| \le |x| + |y|$ (triangle inequality) for all real numbers x and y. (The result was assumed and used in Example 7 of this article.)

(b)   Use the result in (a) to prove that $|x - z| \ge |x| - |z|$ for all real numbers x and z.

(c)   Use the result in (a) to prove that $|x + y + z| \le |x| + |y| + |z|$ for any three real numbers x, y, and z. [See the Hint for Exercise 5(b).]

9. A real-valued function f of a real variable is said to be *even* if and only if $f(-x) = f(x)$ for all $x \in \mathbf{R}$, and *odd* if and only if $f(-x) = -f(x)$ for all $x \in \mathbf{R}$.

(a)   Prove that if f and g are even functions with domain $\mathbf{R}$, then $f + g$, $f - g$, fg, and $f \circ g$ are even functions.

★(b)   Prove that if f and g are odd functions with domain $\mathbf{R}$, then $f + g$, $f - g$, and $f \circ g$ are odd, and fg is even.

(c)   Prove that if f is odd and g is even, then $f \circ g$ and $g \circ f$ are both even.

10. Let $f(x) = x - (1/x)$.

(a)   Prove that for all nonzero values of x, $f(1/x) = f(-x) = -f(x)$.

(b)   Prove that for all nonzero values of x, $(f \circ f \circ f)(x) = x$.

11. *(a)*   Let $f(x) = (ax + b)/(cx - a)$, where a, b, and c are arbitrary real numbers. Show that $f(f(x)) = x$ for all $x \ne a/c$.

(b)   Suppose a, b, c, and d are real numbers satisfying the equation $ad + b = bc + d$. Define functions f and g, with domain $\mathbf{R}$ in each case by the rules $f(x) = ax + b$, $g(x) = cx + d$. Prove that $f(g(x)) = g(f(x))$ for all $x \in \mathbf{R}$.

12. A function f is said to have an *absolute maximum at a point* $x = a$ if and only if $f(x) \le f(a)$ for all x in the domain of f. *Absolute minimum at* a is defined analogously.

(a)   Prove, without using calculus, that $f(x) = 10 - x^2$ has an absolute maximum at $x = 0$.

★(b)   Prove algebraically that $g(x) = 60 + 14x - 2x^2$ has an absolute maximum at $x = \frac{7}{2}$.

(c)   Prove algebraically that if $a > 0$, then $f(x) = ax^2 + bx + c$ has an absolute minimum at $x = -b/2a$. [*Hint:* In (b) and (c) write down carefully, in terms of the preceding definition, exactly what must be proved. Use the algebraic technique of completing the square.]

13. Prove or disprove, for any three sets A, B, and C:

(a) $A - (B - C) = (A - B) - C$ (b) $(A - B)' = A' - B'$

(c) $A \cup (B - A) = A \cup B$ ★(d) $A \cap (B \cup C) = (A \cap B) \cup C$

14. Prove or disprove, for any real number x:

(a) $\sin 2x + 2 \sin x = \cos x + 1$ (b) $\sin 2x \cos x = \sin x$

(c) $\tan^2 x + 4 = 3 \sin^2 x + \sec^2 x + 3 \cos^2 x$

15. Prove or disprove, where m, n, and k are positive integers such that each of the individual quantities is defined, that $\binom{n+m}{k} = \binom{n}{k} + \binom{m}{k}$.

16. Let $U = \{1, 2, 3\}$. Consider the assertion that for all subsets A, B, and C of U, $(A \triangle B) \triangle C = A \triangle (B \triangle C)$; that is, the operation of symmetric difference is associative over this particular universal set U.

(a)   How many particular cases are encompassed by this statement for the given universal set?

(b)   Verify that the statement is true for three such cases.

(c)   Do you believe that symmetric difference is associative in general? How would you go about investigating this possibility?

17. An $m \times n$ real *matrix* is a rectangular array of m rows and n columns of real numbers, called *entries*. The entry in the ith row, jth column is customarily denoted a_{ij} and A itself may be represented

$$A = \begin{pmatrix} a_{11} & a_{12} & \cdots & a_{1n} \\ a_{21} & a_{22} & \cdots & a_{2n} \\ \vdots & & & \\ a_{m1} & a_{m2} & \cdots & a_{mn} \end{pmatrix}$$

which may, in turn, be abbreviated $A = (a_{ij})_{m \times n}$. A is said to be *square* if $m = n$. Some readers are probably familiar with elementary matrix theory, but for those who may not be, we provide here some basic definitions that we use in the following exercises and later in this chapter.

1.   If $A = (a_{ij})_{m \times n}$ and $B = (b_{ij})_{m \times n}$, define $A = B$ if and only if $a_{ij} = b_{ij}$ for all $i = 1, 2, \ldots, m$, and $j = 1, 2, \ldots, n$.

2.   If $A = (a_{ij})_{m \times n}$ and $B = (b_{ij})_{m \times n}$, define $A + B$ by the rule $A + B = (a_{ij} + b_{ij})_{m \times n}$. If $k \in \mathbf{R}$, define $kA = (ka_{ij})_{m \times n}$.

3.   If $A = (a_{ij})_{m \times n}$ and $B = (b_{ij})_{n \times p}$, define AB by the rule $AB = (c_{ij})_{m \times p}$, where $c_{ij} = \sum_{k=1}^{n} a_{ik} b_{kj}$.

4.   If $A = (a_{ij})_{m \times n}$, define A^t, the *transpose* of A, by $A^t = (b_{ij})_{n \times m}$, where $b_{ij} = a_{ji}$ for all $i = 1, 2, \ldots, n$, and $j = 1, 2, \ldots, m$.

5.   A square matrix $A = (a_{ij})_{m \times m}$ is said to be *symmetric* if and only if $A^t = A$ and *antisymmetric* if and only if $A^t = -A$.

6.   If $A = (a_{ij})_{2 \times 2}$, we define *the determinant of A*, denoted $|A|$, by the rule $|A| = a_{11}a_{22} - a_{12}a_{21}$.

Throughout parts (a) through (h), assume and use the facts that when the appropriate quantities are defined, matrix addition and multiplication are associative, matrix addition is commutative, and matrix multiplication distributes over matrix addition. Note that matrix multiplication is not commutative, even when both AB and BA are defined. Assume also that if $A + B$ and AB are defined, then $(A + B)^t = A^t + B^t$, $(AB)^t = B^t A^t$ and $(kA)^t = kA^t$ for any $k \in \mathbf{R}$.

★(a)   Prove that if A and B are $m \times n$ matrices with $A^t = B^t$, then $A = B$.

(b)   Prove that $(A^t)^t = A$ for any matrix A.

(c)   Prove that if A, B, and C are matrices of the same shape, then $(A + B + C)^t = A^t + B^t + C^t$.

(d)   Prove that if the product ABC is defined, then the product $C^t B^t A^t$ is defined and $C^t B^t A^t = (ABC)^t$.

★(e)   Prove that if A and B are symmetric square matrices, then $A + B$ is symmetric.

(f) Prove that if A is any square matrix, then $A + A^t$ is symmetric, whereas $A - A^t$ is antisymmetric.

(g) Prove that if A and B are 2×2 matrices, then $|AB| = |A||B|$.

18. One approach to the inverse trigonometric functions is to define first the two functions $\sin^{-1}$ and $\tan^{-1}$ directly as inverses to sin, restricted to the portion $[-\pi/2, \pi/2]$ of its domain, and tan, restricted to $(-\pi/2, \pi/2)$ respectively. That is, $y = \sin^{-1} x$ if and only if $\sin y = x$, $-\pi/2 \le x \le \pi/2$, and $y = \tan^{-1} x$ if and only if $\tan y = x$, $-\pi/2 < x < \pi/2$. Note that domain $(\sin^{-1})$ = range $(\sin) = [-1, 1]$, and domain $(\tan^{-1})$ = range $(\tan) = (-\infty, \infty)$.

Having done this, we may then define the other four inverse trigonometric functions $\cos^{-1}$, $\cot^{-1}$, $\sec^{-1}$, and $\csc^{-1}$ in terms of $\sin^{-1}$ and $\tan^{-1}$. Specifically, we may let

$$\cos^{-1} x = \pi/2 - \sin^{-1} x \qquad \cot^{-1} x = \pi/2 - \tan^{-1} x$$

$$\sec^{-1} x = \cos^{-1}(1/x) \qquad \csc^{-1} x = \sin^{-1}(1/x)$$

The first definition is motivated by the fact that the cosine of an acute angle equals the sine of its complement, so that $\cos(\pi/2 - \sin^{-1} x) = \sin(\sin^{-1} x) = x$ for any $x \in [-1, 1]$. The other definitions have similar trigonometric motivations. If you have not previously done so in your calculus class, calculate the domain and range of each of the preceding functions and sketch the graph of each. It can be proved, using the definition of inverse of a function, that $\sin^{-1}$ and $\tan^{-1}$ are odd functions; that is, $\sin^{-1}(-x) = -\sin^{-1} x$ and $\tan^{-1}(-x) = -\tan^{-1} x$ for all x in the respective domains. Use these facts to prove:

(a) $\cos^{-1}(-x) = \pi - \cos^{-1} x$, $\qquad -1 \le x \le 1$

(b) $\sec^{-1}(-x) = \pi - \sec^{-1} x$, $\qquad x \le -1 \quad \text{or} \quad x \ge 1$

(c) $\csc^{-1}(-x) = -\csc^{-1} x$, $\qquad x \le -1 \quad \text{or} \quad x \ge 1$

(d) $\cot^{-1}(-x) = \pi - \cot^{-1} x$, $\qquad -\infty < x < \infty$

For a geometric interpretation of these results, see Article 5.2, Exercise 5(c).

19. Critique and complete (recall the instructions for this type of exercise, given in Exercise 11, Article 4.1):

(a) THEOREM   For any sets A, B, and C, $(A \cap B) \triangle (A \cap C) = A \cap (B \triangle C)$

"Proof"

$(A \cap B) \triangle (A \cap C) = A \cap (B \triangle C)$

$\therefore [(A \cap B) \cap (A \cap C)'] \cup [(A \cap B)' \cap (A \cap C)] = A \cap [(B \cap C') \cup (B' \cap C)]$

$\therefore [(A \cap B) \cap (A' \cup C')] \cup [(A' \cup B') \cap (A \cap C)] = (A \cap B \cap C') \cup (A \cap B' \cap C)$

$\therefore [(A \cap B \cap A') \cup (A \cap B \cap C')] \cup [(A' \cap A \cap C) \cup (B' \cap A \cap C)]$
$$= (A \cap B \cap C') \cup (A \cap B' \cap C)$$

$\therefore [\varnothing \cup (A \cap B \cap C')] \cup [\varnothing \cup (B' \cap A \cap C)] = (A \cap B \cap C') \cup (A \cap B' \cap C)$

$\therefore (A \cap B \cap C') \cup (A \cap B' \cap C) = (A \cap B \cap C') \cup (A \cap B' \cap C) \quad \square$

(b) THEOREM   For any sets A and B, $A' - B' = B - A$.

"Proof"   Let A and B be arbitrary sets. Then

$$
\begin{aligned}
A' - B' &= A' \cap B'' &&\text{[Fact 5 (29), Article 1.4]} \\
&= A' \cap B &&\text{[Fact 3 (21), Article 1.4]} \\
&= B \cap A' &&\text{[Fact 2 (16), Article 1.4]} \\
&= B - A &&\text{[Fact 5 (29), Article 1.4]}
\end{aligned}
$$

(c) FACT   If $f(x) = x - (1/x)$, then f is not an even function. (cf; Exercise 9).

Start of "Proof"   Let x be an arbitrary nonzero real number. To prove f is not even, we must prove that $f(-x) \neq f(x) \ldots$.

(d) THEOREM   For any sets A and B, $(A - B)' = A' \cup B$.

Start of "Proof"   Let A and B be arbitrary sets. If $(A - B)' = A' \cup B$, then $(A \cap B')' = A' \cup B \ldots$.

5.2   Conclusions Involving $\forall$ and $\rightarrow$, but Not $\exists$

In this article we consider the problem of proving statements whose conclusion has the logical form $(\forall x)(p(x) \rightarrow q(x))$. Such proofs are common, for many definitions in mathematics have this logical form. Here are a few examples:

EXAMPLE 1   A subset C of $\mathbf{R} \times \mathbf{R}$ is said to be **symmetric with respect to the x axis** (respectively, **y axis** and **origin**) if and only if, for all real numbers x and y, $(x, y) \in C$ implies $(x, -y) \in C$ [respectively, $(-x, y) \in C$ and $(-x, -y) \in C$].

Observe that the logical form of the definition of x-axis symmetry in Example 1 is $(\forall x)(\forall y)\ (p(x, y) \rightarrow q(x, y))$, where $p(x, y)$ is the predicate $(x, y) \in C$ and $q(x, y)$ represents $(x, -y) \in C$.

EXAMPLE 2   A subset I of the set of all real numbers $\mathbf{R}$ is said to be an **interval** if and only if, for all $a, b, c \in \mathbf{R}$, if $a \in I$, $c \in I$, and $a < b < c$, then $b \in I$ (recall Definition 2, Article 1.1).

EXAMPLE 3   A real-valued function $y = f(x)$ is said to be **increasing** on an interval I if and only if, for all x_1 and $x_2 \in I$, if $x_1 < x_2$, then $f(x_1) < f(x_2)$.

EXAMPLE 4   A set A is said to be a **subset** of a set B (A and B both contained in a common universal set U) if and only if, for every $x \in U$, $x \in A$ implies $x \in B$ [recall Definition 1(b), Article 4.1].

EXAMPLE 5   (Some linear algebra background is helpful.) A set of vectors $\{v_1, v_2, \ldots, v_n\}$ in a vector space V is said to be **linearly independent** if and only if, for any n real numbers $\beta_1, \beta_2, \ldots, \beta_n$, if $\beta_1 v_1 + \beta_2 v_2 + \cdots + \beta_n v_n = 0$, then $\beta_1 = \beta_2 = \cdots = \beta_n = 0$.

As indicated, Examples 2 and 4 were encountered earlier in the text, but all except possibly Example 5 should be familiar to you. Also, you should be able to recall other definitions from your mathematical experience that have this logical form.

The problem we wish to confront now is how to go about proving a theorem in which the <u>conclusion</u> is of the same logical form as we have just seen in Examples 1 through 5, that is, the form $(\forall x)(p(x) \to q(x))$.

EXAMPLE 6   Use the definition in Example 2 to prove that if I_1 and I_2 are intervals, then $I_1 \cap I_2$ is an interval.

Solution   The questions we must ask in approaching a proof of a statement such as this one are. (1) "What is my desired conclusion?" (2) "According to the relevant definitions, what must I do in order to arrive at this conclusion?" (3) "What do I have to work with? How can I bring the given hypotheses to bear on the problem?" Implicit in the order of these questions is an important guiding rule, one that we had occasion to state and use earlier in the text, in Article 4.1, after Example 7. The rule states that, in setting up a proof of the type under consideration in this article, we should at the outset focus on the <u>desired conclusion</u>, not on the hypotheses. In the example at hand the desired conclusion is the statement that $I_1 \cap I_2$ is an interval. The proof will be "set up" strictly in terms of the definition of "$I_1 \cap I_2$ is an interval." The hypotheses, that is, the assumptions that I_1 and I_2 are intervals, will be brought in and used in <u>the course of the proof</u>. Our goal is to prove that $I_1 \cap I_2$ is an interval; how is this to be done? By the definition in Example 2, we must show that if a, b, and c are real numbers with a, $c \in I_1 \cap I_2$ <u>and</u> $a < b < c$, <u>then</u> $b \in I_1 \cap I_2$. Hence, to set up the proof, we begin by <u>assuming</u> that a, b, and c are real numbers with $a < b < c$ and a and c both elements of $I_1 \cap I_2$ ("let a, b, and c be real numbers with . . ."). We must prove, on the basis of these assumptions and the given hypotheses, that $b \in I_1 \cap I_2$. By definition of intersection, this means we must show that $b \in I_1$ <u>and</u> $b \in I_2$.

At this stage, the basic structure of the proof has been set; we must <u>now</u> ask how our hypotheses can be brought to bear on the problem. We may reason as follows: Since I_1 is an interval, since $a < b < c$, and since a and c are both in I_1 (since $I_1 \cap I_2 \subseteq I_1$), then $b \in I_1$. An identical argument, with I_2 replacing I_1, shows that $b \in I_2$. Hence $b \in I_1 \cap I_2$ and $I_1 \cap I_2$ is an interval, as claimed.   □

EXAMPLE 7   Prove that if $M > 0$, then the linear function $y = f(x) = Mx + B$ is increasing on **R**.

Solution   Again, we focus first on the desired conclusion that f is increasing on **R**; the hypothesis $M > 0$ will be employed in the course of the proof. To prove that f is increasing, we must show that if x_1 and x_2 are real numbers with $x_1 < x_2$, then $f(x_1) < f(x_2)$. Hence we begin, or set up, the proof by letting real numbers x_1 and x_2 be given with $x_1 < x_2$, that is, we are <u>assuming</u> that $x_1 < x_2$. Now proving that $f(x_1) < f(x_2)$ is clearly the same as proving $Mx_1 + B < Mx_2 + B$. What we have to work with, as we aim toward this conclusion, is the assumption that $x_1 < x_2$ and the hypothesis $M > 0$. Using elementary properties of inequalities, we note that since $x_1 < x_2$ and $M > 0$, then $Mx_1 < Mx_2$. Then since $Mx_1 < Mx_2$, we may conclude $Mx_1 + B < Mx_2 + B$, so that $f(x_1) < f(x_2)$, as desired.   □

Explanatory remarks added considerably to the length of the proof in Example 7. In actual practice, the style of proof you will see in most circumstances, and should try to write, would go something like this: "To prove f is increasing on **R**, assume $x_1 < x_2$. We must prove $f(x_1) < f(x_2)$, that is, $Mx_1 + B < Mx_2 + B$. Since $x_1 < x_2$ and $M > 0$, then $Mx_1 < Mx_2$. Since $Mx_1 < Mx_2$, then $Mx_1 + B < Mx_2 + B$, as desired."

Before looking at another proof, let us review the strategy of the proofs in Examples 6 and 7. In both cases the desired conclusion had essentially the form $(\forall x)(p(x) \to q(x))$. Our first step in both proofs was to let a value of x be given for which <u>we assume</u> that $p(x)$ is satisfied. This x is general, or arbitrarily chosen, as opposed to being a specifically identified or named element, but we fix <u>this</u> x and work <u>with it</u> throughout the remainder of the proof. Our goal was to show that $q(x)$ is valid, using the given hypotheses and the <u>assumption</u> that $p(x)$ is valid. You may have realized already that this approach is really just the choose or pick-a-point method, introduced in Article 4.1 for proofs of set theoretic inclusion, applied in a more general setting. A proof of a conclusion with logical form $(\forall x)(p(x) \to q(x))$, carried out by using the choose method, is an example of a *direct proof*. There are various types of direct proof; we will encounter several in the remainder of this chapter and in Chapter 6. In Article 6.2 we deal with *indirect proof*.

We return in the next two examples to proofs of set theoretic inclusion, but for statements of more complicated logical structure than those studied in Articles 4.1 and 5.1. The theorems proved in Examples 8 and 9 have as their conclusion a statement that one set is a subset of another. We noted, in Example 4, that the definition of "subset" has the logical form $(\forall x)(p(x) \to q(x))$.

EXAMPLE 8   Prove that if A, X, and Y are any sets with $X \subseteq Y$, then $A \cap X \subseteq A \cap Y$.

Solution   You may recall this result as one that we assumed and used in the solution to Example 8, Article 5.1. To prove it, we proceed, as in Examples 6 and 7, by concentrating at the outset on the desired conclusion $A \cap X \subseteq A \cap Y$; we use the hypothesis $X \subseteq Y$ in the course of the argument. Now, how do we go about showing that one set is a subset of another? We saw in Article 4.1 that this is done by choosing an arbitrary element from the first set and trying to show that this object lies in the second set as well. In this case we begin by letting x be an element of $A \cap X$. We must show that this x lies in $A \cap Y$. Somewhere along the line, we will have to use the hypothesis $X \subseteq Y$. So to start, let $x \in A \cap X$ be given. To show that $x \in A \cap Y$, we must prove that $x \in A$ and $x \in Y$. Now since $x \in A \cap X$ and $A \cap X \subseteq A$, then $x \in A$. Also, since $x \in A \cap X$, then $x \in X$. But $X \subseteq Y$, by hypothesis, so that since $x \in X$ and $X \subseteq Y$, we must have $x \in Y$. Since $x \in A$ and $x \in Y$, then $x \in A \cap Y$, as desired.   □

A common error in a proof such as that in Example 8, committed even by students who understand the general pick-a-point approach to proving set inclusion, is to begin the proof in the wrong place, setting it up with reference to the hypothesis rather than to the conclusion. Specifically, in trying to prove that $X \subseteq Y$ implies $A \cap X \subseteq A \cap Y$, many students will erroneously write as their first step "let $x \in X$" rather than the correct "let $x \in A \cap X$." Also, since we have repeatedly suggested focusing on the desired conclusion rather than on the hypotheses in setting up a proof, it is perhaps appropriate that we emphasize that this guiding rule is not to be confused with the common error of beginning a proof by assuming the conclusion. The latter approach, of course, is never valid. In the proof from Example 8 this mistaken approach would have involved starting with the statement "assume (or suppose) that $A \cap X \subseteq A \cap Y$." This is different from the approach we took ("let $x \in A \cap X$. We must prove $x \in A \cap Y \ldots$").
Here is a slightly more complicated example from set theory.

EXAMPLE 9   Prove that if A, B, and C are sets with $A \times B \subseteq A \times C$ and $A \neq \varnothing$, then $B \subseteq C$.

Solution   Again, we focus first on our desired conclusion. We begin the proof that $B \subseteq C$ by letting x be an arbitrary element of B. Our goal is to prove $x \in C$. We have at our disposal the hypotheses $A = \varnothing$ and $A \times B \subseteq A \times C$. We must determine how to make use of these hypotheses. Think about this for a while before proceeding; for instance, what is the significance of the hypothesis that A is nonempty? Let us resume. Since $A \neq \varnothing$, then A contains at least one element, call it a. Since $a \in A$ and $x \in B$, then the ordered pair (a, x) is an element of $A \times B$. Do you see the next step? Since $A \times B \subseteq A \times C$, by hypothesis, and since $(a, x) \in A \times B$, then (a, x) must be an element of $A \times C$. But this implies $x \in C$ and this is precisely what we wanted to prove.   □

As we did after Example 7, let us rewrite the preceding proof with explanatory comments removed. That is, let us write a version of the proof more closely resembling the finished product form of most proofs that appear in print. "Assume A, B, and C are sets with $A \times B \subseteq A \times C$ and $A \neq \emptyset$. To prove $B \subseteq C$, let $x \in B$. We must show $x \in C$. Since $A \neq \emptyset$, there exists $a \in A$, so that $(a, x) \in A \times B$. Since $A \times B \subseteq A \times C$, then $(a, x) \in A \times C$. Hence $x \in C$, as desired."

We noted in the preceding paragraph that the version of the proof given there corresponds to a "finished product." In practice, most mathematicians write their original proofs in two forms. The first may cover reams of paper and involve a number of false starts and failed attempts. More important, this form of a successful proof will usually reveal the "discovery process" of the proof. The second form is the one that a mathematician shows to other people, a compact, cleaned-up, final, elegant kind of proof in which the discovery process may not be shown. In order to understand and communicate mathematics, you must learn to read and write proofs in the latter form. Most proofs contained in our "Solutions," thus far in the text, have more closely resembled the first form. We have tried thereby to expose the thought process and to emphasize common pitfalls involved in the formative stages of a proof. In Book II (Chapter 7 through 10) we will place much more emphasis on writing proofs in compact form only, with more responsibility left to you for understanding the idea behind the proof.

DISPROVING CONCLUSIONS OF THE FORM $(\forall x)(p(x) \rightarrow q(x))$

Suppose now that we wish to <u>disprove</u> a statement whose logical form is $(\forall x)(p(x) \rightarrow q(x))$. Recall first the discussion following Example 8 in Article 5.1. From that discussion, it would be expected that we generally disprove such a statement by giving a specific counterexample rather than a general deductive proof. We must use logic carefully, however, to determine precisely what constitutes a counterexample. In Article 3.3 we saw that the negation of $(\forall x)(p(x) \rightarrow q(x))$ is $(\exists x)[\sim(p(x) \rightarrow q(x))]$. In Article 2.3 we saw that $\sim(p \rightarrow q)$ is logically equivalent to $p \wedge \sim q$. Thus $\sim[(\forall x)(p(x) \rightarrow q(x)]$ is logically equivalent to $(\exists x)(p(x) \wedge \sim q(x))$. To disprove a statement of the form $(\forall x)(p(x) \rightarrow q(x))$, we must show that some value of x exists for which $p(x)$ is true and $q(x)$ is false. In most elementary situations this is done by producing specifically such an x. Let us apply this principle to some of the definitions stated at the outset of this article.

EXAMPLE 10   Write definitions of "a curve C is <u>not symmetric</u> with respect to the x axis" and "a set of vectors $\{v_1, v_2, \ldots, v_n\}$ in a real vector space V is <u>not linearly independent</u>."

Solution   Recall from Example 1 that C is <u>symmetric</u> with respect to the x axis if and only if, <u>for all</u> real numbers x and y, $(x, y) \in C$ implies $(x, -y) \in C$. Hence C is <u>not symmetric</u> with respect to the x axis if and only if <u>there exist</u> real numbers x and y such that $(x, y) \in C$, but $(x, -y) \notin C$.

We negate the definition of linear independence, given in Example 5, in a similar manner. The set $\{v_1, v_2, \ldots, v_n\}$ of vectors is <u>not</u> linearly independent, and in such a case is said to be *linearly dependent*, if and only if <u>there exist</u> n real numbers $\beta_1, \beta_2, \ldots, \beta_n$, such that $\beta_1 v_1 + \beta_2 v_2 + \cdots + \beta_n v_n = 0$, but not all of the betas equal zero, that is $\beta_j \neq 0$ for some j between 1 and n, inclusive. □

EXAMPLE 11   Prove that the set $C = \{(x, x^2) \mid x \in \mathbf{R}\}$ is symmetric with respect to the y axis, but not to the x axis.

Solution   Note first that an ordered pair (x, y) is on the curve C if and only if $y = x^2$. Thus a picture of the curve C is simply the familiar parabola that constitutes the graph of the quadratic function $y = f(x) = x^2$ as illustrated in Figure 5.2. The picture certainly bears out our symmetry claims, but how are we to prove these claims formally?

To show that C is symmetric with respect to the y axis, let (x, y) be an arbitrarily chosen element of C; we must show that $(-x, y) \in C$. By definition of C, $(-x, y) \in C$ if and only if $y = (-x)^2$. Now since $(x, y) \in C$, then $y = x^2$. Since $x^2 = (-x)^2$, then $y = (-x^2)$, as desired. This completes the proof of y axis symmetry.

On the other hand, to show that C is not symmetric with respect to the x axis, note that $(2, 4) \in C$ since $4 = 2^2$, but $(2, -4) \notin C$, since $-4 \neq 2^2$. We have given a specific counterexample to the statement $(\forall x)(\forall y)[(x, y) \in C \rightarrow (x, -y) \in C]$, and that's all there is to it! □

Here is another important type of problem on which the preceding discussion has a bearing. Suppose you are asked to show that a set A is a <u>proper</u> subset of a set B. By Definition 7, Article 1.1, this means $A \subseteq B$

Figure 5.2   *Graph indicates y-axis symmetry, but no x-axis symmetry.*

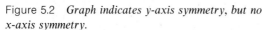
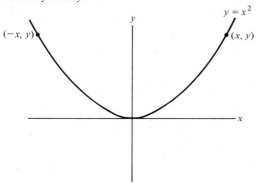

and $B \nsubseteq A$. To prove the latter, we must prove $(\exists x)[(x \in B) \wedge (x \notin A)]$. This is generally best done by producing a specific object x which is in B, but not in A [see Exercise 7(b)].

PROVING STATEMENTS $(\forall x)(p(x) \leftrightarrow q(x))$

The relationship between statements of the form $(\forall x)(p(x) \leftrightarrow q(x))$ and those of the form $(\forall x)(p(x) \rightarrow q(x))$ is the same as the one we noted in Article 4.1 between set equality $A = B$ and set inclusion $A \subseteq B$. Recall that $A = B$ if and only if $A \subseteq B$ and $B \subseteq A$, so that, for instances where a proof by transitivity (cf., Article 5.1) of equality isn't possible or evident, we prove equality of sets by proving mutual inclusion. This kind of proof of set equality, then, involves two proofs, one in each direction, as in Example 9, Article 4.1.

The logical basis for this approach to sets, as well as for the approach we wish to take now in more general situations, is the equivalence

$$(\forall x)(p(x) \leftrightarrow q(x)) \leftrightarrow (\forall x)[(p(x) \rightarrow q(x)) \wedge (q(x) \rightarrow p(x))]$$
$$\leftrightarrow (\forall x)(p(x) \rightarrow q(x)) \wedge (\forall x)(q(x) \rightarrow p(x))$$

The first equivalence follows from the tautology

$$(p \leftrightarrow q) \leftrightarrow [(p \rightarrow q) \wedge (q \rightarrow p)] \qquad [\text{Theorem 1(m), Article 2.3}]$$

whereas the second follows from the equivalence

$$(\forall x)[r(x) \wedge s(x)] \leftrightarrow (\forall x)(r(x)) \wedge (\forall x)(s(x)) \qquad [\text{Theorem 1(c), Article 3.3}]$$

Thus we may write a proof of equivalence by writing two proofs of implication of the type we've been discussing thus far in this article, one in each direction.

EXAMPLE 12   Let f be a real-valued function with domain $\mathbf{R}$. Prove that f is even; that is, $f(-x) = f(x)$ for all $x \in \mathbf{R}$ (recall Exercise 9, Article 5.1) if and only if the set of points in the xy plane $C = \{(x, f(x)) | x \in \mathbf{R}\}$ is symmetric with respect to the y axis.

Solution   Again, we must argue in two directions. Such proofs are often presented in the following format:

($\Rightarrow$) (This arrow means we are proving that if f is even, then C is symmetric.) Suppose f is even. To prove the set $C = \{(x, f(x)) | x \in \mathbf{R}\}$ is symmetric with respect to the y axis, let $(x, y) \in C$. We must prove $(-x, y) \in C$, that is, prove that $y = f(-x)$. Now since $(x, y) \in C$, then $y = f(x)$. Since f is even, we have $f(x) = f(-x)$. Hence $y = f(x) = f(-x)$, so that $y = f(-x)$, as desired.

($\Leftarrow$) Conversely, suppose that C is symmetric with respect to the y axis. To prove f is even, let $x \in \mathbf{R}$ be arbitrarily chosen. We must show that $f(-x) = f(x)$. By definition of C, the point $(x, f(x)) \in C$. By the assumed symmetry, since $(x, f(x)) \in C$, then $(-x, f(x)) \in C$. Now, again by definition of C, we know that $(-x, f(-x)) \in C$. Since C is the graph of a function, and so can have no more than one y value corresponding to any given x value, and since both $f(x)$ and $f(-x)$ correspond to $-x$, we must have $f(x) = f(-x)$, as desired.   □

The proof in Example 12 is perhaps the most difficult one we have presented thus far, although the result itself is exceedingly plausible. Sometimes a result can seem so "obvious" that we fail to notice that the definitions involved are distinct and that there indeed is something to be proved. A formal proof, in such a case, is merely a rigorous explanation of why the result is obvious. Since intuition can mislead, it is important, at all levels of mathematics, to know how to write a formal proof, if pressed, of all mathematical statements that we claim are true, even though we do not, in practice, write out every such proof.

In this article we have stated that, for many proofs, the correct approach—the proper "setting-up" of the argument—is a very large part of the "battle." Although this is true, there are, of course, many proofs that are more complicated and require more than just the proper technical approach, both in terms of prior knowledge of relevant mathematics and in terms of facility with further proof techniques. The ⇐ part of Example 12 demonstrated both needs. At the very end of the proof, we had to call on some general knowledge about what a function is (i.e., "no x value has two distinct corresponding y values"). Just before that, when we noted that the ordered pair $(-x, f(-x)) \in C$, we were implicitly using a technique of proof known as *specialization*. We knew that C consisted of all ordered pairs of the form $(a, f(a))$, where a ranges over all real numbers. Thus, in particular, the ordered pair $(-x, f(-x))$ must be in C, where x is the arbitrary real number whose value we fixed at the start of the proof. Specialization is one of two very useful techniques we will focus on in the next article (*division into cases* being the other). At the end of that article, we will be able to handle a wider variety of problems calling for the derivation of conclusions involving ∀ and → than in the exercises that follow.

Exercises

1. Let A and B be arbitrary sets. Prove:

(a) $A \cap B = A$ if and only if $A \subseteq B$

(b)   If $A \cup B = B$, then $A \subseteq B$ (The converse is also true. It will appear as an exercise at the end of the next article.)

(c)   If C is a nonempty set such that $A \times C = B \times C$, then $A = B$ (recall Example 9. Note also the connection between this exercise and Exercise 5, Article 1.3.).

(d)   If $A \times B = B \times A$, $A \neq \varnothing$, and $B \neq \varnothing$, then $A = B$

2. Recall (Definition 5, Article 1.1) that the power set $\mathscr{P}(A)$ of a set A is the set of all subsets of A. Thus $X \in \mathscr{P}(A)$ if and only if $X \subseteq A$.

★(a)   Prove that, for any sets A and B, if $A \subseteq B$, then $\mathscr{P}(A) \subseteq \mathscr{P}(B)$.

(b)   Prove that, for any sets A and B, $\mathscr{P}(A \cap B) = \mathscr{P}(A) \cap \mathscr{P}(B)$.

3. (a)   Use the definition of *interval* (Example 2) to show that each of the first eight types of sets listed in Definition 3, Article 1.1 (e.g., $[a, b]$, (a, ∞), etc.) is an interval. (*Note:* Assume throughout this proof that if p, q, and r are any real numbers with $p \leq q$ and $q \leq r$, then $p \leq r$.)

(b)   Prove that if $\{I_n \,|\, n = 1, 2, \ldots\}$ is a collection of <u>intervals</u> indexed by the set of all positive integers, then $\bigcap_{n=1}^{\infty} I_n$ is an interval.

(c)   Prove or disprove: If I_1 and I_2 are intervals, then $I_1 \cup I_2$ is an interval. See also Exercise 15, Article 5.3.)

4. (a)   Prove that the curve $C_1 = \{(x, |x|) \,|\, x \in \mathbf{R}\}$ is symmetric with respect to the y axis, but not to the x axis.

(b)   Prove that the curve $C_2 = \{(x, x^3) \,|\, x \in \mathbf{R}\}$ is symmetric with respect to the origin, but not to the x axis.

(c)   Let f be a real-valued function with domain $\mathbf{R}$. Prove that f is *odd*; that is, $f(-x) = -f(x)$ for all $x \in \mathbf{R}$, if and only if the set $C_3 = \{(x, f(x)) \,|\, x \in \mathbf{R}\}$ is symmetric with respect to the origin.

5. A subset C of $\mathbf{R} \times \mathbf{R}$ is said to be **symmetric with respect to the point** (h, k) if and only if, whenever $(x + h, y + k) \in C$, then $(-x + h, -y + k) \in C$.

(a)   Prove that if C is the graph of a function $y = f(x)$, then C is symmetric with respect to the point (h, k) if and only if $f(-x + h) = 2k - f(x + h)$ for every x such that $x + h$ is in the domain of f.

★(b)   Show that the graph of the function $y = f(x) = 1 + (1/(x - 1))$ is symmetric with respect to the point $(1, 1)$.

(c)   Use Exercise 18, Article 5.1, to conclude that the graphs of the functions $\cos^{-1}$, $\tan^{-1}$, and $\cot^{-1}$ are each symmetric with respect to the point $(0, \pi/2)$.

6. A function f, mapping real numbers to real numbers, is said to be **one to one** on an interval I if and only if, for any real numbers x_1 and x_2 in the interval I, if $f(x_1) = f(x_2)$, then $x_1 = x_2$.

(a)   Prove that $f(x) = x^2$ is not one to one on $\mathbf{R}$.

(b)   Prove that, if $M \neq 0$, then the linear function $y = f(x) = Mx + B$ is one to one on $\mathbf{R}$.

(c)   Prove that if f is increasing on an interval I, then f is one to one on I. (*Hint:* contrapositive)

7. Consider the curve C_1 in the xy plane described parametrically by the equations $x = \cos t$, $y = \sin t$, where t is any real number; that is, $C_1 = \{(\cos t, \sin t) \,|\, t \in \mathbf{R}\}$. Note that a point (x, y) in the xy plane is on C_1 if and only if there exists a real number t such that $x = \cos t$ and $y = \sin t$.

(a)   Let C_2 be the curve $\{(x, y) \in \mathbf{R} \times \mathbf{R} \,|\, x^2 + y^2 = 1\}$. Use well-known properties of sine and cosine to prove that $C_1 \subseteq C_2$. (In fact, these curves are the same; that is, $C_1 = C_2$. We will consider the reverse inclusion in Article 6.1.)

(b)   Let C_3 be the curve in the xy plane described parametrically by $x = \cosh t$
and $y = \sinh t$. Use well-known properties of sinh and cosh to prove that $C_3 = \{(\cosh t, \sinh t) \mid t \in \mathbf{R}\}$ is a <u>proper subset</u> of $\{(x, y) \in \mathbf{R} \times \mathbf{R} \mid x^2 - y^2 = 1\} = C_4$.
(Recall the paragraph immediately following Example 11.)

8. A curve C described by an equation $F(r, \theta) = 0$ in polar coordinates has the
property that a point with polar representation (r, θ) is on C if and only if an
ordered pair either of the form $(r, \theta + 2n\pi)$ or of the form $(-r, \theta + (2n + 1)\pi)$ satisfies the defining equation, for some positive integer n. (For most curves, it suffices
to consider the case $n = 0$.) Let curves C_1 and C_2 in the xy plane be defined by
$C_1 = \{(r, \theta) \mid r = \cos\theta + 1\}$ and $C_2 = \{(r, \theta) \mid r = \cos\theta - 1\}$. Prove that $C_1 = C_2$.

9. A subset S of the real line $\mathbf{R}$ is said to be **convex** if and only if, for all $x, y \in S$
and for every real number t satisfying $0 \le t \le 1$, the real number $tx + (1 - t)y$ is
an element of S.

★(a)   Prove that $[0, 1]$ is convex.
(b)   Prove that $[0, 1] \cup [2, 3]$ is not convex.
(c)   Prove that if S_1 and S_2 are convex, then $S_1 \cap S_2$ is convex.
(d)   Prove that if I is an interval in $\mathbf{R}$, then I is convex. [In fact, the converse
of (d) is true as well. Its proof will be considered in Article 6.1.]

10. (a)   Suppose that T is a linearly independent subset of a vector space V and
that $S \subseteq T$. Prove that S is linearly independent.
(b)   Let $\mathbf{v}_1$, $\mathbf{v}_2$, and $\mathbf{v}_3$ be linearly independent vectors in a vector space V and let
c be a nonzero scalar. Prove that the sets $\{\mathbf{v}_1, c\mathbf{v}_2, \mathbf{v}_3\}$ and $\{\mathbf{v}_1 + c\mathbf{v}_2, \mathbf{v}_2, \mathbf{v}_3\}$ are
also linearly independent. (*Note:* some familiarity with elementary properties of
vector addition and scalar multiplication is needed for this proof.)

11. A square matrix $A = (a_{ij})_{m \times m}$ is said to be a **diagonal matrix** if and only if, for
all $i, j = 1, 2, \ldots, m$, $i \ne j$ implies $a_{ij} = 0$. A is **upper** (respectively, **lower**) **triangular**
if and only if $i > j$ (respectively, $i < j$) implies $a_{ij} = 0$ for all $i, j = 1, 2, \ldots, m$.

(a)   Give examples of a:
(i) 3×3 diagonal matrix
(ii) 4×4 upper triangular matrix
(iii) 3×3 matrix that is lower triangular and not diagonal.
(b)   Prove that an $m \times m$ diagonal matrix is necessarily upper triangular.
(c)   Prove that an $m \times m$ diagonal matrix is necessarily lower triangular.

12. Critique and complete (recall instructions in Exercise 11, Article 4.1).

(a)   FACT   The subset $C = \{(x, x^5 + x^3) \mid x \in \mathbf{R}\}$ is symmetric with respect to the
origin.

"Proof"   Let $x = 3$ and note that the point $(3, 270) \in C$, since $y = 270 = 3^5 + 3^3$.
Note also that $(-3, -270) \in C$, since $-270 = -243 - 27 = (-3)^5 + (-3)^3$.
Since (x, y) and $(-x, -y)$ are both on C, the desired symmetry is established.
(b)   THEOREM   A linear function $y = f(x) = Mx + B$ is increasing on $\mathbf{R}$ <u>if and
only if $M > 0$</u>.

"Proof"   We may prove the desired equivalence by proving implication in each
direction. In other words, we may prove that if $M > 0$, then f is increasing on $\mathbf{R}$
<u>and if f is increasing on $\mathbf{R}$, then $M > 0$</u>. ($\Rightarrow$) Done in Example 7. ($\Leftarrow$) Let x_1

and x_2 be real numbers such that $x_1 < x_2$. Then $M = M(x_2 - x_1)/(x_2 - x_1) = [M(x_2 - x_1) + (B - B)]/(x_2 - x_1) = [(Mx_2 + B) - (Mx_1 + B)]/(x_2 - x_1) > 0$, since $Mx_1 + B < Mx_2 + B$, by our assumption that f is increasing.

(c) FACT   The subset $S = [0, 1] \cup [2, 3]$ of **R** is not an interval.

Start of "Proof"   Using the logical negation of the definition of "interval," as stated in Example 2, it is sufficient to show that there exist real numbers a, b, and c such that $a < b < c$, $a \in S$ and $c \in S$ but $b \in S$.

(d) THEOREM   For any subsets X and Y of a universal set U, if $X \subseteq Y$, then $X' \cup Y = U$.

Start of "Proof"   Let X and Y be sets and let w be an arbitrarily chosen element of X. We must prove $w \in Y$ . . . .

(e) FACT $[0, 2]$ is not a subset of $[1, 3]$.

Start of "Proof"   Let x be an arbitrary element of $[0, 2]$. We must prove $x \notin [1, 3]$ . . . .

5.3   Proof by Specialization and Division into Cases

Proofs of theorems whose conclusion has the form $(\forall x)(p(x) \rightarrow q(x))$, such as those contained in the preceding article, can vary greatly according to the specific problems encountered in adapting the assumption that $p(x)$ is valid, possibly together with some given hypotheses, toward the desired conclusion $q(x)$. In particular, consider these problems:

EXAMPLE 1   Prove that if a subset C of **R** $\times$ **R** is symmetric with respect to both the x axis and the origin, then C is symmetric with respect to the y axis.

EXAMPLE 2   Given sets A, B, and X, prove that if $A \cap X \subseteq B \cap X$ and $A \cap X' \subseteq B \cap X'$, then $A \subseteq B$.

Both these statements are of the type considered in Article 5.2, since the conclusion of each (i.e., "C is symmetric with respect to the y axis" and "A is a subset of B") has a definition of logical form $(\forall x)(p(x) \rightarrow q(x))$. Thus in each case we should begin the proof by focusing on that conclusion and setting up the proof in terms of its definition.

Specifically, in Example 1, we start by assuming that the ordered pair (x, y) is an element of C; we must prove that $(-x, y) \in C$, using the given hypotheses. In Example 2 we begin by letting x be an arbitrary element of A. We must prove $x \in B$. To accomplish this, we will somehow have to make use of the two given hypotheses, involving a third set X. Before reading on, think about these two examples. Can you determine how to complete the proof of one or both of them? Take some time now to try to write out the proofs. Don't, however, become discouraged if you can't do them at this stage. If you can prove the symmetry property in Example 1, then you already have an implicit grasp of a proof technique known as *specialization*. If you can handle Example 2 now, then you are able to deal with a proof that calls for a *division into cases*.

These two methods will be useful throughout the remainder of the text. Regardless of the logical form of the desired conclusion of a theorem, these two methods are basic tools of the mathematician for adapting given hypotheses toward that conclusion.

SPECIALIZATION

Repeatedly we have stressed the fact that a general assertion $(\forall x)(p(x))$ cannot be proved by verifying a particular instance $p(a)$, where a is a specific element of the domain of discourse of $p(x)$. But frequently, in deriving a conclusion on the basis of an assumption or hypothesis $(\forall x)(p(x))$, we find that a particular case of the latter proves to be just what is needed to get the desired result. In such situations the special case may involve either the substitution of a specific constant a for the variable x (see Example 3) or the replacement of x by some expression involving an arbitrary quantity y whose value was fixed as a part of the initial setting up of the proof (see Example 4).

The first exposure most students get to proofs involving the method of specialization is in proofs of certain theorems in trigonometry.

EXAMPLE 3   Suppose it is known (i.e., has been assumed as an axiom or has already been proved) that $\sin(x + a) = \sin x \cos a + \cos x \sin a$ for all real numbers x and a. Prove that $\sin(x + (\pi/2)) = \cos x$, for all real numbers x.

Solution   Let x be an arbitrary real number. Consider the special case $a = \pi/2$ of the known identity. This gives

$$\sin(x + (\pi/2)) = \sin x \cos(\pi/2) + \cos x \sin(\pi/2)$$
$$= (\sin x)(0) + (\cos x)(1)$$
$$= \cos x, \quad \text{as desired.} \quad \square$$

EXAMPLE 4   Suppose it is known that $\sin x = \cos((\pi/2) - x)$ for all real numbers x. Use this result to prove that $\cos x = \sin((\pi/2) - x)$ for all real numbers x.

Solution   Let x be an arbitrary real number. Recalling that $\sin x' = \cos((\pi/2) - x')$ for any real number x' is known to be true, consider the quantity $\sin((\pi/2) - x)$. Letting $x' = (\pi/2) - x$ in the equation of the previous sentence, we have $\sin((\pi/2) - x) = \sin x' = \cos((\pi/2) - x') = \cos((\pi/2) - ((\pi/2) - x)) = \cos x$, which is precisely what we wanted to prove. $\square$

Note that the proof of Example 3 employed a straightforward substitution, whereas that of Example 4 was somewhat more intricate, involving a fairly "clever" choice of x', in terms of the arbitrary x that we chose at the outset of the proof. Some of the most ingenious proofs in mathematics involve specialization, especially in the latter form. You will often encounter proofs in future studies, and perhaps already have, that left you wondering; "How did anyone ever think of that?" The next time this occurs, try to notice whether the key step is, in fact, a clever application of the specialization technique. We now apply this technique to Example 1.

Solution to Example 1   We must prove that C has y-axis symmetry, given that it has x-axis and origin symmetry. To do this, we begin by letting (x, y) be an arbitrary element of C. We must prove that $(-x, y) \in C$. The question is how to take advantage of our two hypotheses. Well, first, note that since C has x-axis symmetry, by hypothesis, and since $(x, y) \in C$, by assumption, then $(x, -y) \in C$. Now comes the tricky part. We have shown that $(x, -y) \in C$ and have not yet used the hypothesis that C is symmetric with respect to the origin. This hypothesis says that $(-x, -y) \in C$ whenever $(x, y) \in C$; in particular then, since $(x, -y) \in C$, we must have that $(-x, -(-y)) \in C$. But $(-x, -(-y)) = (-x, y)$, so that $(-x, y) \in C$, as desired. $\square$

The proof in Example 1 illustrates the power and generality of universal quantification {recall the theorem of the predicate calculus $[(\forall x)(p(x))] \rightarrow p(a)$, Theorem 2(d), Article 3.3}. If a statement, say, of the form $p(x) \rightarrow q(x)$ is known to be true for all x, then $p(a) \rightarrow q(a)$ is true for any specific value of a, so that, if $p(a)$ can be proved, we may conclude $q(a)$ by the principle of *modus ponens* [Example 5 and Theorem 2(e), Article 2.3]. This description applies to the preceding proof, letting $p(x, y)$ represent "$(x, y) \in C$" and $q(x, y)$ stand for "$(-x, -y) \in C$," while a is taken to be the ordered pair $(x, -y)$. Other examples of applications of this technique occur in Exercises 5(c) and 8.

DIVISION INTO CASES

Often, in the course of setting up a proof, we arrive at a point where there is a natural division of the argument into a finite number of cases. As we will see, these cases must always be "exhaustive" and are often "mutually exclusive." As one example, it may be that, in trying to prove something about an integer m, there is an advantage in considering the two possibilities (i.e., dichotomy) m even and m odd. Or else, in dealing with a real number x, we might be able to use the three cases (i.e., trichotomy), $x < 0$, $x = 0$, and $x > 0$, to advantage. If we know that an object x is in the union of two sets A and B and are trying to derive some conclusion from this, the two cases $x \in A$ and $x \in B$ (which may fail to be mutually exclusive in many situations), may work to our advantage. Other situations will be demonstrated in subsequent examples.

In order to use "division into cases" correctly, we must keep two key ideas in mind. The first involves the terms "mutually exclusive" and "exhaustive." The former means that categories are nonoverlapping; no specific example falls into more than one category. The latter term means that categories include all possibilities; each specific example falls into at least one category. The cases in an argument in which the technique under discussion is employed <u>must be exhaustive</u>; often, but not always, cases are mutually exclusive. Thus in dealing with real numbers, we find that the division into rational and irrational is a valid approach, but the division into positive and negative is inadequate, failing to be exhaustive (zero is left out). A division into nonpositive and nonnegative, being overlapping or not mutually exclusive (since zero occurs twice), may lead to difficulties. The second key idea is that if an argument is going to be divided into cases, something should be gained in the proof through such a division. The argument leading to the desired conclusion under Case I should be different from that under Case II and all other cases. In particular, the argument within each case should contain statements that are valid for that case only. Indeed, any two cases for which the arguments are identical should be combined into a single case.

We demonstrate some of these ideas by considering the problem presented at the beginning of this article, under Example 2.

Solution to Example 2   Recall we have been given sets A, B, and X satisfying $A \cap X \subseteq B \cap X$ and $A \cap X' \subseteq B \cap X'$. In order to prove $A \subseteq B$, our desired conclusion, we began, in the discussion following Example 2, by letting x be an arbitrary element of A. We must prove that $x \in B$; our difficulty is in determining how to make use of the given hypotheses and, in particular, how to involve the third set X in the argument. The key is to recall the elementary theorems of set theory, $X \cup X' = U$ and $X \cap X' = \emptyset$. Our chosen element x is either in X or in X' and may not be in both X and X'. Since we have no way of knowing whether $x \in X$ or $x \in X'$, we consider both instances, in the hope that, <u>within each case</u>, we can derive the desired conclusion.

Case I: If $x \in X$, then since $x \in A$, we have $x \in A \cap X$. But $A \cap X \subseteq B \cap X$, thus since $x \in A \cap X$, we may conclude $x \in B \cap X$. Since $B \cap X \subseteq B$, this leads directly to the desired conclusion $x \in B$.

Case II: If $x \in X'$, then $x \in A \cap X'$. Since $A \cap X' \subseteq B \cap X'$, then $x \in B \cap X'$, so that $x \in B$, again as desired. $\square$

Note that the argument <u>under each case</u> concluded with the desired result $x \in B$. Note also that the arguments given under the two cases differed in an essential way; Case I used one hypothesis exclusively whereas Case II used the other. Finally, notice the relationship between the result proved in Example 2 and Exercise 4, Article 1.3.

Many definitions in mathematics are structured in such a way as to lend themselves readily to "proof by cases" of theorems involving them. Look for this especially in definitions whose statement involves cases. One such situation is given in Example 5.

EXAMPLE 5   Recall that the *absolute value* $|x|$ of a real number x is defined by

$$|x| = \begin{cases} x, & x \geq 0 \\ -x, & x < 0 \end{cases}$$

Prove that $|xy| = |x||y|$ for real numbers x and y.

Solution   In proofs such as this the counting techniques introduced in Article 1.5 may be of value. If a proof is going to be divided into cases, according to certain criteria, it may be a nontrivial problem to count, and list systematically, all the cases [recall in particular Exercise 11(c) of Article 1.5]. In this particular instance, which is identical to counting the subsets of a two-element set or to listing the rows of a truth table based on two letters, there are exactly $2^2 = 4$ cases, including:

Case I: If $x \geq 0$ and $y \geq 0$, then $xy \geq 0$ and $|xy| = xy = |x||y|$.

Case II: If $x \geq 0$ and $y < 0$, then $xy \leq 0$ and $|xy| = -(xy) = x(-y) = |x||y|$.

Note that in each of these two cases we are able to use a very brief proof by transitivity. Notice also that in Case II we use the fact that $|x| = -x$ if $x \leq 0$, since $|0| = 0 = -0$. The formulation and completion of the other two cases are left as an exercise [Exercise 12(a)].   □

Sometimes in a proof the course of the argument leads to a statement "either p_1 or p_2 or ... or p_n" from the given hypotheses, where the statements p_i are exhaustive, but may not be mutually exclusive. In such situations it may be appropriate to divide the argument at that stage into n cases and to try to derive the desired conclusion within each of those cases. Cases in point are Exercises 2(d) and 4(a).

Exercises

1. *(a)*   Prove that if A, B, and X are sets with $A \subseteq X$ and $B \subseteq X$, then $A \cup B \subseteq X$.
(b)   Prove that if A and B are sets such that $A \subseteq B$, then $A \cup B = B$.

2. *(a)*   Prove that if A, X, and Y are sets with $X \subseteq Y$, then $A \cup X \subseteq A \cup Y$.
(b)   Prove or disprove the converse of the statement in (a); that is, if A, X, and Y are sets with $A \cup X \subseteq A \cup Y$, then $X \subseteq Y$. (If true, this would mean that the only way we can have $A \cup X \subseteq A \cup Y$ is if $X \subseteq Y$.)

(c)   Prove or disprove the converse of the theorem proved in Example 8, Article 5.2, namely, if A, X, and Y are sets such that $A \cap X \subseteq A \cap Y$, then $X \subseteq Y$.

(d)   Prove that if A, X, and Y are sets satisfying the properties $A \cap X \subseteq A \cap Y$ and $A \cup X \subseteq A \cup Y$, then $X \subseteq Y$ [recall Exercise 3(a), Article 1.3].

(e)   Use the result of (d) to prove that if A, X, and Y are sets satisfying $A \cap X = A \cap Y$ and $A \cup X = A \cup Y$, then $X = Y$.

(f)   Recall from Exercise 10, Article 3.3, the definition of *a complement* of a set. Use (e) to show that if a set A has a complement, this complement is unique.

3. Prove that if A, B, and X are sets satisfying $A \cup X \subseteq B \cup X$ and $A \cup X' \subseteq B \cup X'$, then $A \subseteq B$.

4. ★(a)   Prove, by the choose method, that if X, A, and B are sets such that $X \subseteq B$, then $X \cup (A \cap B) \subseteq (X \cup A) \cap B$. (*Note:* The reverse inclusion is true for any three sets X, A, and B, that is, without the hypothesis $X \subseteq B$. Its proof will be considered in Article 6.2.)

(b)   Show by example that the converse of the theorem in (a) is false. Specifically, show that there exist sets X, A, and B such that $X \cup (A \cap B) = (X \cup A) \cap B$, but X is not a subset of B.

(c)   Prove that if X and B are sets, from a universal set U, satisfying the property $X \cup (A \cap B) = (X \cup A) \cap B$ for· every set A from U, then necessarily $X \subseteq B$. [*Note:* This result is called a *partial converse* of the theorem in (a). *Hint:* For the proof, use specialization.]

(d)   Is there any logical conflict between the results of (b) and (c)? Interpret these results in the light of Exercise 11, Article 3.4.

(e)   Prove that if X and Y are sets having the property that, for every set A (from the common universal set that also contains X and Y), $A \cap X \subseteq A \cap Y$, then $X \subseteq Y$. [This is a partial converse to the theorem in Example 8, Article 5.2. Recall Exercise 2(c).]

5. (Continuation of Exercise 2, Article 5.2)

(a)   Prove that if A and B are sets, then $\mathscr{P}(A) \cup \mathscr{P}(B) \subseteq \mathscr{P}(A \cup B)$.

(b)   Give an example to show that the reverse inclusion in (a) need not be true.

(c)   Prove that, for any sets A and B, if $\mathscr{P}(A) \cup \mathscr{P}(B) = \mathscr{P}(A \cup B)$, then either $A \subseteq B$ or $B \subseteq A$. [*Hint:* Use specialization followed by division into cases. Note that $A \cup B$ itself is an element of $\mathscr{P}(A \cup B)$, since $A \cup B \subseteq A \cup B$.]

(d)   In view of the results from (a) and (c), what relationship exists between $\mathscr{P}(A) \cup \mathscr{P}(B)$ and $\mathscr{P}(A \cup B)$ for any two sets A and B, neither of which is a subset of the other?

6. Prove by the choose method (in particular, do <u>not</u> use distributivity) that if A and B are sets, then $(A \cap B) \cup (A \cap B') = A$.

7. Use distributivity and previously proved identities involving union and intersection to give a proof <u>by transitivity</u> (as in Article 5.1) that if A, B, and X are subsets of a universal set U, and:

(a)   If $X \subseteq B$, then $X \cup (A \cap B) = (X \cup A) \cap B$

★(b)   If $A \cap X = B \cap X$ and $A \cap X' = B \cap X'$, then $A = B$

(c)   If $A \cup X = B \cup X$ and $A \cup X' = B \cup X'$, then $A = B$

(d)   If $A \cap X = B \cap X$ and $A \cup X = B \cup X$, then $A = B$

8. (a)   Prove that if a subset C of $\mathbf{R} \times \mathbf{R}$ is symmetric with respect to both the x axis and the y axis, then it is symmetric with respect to the origin.

(b)   Prove that if a subset C of $\mathbf{R} \times \mathbf{R}$ is symmetric with respect to both the origin and the y axis, then it is symmetric with respect to the x axis.

9. Assume it is known that $\cos(x - y) = \cos x \cos y + \sin x \sin y$ for all real numbers x and y. Use the additional facts that $\cos^2 x + \sin^2 x = 1$ for all $x \in \mathbf{R}$, $\cos(\pi/2) = 0$, $\sin(\pi/2) = 1$, $\cos 0 = 1$, $\sin 0 = 0$, and $\sin(-\pi/2) = -1$, to prove:

(a) $\cos((\pi/2) - y) = \sin y$ for all $y \in \mathbf{R}$ (This is the result we assumed in Example 4.)

(b) $\cos(-y) = \cos y$ for all $y \in \mathbf{R}$ (i.e., cosine is an *even* function.)

(c) $\cos(x + (\pi/2)) = -\sin x$ for all $x \in \mathbf{R}$

(d) $\sin(-x) = -\sin x$ for all $x \in \mathbf{R}$ [i.e., sine is an *odd* function. *Hint:* Use the results of (a) and (c).]

(e) $\sin(x + (\pi/2)) = \cos x$ for all $x \in \mathbf{R}$ [*Hint:* Use (a).]

(f) $\cos(x + y) = \cos x \cos y - \sin x \sin y$ for all $x, y \in \mathbf{R}$

(g) $\sin(x + y) = \sin x \cos y + \cos x \sin y$ for all $x, y \in \mathbf{R}$ [*Hint:* Use (a) and Example 4.]

(h) $\sin(x - y) = \sin x \cos y - \cos x \sin y$ for all $x, y \in \mathbf{R}$

(i) $\sin 2x = 2 \sin x \cos x$ for all $x \in \mathbf{R}$

10. Use the results from Exercise 9 to prove further that:

★(a) $\sin x - \sin y = 2 \cos((x + y)/2) \sin((x - y)/2)$ for all $x, y \in \mathbf{R}$

(b) $\cos 2x = 1 - 2 \sin^2 x = 2 \cos^2 x - 1$ for all $x \in \mathbf{R}$

(c) $\cos^2 x = (1 + \cos 2x)/2$ for all $x \in \mathbf{R}$

(d) $\sin^2 x = (1 - \cos 2x)/2$ for all $x \in \mathbf{R}$

(e) $\tan(x - y) = (\tan x - \tan y)/(1 + \tan x \tan y)$,   whenever $x, y \in \mathbf{R}$ and $x \neq y + [(2n + 1)\pi/2]$, for any integer n

11. For given real numbers x and y we define:

$$\max(x, y) = x \vee y = \begin{cases} x, & y \leq x \\ y, & x \leq y \end{cases} \quad \text{and} \quad \min(x, y) = x \wedge y = \begin{cases} y, & y \leq x \\ x, & x \leq y \end{cases}$$

Prove that, for any real numbers x, y, and z:

(a) $x \wedge (y \wedge z) = (x \wedge y) \wedge z$

(b) $(x \wedge y) + (x \vee y) = x + y$

(c) $(-x) \wedge (-y) = -(x \vee y)$

(d) $(x \vee y) + z = (x + z) \vee (y + z)$

(e)   If $z > 0$, then $z(x \vee y) = (zx) \vee (zy)$

12. (a)   Complete the proof from Example 5 that $|xy| = |x||y|$ for all real numbers x and y.

(b)   Recall from Exercise 8, Article 5.1, that $|x + y| \leq |x| + |y|$ for all $x, y \in \mathbf{R}$ and $|x| \leq y$ if and only if $-y \leq x \leq y$, where $x, y \in \mathbf{R}$ and $y \geq 0$. Prove that:

(i) $|x| = x \vee (-x)$ for any $x \in \mathbf{R}$

★ (ii) $x \vee y = \frac{1}{2}(x + y + |x - y|)$ for any $x, y \in \mathbf{R}$

(iii) $x \wedge y = \frac{1}{2}(x + y - |x - y|)$ for any $x, y \in \mathbf{R}$

(iv) $(x \vee y) - (x \wedge y) = |x - y|$ for any $x, y \in \mathbf{R}$

13. Let $A = (a_{ij})_{n \times n}$ and $B = (b_{ij})_{n \times n}$ be square matrices. Recall Exercise 11 from Article 5.2 and prove:

(a) If A is diagonal, then $A = A^t$.

(b) If A is both upper and lower triangular, then A is diagonal. [What theorem emerges from the combination of this fact with the results of (b) and (c) of Exercise 11, Article 5.2?]

★(c) If A and B are diagonal matrices, then their product AB is a diagonal matrix.

(d) If A and B are upper (resp., lower) triangular matrices, then their product AB is an upper (resp., lower) triangular matrix.

14. Suppose that I_1 and I_2 are intervals on the real line such that $I_2 \cap I_2 \neq \varnothing$. Prove that $I_1 \cup I_2$ is an interval.

15. Critique and complete (instructions in Exercise 11, Article 4.1):

(a) THEOREM For any real numbers x, y, and z, $x \vee (y \vee z) = (x \vee y) \vee z$ (recall Exercise 11).

"Proof" We divide the argument into the cases $x < y < z$ and $x > y > z$. In the first case $x \vee (y \vee z) = x \vee z = z = y \vee z = (x \vee y) \vee z$, so that $x \vee (y \vee z) = (x \vee y) \vee z$, as desired. In the second case $x \vee (y \vee z) = x \vee y = x = x \vee z = (x \vee y) \vee z$, so that the desired result holds in this case as well. In either case we have the desired conclusion.

(b) THEOREM For any positive real numbers x and y, $\ln (x/y) = \ln x - \ln y$. [*Note:* Assume we already proved that (1) $\ln (xy) = \ln x + \ln y$ for any positive real numbers x and y and (2) $\ln 1 = 0$.]

"Proof" Let x be an arbitrary real number; we begin by using the special case $y = 1/x$ in (1). By (2), we have $0 = \ln 1 = \ln (x \cdot 1/x) = \ln x + \ln (1/x)$. Hence $\ln (1/x) = -\ln x$ for any $x > 0$. Next, let x and y be arbitrary positive real numbers. Then $\ln (x/y) = \ln (x \cdot 1/y) = \ln x + \ln (1/y) = \ln x - \ln y$, as desired.

(c) THEOREM For any sets X and Y in U, if $Y = X \cup (Y \cap X')$, then $X \subseteq Y$.

Start of "Proof" Let x be an arbitrary element of U. Clearly either $x \in X$ or $x \in X'$. We will divide the argument into these two cases . . . .

(d) THEOREM If a function f, mapping reals to reals, is decreasing on an interval I (i.e., if $x_1 < x_2$ implies $f(x_1) > f(x_2)$ for any $x_1, x_2 \in \mathbf{R}$), then f is one to one on I.

Start of "Proof" Assume f is decreasing on I. To show f is one to one on I, assume that x_1 and x_2 are elements of I such that $f(x_1) = f(x_2)$. We must prove $x_1 = x_2$. For suppose $x_1 \neq x_2$. Then . . . . (*Note:* This approach anticipates *indirect proof*, to be studied in Article 6.2.)

(e) FACT The function $f(x) = a^x$ ($a > 0$, $a \neq 1$) is one to one on $\mathbf{R}$. [*Note:* Use the results of (d), and Exercise 6(c), Article 5.2, together with the derivative formula $d/dx(a^x) = a^x \ln a$ where $a > 0$ and $a \neq 1$, and well-known facts about the significance of the sign of the first derivative.]

Start of "Proof" We consider the sign of the derivative of the function $f(x) = a^x$. Since $a > 0$ and $a \neq 1$, then either $a > 1$ or $0 < a < 1$. . . .

5.4 Proof by Mathematical Induction

Proof by mathematical induction is a special method of proof, appropriate for use in particular situations. In this article we introduce the principle of mathematical induction and discuss under what circumstances and exactly how this important principle is applied. The following example gives several statements that, it turns out, are theorems that are provable by mathematical induction.

EXAMPLE 1 Test the truth of each of the following statements for at least five particular elements of the specified universal set:

(a) For all positive integers n, 4 divides $5^n - 1$.
(b) $1 + 2 + 3 + \cdots + n = [n(n + 1)]/2$ for any $n = 1, 2, 3, \ldots$.
(c) If $n \in \mathbf{N}$ and $n \geq 5$, then $4^n \geq n^4$.
(d) If $f_1, f_2, \ldots, f_n$ are n functions differentiable on $\mathbf{R}$, where n is an arbitrary positive integer, then their sum $f_1 + f_2 + \cdots + f_n$ is differentiable on $\mathbf{R}$ and $(d/dx)(f_1 + f_2 + \cdots + f_n) = df_1/dx + df_2/dx + \cdots + df_n/dx$.

Outline of solution It is left to you to provide most of the verifications, but we note, for example, that in (a), if $n = 1$, then $5^n - 1 = 5 - 1 = 4$, which is indeed divisible by 4. Furthermore, if $n = 6$, then $5^n - 1 = 5^6 - 1 = 15{,}625 - 1 = 15{,}624$, which again is divisible by 4. In (b) we observe that, for $n = 10$, the sum $1 + 2 + 3 + \cdots + 10$ equals 55, while the formula $[n(n + 1)]/2$ also equals 55 when 10 is substituted for n. If $n = 100$, then you can verify that both quantities equal 5,050. In (c), if $n = 5$, then $4^n = 4^5 = 1{,}024 > 625 = 5^4$, as claimed. Note that statement (c) says nothing about the inequality if $n = 1, 2, 3,$ or 4. You should try the inequality in some of these cases as well, keeping in mind, however, that none of these can serve as a counterexample to (c). As an illustration of (d), we may let $n = 5$ and consider the functions $f_i(x) = x^i$ for $i = 1, 2, 3, 4, 5$. For this specific situation the theorem asserts that $(d/dx)(x + x^2 + x^3 + x^4 + x^5) = 1 + 2x + 3x^2 + 4x^3 + 5x^4$, a result that, although laborious to derive from the definition of derivative, is of a type familiar to every calculus student. $\square$

What do the statements in Example 1 have in common? Compared, say, to the trigonometric identity "$\cos 2x = 2 \cos^2 x - 1$ for all $x \in \mathbf{R}$," or the theorem of set theory "$A \cap (B \cup C) = (A \cap B) \cup (A \cap C)$ for all sets A, B, and C," what distinguishes these statements? The answer lies in the nature of the particular cases used to test the truth of the statements. Choosing a special case of any of these statements involves choosing a positive integer n. The reason for this, in turn, is that each of statements (a), (b), and (d) contains the quantification "for all positive integers n," in symbols ($\forall n \in \mathbf{N}$).

To a very large extent, theorems whose statement involves the phrase "for all positive integers n," are the theorems for which an induction proof is appropriate. As we will see later, induction proofs may be appropriate in a slightly more general context that includes (c) of Example 1.

Suppose now we wish to prove a statement $(\forall n)(p(n))$, where $\mathbf{N}$ is the domain of discourse for the predicate $p(n)$. Denote by S the subset of $\mathbf{N}$ consisting of all positive integers for which $p(n)$ is true. In the terminology of Chapter 3, S is the truth set of $p(n)$. By definition, S is a subset of $\mathbf{N}$. To prove our theorem, we must prove that S equals $\mathbf{N}$. Clearly a criterion giving a general approach to proving that a subset S of $\mathbf{N}$ actually equals $\mathbf{N}$ should have potential for being applied to this situation. The principle of mathematical induction is just such a criterion.

THEOREM   1 (Principle of Mathematical Induction)
Let S be a subset of the set $\mathbf{N}$ of all positive integers satisfying the properties:

(i) $1 \in S$
(ii)   For all $n \in \mathbf{N}$, if $n \in S$, then $n + 1 \in S$.

Then $S = \mathbf{N}$

It is intuitively evident that $\mathbf{N}$ satisfies conditions (i) and (ii) of Theorem 1. Another way of stating Theorem 1 is that no proper subset of $\mathbf{N}$ satisfies both conditions (i.e., the only subset of $\mathbf{N}$ satisfying both conditions is $\mathbf{N}$ itself). We defer a formal proof in the text of Theorem 1 until Chapter 10, where we study $\mathbf{N}$ as a number system and consider a number of its properties (see also Exercise 9(d), Article 6.3). We note here, however, that the result is not difficult to believe. For example, assume that a subset S of $\mathbf{N}$ satisfies (i) and (ii) and suppose we wish to conclude $3 \in S$. To do this, we observe simply that $1 \in S$, by (i). Combining this fact with (ii), using specialization, we conclude that $2 = 1 + 1 \in S$. Since $2 \in S$, then, again using (ii), we conclude $3 = 2 + 1 \in S$, as desired. The same argument, involving n repetitions, can in theory be used to prove that any given positive integer n is in S.

We shift our attention now away from the validity of Theorem 1 and toward its application.

EXAMPLE 2   Prove that the sum of the first n odd positive integers is given by the formula n^2, in symbols, for all $n \in \mathbf{N}$, $1 + 3 + 5 + \cdots + (2n - 1) = n^2$.

Solution   Before attempting to write a proof of a statement, we find it a good idea to try a few cases, to see whether the result stated is reasonable. For example, if $n = 10$, the result states that $1 + 3 + 5 + \cdots + 17 + 19 = 100$, as computation quickly verifies. You should try several other cases.

Now for the proof, let S be the subset of $\mathbf{N}$ consisting of those positive integers m for which the result is true. Our claim is that $S = \mathbf{N}$. To prove this, it is sufficient, by Theorem 1, to prove (i) $1 \in S$ and (ii) for each $m \in \mathbf{N}$, if $m \in S$, then $(m + 1) \in S$.

1. Clearly $1 \in S$, since $1^2 = 1 =$ the sum of the "first 1" odd positive integers.
2. Let $m \in S$ be given. Hence $1 + 3 + \cdots + (2m - 1) = m^2$. (The assumption $m \in S$ with which step (2) begins in every induction proof is often called the *induction hypothesis* or the *inductive assumption*.) To prove $m + 1 \in S$, we must prove

$$1 + 3 + 5 + \cdots + (2m - 1) + 2(m + 1) - 1 = (m + 1)^2.$$

In the course of the latter proof in turn we must make use of the induction hypothesis. Note now that

$$[1 + 3 + 5 + \cdots + (2m - 1)] + [2(m + 1) - 1]$$
$$= [1 + 3 + 5 + \cdots + (2m - 1)] + (2m + 1)$$
$$= m^2 + (2m + 1) \qquad \text{(We have just used the}$$
$$\text{induction hypothesis.)}$$
$$= (m + 1)^2.$$

This is precisely what was needed to prove $m + 1 \in S$, so that condition (ii) is verified and the proof is complete. $\square$

EXAMPLE 3   Assume that the product rule for the derivative $(fg)'(x) = f(x)g'(x) + f'(x)g(x)$ is known. Use this rule to prove that, for all positive integers n, if $f(x) = x^n$, then $f'(x) = nx^{n-1}$.

Solution   Every student with a calculus background is familiar with this rule. Since its statement involves the phrase "for all positive integers n," it is a candidate for proof by mathematical induction. We begin such a proof by letting S be the set of those positive integers m for which the theorem is true: If m is a positive integer, then $m \in S$ if and only if $(d/dx)(x^m) = mx^{m-1}$. To prove $S = \mathbf{N}$, we must prove (1) $1 \in S$ and (2) for all $m \in \mathbf{N}$, if $m \in S$, then $m + 1 \in S$.

1. Clearly $1 \in S$, since $(d/dx)(x^1) = dx/dx = 1$ and $1x^{1-1} = 1x^0 = x^0 = 1$.
2. Assume $m \in S$. To prove $m + 1 \in S$, we must show that $(d/dx)(x^{m+1}) = (m + 1)x^m$, using the inductive assumption that $(d/dx)(x^m) = mx^{m-1}$. Now

$$(d/dx)(x^{m+1}) = (d/dx)(x^m \cdot x)$$
$$= x^m(dx/dx) + x[(d/dx)(x^m)] \qquad \text{(by the product rule)}$$
$$= x^m(1) + (x)(mx^{m-1}) \qquad \text{(by the induction}$$
$$\text{hypothesis)}$$
$$= x^m + mx^m$$
$$= (m + 1)x^m, \qquad \text{as desired} \quad \square$$

Students sometimes complain that the actual induction proof seems like an afterthought, after a "seemingly sufficient" number of special cases of a statement have been verified as true. Keep in mind that no (necessarily finite) number of verifications of specific cases is ever enough to prove that a statement is true for every positive integer. Exercise 11 is a case in point. A second complaint often heard is that, in the course of an induction proof, assumption is made of what we are trying to prove when the induction hypothesis is stated. For instance, in Example 1, we wanted to prove $p(n)$: $1 + 3 + \cdots + (2n - 1) = n^2$; did we not <u>assume</u> precisely that equation at the start of part (2) of the proof? The distinction lies in the use of quantifiers. Our desired result in Example 1 is $(\forall n)(p(n))$. Our assumption is simply $p(m)$, where m is some fixed positive integer, our goal being to deduce $p(m + 1)$ <u>for that</u> m. A third problem is that because part (i) of most induction proofs is often trivial to prove, students are sometimes tempted to omit it or gloss over it. Exercise 10 demonstrates the dangers of such an attitude.

CATEGORIES OF INDUCTION PROOF

There are certain mathematical situations that lend themselves especially well to proof by induction. In the following paragraphs we consider three such situations. These three categories are by no means exhaustive.

Summation formulas. The result in Example 2 is a simple representative of a large class of theorems whose proofs use the induction technique. Such a theorem is known as a *summation formula*, a formula that yields, for each positive integer n, the sum of n numbers of a prescribed form. Part (b) of Example 1 is also in this category. Formulas of this type are often said to be a *closed form* representation of the given sum.

Summation formulas are usually expressed by means of *summation notation*, whereby we abbreviate a sum $x_1 + x_2 + \cdots + x_n$ by the symbol $\sum_{k=1}^{n} x_k$. Using this notation, we may rewrite Example 2 in the form $\sum_{k=1}^{n} (2k - 1) = n^2$ and Example 1(b) as $\sum_{k=1}^{n} k = [n(n + 1)]/2$. The variable k in such a formula is a dummy variable (recall the discussion following Example 1, Article 3.2); the letters i, j, and k are the letters most commonly used for this purpose. As further examples, the symbol $\sum_{j=3}^{n} (2j)$ represents the sum $6 + 8 + 10 + \cdots + 2n$, while $\sum_{i=1}^{5} (-1)^i \, i$ stands for $-1 + 2 - 3 + 4 - 5$.

Here are two more examples of induction proofs of summation formulas. It should be noted that the induction method is of no assistance in discovering the formula, but only for proving that a given formula actually represents a particular sum.

EXAMPLE 4   Prove that, for each positive integer n, the sum $\sum_{k=1}^{n} (k/2^k)$ is given by the formula $2 - [(n + 2)/2^n]$. (You should first "try out" the formula for several special cases.)

Solution   Let S be the truth set of $p(n)$: $\sum_{k=1}^{n} (k/2^k) = 2 - [(n + 2)/2^n]$. To prove $S = \mathbf{N}$, we need only verify (i) and (ii) of Theorem 1.

1. $1 \in S$, since $\sum_{k=1}^{1} (k/2^k) = 1/2^1 = \frac{1}{2} = 2 - (\frac{3}{2}) = 2 - [(1 + 2)/2^1]$.
2. Assume $m \in S$. To prove $m + 1 \in S$, we must show that $\sum_{k=1}^{m+1} (k/2^k) = 2 - [((m + 1) + 2)/2^{m+1}]$. First, we note that we can express $\sum_{k=1}^{m+1} (k/2^k)$ as $\sum_{k=1}^{m} (k/2^k) + [(m + 1)/2^{m+1}]$.

Applying the induction hypothesis, we transform the latter expression to

$$[2 - ((m + 2)/2^m)] + ((m + 1)/2^{m+1})$$

which equals

$$[2^{m+2} - 2(m + 2) + (m + 1)]/2^{m+1}$$

Simplifying, we get

$[2^{m+2} - (m + 3)]/2^{m+1}$, that is, $2 - [((m + 1) + 2)/2^{m+1}]$, as desired. $\quad\square$

In the next example of an induction proof we verify a basic property of summation notation.

EXAMPLE 5   Suppose n is a positive integer and $x_1, x_2, \ldots, x_n, y_1, y_2, \ldots, y_n$ are $(2n)$ real numbers. Prove that $\sum_{k=1}^{n} (x_k + y_k) = \sum_{k=1}^{n} x_k + \sum_{k=1}^{n} y_k$.

Proof   Let S be the truth set of $p(n)$: $\sum_{k=1}^{n} (x_k + y_k) = \sum_{k=1}^{n} x_k + \sum_{k=1}^{n} y_k$. We claim $S = \mathbf{N}$. We must verify (i) and (ii) of Theorem 1.

1. $1 \in S$, since $\sum_{k=1}^{1} (x_k + y_k) = x_1 + y_1 = \sum_{k=1}^{1} x_k + \sum_{k=1}^{1} y_k$.
2. Assume $m \in S$. To prove $m + 1 \in S$, we must show

$$\sum_{k=1}^{m+1} (x_k + y_k) = \sum_{k=1}^{m+1} x_k + \sum_{k=1}^{m+1} y_k.$$

This follows from the string of equations,

$$\sum_{k=1}^{m+1} (x_k + y_k) = \left[\sum_{k=1}^{m} (x_k + y_k)\right] + (x_{m+1} + y_{m+1})$$

$$= \left[\sum_{k=1}^{m} x_k + \sum_{k=1}^{m} y_k\right] + (x_{m+1} + y_{m+1})$$

$$= \left[\left(\sum_{k=1}^{m} x_k\right) + x_{m+1}\right] + \left[\left(\sum_{k=1}^{m} y_k\right) + y_{m+1}\right]$$

$$= \sum_{k=1}^{m+1} x_k + \sum_{k=1}^{m+1} y_k, \qquad \text{as desired.}$$

You should apply justifications for each of the preceding steps, noting especially where the induction hypothesis is used. $\quad\square$

Generalization. Many theorems or axioms whose familiar statement says something about two objects are generalized to "any finite number" by an induction proof.

EXAMPLE 6   Use induction and the distributive axiom to prove the law of *generalized distributivity* of multiplication over addition, that is, for any positive integer n,

$$a(b_1 + b_2 + \cdots + b_n) = ab_1 + ab_2 + \cdots + ab_n,$$

where $a, b_1, \ldots, b_n$ are real numbers.

Solution   In proofs of this type induction is done on the number m of objects involved, in this case the number of real numbers over which we are distributing a. Also, the "known" distributive law is simply the case $m = 2$, which is thereby known to be true. Let S be the set of those positive integers m such that "distributivity across m real numbers" is valid. Condition (i) of the induction principle says that $ab_1 = ab_1$, which is true. For condition (ii), assume $m \in S$. This means that $a(b_1 + b_2 + \cdots + b_m) = ab_1 + ab_2 + \cdots + ab_m$ for any real number a and for any m real numbers $b_1, b_2, \ldots, b_m$. To show $m + 1 \in S$, let $a \in \mathbf{R}$ and let $c_1, c_2, \ldots, c_m, c_{m+1}$ be any $(m + 1)$ real numbers. Then

$$
\begin{aligned}
a(c_1 + c_2 &+ \cdots + c_m + c_{m+1}) \\
&= a[(c_1 + c_2 + \cdots + c_m) + c_{m+1}] \\
&= a(c_1 + c_2 + \cdots + c_m) + ac_{m+1} \\
&= (ac_1 + ac_2 + \cdots + ac_m) + ac_{m+1} \\
&= ac_1 + ac_2 + \cdots + ac_m + ac_{m+1}, \qquad \text{as desired}
\end{aligned}
$$

Note, finally, that generalized distributivity can be expressed by summation notation, namely, the equation $\sum_{k=1}^{n} (ab_k) = a\sum_{k=1}^{n} b_k$. $\square$

Notice that the step leading from line 2 to line 3 was based on the ordinary distributive law (i.e., the case $n = 2$ of generalized distributivity), whereas we went from line 3 to line 4 by means of the induction hypothesis. The pattern of an essentially two-step argument, using first the known case $n = 2$, followed by using the induction hypothesis, is the usual one when induction is used for the purpose of generalization. Note that (d) of Example 1 is a problem in this category, as are the two parts of Exercise 6.

It may be appropriate, at this point, to note that the results of Examples 5 and 6 are among a number of "basic properties of summation notation" that are proved by induction. These include additional results such as $\sum_{k=1}^{n} c = nc$ (for any $n \in \mathbf{N}$ and $c \in \mathbf{R}$) and $\sum_{k=1}^{n} x_k = \sum_{k=1+i}^{n+i} x_{k-i}$ (for any positive integers n and i, and real numbers $x_1, x_2, \ldots, x_k$). Generalizations of these and other basic summation notation properties are the subject of Exercise 15.

The results in Examples 5 and 6, when combined with an elementary summation formula such as $\sum_{k=1}^{n} k = [n(n + 1)]/2$ [recall Example 1(b)] can be used to produce quick and easy (noninduction) proofs of additional summation properties. For example, we may prove that $\sum_{k=1}^{n} (4k - 5) = 2n^2 - 3n$ for all $n \in \mathbf{N}$ by either an induction argument or by the argument:

$$\sum_{k=1}^{n} (4k - 5) = \left(\sum_{k=1}^{n} 4k\right) - \left(\sum_{k=1}^{n} 5\right) = \left(\sum_{k=1}^{n} k\right) - \left(\sum_{k=1}^{n} 5\right)$$
$$= 4[(n(n + 1))/2] - 5n = 2(n^2 + n) - 5n = 2n^2 - 3n$$

You should supply justifications for each step of this argument, and see Exercise 4 for similar type problems.

Results about divisibility. If a and b are integers, we say that a divides b, denoted $a|b$, if and only if there exists an integer n such that $b = na$. In Article 6.1 we will verify a number of properties of divisibility, the results of which we assume and use for the time being. These include:

1. $a|a$ for all $a \in \mathbf{Z}$
2. $\forall a, b, c \in \mathbf{Z}$, if $a|b$, then $a|bc$
3. $\forall a, b, c \in \mathbf{Z}$, if $a|b$ and $a|c$, then $a|(b + c)$
4. $\forall a, b, c \in \mathbf{Z}$, if $a|b$ and $b|c$, then $a|c$

A number of properties of divisibility are valid "for all positive integers n," and hence lend themselves to proof by induction. The next example presents one such property.

EXAMPLE 7   Prove that 6 divides $7^n - 1$ for all positive integers n.

Solution   Define S in the usual fashion. Note that $1 \in S$ since $7^1 - 1 = 6$ and 6 divides itself. Now suppose $m \in S$. To prove $m + 1 \in S$, we must prove that 6 divides $7^{m+1} - 1$, using the inductive assumption that 6 divides $7^m - 1$. Now $7^{m+1} - 1 = 7(7^m - 1) + 6$. Since 6 divides $7^m - 1$, then 6 divides $7(7^m - 1)$ by (2). Clearly $6/6$ [by (1)]. By (3), we have that 6 divides the sum of 6 and $7(7^m - 1)$. But this sum equals $7^{m+1} - 1$, so that 6 divides $7^{m+1} - 1$, as we wished to prove. $\square$

INDUCTIVE SETS

Part (c) of Example 1 is a theorem that is true not for all positive integers, but rather, for all integers greater than or equal to a particular positive integer n_0, in this case $n_0 = 5$. A slight variation in the induction principle can be used to prove theorems of this type. We introduce a concept helpful toward this end in Definition 1.

DEFINITION 1

A subset S of the set **N** of all positive integers is said to be **inductive** if and only if $m \in S$ implies $m + 1 \in S$ for all positive integers m.

Since the condition of Definition 1 is simply condition (ii) of Theorem 1, it is clear that **N** itself is inductive. In fact, for any positive integer n, the subset $\{n, n + 1, n + 2, \ldots\}$ of **N** is also inductive. Furthermore, we have the following theorem.

THEOREM 2

Suppose S is an inductive subset of **N** containing a positive integer m_0. Then S contains m for every positive integer m greater than m_0: that is, $\{m_0, m_0 + 1, m_0 + 2, \ldots\} \subseteq S$.

Proof   Consider the set $T = S \cup \{1, 2, \ldots, m_0 - 1\}$. Clearly $1 \in T$ and T is inductive (Verify the latter claim, using the technique of division into cases together with the fact that S is inductive). Hence, by Theorem 1, $T = \mathbf{N}$. Choose $m \in \mathbf{N}$ such that $m > m_0$. We will have completed the proof if we can show $m \in S$. Since $T = \mathbf{N}$, then we have $m \in \mathbf{N} = T = S \cup \{1, 2, \ldots, m_0 - 1\}$. Since $m > m_0$, then $m \notin \{1, 2, \ldots, m_0 - 1\}$ so that we may conclude $m \in S$, as desired.

The upshot of Theorem 2 is that we may prove a theorem asserting $(\forall n \geq n_0)(p(n))$ by proving that the truth set S of $p(n)$ satisfies (i) $n_0 \in S$ and (ii) S is inductive. In fact, we may substitute for (ii) the slightly weaker condition (ii)': for all $m \in \mathbf{N}$, $m \in S$ and $m \geq n_0$ together imply $m + 1 \in S$.

EXAMPLE 8   Prove that if n is an integer and $n \geq 4$, then $2^n < n!$.

Solution   Let S be the truth set of $p(n)$: $2^n < n!$. We claim that $\{4, 5, 6, \ldots, \} \subseteq S$. Note first that $4 \in S$ since $2^4 = 16 < 24 = 4!$. Second, suppose that $m \geq 4$ and $m \in S$, so that $2^m < m!$. We must prove, on the basis of these assumptions, that $2^{m+1} < (m + 1)!$. But $2^{m+1} = 2(2^m) < 2(m!) < (m + 1)m! = (m + 1)!$, as desired.

Note that the induction hypothesis was used in the step $2(2^m) < 2(m!)$.

$\square$

You may have already conjectured that *every inductive subset of N has the form* $\{m, m + 1, m + 2, \ldots\}$ *for some positive integer m*. This conjecture is nearly true; in order to make it true, we must insert the word *nonempty* before "inductive." The reason for this is that the empty set $\varnothing$ is inductive. The latter fact is another reason we must never neglect to verify condition (i) in any induction proof. If a statement $p(n)$ with domain of discourse **N** has a truth set that is inductive [i.e., condition (ii) can be proved], it may still be the case that $p(n)$ is false for all $n \in \mathbf{N}$, that is, $S = \varnothing$ (see Exercise 10). But if $p(n)$ has an inductive truth set and furthermore is true for at least one positive integer n_0, then it is true for infinitely many positive integers; specifically it is true for at least all positive integers $m \geq n_0$.

In Chapter 10 we will deal with other forms of the induction principle, as well as with "definition by induction," in the context of a development of the number system of positive integers.

Exercises

1. Use induction to prove parts (a) through (d) of Example 1, that is, prove that if $n \in \mathbf{N}$, then:

(a) 4 divides $5^n - 1$ (b) $\sum_{k=1}^{n} k = [n(n + 1)]/2$

(c) $4^n > n^4$, if $n \geq 5$ (d) $(d/dx)[\sum_{k=1}^{n} f_k] = \sum_{k=1}^{n} (df_k/dx)$

2. Prove, by induction, that for all positive integers n:

(a) $\sum_{i=1}^{n} i^2 = [n(n + 1)(2n + 1)]/6$ (b) $\sum_{k=1}^{n} k^3 = \frac{1}{4}(n^4 + 2n^3 + n^2)$

(c) $\sum_{j=1}^{n} j^4 = \frac{1}{5}n(n^4 + (\frac{5}{2})n^3 + (\frac{5}{3})n^2 - (1/6))$

3. Use induction to prove that for all positive integers n;

(a) $\sum_{j=1}^{n} 1/j(j + 1) = n/(n + 1)$

★(b) $\sum_{k=1}^{n} k(k + 1) = [n(n + 1)(n + 2)]/3$

(c) $\sum_{k=1}^{n} (3k^2 - 3k + 1) = n^3$

(d) $1 + 2 + 4 + \cdots + 2^{n-1} = 2^n - 1$

4. Use either an induction argument, or a noninduction proof that employs previously noted summation formulas, to prove that for all positive integers n:

(a) $\sum_{k=1}^{n} (2k) = n(n + 1)$

(b) $5 + 10 + 15 + \cdots + 5n = [5n(n + 1)]/2$

(c) $\sum_{k=1}^{n} (4k - 3) = 2n^2 - n$

(d) $\sum_{k=1}^{n} (3k - 2) = (\frac{3}{2})n^2 - (\frac{1}{2})n$

5. (a)   Use induction, together with the facts $\cos (x + y) = \cos x \cos y - \sin x \sin y$ and $\cos (\pi) = -1$, to prove that $\cos (n\pi) = (-1)^n$ for all $n \in \mathbf{N}$.

(b) Suppose a real-valued function f having domain $\mathbf{R}$ has the property $f(x + T) = f(x)$ for all $x \in \mathbf{R}$. Use induction to prove that $f(x + nT) = f(x)$ for all $x \in \mathbf{R}$ and $n \in \mathbf{N}$.

(c)   Prove by induction that $\sum_{i=1}^{n} \sin (2i - 1)x = (1 - \cos 2nx)/2 \sin x$, whenever x is not an integral multiple of π.

6. (a)   Assuming the truth of the triangle inequality, $|x + y| \leq |x| + |y|$ for all x, $y \in \mathbf{R}$, prove by induction on n the *generalized triangle inequality*, if $x_1, x_2, \ldots,$ $x_n \in \mathbf{R}$, where n is a positive integer, then $|\sum_{k=1}^{n} x_k| \leq \sum_{k=1}^{n} |x_k|$.

(b) Suppose it is known that if $\lim_{x \to a} f(x)$ and $\lim_{x \to a} g(x)$ both exist, then $\lim_{x \to a}(f + g)(x)$ exists and equals $\lim_{x \to a} f(x) + \lim_{x \to a} g(x)$ (i.e., the limit of a sum is the sum of the limits, provided both limits exist). Prove by induction that if $f_1(x), f_2(x), \ldots, f_n(x)$ are n functions such that $\lim_{x \to a} f_i(x)$ exists for each $i = 1, 2, \ldots, n$, then $\lim_{x \to a} (\sum_{i=1}^{n} f_i(x))$ exists and equals $\sum_{i=1}^{n} \lim_{x \to a} f_i(x)$.

7. *(a)* Prove, by induction, that 3 divides $4^n - 1$ for all $n \in \mathbf{N}$.
   (b) Prove that, for any $x \in \mathbf{Z}$, $x - 1$ divides $x^n - 1$ for all $n \in \mathbf{N}$.
   (c) Prove that 5 divides $8^n - 3^n$ for all $n \in \mathbf{N}$.
   ★*(d)* Prove that, for any integers x and y, $x - y$ divides $x^n - y^n$, $n = 1, 2, 3, \ldots$
   (e) Prove that 6 divides $n^3 - n$ for all $n \in \mathbf{N}$.

8. Prove, using the modified induction approach suggested by Theorem 2;

(a) If $n \geq 5$, then $n^2 < 2^n$ ★*(b)* If $n \geq 10$, then $n^3 < 2^n$
(c) If $n \geq 17$, then $n^4 < 2^n$ *(d)* If $n \geq 9$, then $4^n < n!$
(e) If $n \geq 2$, then $\sum_{k=1}^{n} (1/\sqrt{k}) > \sqrt{n}$.

9. *(a)* Prove that if x is a real number greater than -1 and if n is a positive integer, then $(1 + x)^n \geq 1 + nx$.
   (b) Prove that if n is a positive integer and

   (i) If $x > 1$, then $x^n > 1$ *(ii)* If $x < 0$, then $x^{2n-1} < 0$
   (iii) If $x \neq 0$, then $x^{2n} > 0$ *(iv)* If $x \geq 1$, then $x^n \geq x$
   (v) If $0 < a < b$, then $0 < a^n < b^n$

   (c) Prove that if $|a_1| \leq 1$ and $|a_k - a_{k-1}| \leq 1$ for all $k = 1, 2, \ldots, n$, then $|a_n| \leq n$.

10. Each of the following predicates over $\mathbf{N}$ is <u>false for all positive integers</u>. Verify in each case that the condition $(\forall n)(p_i(n) \rightarrow p_i(n + 1))$ is true:

(a) $p_1(n)$, $n = n + 1$ *(b)* $p_2(n)$, $\sum_{i=1}^{n} 2^{i-1} = 2^n$
(c) $p_3(n)$, $\sum_{k=1}^{n} 2k = (n + (\frac{1}{2}))^2$ *(d)* $p_4(n)$, $\sum_{k=1}^{n} (2k - 1) = n^2 + 5$

11. The formula $n^2 - n + 41$ yields primes for $n = 1, 2, 3, \ldots, 40$.

(a) Verify this for five specific cases.
(b) Prove or disprove that this formula yields a prime for all positive integers n.

12. ★*(a)* Prove that the empty set $\varnothing$ is inductive.
   (b) Use Theorem 2, together with the well-ordering principle for $\mathbf{N}$ (i.e., the axiom *every nonempty subset of $\mathbf{N}$ has a smallest element*), to prove that every nonempty inductive subset of $\mathbf{N}$ has the form $\{m, m + 1, m + 2, \ldots\}$ for some positive integer m.
   (c) Conclude from (b) that every inductive subset of $\mathbf{N}$ is either empty or infinite.

13. *(a)* Prove, by induction on n, that if A is a set with n elements ($n \in \mathbf{N}$), then $\mathcal{P}(A)$ has 2^n elements.
   (b) Assume that the sum of the interior angles of a a triangle is $180°$. Use this result to prove, by induction, that the sum of the interior angles of an n-sided convex polygon ($n \geq 3$) is $180°$ times $(n - 2)$.

14. Determine what is wrong with the following "proof" by induction of the "theorem": All sets in any collection of n sets are equal.

"Proof"   Let S be the set of those positive integers for which the result is true. Thus $m \in S$ if and only if all sets in any collection of m sets are equal. (1) Clearly $1 \in S$, since every set equals itself. (2) Assume $m \in S$. To prove $m + 1 \in S$, let $\{A_1, A_2, \ldots, A_{m+1}\}$ be a collection of $m + 1$ sets. We claim that $A_1 = A_2 = \cdots = A_{m+1}$. Now since $\{A_1, A_2, \ldots, A_m\}$ is a collection of m sets, then $A_1 = A_2 = \cdots = A_m$ by the induction hypothesis. For the same reason, $A_2 = A_3 = \cdots = A_m = A_{m+1}$. Hence we conclude $A_1 = A_2 = \cdots = A_m = A_{m+1}$, as desired.

15. This exercise contains a list of basic properties of summation notation and is included primarily as a reference. These properties are particularly relevant to the theoretical development of the definite integral and to series solutions of differential equations, as well as to proving the binomial theorem (Exercise 16). A feature of these formulas, not emphasized in the text's treatment of "summation," is the summing from an arbitrary starting point, rather than necessarily from $m = 1$. Let us assume the following as a definition: $(*)$ $\sum_{k=m}^{n} x_k = \sum_{k=1}^{n} x_k - \sum_{k=1}^{m-1} x_k$. Note that the special cases $m = 1$ of (c) and (e) were proved by induction on n in the text (Examples 5 and 6). <u>Assume</u> the truth of the case $m = 1$ in the remainder of the properties and use the preceding definition $(*)$ to prove (assuming $m, n \in \mathbf{N}$, $m < n$, $c \in \mathbf{R}$, all $x_k \in \mathbf{R}$):

(a) $\sum_{k=m}^{n} x_k = \left(\sum_{k=m}^{n-1} x_k\right) + x_n$ (b) $\sum_{k=m}^{n} x_k = x_m + \left(\sum_{k=m+1}^{n} x_k\right)$

(c) $\sum_{k=m}^{n} (x_k + y_k) = \sum_{k=m}^{n} x_k + \sum_{k=m}^{n} y_k$

(d) $\sum_{k=m}^{n} c = (n - m + 1)c$ (e) $\sum_{k=m}^{n} cx_k = c \sum_{k=m}^{n} x_k$

(f) $\sum_{k=m}^{n} x_k = \sum_{k=m+i}^{n+i} x_{k-i}$ (g) $\sum_{k=m}^{n} x_k = \sum_{k=m-i}^{n-i} x_{k+i}$

(h) $\sum_{k=m}^{n} x_k = \sum_{j=m}^{n} x_j$

16. *(a)* Use induction to prove the binomial theorem: If x and y are real numbers and n is a positive integer, then $(x + y)^n = \sum_{k=0}^{n} \binom{n}{k} x^{n-k} y^k$. [Recall the result from Exercise 15(f) and the formula $\binom{n+1}{k} = \binom{n}{k} + \binom{n}{k-1}$ from Exercise 7(a), Article 5.1.]

(b) Use specialization to conclude from the result in (a) that $2^n = \sum_{k=0}^{n} \binom{n}{k}$ (recall Exercise 11, Article 1.5).

17. Critique and complete (instructions in Exercise 11, Article 4.1).

(a) THEOREM For all positive integers n and for all real numbers x such that $\sin x \neq 0$ (i.e., x is not an integral multiple of π), $\sum_{k=1}^{n} \cos (2k - 1)x = (\sin 2nx)/2 \sin x$.

"Proof" Define S in the usual manner. To prove the theorem (i.e., to prove $S = \mathbf{N}$), we must verify (i) and (ii) of Theorem 1:

(i) The case $n = 1$ is the equation $\cos x = \sin 2x/2 \sin x$, which is true by the double-angle formula for sine.

(ii) Assume $m \in S$. To prove $m + 1 \in S$, we must show that

$$\sum_{k=1}^{m+1} \cos (2k - 1)x = (\sin 2(m + 1)x)/2 \sin x$$

Now $\sum_{k=1}^{m+1} \cos (2k - 1)x = \sum_{k=1}^{m} \cos (2k - 1)x + \cos (2m + 1)x$, which by induction hypothesis equals $[\sin 2mx/2 \sin x] + \cos (2m + 1)x$. But the latter quantity equals

$[\sin 2mx + 2 \sin x \cos (2m + 1)x]/2 \sin x$, which equals

$[\sin 2mx + 2 \sin x(\cos 2mx \cos x - \sin 2mx \sin x)]/2 \sin x$

Finally, we have

$[\sin 2mx + 2 \sin x(\cos 2mx \cos x - \sin 2mx \sin x)]/2 \sin x$

$= [\sin 2mx - 2 \sin^2 x \sin 2mx + 2 \sin x \cos x \cos 2mx]/2 \sin x$

$= [(1 - 2 \sin^2 x) \sin 2mx + (2 \sin x \cos x) \cos 2mx]/2 \sin x$

$= [\cos 2x \sin 2mx + \sin 2x \cos 2mx]/2 \sin x$

$= [\sin (2x + 2mx)]/2 \sin x$

$= \sin [2(m + 1)x]/2 \sin x,$ as desired

(b)   THEOREM   If $n \in \mathbf{N}$ and x is a positive real number then $x^{2n-1} > 0$.

"Proof"   Assume $x^{2n-1} > 0$. Since $x > 0$, then $x^{2n} = x(x^{2n-1}) > 0$, as desired.

(c)   THEOREM   If $n \in \mathbf{N}$, then $\sum_{k=1}^{n} r^{k-1} = (1 - r^n)/(1 - r), r \neq 1$.

Start of "Proof"   The theorem is clearly true for $n = 1$, since $r^0 = 1 = (1 - r)/(1 - r)$. To verify condition (ii), assume the theorem true for m. To show the theorem true for $m + 1$, we must prove that $\sum_{k=1}^{m} r^k = [(1 - r^m)/(1 - r)] + 1 \ldots$.

Methods of Mathematical Proof, Part II: Advanced Methods
CHAPTER 6

The question of what constitutes an *advanced*, as opposed to elementary, method of mathematical proof is largely subjective. In truth, the difficulty of a given proof depends more on the details of the particular theorem than on the logical structure of the conclusion of that theorem. Our criteria for inclusion under the "advanced" designation are based partly on experience with students' reaction to various kinds of proofs, and partly on the difficulty of the applications involved in illustrating these categories. On this basis, proofs involving existence, uniqueness, and various indirect methods are categorized in this text as advanced. Many of the exercises in this chapter are more difficult, and specialized, than those in Chapter 5; some may be appropriate primarily for those who have already had experience in junior-senior level courses.

6.1 Conclusions Involving ∀, Followed by ∃ (Epsilon-Delta Proofs Optional)

Many important definitions in mathematics involve the existential quantifier ∃. Such definitions are virtually nonexistent in precalculus mathematics and occur relatively infrequently in the standard calculus sequence. The best known of these is the epsilon-delta definition of limit, discussed earlier in Article 4.3. But in junior-senior level mathematics, definitions involving ∃ abound. As a consequence, many of the proofs that students at that level are asked to understand or write are of statements whose conclusion involves the universal quantifier ∀ followed by the existential quantifier ∃. Proofs of this type will be the object of our study in this article. Here are a few important definitions that involve the quantifier ∃.

EXAMPLE 1 (Elementary Algebra)   A real number x is said to be **rational** if and only if there exist integers p and q ($q \neq 0$) such that $x = p/q$.

EXAMPLE 2 (Elementary Number Theory)   Let m and n be integers. We say that **m divides n**, denoted $m|n$, if and only if there exists an integer r such that $n = mr$ (recall Exercise 7, Article 3.4 and Example 7, Article 5.4).

EXAMPLE 3 (Linear Algebra)   A square matrix $A_{n \times n}$ is said to be **invertible** if and only if there exists a matrix $B_{n \times n}$ such that $AB = BA = I_n$, where I_n is the $n \times n$ identity matrix, that is, $I_n = (\delta_{ij})_{n \times n}$, where $\delta_{ij} = \begin{cases} 1, & i = j \\ 0, & i \neq j \end{cases}$.

EXAMPLE 4 (Elementary Topology)   Let S be a subset of the real numbers $\mathbf{R}$. An element $x \in S$ is said to be an **interior point** of S if and only if there exists $\delta > 0$ such that $N(x; \delta) \subseteq S$, where $N(x; \delta)$ represents the open interval $(x - \delta, x + \delta)$ and is referred to as the δ neighborhood of x. Note that $N(x; \delta) = \{y \in \mathbf{R} \mid |x - y| < \delta\}$. S is said to be an **open** subset of $\mathbf{R}$ if and only if each of its points is an interior point.

EXAMPLE 5 (Advanced Calculus)   An infinite sequence $\{x_n\}$ of real numbers is said to **converge to the real number x**, denoted $x_n \to x$ or $\lim_{n \to \infty} x_n = x$, if and only if, to every positive real number ε, there corresponds a positive integer N such that $|x_n - x| < \varepsilon$ whenever $n \geq N$. In symbols, $x_n \to x \Leftrightarrow$

$$(\forall \varepsilon > 0)(\exists N \in \mathbf{N})(\forall n \in \mathbf{N})[(n \geq N) \to (|x_n - x| < \varepsilon)].$$

Before studying some proofs of statements whose conclusion involves the sequence (∀)(∃) of quantifiers, let us state some principles governing the approach to take to such proofs. Especially, let us review some facts involving *dependence* between quantified variables. In discussing the logical relationship between statements of the form $(\exists y)(\forall x)p(x, y)$ and $(\forall x)(\exists y)p(x, y)$ (the first of these is in general stronger than the second; recall Theorem 1, Article 3.4), we saw that the sequence $(\forall x)(\exists y)$ of quantified variables in the weaker statement signals a *possible dependence* of y on x, which, however, does not occur if the corresponding stronger statement $(\exists y)(\forall x)p(x, y)$ is also true. The student may do well to review Article 3.4, Exercises 6 and 7, and the remark immediately preceding Theorem 2. The next example deals with some general situations.

EXAMPLE 6   Let $q(x, y)$, $r(x, y, z)$, and $s(x, y, z)$ be propositional functions, where x, y, z come from a common domain of discourse U. Discuss the basic approach to a proof in each of the following cases, where P represents a set of hypotheses throughout.

(a)   Given P, prove $(\forall x)(\exists y)q(x, y)$
(b)   Given P, prove $(\forall x)(\forall y)(\exists z)r(x, y, z)$
(c)   Given P, prove $(\forall x)(\exists y)(\exists z)r(x, y, z)$
(d)   Given P, prove $(\forall x)(\exists y)(\forall z)[r(x, y, z) \rightarrow s(x, y, z)]$

Discussion   (a)   As we did repeatedly in Chapter 5, we note here that, in setting up a proof, we should focus on the desired conclusion, with the hypotheses brought into play only as the proof progresses. In the first case, the proof should begin "let $x \in U$ be given" or "let x be an arbitrary element of U," or simply "let $x \in U$." Now what must we prove? We must prove that there exists a corresponding $y \in U$ such that $q(x, y)$ is true; in essence, we must produce a y that, in combination with the given x, makes the predicate $q(x, y)$ into a true statement. The key in every such proof (and here is generally where the hypotheses P are used) is to determine the relationship between y and x, or more accurately, the dependence of y on x. Proceed in such a proof with the expectation that the y you are looking for (which may or may not be unique—we will pursue that issue in Article 6.3) will be defined in terms of x, or possibly defined in terms of some other quantity that is defined in terms of x. Specific examples will soon follow, starting with Example 7. After y is selected, the proof concludes with the (sometimes anticlimactic) verification that $q(x, y)$ is true for the arbitrary x and this corresponding y.

(b)   Start the proof with the statement "let $x \in U$ and $y \in U$ be given. We must produce $z \in U$ such that $r(x, y, z)$ is true." In general, it must be expected that z will depend on both x and y, and that the key to the choice of z will lie somewhere among the hypotheses P. After z, which often will be an expression involving x and y explicitly, is selected, the proof is completed by verifying $r(x, y, z)$.

(c)   Start with "let $x \in U$ be given. We must produce $y \in U$ and $z \in U$ such that $r(x, y, z)$ is true." In this case the burden of proof is to produce two quantities, each of which should be expected to depend on the given x. The key to the choice of y and z must again be contained in the hypotheses P.

(d)   This is by far the most complicated case, arising in undergraduate mathematics almost exclusively in connection with various limit concepts. Such a proof should begin "let $x \in U$ be given. We must produce $y \in U$ (with y expected to depend on x and perhaps to be defined in terms of x) having the property that, for any $z \in U$, if $r(x, y, z)$ is true, then $s(x, y, z)$ is true." Especially critical in this type of proof is the choice of y. Once y has been designated, the proof concludes (not quite so anticlimactically as in parts (a)(b)(c)) by letting z be an arbitrarily chosen element of U and <u>assuming</u> that $r(x, y, z)$ is true. The final step is to conclude from this assumption, and perhaps the hypotheses P, that $s(x, y, z)$ is true as well. □

The descriptions in Example 6 may seem vacuous and, indeed, may overly abstract at this point, but we predict that you will be drawn back to this example after studying some actual proofs of this type and especially in the course of attempting the exercises at the end of the article.
We now begin to consider some specific proofs.

EXAMPLE 7 Prove that if m, n, and p are integers such that $m|n$ and $m|p$, then $m|(n + p)$.

Solution Let m, n, and p be integers satisfying the given hypotheses. According to the definition of "divides," we must produce an integer q such that $n + p = mq$. The key to the choice of q lies in the hypotheses. Since $m|n$, we know that there exists an integer q_1 such that $n = mq_1$. Since $m|p$, there must exist an integer q_2 such that $p = mq_2$. Let us look now at the situation. How are we to arrive at the desired q that will relate $n + p$ to q? If we note that $n + p = mq_1 + mq_2$ which in turn equals $m(q_1 + q_2)$, our choice is clear. Resuming the proof now, we make the assertion "let $q = q_1 + q_2$." Note first that since q_1 and q_2 are integers, then $q_1 + q_2$ is an integer. Second, note that we have $mq = m(q_1 + q_2) = mq_1 + mq_2 = n + p$, as desired. □

Here are a few observations regarding the proof in Example 7. You may object that, according to Example 6, we were to expect q to be defined in terms of m, n, and p. Instead, q turned out to be defined in terms of q_1 and q_2. Is there any conflict here? No, because q_1 depended on n and m, while q_2 depended on p and m, so that q ultimately <u>did depend</u> on m, n, and p, as expected. Second, you should note and avoid a common error in a proof such as this. In writing out what is known at the start of the proof, it is easy, but mistaken, to write "since $m|n$ and $m|p$, then there exists an integer q such that $n = mq$ and $p = mq$." There is nothing in the hypotheses to indicate that <u>the same</u> q works for both of the pairs m, n, and m, p. Accordingly, the proof must be set up with two different symbols q_1 and q_2 being employed in the two applications of the definition of divides. Finally, we rewrite the proof in a "final" form: "Assume m, n, and p are integers such that $m|n$ and $m|p$. We must find an integer q such that $n + p = mq$. Since $m|n$ and $m|p$, there exist integers q_1 and q_2 such that $n = mq_1$ and $p = mq_2$. Let $q = q_1 + q_2$. Clearly q is an integer and $mq = m(q_1 + q_2) = mq_1 + mq_2 = n + p$, as desired."

EXAMPLE 8 Let A and B be invertible $n \times n$ matrices. Prove that their product AB is again invertible.

Solution   Let A and B be given invertible $n \times n$ matrices. We must find a matrix $X_{n \times n}$ such that $(AB)X = X(AB) = I_n$. Now since A is invertible, there exists an $n \times n$ matrix C such that $AC = CA = I_n$. Since B is invertible, there corresponds an $n \times n$ matrix D such that $BD = DB = I_n$. We get the desired X from C and D, namely, by letting $X = DC$. Note that $(AB)X = (AB)(DC) = A(BD)C = A(I_n)C = AC = I_n$. Verify that $X(AB) = I_n$. □

Obviously, the key to the preceding proof, once the setting-up is completed, is the choice $X = DC$ of X in terms of D and C. If you had never seen this proof before, how might you have discovered that $X = DC$ was the proper choice? Back in Chapter 1 we emphasized two main methods of discovery that mathematicians use and that are worth recalling here. One was drawing a picture (a method we will use in the next example); the other was carrying out computations in specific examples. Assuming that you have some computational familiarity with matrices, you might look at a particular pair of invertible matrices, say $A = \begin{pmatrix} 2 & 3 \\ 1 & 4 \end{pmatrix}$ and $B = \begin{pmatrix} -1 & 1 \\ 0 & 2 \end{pmatrix}$. Computations yield

$$AB = \begin{pmatrix} -2 & 8 \\ -1 & 9 \end{pmatrix}, \qquad C = \begin{pmatrix} \frac{4}{5} & -\frac{3}{5} \\ -\frac{1}{5} & \frac{2}{5} \end{pmatrix},$$

$$D = \begin{pmatrix} -1 & \frac{1}{2} \\ 0 & \frac{1}{2} \end{pmatrix}, \quad \text{and} \quad X = \begin{pmatrix} -\frac{9}{10} & \frac{4}{5} \\ -\frac{1}{10} & \frac{1}{5} \end{pmatrix}.$$

After some experimentation, you might finally notice the relationship $X = DC$, and this observation should lead to the speculation that the choice $X = DC$ of X will work in general.

In the next example we use geometric motivation for our selection of the existentially quantified unknown, as we apply definitions from Example 4.

EXAMPLE 9   Suppose S and T are both open subsets of **R**. Prove that $S \cap T$ and $S \cup T$ are both open.

Solution   We deal first with intersection. Let S and T be arbitrary open subsets of **R**. According to the definition of "open," in order to prove that $S \cap T$ is open, we must show that each point of $S \cap T$ is an interior point. So begin by letting x be an arbitrary point in $S \cap T$. (*Note:* We are using here, almost unconsciously, proof-writing techniques over which we labored hard in Article 5.2. In particular, we are setting up our proof in terms of the desired conclusion, not the hypotheses.) To prove that x is an interior point of $S \cap T$, we must produce a positive real number δ such that the δ neighborhood $N(x; \delta)$ of x is a subset of

$S \cap T$. The key is the choice of δ; we can go no further in the proof until we've decided what δ should be.

Now what do our hypotheses tell us? Since S is open and $x \in S$, then x is an interior point of S. (Note the implicit use of "specialization." Every point of S is an interior point of S; hence our particular point x must be an interior point.) Similarly, x is an interior point of T. Using the definition of "interior point" twice, we see that there exist positive real numbers δ_1 and δ_2 such that $N(x; \delta_1) \subseteq S$ and $N(x; \delta_2) \subseteq T$. Examples 7 and 8 may have conditioned you to expect that we will define the desired δ in terms of δ_1 and δ_2. (Perhaps we should say that if you have already made a mental note that we will doubtless define δ in terms of δ_1 and δ_2, then you're making good progress.) But the question is, "How to do it?" Let us draw some pictures, such as those shown in Figure 6.1.

Figure 6.1*b* illustrates the two values of δ_1 and δ_2. Any point within δ_1 of x is inside S; any point within δ_2 of x is inside T. We want to choose δ small enough (but still positive) so that any point within δ of x will be inside both S and T. Finally, then, how will we choose δ? Why not let δ be the smaller of δ_1 and δ_2? In symbols $\delta = \min \{\delta_1, \delta_2\}$! This choice seems reasonable; if it is correct, we ought to be able to complete the proof by showing $N(x; \delta) \subseteq S \cap T$. To do this, in turn, we recall the choose method and let $y \in N(x; \delta)$. We claim that $y \in S \cap T$. Now $|x - y| < \delta \le \delta_1$ so that $y \in N(x; \delta_1) \subseteq S$ so $y \in S$. Also, $|x - y| < \delta \le \delta_2$ so that $y \in N(x; \delta_2) \subseteq T$. Hence $y \in S \cap T$ so that $N(x; \delta) \subseteq S \cap T$, and our proof is complete.

Figure 6.1 *A picture suggests how to complete the proof that the intersection of two open sets is open. (a) A picture of a two-dimensional version of the situation described in Example 9. (b) In this case, we take $\delta = \delta_2$, since $\delta_2 < \delta_1$.*

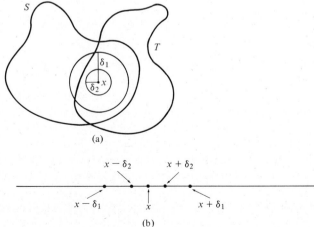

(a)

(b)

We deal next with union. To prove $S \cup T$ is open, let $x \in S \cup T$. To prove that x is an interior point of $S \cup T$, we must produce $\delta > 0$ such that $N(x; \delta) \subseteq S \cup T$. Since x is either in S or T (but we don't know which one), and since our hypotheses deal with properties of S and T individually, this proof is clearly a candidate for division into cases. Our strategy is to divide the proof into the two cases $x \in S$ and $x \in T$, and see whether, in each case, we can arrive at the desired conclusion. Now if $x \in S$, then since S is open, there exists a positive δ_1 such that $N(x; \delta_1) \subseteq S$. But since $S \subseteq S \cup T$, we may let $\delta = \delta_1$ for this case, noting that $N(x; \delta) = N(x; \delta_1) \subseteq S \subseteq S \cup T$, so that x is, indeed, an interior point of $S \cup T$. Similarly, if $x \in T$, then $\exists \delta_2 > 0$ such that $N(x; \delta_2) \subseteq T$. Letting $\delta = \delta_2$, we conclude again in this case that $N(x; \delta) = N(x; \delta_2) \subseteq T \subseteq S \cup T$, as desired.   □

The theorem that union and intersection of two open sets is open is generally taught in a course in advanced calculus and/or elementary topology. If you have not already seen these proofs, then it is worth noting that their complexity is fairly representative of many proofs in courses at that level. Two final remarks: (1) You should realize now that techniques that were stressed individually in Chapters 4 and 5 (e.g., cases, specialization, choose) are beginning to be used, several at a time, in individual proofs. (2) You should know that examples such as 7, 8, and 9 illustrate that an important aspect of proof writing is the careful interpretation of definitions.

EPSILON-DELTA PROOFS

Let us now turn to the problem of writing epsilon-delta proofs that $L = \lim_{x \to a} f(x)$. Such proofs may arise in connection with specific functions, as in $25 = \lim_{x \to 5} x^2$ or $Ma + B = \lim_{x \to a} (Mx + B)$, or may be required for the purpose of establishing a more general theorem, such as "if $\lim_{x \to a} f(x) = L_1$ and $\lim_{x \to a} g(x) = L_2$, then $\lim_{x \to a} (f(x) + g(x)) = L_1 + L_2$."

A typical epsilon-delta proof is structured as follows. Begin by letting $\varepsilon > 0$ be given. The crux of the proof is to define, in terms of this ε, a $\delta > 0$ having the property that, whenever x is a real number satisfying the inequalities $0 < |x - a| < \delta$ (i.e., x is within δ of a, but $x \neq a$), then its corresponding $f(x)$ satisfies $|f(x) - L| < \varepsilon$ [i.e., $f(x)$ is within ε of L]. The problem, inevitably, is how to choose δ. The key for many specific functions is to look for a relationship between the quantities $|x - a|$ and $|f(x) - L|$. Note, in particular, that if a positive constant k can be found such that $|f(x) - L| \leq k|x - a|$ for all x within some neighborhood $N(a; \delta_1)$ of a (with the possible exception of $x = a$ itself), then $\delta = \min\{\delta_1, \varepsilon/k\}$ will do the job. For if $0 < |x - a| < \delta$, then $0 < |x - a| < \delta_1$ and so $|f(x) - L| \leq k|x - a| \leq (\varepsilon/\delta)(|x - a|) < (\varepsilon/\delta)(\delta) = \varepsilon$, as desired. Let us look now at some examples.

EXAMPLE 10   Prove that $\lim_{x \to 3} (4x + 7) = 19$.

Solution   Note that $f(x) = 4x + 7$, $a = 3$, $L = 19$ in this problem. Let $\varepsilon > 0$ be given. We must produce $\delta > 0$ such that whenever $0 < |x - 3| < \delta$, then $|f(x) - L| = |4x + 7 - 19| = |4x - 12| < \varepsilon$. Let us look for a relationship between $|x - a|$ and $|f(x) - L|$; in this case it's easy to spot since $|4x - 12| = 4|x - 3|$ for every real number x. Hence we simply let $\delta = \varepsilon/4$. Note that if $0 < |x - 3| < \delta$, then $|f(x) - 19| = |4x - 12| = 4|x - 3| < 4\delta = 4(\varepsilon/4) = \varepsilon$, as desired.   □

Note that if $f(x)$ is a linear function $y = Mx + B$, we can always use $|M|$ as the positive constant k satisfying $|f(x) - L| \le k|x - a|$. (Verify this.) Furthermore, this inequality is valid <u>for all real</u> x so that we do not need to deal with the neighborhood $N(x; \delta_1)$ referred to prior to Example 10. Hence the choice of δ in terms of ε in any epsilon-delta proof involving a linear function is particularly simple: Just take delta to be epsilon divided by the absolute value of the slope!

EXAMPLE 11   Prove that $\lim_{x \to 5} x^3 = 125$.

Solution   Let $\varepsilon > 0$ be given. Our goal is to produce $\delta > 0$ such that whenever x satisfies $0 < |x - 5| < \delta$, then $f(x)$ satisfies $|f(x) - 125| < \varepsilon$; that is, $|x^3 - 125| = |x - 5||x^2 + 5x + 25| < \varepsilon$. Now your first impulse, based on the solution to Example 10, might be to assert that δ can be taken to equal $\varepsilon/|x^2 + 5x + 25|$. The problem with this suggestion is subtle, but crucial. The definition of limit contains the sequence of quantifiers $(\forall \varepsilon > 0)(\exists \delta > 0)(\forall x)$, not $(\forall \varepsilon > 0)(\forall x)(\exists \delta > 0)$. That is, the δ we are charged to find may depend on ε only, not on ε and x! Hence we must take the approach outlined before Example 10. Namely, we must ask whether there is some neighborhood $N(5; \delta_1)$ of 5 and a positive constant M such that $|x^2 + 5x + 25| \le M$ whenever $0 < |x - 5| < \delta_1$. Let us try $\delta_1 = 1$; that is, suppose that $0 < |x - 5| \le 1$. Then $-1 \le x - 5 \le 1$ and $x = 5 \ne 0$, so that $4 \le x \le 6$ and $x \ne 5$. Since $x \le 6$, then we may conclude $|x^2 + 5x + 25| \le 36 + 30 + 25 = 91$. That is, $|x^2 + 5x + 25| \le 91$. Thus our choice of δ is dictated by the rule given just prior to Example 10, with $\delta_1 = 1$ and $k = 91$; let $\delta = \min\{1, \varepsilon/91\}$. Then if $0 < |x - 5| < \delta$, we have both $0 < |x - 5| < 1$ so that $|x^2 + 5x + 25| \le 91$, and $0 < |x - 5| < \varepsilon/91$. Hence

$$|f(x) - 125| = |x^3 - 125|$$
$$= |x - 5||x^2 + 5x + 25| \le 91|x - 5| < 91(\varepsilon/91) = \varepsilon. \quad □$$

A final version of this proof begins: "Let $\varepsilon > 0$. We must find $\delta > 0$ such that if $0 < |x - 5| < \delta$, then $|x^3 - 125| < \varepsilon$. If $0 < |x - 5| < 1$, then $|x^2 + 5x + 25| \le 91$. Let $\delta = \min\{1, \varepsilon/91\} \ldots$"

In most theorems about general properties of limits the hypotheses include a statement about the existence and value of one or more limits. In such cases the epsilon-delta proof of a conclusion about limits will often use in a crucial way the technique of specialization, introduced in Article 5.3.

EXAMPLE 12   Assume that $\lim_{x \to a} f(x) = L_1$ and $\lim_{x \to a} g(x) = L_2$. Prove that $\lim_{x \to a} (f + g)(x) = L_1 + L_2$.

Solution   Let $\varepsilon > 0$ be given; we fix this ε here at the outset and note that we work <u>with it</u> throughout the remainder of the proof. We must produce $\delta > 0$ such that whenever x is a real number satisfying $0 < |x - a| < \delta$, then $(f + g)(x)$ satisfies $|(f + g)(x) - (L_1 + L_2)| < \varepsilon$. Now our hypotheses will tell us something about the quantities $|f(x) - L_1|$ and $|g(x) - L_2|$, and we note for future reference that the quantity we wish to make less than ε can be related to these two quantities by the inequality

$$|(f + g)(x) - (L_1 + L_2)| = |(f(x) - L_1) + (g(x) - L_2)|$$
$$\leq |f(x) - L_1| + |g(x) - L_2| \tag{1}$$

Now precisely how can we make use of our hypotheses? Since $\lim_{x \to a} f(x) = L_1$, then corresponding to any positive real number, and in particular to our given ε, divided by 2, there is a positive δ_1 having the property that whenever $0 < |x - a| < \delta_1$, then $|f(x) - L_1| < \varepsilon/2$. Similarly, there exists $\delta_2 > 0$ such that whenever $0 < |x - a| < \delta_2$, then $|g(x) - L_2| < \varepsilon/2$. Now if we can choose δ so small as to make both these inequalities concerning f and g true at the same time, we will be very close to our final goal, due to expression (1). How shall we choose δ? Recalling the argument in the first part of Example 9, we let $\delta = \min \{\delta_1, \delta_2\}$. Then if x satisfies $0 < |x - a| < \delta$, it will automatically satisfy both $0 < |x - a| < \delta_1$ and $0 < |x - a| < \delta_2$, so that

$$|(f + g)(x) - (L_1 + L_2)| = |(f(x) - L_1) + (g(x) - L_2)|$$
$$\leq |f(x) - L_1| + |g(x) - L_2|$$
$$< \varepsilon/2 + \varepsilon/2 = \varepsilon, \text{ as desired.} \quad \square$$

Note the role of specialization in the preceding proof. We have set up the proof that $(f + g)(x)$ tends to $L_1 + L_2$, as x tends to a, by fixing a value of ε at the outset. Our two hypotheses, involving f and g separately, indicate that something works for any positive real number, and so we can conclude that this something works for the <u>particular</u> positive number $\varepsilon/2$. Proofs of other limit theorems (e.g., Exercises 15, 18) call for similar applications of the specialization technique.

Students often ask why $\varepsilon/2$ is used in this proof and how they can ever be expected to think of such a "trick" in writing their own proofs. The first question can be answered on two levels. We use $\varepsilon/2$ (1) because there is no reason we shouldn't (we violate no rules in doing so) and (2) because it works! The best answer we can give to the second question is that most students have considerable difficulty in writing epsilon-delta proofs (largely because of deficiencies in logical background and lack of experience in writing <u>any kind</u> of proof—the very weaknesses you may be eliminating as you work through this text) and only begin to overcome that difficulty with much effort and experience. Although all the information needed to write proofs such as those in Exercises 12 through 19 has been provided in this article, do not be surprised or discouraged if you have difficulty in your early attempts. Finally, even after you have mastered these proofs, through a process of studying a number of similar proofs written by others and your own maturing in mathematics, keep in mind that a still higher level to attain is the ability to discover, on your own, original proof techniques (such as the use of $\varepsilon/2$) and perhaps, at some stage, prove theorems previously unproved and solve mathematical problems previously unsolved. This pursuit is the goal of mathematical study at the graduate level; an undergraduate student who is able to do many of the following exercises, shows promise of possible success at that level.

Exercises

1. Use the definition in Example 1 and the ordinary rules for addition and multiplication of fractions, together with the fact that $\mathbf{Z}$ is closed under addition and multiplication, to prove

(a)   If x and y are rational, then xy is rational
(b)   If x and y are rational, then $x + y$ is rational
(c)   If x and y are rational and $y \neq 0$, then x/y is rational

2. Use the definition in Example 2 to prove that, for any $m, n, p \in \mathbf{Z}$

(a)   If $m \mid n$ and $n \mid p$, then $m \mid p$
(b)   If $m \mid n$ and $n \mid m$, then $n = m$ or $n = -m$
(c) $m \mid m$ *(d)* $1 \mid n$
(e) $m \mid 0$ *(f)*   If $m \mid n$ and $m \mid p$, then $m \mid np$
(g)   If $m \mid n$, then $m \mid (-n)$
(h)   Based on your proof in (f), can you improve upon the result in (f), that is, state and prove a stronger theorem (due to a weaker hypothesis) than the one in (f)? (*Note:* Reread the fourth and fifth paragraphs under the heading "Mathematical Significance of Tautologies Involving the Conditional," following Theorem 2, Article 2.3. Recall also Exercise 7, Article 2.3.)

3. *(a)*   Prove that if $U = \mathbf{Z}$, then:

   (i) $(\forall m)(\exists n)(m \mid n)$
   (ii) $(\exists n)(\forall m)(m \mid n)$
   (iii) $(\forall n)(\exists m)(m \mid n)$
   (iv) $(\exists m)(\forall n)(m \mid n)$ [recall Exercise 7(b), Article 3.4]

(b) An integer n is said to be **even** if and only if there exists an integer m (necessarily unique) such that $n = 2m$, and **odd** if and only if $n = 2m + 1$ for some integer m (where m again is uniquely determined by n). Assume that every integer is either even or odd, and not both even and odd.

★(i)   What tautology of the propositional calculus would enable us to conclude, from the preceding assumption, that an integer m is even if and only if it is not odd? Formulate and verify, by using a truth table, such a tautology.

(ii)   Prove that if n is even, then $n + 1$ is odd, $n + 2$ is even, and $n + 3$ is odd.

(iii)   Prove that if m is even, then m^2 is even.

(iv)   Prove that if m is odd, then m^2 is odd.

4. Recall from Definition 7, ff., Article 1.2, that an object x is in the cartesian product $A \times B$ of two sets A and B, if and only if there exist elements $a \in A$ and $b \in B$ such that $x = (a, b)$. Prove that, if W, X, Y, and Z are arbitrary sets, then:

★(a) $(X \cup Y) \times Z = (X \times Z) \cup (Y \times Z)$

(b) $(X \cap Y) \times Z = (X \times Z) \cap (Y \times Z)$

(c) $(X - Y) \times Z \subseteq (X \times Z) - (Y \times Z)$

(d)   if $W \subseteq X$ and $Y \subseteq Z$, then $W \times Y \subseteq X \times Z$.

[*Note:* The reverse inclusion in (c) is true as well. See Exercise 1(e), Article 6.2.]

5. [Continuation of Exercise 7(a), Article 5.2] Let $C_1 = \{(\cos t, \sin t) | t \in \mathbf{R}\}$ and $C_2 = \{(x, y) \in \mathbf{R} \times \mathbf{R} | x^2 + y^2 = 1\}$. Recall that $(x, y) \in C_1$ if and only if $\exists t \in \mathbf{R}$ such that $x = \cos t$ and $y = \sin t$.

(a)   Prove that $C_2 \subseteq C_1$. [*Hint:* Given $(x, y) \in C_2$, let $t = \sin^{-1} y$. Clearly $y = \sin t$. Use identities from Exercise 18, Article 5.1, to prove that $x = \cos t$.]

(b)   Prove that C_1 is symmetric with respect to the x-axis and the origin. Use these results and Example 1, Article 5.3, to conclude that C_1 is symmetric with respect to the y axis.

6. (Continuation of Exercise 9, Article 5.2) (a)   Suppose x, y, and z are real numbers with $x < z < y$. Prove that there exists a real number t, $0 < t < 1$, such that $z = tx + (1 - t)y$. (*Hint:* On what quantities would you expect the desired t to depend?)

★(b)   Prove that if S is a convex subset of $\mathbf{R}$, then S is an interval. (*Note:* Combining this result with Exercise 9, Article 5.2, we conclude that a subset S of $\mathbf{R}$ is convex if and only if it is an interval.)

7. (a)   Assume that the inverse of an $n \times n$ matrix, if it exists, is unique [to be proved in Article 6.3, Exercise 5(a)]. Prove that if A, B, and C are invertible $n \times n$ matrices, then:

(i) A^{-1} is invertible.

(ii) ABC is invertible.

(iii)   The matrix cA is invertible, where c is a nonzero real number.

(iv)   If $AD = AF$, where D and F are arbitrary $n \times n$ matrices, possibly noninvertible, then $D = F$. (*Hint:* Write a proof by transitivity.)

(b)   Prove that if A is any square matrix, then A can be expressed in the form $A = B + C$, where B is a symmetric matrix and C is antisymmetric [recall Exercise 17(f), Article 5.1].

8. *(a)* Prove that $\frac{1}{2}$ is an interior point of $[0, 1]$.

(b) Prove that 1 is not an interior point of $[0, 1]$.

(c) Prove that the set **N** of all positive integers has no interior points. Is **N** open in **R**.

(d) Prove that any interval of the form (a, b), where $a \neq b$, is an open subset of **R**.

(e) Prove that **R** is an open subset of itself.

(f) Prove that if S_1, S_2, and S_3 are open subsets of **R**, then both $S_1 \cap S_2 \cap S_3$ and $S_1 \cup S_2 \cup S_3$ are open subsets of **R**.

(g) Use an induction argument to prove that the union and intersection of any finite collection of open subsets of **R** is an open subset of **R**.

(h) Generalize one of the arguments in Example 9 to show that if $\{S_i | i = 1, 2, 3, \ldots\}$ is a family of open subsets of **R**, indexed by **N**, then $\bigcup_{i=1}^{\infty} S_i$ is open in **R**. Does the other argument in Example 9 generalize to such an infinite collection, that is, can we conclude that $\bigcap_{i=1}^{\infty} S_i$ is necessarily open in **R**?

9. Let S be a subset of **R**. A real number a, which may or may not lie in S, is said to be a *point of accumulation of S* if and only if every neighborhood $N(a; \delta)$ of a contains points of S other than a itself. This definition may be represented $(\forall \delta > 0)(N'(a; \delta) \cap S \neq \varnothing)$, where $N'(a; \delta) = N(a; \delta) - \{a\}$ is called the *deleted δ neighborhood* of a. S is said to be a *closed* subset of **R** if and only if S contains all its points of accumulation.

(a) Prove that 1 is a point of accumulation of $(0, 1)$. (Thus a point of accumulation of a set need not lie in the set.)

★*(b)* Write the logical negation of the definition of point of accumulation and use it to prove that 2 <u>is not</u> a point of accumulation of $(0, 1) \cup \{2\}$. (Thus a point in a set need not be a point of accumulation of that set.)

(c) Prove that, for any $\mu > 0$, $-\mu$ is not a point of accumulation of $[0, 1]$.

(d) Prove that 0 is a point of accumulation of the set $S = \{1, \frac{1}{2}, \frac{1}{3}, \ldots\}$. Is this set closed? (*Note:* You may assume the Archimedean property, introduced following Example 2, Article 4.2.)

(e) Prove that the set $\mathbf{N} = \{1, 2, 3, \ldots\}$ of all positive integers has no accumulation points. Is this set closed in **R**?

(f) Prove that any interval of the form $[a, b]$, where $a \neq b$, is closed in **R**.

(g) Prove that **R** is a closed subset of itself.

10. (Continuation of Exercises 8 and 9) *(a)* Give an example of a subset of **R** that is neither open nor closed.

(b) Give an example of a subset of **R** that is both open and closed.

(c) Prove that if a subset S of **R** is closed in **R**, then its complement S' is open in **R**. (The converse is true as well; it will be considered in Exercise 11(a), Article 6.2.)

11. Throughout our discussion of limit in Article 4.3, whenever we considered $\lim_{x \to a} f(x)$, we assumed f to be a function defined in an open interval containing a. In the terminology of Exercise 9 this assumption implies that a is a point of accumulation of the domain of f. Prove that if a is not a point of accumulation of the domain of f [recall Exercise 9(b)], then $L = \lim_{x \to a} f(x)$ is true <u>for any value</u> of L (thus rendering the definition of limit worthless in that circumstance).

12. Use an epsilon-delta argument to prove:

(a) $\lim_{x \to 4} (-3x + 6) = -6$

(b) $\lim_{x \to 9} x^2 + 5 = 86$

(c) $\lim_{x \to 1} 2x^2 + 3x + 1 = 6$

13. Use an epsilon-delta argument to prove:

(a) $\lim_{x \to 3} f(x) = 11$,   where $f(x) = \begin{cases} 2x + 5, & x \neq 3 \\ 2, & x = 3 \end{cases}$

★(b) $\lim_{x \to 0} g(x) = 0$,   where $g(x) = \begin{cases} x, & x \text{ rational} \\ 0, & x \text{ irrational} \end{cases}$

(c) $\lim_{x \to 0^+} x \sin(1/x) = 0$.   [*Note:* $|\sin 1/x| \leq 1$ for all $x > 0$, so that $|x \sin 1/x| \leq |x|$ for all positive real numbers x (recall Exercise 5, Article 4.3).]

14. Use an epsilon-delta argument to prove:

(a)   If $f(x) = K$ is a constant function defined on IR, then $\lim_{x \to a} f(x) = k$, for any $a \in IR$.

(b)   If $\lim_{x \to a} f(x) = L$ and K is any real number, then $\lim_{x \to a} (kf(x)) = kL$.

15. Use an argument similar to the proof in Example 12 and the definitions in Exercises 4 and 8 of Article 4.3, to prove:

(a)   If $\lim_{x \to a^+} f(x) = L_1'$ and $\lim_{x \to a^+} g(x) = L_2$, then $\lim_{x \to a^+} (f + g)(x) = L_1 + L_2$.

(b)   If $\lim_{x \to \infty} f(x) = L_1$ and $\lim_{x \to \infty} g(x) = L_2$, then $\lim_{x \to \infty} (f + g)(x) = L_1 + L_2$.

16. (a)   Prove that if $\lim_{x \to a} f(x) = L$ where $L > 0$, then there exists $\delta > 0$ such that $f(x) > 0$ for all $x \in N'(a; \delta)$. [Recall from Exercise 9 that $N'(a; \delta) = N(a; \delta) - \{a\}$.]

(b)   Conclude from (a) that if f is continuous at a and $f(a) > 0$, then there exists $\delta > 0$ such that $f(x) > 0$ for all $x \in (a - \delta, a + \delta)$.

(c)   Let f be continuous on an open interval $a < x < b$ containing the real number x_0 and suppose $f'(x_0) > 0$. Prove that there exists a neighborhood $N(x_0; \delta)$ of x_0 such that if $x \in N(x_0; \delta)$ and $x < x_0$, then $f(x) < f(x_0)$, while if $x \in N(x_0; \delta)$ and $x > x_0$, then $f(x) > f(x_0)$. [*Hint:* Apply the epsilon-delta definition of limit with $\varepsilon = f'(x_0)/2$, using the fact that $f'(x_0) = \lim_{x + x_0} (f(x) - f(x_0))/(x - x_0)$.]

17. (a)   (Sandwich or Pinching Theorem) Suppose that three functions f, g, and h are all defined in some neighborhood $N(a; r)$ of a point a, and that $f(x) \leq g(x) \leq h(x)$ for all values of x in this neighborhood, with the possible exception of a itself. Suppose furthermore that $\lim_{x \to a} f(x) = \lim_{x \to a} h(x) = L$. Prove, by using an epsilon-delta argument, that $\lim_{x \to a} g(x) = L$.

(b)   Use (a) to prove that $\lim_{x \to 0} x \sin(1/x) = 0$.

(c)   Suppose f is a bounded function (i.e., there exists $M > 0$ such that $|f(x)| \leq M$ for all $x \in \mathbf{R}$) and g is a function satisfying $\lim_{x \to a} g(x) = 0$. Prove that $\lim_{x \to a} f(x)g(x) = 0$.

18. Prove that if $\lim_{x \to a} f(x) = L_1$ and $\lim_{x \to a} g(x) = L_2$, then $\lim_{x \to a} (fg)(x) = L_1 L_2$. (*Hint:* Note that $|(fg)(x) - L_1 L_2| \leq |g(x)||f(x) - L_1| + |L_1||g(x) - L_2|$, and that by using the fact that $\lim_{x \to a} g(x) = L_2$ with $\varepsilon = 1$, we can conclude that $|g(x)| < |L_2| + 1$ for all x within some deleted δ neighborhood of a.)

19. Prove that $\lim_{x \to a} f(x)$ exists if and only if both $\lim_{x \to a^+} f(x)$ and $\lim_{x \to a^-} f(x)$ exist and are equal.

20. (Some prior familiarity with infinite sequences beneficial in Exercises 20, 21, and 22) A real number x is said to be a *limit of a sequence* $\{x_n\}$, denoted $x = \lim_{n \to \infty} x_n$ or simply $x_n \to x$ (we also say that the sequence x_n *converges* to x) if and only if $\forall \varepsilon > 0$, $\exists$ a positive integer N such that $|x_n - x| < \varepsilon$ whenever $n \ge N$. This means that any ε neighborhood of x, no matter how narrow, must contain all but a finite number (namely, some or all of the first N, where N depends on ε) of the terms in the sequence. The Archimedean property of the real numbers, which we assume, says in essence that the sequence $1/n$ converges to 0; that is, $\lim_{n \to \infty} 1/n = 0$ (recall Example 2 ff., Article 4.2).

(a) Write the logical negation of the definition of sequential convergence; that is, What is true if $x \ne \lim_{n \to \infty} x_n$?

(b) Prove that $0 \ne \lim_{n \to \infty} x_n$, where $x_n = \begin{cases} 1/n, & n \text{ even} \\ 1, & n \text{ odd} \end{cases}$.

(c) Prove that $0 = \lim_{n \to \infty} x_n$, where $x_n = \begin{cases} 1/n, & n > 10{,}000 \\ 1, & 1 \le n \le 10{,}000 \end{cases}$.

(d) Prove that, if $x_n \to x$ and k is a real number, then $kx_n \to kx$.

(e) Prove that $0 = \lim_{n \to \infty} x_n$, where $x_n = \begin{cases} 1/n, & n \text{ even} \\ -1/n, & n \text{ odd} \end{cases}$.

(f) Prove that if $x_n \to x$ and $y_n \to y$, then $x_n + y_n \to x + y$ [recall Exercise 15(b)].

21. (Continuation of 20) A real number x is said to be a *cluster point of a sequence* $\{x_n\}$, if and only if, for all $\varepsilon > 0$ and for all positive integers N, there exists $n \ge N$ such that $|x_n - x| < \varepsilon$. This means that any ε neighborhood of x, no matter how narrow, must contain infinitely many terms of the sequence.

(a) Write the logical negation of the definition of cluster point.
(b) Show that 1 is not a cluster point of the sequence $\{x_n\}$ defined by $x_n = 1/n$.
(c) Show that $+1$ and -1 are both cluster points of the sequence $\{x_n\}$ defined by $x_n = (-1)^n$. Thus cluster points of a sequence are not necessarily unique. (We will see in Article 6.3 that a limit of a sequence, if it exists, is unique.)
(d) Prove that if $\lim_{n \to \infty} x_n = x$, then x is a cluster point of $\{x_n\}$. What does this say about the relative strength of the properties "x is a cluster point of $\{x_n\}$" and "x is a limit of $\{x_n\}$"?
(e) Prove that 2 is a cluster point of the sequence $\{x_n\}$ defined by

$$x_n = \begin{cases} n, & n \ne 5k \text{ for any positive integer } k \\ 2, & n = 5k \text{ for some positive integer } k \end{cases}$$

Does this sequence have any other cluster point(s)? Does it have a limit?

22. A sequence $\{x_n\}$ is said to be a *Cauchy*, or *fundamental*, sequence if and only if, for all $\varepsilon > 0$, there exists $N \in \mathbf{N}$ such that $m \ge N$ and $n \ge N$ imply $|x_m - x_n| < \varepsilon$.

(a) Prove that if $\{x_n\}$ converges, then $\{x_n\}$ is Cauchy.
(b) Prove that if $\{x_n\}$ is Cauchy, and if x is a cluster point of $\{x_n\}$, then $\{x_n\}$ converges to x.

6.2   Indirect Proofs

An *indirect proof* is a proof in which we establish the truth of a statement distinct from, but logically equivalent to, the desired result. Most indirect proofs that you might either read or have to write at the undergraduate level fall into one of three categories, each corresponding to an important tautology from the propositional calculus.

1. *Derivation of a conclusion involving the disjunction of two statements.* According to the tautology $[p \to (q \lor r)] \leftrightarrow [(p \land \sim q) \to r]$ [Theorem 1(p), Article 2.3], we may derive a conclusion of the form $q \lor r$ from a hypothesis p by assuming true the negation of one part of the conclusion, that is, by adding $\sim q$ to our list of hypotheses, and by trying, on that basis, to establish the truth of the other part, that is, to prove r.
2. *Proof by contrapositive.* According to the tautology $(p \to q) \leftrightarrow (\sim q \to \sim p)$ [Theorem 1(n), Article 2.3; see also Theorem 2(f), Article 2.3], we may prove that a conclusion q follows from a hypothesis p by showing that the truth of the negation of q implies that the hypothesis is false; that is, $\sim p$ is true.
3. *Proof by contradiction,* also known as *reductio ad absurdum.* According to the tautology $[\sim p \to (q \land \sim q)] \to p$ [Theorem 2(g), Article 2.3], we may establish p by proving that the assumption of the negation of p leads to a logical impossibility, that is, a contradiction.

It is important to understand the logical basis of these approaches and to know how to write proofs in these forms; equally important, however, is the ability to recognize when an indirect approach is appropriate, as opposed to direct methods outlined thus far in the text. We stress at the outset that the methods of this article are intended to supplement, not substitute for, direct methods. As a general rule, most mathematicians regard a direct proof as preferable, from the point of view of both clarity and aesthetic appeal, to an indirect proof, when the former is possible. Putting it differently you should try to develop a sense of the situations in which an indirect approach (particularly contrapositive and contradiction) is the route to take; do not fall into a habit of overusing these methods.

We now consider in sequence the three cases just outlined.

DERIVATION OF CONCLUSIONS INVOLVING DISJUNCTION

In Article 5.3 we considered the situation of a <u>hypothesis</u> having the form of a disjunction $p_1 \lor p_2 \lor \cdots \lor p_n$ of statements. In that instance we suggested that a division of an argument into cases is often an appropriate and fruitful path. Now we wish to consider the situation in which the <u>desired conclusion</u> is a disjunction. This can present difficulties, because most arguments in mathematics are geared toward a single conclusion at a time. Indeed, if our conclusion is a <u>conjunction</u> $q_1 \land q_2 \land \cdots \land q_n$, we most often break up the proof into n separate derivations, each of which establishes one of the components q_i, that is, we derive each component of the conclusion separately [see Exercise 3(c)]. No such luxury is generally available when disjunction is involved in the conclusion, since the hypothesis usually does not need to imply any components of the conclusion, taken individually. (*Note*: Exercise 4 illustrates an exception to this statement.) A simple example of this difficulty occurs in the following theorem about real numbers:

EXAMPLE 1   Assume it is known that multiplication of real numbers is associative, that nonzero real numbers have multiplicative inverses, and that $a \cdot 0 = 0$ for any real number a. Prove that if x and y are real numbers with $xy = 0$, then $x = 0$ or $y = 0$.

Discussion   Our theorem involves one simple hypothesis and a conclusion involving the disjunction of two statements. Approaching the proof directly, we seem to have no way of getting at the desired conclusion. In particular, neither specialization nor division into cases, the two methods of adapting a hypothesis toward a desired conclusion that we studied in Article 5.3, appears applicable here. We will return to this problem shortly.

A more or less standard approach to problems of the type presented in Example 1 is to take advantage of a generalization of Theorem 1(p), Article 2.3. You may verify that, for any positive integer n, the statement form

$$[p \to (q_1 \lor q_2 \lor \cdots \lor q_n)] \leftrightarrow [(p \land \sim q_1 \land \sim q_2 \land \cdots \land \sim q_{n-1}) \to q_n]$$

is a tautology. We may approach the derivation of $q_1 \lor q_2 \lor \cdots \lor q_n$ from p by assuming as true the negation of all but one (any one) of the components of the conclusion, and then trying, on the basis of these additional assumptions, to prove that the one remaining component must be true. This approach has a dual advantage: (1) to replace a logically complicated desired conclusion by a relatively simple one and (2) to give us one or more additional hypotheses. Let us now return to Example 1.

Solution to Example 1   This specific problem was alluded to in Article 2.1, where we suggested the approach to be carried out now. To derive the conclusion "either $x = 0$ or $y = 0$" from the hypothesis "$xy = 0$," we begin by assuming $x \neq 0$. We will try to use the hypothesis $xy = 0$ and the supposition $x \neq 0$ to prove that $y = 0$. If we can do this, our proof is complete, according to the tautology quoted earlier. What is the significance of a nonzero value for x? One fact that is true about a nonzero real number x but is not true about zero is that the multiplicative inverse (i.e., reciprocal) x^{-1} exists. Note that, on the one hand, $x^{-1}(xy) = x^{-1}(0) = 0$. On the other hand, however, $x^{-1}(xy) = (x^{-1}x)y = 1 \cdot y = y$. Combining these two strings of equations into a single string, we have a proof by transitivity, $y = 1 \cdot y = (x^{-1}x)y = x^{-1}(xy) = x^{-1}(0) = 0$, of the desired conclusion $y = 0$. □

Note that we do not need to repeat the argument just given with the roles of x and y reversed; that is, we do not need to prove also that if $xy = 0$ and $y \neq 0$, then $x = 0$. In deriving a conclusion $q \vee r$ from p, we may assume the negation of whichever of q or r is more convenient, and try to derive the remaining one. Doing it both ways is not necessary.

The preceding method may be convenient for proofs of set inclusion, in which we are trying to prove that a set A is a subset of the union of two sets X and Y. In this situation our desired conclusion has the form "either $x \in X$ or $x \in Y$."

EXAMPLE 2   Prove that if A, B, and C are sets, then $(A \cup B) \cap C \subseteq A \cup (B \cap C)$ [recall Exercise 4(a), Article 5.3].

Solution   Proceeding by the choose method, let x be an arbitrary element of $(A \cup B) \cap C$. To show $x \in A \cup (B \cap C)$, we must prove that either $x \in A$ or $x \in B \cap C$. Suppose $x \notin A$. Our theorem will be proved if we can show that $x \in B \cap C$, that is, $x \in B$ and $x \in C$. Since our "new" conclusion involves only conjunction, we may derive it by proving its two-component statements, one at a time. To show $x \in C$, we note simply that since $x \in (A \cup B) \cap C$ (by assumption), then $x \in C$. So the real problem, and the place where we presumably will have to *use* our supposition $x \notin A$, must be in proving $x \in B$. Now since $x \in (A \cup B) \cap C$, then $x \in A \cup B$; that is, either $x \in A$ or $x \in B$. But, by our supposition, we know $x \notin A$. Hence we must have $x \in B$, as desired. $\square$

Note that the tautology $[(p \vee q) \wedge \sim p] \rightarrow q$ [Theorem 2(k), Article 2.3] was used implicitly in the second sentence from the end of the solution to Example 2. We will see further examples of use of the indirect technique of deriving a conclusion involving disjunction later in the text.

PROOF BY CONTRAPOSITIVE

In Articles 5.2 and 5.3 we considered the problem of deriving a conclusion of the form $(\forall x)(p(x) \rightarrow q(x))$ from a given set of hypotheses. You will recall our guiding rule of focusing first on that conclusion and setting up the proof, by using the choose method, letting x be an arbitrary object for which $p(x)$ is true. The goal then is to prove that $q(x)$ is true for this x, where the hypotheses are incorporated into the proof after the initial setting-up is completed.

One of the situations we wish to consider, as we study proof by contraposition, is a "mirror image" of the one just described. Suppose the hypothesis of our conjecture has the logical form $(\forall x)(p(x) \rightarrow q(x))$. Suppose, in addition, that our desired conclusion is a simple statement. This situation can be difficult, if not impossible, to deal with by direct methods.

EXAMPLE 3   Prove that if a linear function $y = f(x) = Mx + B$ is increasing on **R**, then $M > 0$.

Discussion   You may recall the proof of the converse of this result from Example 7, Article 5.2; a simple direct proof by the choose method sufficed. In this case, however, the hypothesis has the form

$$(\forall x_1)(\forall x_2)[(x_1 < x_2) \rightarrow (Mx_1 + B < Mx_2 + B)],$$

whereas the conclusion is the simple statement $M > 0$. Since the conclusion is a simple statement (involving no quantifiers or connectives), the only direct method applicable to deriving it is proof by transitivity. But since the hypothesis is an "if . . . then" statement and so requires the assumption $x_1 < x_2$ in order to "activate" its conclusion, it may not be evident how to incorporate that hypothesis into such an argument.

Solution to Example 3   Because of the difficulty just described, we will give a proof by contrapositive. Suppose $M \leq 0$. Let $x_1 = 3$ and $x_2 = 5$ and note that $x_1 < x_2$. But since $M \leq 0$, then $Mx_1 = 3M \geq 5M = Mx_2$, so that $3M + B \geq 5M + B$, and thus $f(3) \geq f(5)$. We have proved the existence of real numbers x_1 and x_2 with $x_1 < x_2$, but $f(x_1) \geq f(x_2)$, thus proving the negation of the original hypothesis.   □

EXAMPLE 4   Suppose that a set A (from a universal set U) has the property that $A \subseteq B$ for all $B \subseteq U$. Prove that $A = \emptyset$.

Solution   Note again the simple logical form of the conclusion, compared to the hypothesis which like the hypothesis in Example 3, involves both the universal quantifier and implication arrow, the latter as part of the definition of "subset." We will proceed by contraposition and begin by assuming $A \neq \emptyset$. To contradict the hypothesis, we must prove that there exists a set $B \in \mathscr{P}(U)$ such that $A \nsubseteq B$. We take $B = \emptyset$ and note that since $A \neq \emptyset$, there exists an element x in A. Since $B = \emptyset$, then $x \notin B$. Hence $A \nsubseteq B$, as desired.   □

Proof by contrapositive can be useful in deriving results whose hypothesis, although not necessarily of the form $(\forall x)(p(x) \rightarrow q(x))$, is of a more complicated logical structure than the conclusion.

EXAMPLE 5   Suppose that a is a real number satisfying the property $(\forall \mu > 0)(|a| < \mu)$. Prove that $a = 0$.

Solution   Suppose $a \neq 0$. Then $\frac{1}{2}|a| > 0$. Letting $\mu = \frac{1}{2}|a|$, we note that clearly $\mu > 0$, and also, since $1 > \frac{1}{2}$, then $|a| = (1)(|a|) > \frac{1}{2}|a| = \mu$; that is, $(\exists \mu > 0)(|a| > \mu)$ so that we have $(\exists \mu > 0)(|a| \geq \mu)$, the logical negation of the hypothesis.   □

The underlined result in Example 5 is of interest in its own right, since it is an important tool for proving uniqueness, in connection with limits. We will employ it in Article 6.3.

In some situations in which a desired conclusion is of the form $(\forall x)(p(x) \rightarrow q(x))$, the relationship between this conclusion and the hypotheses may be such as to make it advantageous to prove the equivalent form $(\forall x)(\sim q(x) \rightarrow \sim p(x))$ of the conclusion instead. This situation occurred in Exercise 6(c), Article 5.2, as we now demonstrate.

EXAMPLE 6   Prove that if f is increasing on an interval I, then f is one to one on I.

Solution   By definition of "one to one," we must show that if x_1 and x_2 are real numbers with $f(x_1) = f(x_2)$, then $x_1 = x_2$. Our hypothesis that f is increasing has, however, the reverse format, namely, if $x_1 < x_2$, then $f(x_1) < f(x_2)$. Thus it is easier for us to derive the conclusion by assuming $x_1 \neq x_2$ and trying to prove $f(x_1) \neq f(x_2)$. A division into cases presents itself immediately. If $x_1 \neq x_2$, then either $x_1 < x_2$, in which case $f(x_1) < f(x_2)$ so that $f(x_1) \neq f(x_2)$, or $x_1 > x_2$, so that $f(x_1) > f(x_2)$ and again $f(x_1) \neq f(x_2)$, as desired.   □

We could also have deduced the result in Example 6 using a full contraposition argument. That is, assume f is not one to one and prove that f cannot be increasing. This approach is left for Exercise 5(a).

A very common application of proof by contrapositive arises when a theorem of the form $(p \wedge q) \rightarrow r$ is known, and we are asked to prove the corresponding statement of the form $(p \wedge \sim r) \rightarrow \sim q$. In fact, the two statement forms are logically equivalent [Exercise 9(a)], so that the latter statement can always be proved. In specific applications a brief and routine argument by contrapositive is the best approach, as the next example demonstrates.

EXAMPLE 7   Suppose that a subset C of $\mathbf{R} \times \mathbf{R}$ is symmetric with respect to the y axis, but not with the origin. Use the result of Exercise 8(a), Article 5.3, to prove that C is not symmetric with respect to the x axis.

Solution   Suppose C were symmetric with respect to the x axis. By the cited exercise, since C is symmetric with respect to both the x axis (by assumption) and the y axis (by hypothesis), then C is symmetric with respect to the origin. This establishes the negation of the hypothesis "but not with the origin" and so proves the theorem.   □

At the outset of this article, overzealousness in applying indirect methods of proof was discouraged. Proof by contrapositive is particularly subject to overuse. The reason for this, perhaps, is that starting a proof is often a difficult step, and the approach "assume the conclusion false" is an easy way of at least getting started. But this approach, when used instead of a readily available direct argument, can lead nowhere or to a convoluted argument or at best to an argument that is not so well presented as it could be. In Exercise 15 you are asked to examine difficulties that can arise if the approach of contraposition is taken to theorems proved by direct methods earlier in the text.

We conclude our consideration of proof by contrapositive with a reminder that such a proof always begins with the assumption of the negation of the desired conclusion; it is never appropriate to begin a proof by assuming the negation of one or more of the hypotheses.

PROOF BY CONTRADICTION

This method of proof is based on the principle "if the negation of a statement leads to a logical impossibility, the statement must be true." Actually, proof by contradiction has already been employed at two earlier stages of the text. The more recent was in the preceding section; proof by contrapositive can be viewed as a special instance of proof by contradiction. In a proof by contrapositive that p implies q, we have p as a hypothesis and assume $\sim q$. If we can derive $\sim p$ from $\sim q$, we then have $p \wedge \sim p$, a contradiction. An earlier instance of proof by contradiction occurred in Article 4.1 (Example 11), in connection with proofs that a given set equals the empty set. Here is another example in this category.

EXAMPLE 8   Prove that if A and B are sets such that $(B \cap A') \cup (B' \cap A) = B$, then $A = \emptyset$. [Recall Exercise 3(f), Article 5.1. How is that result related to the one just stated?]

Solution   Assume $A \neq \emptyset$, so that there exists x such that $x \in A$. We will try to arrive at a contradiction. Clearly we must find some way to involve the set B in the argument; indeed, if the existence of this element x is going to lead to a contradiction, we will have to find some way to relate x to B. Now what can we say about this relationship? Do we know $x \in B$, for example? No, we do not; nor do we know that $x \notin B$. What we <u>do know</u> is that either $x \in B$ or $x \notin B$ (i.e., $x \in B'$). Let us divide the argument into cases according to those two possibilities:

Case I: If $x \in B$, then either $x \in B \cap A'$ or $x \in B' \cap A$, by the equation $B = (B \cap A') \cup (B' \cap A)$. But $x \notin B' \cap A$, since $x \notin B'$, so $x \in B \cap A'$, which means $x \in A'$. Since $x \in A$, we have the contradiction $x \in A \cap A' = \emptyset$.

Case II: If $x \in B'$, then since $x \in A$, we have $x \in B' \cap A$. Since $B' \cap A \subseteq (B' \cap A) \cup (B \cap A') = B$, then $x \in B$. Thus we have $x \in B \cap B' = \emptyset$, again a contradiction.

Since both cases lead to a contradiction, and since these two cases are clearly exhaustive, our assumption $A \neq \emptyset$ must be false. We may conclude $A = \emptyset$, as desired.   □

Two classic proofs by contradiction are the proofs that $\sqrt{2}$ is irrational and that there exist infinitely many primes. The latter will be held off until the next article; proof by contradiction is one of the primary methods of proving existence, part of the subject of that article. We consider the former in the next example.

EXAMPLE 9   Prove that $\sqrt{2}$ is irrational; that is, there do not exist integers p and q such that $(p/q)^2 = 2$.

Solution   Proceeding by contradiction, we suppose that such integers exist. Note that if any such pair of integers exists, as we suppose, then surely a pair (p, q) exists having no factors in common. Now $2 = (p/q)^2 = (p^2/q^2)$ means that $2q^2 = p^2$. Hence p^2 is even. By Exercise 6(a), p is even. Hence we can express p as $p = 2n$, where n is an integer. Hence $2q^2 = p^2 = (2n)^2 = 4n^2$, so that $q^2 = 2n^2$. This means that q^2 is even so that q is even, again by Exercise 6(a). Hence p and q are both even; but this contradicts the assumption that p and q have no factors in common. Thus a pair of integers of the type described at the outset must not exist, as desired.   □

Exercises

1. Let A, B, and C be sets. Prove:

(a) $A \times \varnothing = \varnothing$
(b) If $A \times B = A \times C$, then either $A = \varnothing$ or $B = C$
(c) If $A \times B = B \times A$, then either $A = \varnothing$, $B = \varnothing$, or $A = B$
(d) If $A \times B = \varnothing$, then either $A = \varnothing$ or $B = \varnothing$
★(e) $(A \times C) - (B \times C) \subseteq (A - B) \times C$ [recall Exercise 4(d), Article 6.1].
(f) If $A \cap B' = \varnothing$, then $A \subseteq B$ [recall Example 12, Article 4.1. How is the theorem of that example related to the result of this exercise?].
★(g) If $A' \cup B = U$, then $A \subseteq B$ [recall Exercise 8(a), Article 4.1 and Exercise 10(c), Article 3.2]
(h) If $(A' \cup B) \cap (A \cup B') = U$, then $A = B$ [recall Exercise 3(g), Article 5.1 and Exercise 9(c), Article 3.2].

2. Suppose it is known that if m, a, and b are integers such that m divides ab, and m and a have no factors in common, then m divides b. Suppose also that it is known that if m is prime, then either $m|a$ or m has no factors in common with a. Use these facts to prove that if p, a, and b are integers such that p is prime and $p|ab$, then either p divides a or p divides b.

3. (a) Verify, by using a truth table, the tautology

$$[(p \to q_1) \vee (p \to q_2)] \to [p \to (q_1 \vee q_2)]$$

(b) (i) Prove that if A, B, C, and D are nonempty sets such that $A \times B \subseteq C \times D$, then $A \subseteq C$ and $B \subseteq D$.

(ii) Prove, by the choose method, that if A, B, and C are sets, then $A \cup (B \cap C) \subseteq (A \cup B) \cap (A \cup C)$.

(c) Describe the <u>general approach</u> you would take to prove these theorems:

(i) If a subset S of **R** is compact, then S is closed and bounded.

(ii) If A and B are sets such that $A \cup B$ is finite, then A is finite and B is finite.

(iii) The subset $2Z$ of **R** consisting of all even integers is closed under addition <u>and</u> multiplication.

[*Note:* It is not necessary to know the meaning of technical terms, such as "bounded," in order to do (c).]

4. *(a)* Verify the tautology

$$[(p_1 \rightarrow q_1) \wedge (p_2 \rightarrow q_2)] \rightarrow [(p_1 \vee p_2) \rightarrow (q_1 \vee q_2)]$$

(b) Use the result in Example 1 to show that if x satisfies the equation $x^2 + 2x - 35 = 0$, then either $x = 5$ or $x = -7$.

(c) Prove that if x, a, and b are real numbers satisfying the equation $xa = xb$, then either $x = 0$ or $a = b$. (Use the result of Example 1.)

5. *(a)* Give a proof by contrapositive that if a function f (mapping **R** to **R**) is increasing, then f is one to one.

(b) Prove that if $f(x) = Mx + B$ is one to one, then $M \neq 0$.

6. *(a)* Prove that if m is an integer such that m^2 is even, then m is even.

(b) Prove that if m is an integer such that m^2 is odd, then m is odd [recall Exercise 3(b), Article 6.1].

7. It is a familiar property (transitivity) of equality of real numbers that if $a = b$ and $b = c$, then $a = c$. Use this property to show that if f, g, and h are real-valued functions of a real variable with $A = \{x \in \mathbf{R} \mid f(x) \neq g(x)\}$, $B = \{x \in \mathbf{R} \mid g(x) \neq h(x)\}$, and $C = \{x \in \mathbf{R} \mid f(x) \neq h(x)\}$, then $C \subseteq A \cup B$.

★**8.** [Continuation of Exercise 16(c), Article 6.1] Let f be a real-valued function defined on an open interval (a, b). Suppose f has a relative maximum at a point $x_0 \in (a, b)$; that is, suppose there exists $\delta > 0$ such that $f(x_0) > f(x)$ for every $x \in (x_0 - \delta, x_0 + \delta)$. Suppose finally that $f'(x_0)$ exists. Prove that $f'(x_0) = 0$.

9. *(a)* Verify, by using a truth table, that $[(p \wedge q) \rightarrow r] \leftrightarrow [(p \wedge \sim r) \rightarrow \sim q]$ is a tautology.

(b) Suppose it is known that the sum of two rational numbers is rational. Prove that if x is rational and $x + y$ is irrational, then y is irrational. Can we conclude y is irrational if we know that <u>both</u> x and $x + y$ are irrational?

★*(c)* Given sets A, B, and C such that A is a subset of B and A is not a subset of C. Prove that B is not a subset of C.

(d) If m, n, and p are integers such that m divides n and m does not divide p, prove that n does not divide p.

(e) Prove that if S_1 and S_2 are subsets of **R** such that S_1 is convex and $S_1 \cap S_2$ is not convex, then S_2 is not convex (recall Exercise 9, Article 5.2).

10. *(a)* Prove or disprove: If real numbers x and y are irrational, then $x + y$ is irrational? xy is irrational?

(b)   A subset S of $\mathbf{R}$ is said to be *closed under addition* if and only if $x + y \in S$ whenever $x \in S$ and $y \in S$. Suppose the subset S of $\mathbf{R}$ is closed under addition and has the further property that $-x \in S$ whenever $x \in S$. Prove that if $x \in S$ and $y \notin S$, then $x + y \notin S$. (*Note:* $\mathbf{Z}$ and $\mathbf{Q}$ both satisfy the hypotheses of this theorem.)

(c)   A subset S of $\mathbf{R}$ is said to be *closed under multiplication* if and only if $xy \in S$ whenever $x \in S$ and $y \in S$. Suppose the subset S of $\mathbf{R}$ is closed under multiplication and has the further property that $1/x \in S$ whenever $x \in S$ and $x \neq 0$. Prove that if $x \in S$, $x \neq 0$, and $y \notin S$, then $xy \notin S$. (*Note:* $\mathbf{Q}$ satisfies the hypotheses of this theorem.)

★(d)   Use the result of Example 9, together with the result of (c), to show that, for any real number x, either $\sqrt{2} + x$ or $\sqrt{2} - x$ is irrational.

(e)   Assume it is known that $\sqrt{n}$ is irrational whenever the positive integer n is not a perfect square. Use this fact to prove that $\sqrt{2} + \sqrt{3}$ is irrational.

11. (a)   [Continuation of Exercise 10(c), Article 6.1] Use proof by contrapositive to show that if a subset S of $\mathbf{R}$ is open, then its complement S' is closed.

(b)   Use (a) and Exercise 8(e), Article 6.1, to show that $\varnothing$ is a closed subset of $\mathbf{R}$.

★(c)   Prove that $\varnothing$ is an open subset of $\mathbf{R}$.

(d)   Prove that $\varnothing$ is an interval in $\mathbf{R}$. (*Hint:* Using the definition from Example 2, Article 5.2, consider what must be the case if $\varnothing$ is not an interval.)

12. Suppose that S is a linearly dependent subset of a vector space V and that $S \subseteq T$. Prove that T is linearly dependent [recall Exercise 10(a), Article 5.2].

13. Prove that if x and y are real numbers with $y \leq x + \mu$ for every $\mu > 0$, then $y \leq x$.

14. Suppose $\{x_n\}$ and $\{y_n\}$ are infinite sequences of real numbers such that $x_n \to x$, $y_n \to y$, and $x_n < y_n$ for all $n = 1, 2, 3, \ldots$. Prove that $x \leq y$. Is it possible to prove $x < y$? (Recall Exercise 20, Article 6.1.)

15. Each of the following theorems was proved earlier in the text (either as an exercise or example) by direct methods. For each of them, set up a proof by contrapositive and compare the effectiveness of this approach with that of the corresponding direct proof.

(a)   If m, n, and p are integers such that $m \mid n$ and $m \mid p$, then $m \mid (n + p)$.

★(b)   If A, B, and C are sets with $A \subseteq B$ and $B \subseteq C$, then $A \subseteq C$.

(c)   If A, B, and X are sets with $A \cap X \subseteq B \cap X$ and $A \cap X' \subseteq B \cap X'$, then $A \subseteq B$.

16. Suppose f and g are both functions defined on an open interval containing a, where a is a real number. Prove that if $\lim_{x \to a} f(x) = L \neq 0$ and $\lim_{x \to a} g(x) = 0$, then $\lim_{x \to a} f(x)/g(x)$ does not exist (recall Exercise 18, Article 6.1).

6.3 Existence and Uniqueness (Optional)

In this article we consider how to prove two types of mathematical theorem:

1.   Prove that *at least* one object exists satisfying a given mathematical property (existence).

2.   Prove that *at most* one object exists satisfying a given mathematical property (uniqueness).

You may recall the notation $(\exists!x)(p(x))$ and the accompanying formal definition of "unique existence" from Exercise 9, Article 3.3. Specific instances of the themes of existence and uniqueness occur in a variety of mathematical settings, as the following example shows.

EXAMPLE 1 (a) Show that there is a unique real solution to the equation $x - 5 = \sqrt{(x + 7)}$ (existence <u>and</u> uniqueness; see Example 2).
  (b) Show that there exists an "upper bound" for the interval $[0, 1]$ (existence only; see Example 7).
  (c) Show that if f is a function defined on an open interval containing a point a, then $\lim_{x \to a} f(x)$, if it exists, is unique (uniqueness only; see Example 5).
  (d) Show that if m and n are integers, not both zero, then they have a unique *greatest common divisor* (existence and uniqueness; see Example 10).
  (e) Show that there exists an infinite number of primes (existence only; see Example 9).

Techniques of proof pertaining to these two themes are different; yet we treat them in the same article because, as parts (a) and (d) of Example 1 illustrate, the two themes often occur together as two parts of a single problem, one part being the "flip side" of the other. Indeed, the dual theme of *existence and uniqueness* runs through mathematics at all levels, beginning in high school algebra. Another reason for treating them together is that sometimes the process by which uniqueness is proved provides the key to the proof of existence, as in the following example.

EXAMPLE 2 Show that both the equations $7x - 5 = 0$ and $x - 5 = \sqrt{(x + 7)}$ have unique real solutions.

Solution Both these equations may be approached through normal algebraic manipulations, directed toward solving the equation, namely:

$$7x - 5 = 0 \quad \text{and} \qquad\qquad x - 5 \;=\; \sqrt{(x + 7)}$$
$$\Rightarrow \qquad 7x = 5 \qquad\qquad\qquad \Rightarrow \qquad (x - 5)^2 = x + 7$$
$$\Rightarrow \qquad x = \tfrac{5}{7} \qquad\qquad \Rightarrow \quad x^2 - 10x + 25 = x + 7$$
$$\Rightarrow \quad x^2 - 11x + 18 = 0$$
$$\Rightarrow \quad (x - 9)(x - 2) \;=\; 0$$
$$\Rightarrow \quad x = 9 \text{ or } x = 2$$

At first glance, the second equation appears to have two solutions, but substitution of both candidates into the original equation reveals that $x = 2$ does not satisfy the equation, since $-3 \neq \sqrt{9}$. This example illustrates the general fact that the process of solving an equation algebraically never proves that any number actually solves the equation, and so, in particular, <u>never proves existence</u> of a solution. The reasoning underlying the two preceding derivations is that <u>if</u> x is a solution to the given equation, <u>then</u> x must equal $\frac{5}{7}$ in the first case, and either 2 or 9 in the second. That is, these numbers are the only *candidates*, or possible solutions. Existence is proved in this situation only when it is verified <u>by substitution</u> that at least one of the candidates is an actual solution. In our examples substitution of $x = \frac{5}{7}$ satisfies the first equation, while substitution of $x = 9$ satisfies the second. On the other hand, the process of solving an equation may prove uniqueness, as it did for our first equation. For the second equation, it was the process of solving the equation, together with the results of the substitution of the two candidates, that led to the conclusion of uniqueness.   □

In Example 2 uniqueness is proved, in the concrete setting of an explicit equation, by showing that only a specific "named" object (i.e., the specific number $x = \frac{5}{7}$ in the first case; the number $x = 9$ in the second) may have the desired property, namely, of solving the equation. In more abstract settings there are three other possible approaches to a proof of uniqueness. The most common is: Assume x_1 and x_2 are both objects satisfying the property $p(x) \cdots$; prove that $x_1 = x_2$. Another approach may be taken when we are given that $p(a)$ is true for some specific a and are asked to prove that a is the only such object. In such a case we proceed by letting x be any object satisfying $p(x)$ and trying to prove $x = a$. A third approach to proving uniqueness is argument by contradiction. Each of these three approaches will be demonstrated in the following section.

UNIQUENESS

Our next three examples illustrate proofs of uniqueness in an abstract setting, that is, with no knowledge of a specific object a for which $p(a)$ is true. In each proof we adopt the approach: Assume that x_1 and x_2 are objects such that $p(x_1)$ and $p(x_2)$ both hold, and try to prove $x_1 = x_2$.

EXAMPLE 3   Recall from Exercise 10, Article 3.3, that a set Y is called *a complement* of a set X if and only if $X \cup Y = U$ and $X \cap Y = \emptyset$. Prove that every set has <u>at most one</u> complement.

Solution   Note first that by using the words "at most one complement" rather than "has a unique complement," we are completely avoiding the question of existence in this example [see, however, Exercise 2(a)]. We approach this proof as follows: Given a set X, suppose Y_1 and Y_2 are both complements of X. We claim $Y_1 = Y_2$. Now, by our assumption, we have

$$X \cup Y_1 = X \cup Y_2 = U \quad \text{and} \quad X \cap Y_1 = X \cap Y_2 = \emptyset$$

We could prove $Y_1 = Y_2$ by proving mutual inclusion through the choose method. Instead, we note that

$$Y_1 = Y_1 \cap U = Y_1 \cap (X \cup Y_2)$$
$$= (Y_1 \cap X) \cup (Y_1 \cap Y_2)$$
$$= \varnothing \cup (Y_1 \cap Y_2)$$
$$= Y_1 \cap Y_2$$

so that $Y_2 \subseteq Y_1$, by Example 9, Article 4.1. A completely analogous argument, with the roles of Y_1 and Y_2 reversed, shows $Y_1 \subseteq Y_2$, so that we may conclude $Y_1 = Y_2$, as desired. □

EXAMPLE 4   A real number u is called a **least upper bound** of a set $S \subseteq \mathbf{R}$ if and only if (i) $x \le u$ for all $x \in S$ and (ii) To every $\beta > 0$, there corresponds $y \in S$ such that $y > u - \beta$. Prove that a subset S of $\mathbf{R}$ has <u>at most one</u> least upper bound.

Solution   Suppose u_1 and u_2 are both least upper bounds for S. We claim $u_1 = u_2$ and will proceed to use an argument by contrapositive to prove it. If $u_1 \ne u_2$, we may assume with no loss of generality that $u_1 < u_2$. We will apply the technique of specialization to part (ii) of the definition, letting $\beta = \frac{1}{2}(u_2 - u_1)$. Then, by (ii), there exists $y \in S$ such that $y > u_2 - \beta = u_2 - \frac{1}{2}(u_2 - u_1) = \frac{1}{2}(u_1 + u_2) > \frac{1}{2}(u_1 + u_1) = u_1$. But $y > u_1$ and $y \in S$ contradicts property (i) for u_1. Thus $u_1 = u_2$, as desired. With uniqueness thus established, we often denote the least upper bound of a set S, when it exists, by *lub S*. □

An important property of <u>limit of a function at a point</u> a is that such limits are unique when they exist, provided that f is defined in an open interval containing a. Our general approach to proving this uniqueness is the same abstract one taken in Examples 3 and 4. But due to the underlying complexity, involving the epsilon-delta definition of limit, of the assumption that L_1 and L_2 both satisfy the definition of $L = \lim_{x \to a} f(x)$, we must resort to a different approach to prove that $L_1 = L_2$. Recall from Example 5, Article 6.2, that if a is a real number having the property $(\forall \mu > 0)(|a| < \mu)$, then $a = 0$. We use this result in the next example.

EXAMPLE 5   Prove that if L_1 and L_2 are real numbers, both satisfying the definition of $L = \lim_{x \to a} f(x)$, where f is defined in an open interval containing a, then $L_1 = L_2$.

Solution   Using the result of Example 5, Article 6.2, we attempt to show $L_1 = L_2$ by the following approach. Let $\mu > 0$ be given; we claim $|L_1 - L_2| < \mu$. If we can prove this, we may conclude $L_1 = L_2$, by the cited example. Now since $L_1 = \lim_{x \to a} f(x)$, then corresponding to any positive real number, and in particular to our given μ divided by 2, there exists $\delta_1 > 0$ such that $|f(x) - L_1| < \mu/2$ whenever $0 < |x - a| < \delta_1$. Similarly for L_2, there exists $\delta_2 > 0$ such that $|f(x) - L_2| < \mu/2$ whenever $0 < |x - a| < \delta_2$. Now since f is defined in some open interval containing a, there exists a point x_0 in the domain of f that is within both δ_1 and δ_2 distance of a. For this x_0, we may note that

$$
\begin{aligned}
|L_1 - L_2| &= |L_1 - f(x_0) + f(x_0) - L_2| \\
&\leq |L_1 - f(x_0)| + |f(x_0) - L_2| \\
&= |f(x_0) - L_1| + |f(x_0) - L_2| \\
&< \mu/2 + \mu/2 \\
&= \mu
\end{aligned}
$$

We have established that, for an arbitrary $\mu > 0$, $|L_1 - L_2| < \mu$, so that $L_1 = L_2$, as desired. $\square$

Among the exercises [Exercise 6(b)], you will be asked to mimic the preceding proof to show that an infinite sequence has at most one limit. Note also that the result of Example 5 can be derived through an indirect argument that is quite worthwhile. In Exercise 6(a) you are asked to provide such a proof.

In the next example we illustrate the type of uniqueness proof in which we have to prove that a specific named object a is the only object satisfying a given property $p(x)$.

EXAMPLE 6   Show that the empty set $\varnothing$ is the only set W that may have the property that there exist distinct sets A and B such that $A \times W = B \times W$.

Solution   Suppose that W is an arbitrary set such that $A \times W = B \times W$ for some pair of distinct sets A and B. We claim $W = \varnothing$. Proceeding indirectly, we note that if $W \neq \varnothing$ and $A \times W = B \times W$, then by Example 9, Article 5.2, we may conclude $A = B$, contradicting our assumption. Thus $W = \varnothing$, as claimed. $\square$

Note that to prove the theorem "$\varnothing$ is the only set W having the property . . . ," we must verify additionally that there do indeed exist distinct sets A and B such that $A \times \varnothing = B \times \varnothing$. (This is the *existence* side of the existence-uniqueness duality.) Of course, this is true since $A \times \varnothing = B \times \varnothing = \varnothing$ for any sets A and B, so that we may, for example, let $A = \{1\}$ and $B = \{2\}$.

Proofs of uniqueness similar in type to the one in Example 6 are found in Exercises 3(a, b), 4, and 6(c), among others.

EXISTENCE

There are essentially two elementary approaches to proving existence of an object satisfying a given property or collection of properties. One is the direct approach; we prove existence by producing an object of the desired type. In many cases we produce such an object by naming one explicitly, as in Examples 7 and 8. Existence proofs likely to be encountered by undergraduates in which this can be done are often of the easier variety. In more advanced settings we often give a direct proof of existence with reference to some abstract axiom asserting existence. We see a demonstration of this approach in Example 10.

The other approach to proving existence is <u>indirect</u> and based on the method of *reductio ad absurdum*. We begin such an argument with an assumption of nonexistence and try to arrive at a contradiction. This approach is demonstrated in Example 9.

EXAMPLE 7 A subset S of **R** is said to be *bounded above in **R*** if and only if there exists a real number u such that $x \leq u$ for all $x \in S$. A number u with this property is called an *upper bound* for S. Prove that the interval $[0, 1]$ is bounded above in **R**.

Solution Note that a <u>least upper bound</u> of S (cf., Example 4) is, by virtue of part (i) of its definition, an upper bound for S. Now clearly the real number 2 has the property that $x \leq 2$ for all $x \in [0, 1]$. In fact, any real number not less than 1 could be chosen as u. This is a case in which an object of the desired type, whose existence we have just demonstrated, is highly nonunique. □

EXAMPLE 8 Let f be a function mapping real numbers to real numbers and let A be a subset of the domain of f. We say that a real number y is in the *image of A under f*, abbreviated $y \in f(A)$, if and only if there exists $x \in A$ such that $y = f(x)$. Prove that $4 \in f(A)$, where $f(x) = x^2$ and $A = [0, 4]$.

Solution To prove $4 \in f(A)$, we must produce $x \in [0, 4]$ such that $4 = f(x) = x^2$. Since $2^2 = 4$ and $2 \in [0, 4]$, we let $x = 2$. Note that in this case the object we have produced to prove existence is also unique, as you should verify. □

A famous example of an <u>indirect</u> proof of existence is provided in Example 9.

EXAMPLE 9 Prove that there exist infinitely many primes.

Solution If the desired result were false, we could list all the primes; suppose that $p_1, p_2, \ldots, p_N$ is such a listing. We arrive at a contradiction by constructing a number that is not in the list which must be prime. Namely, let $p = (p_1 p_2 \cdots p_N) + 1$. Clearly each p_i divides the product $p_1 p_2 \cdots p_N$; hence none of the p_i can divide p. For if a certain p_i divided both p and $p_1 p_2 \cdots p_N$, then it would divide their difference, which is 1, and consequently would equal 1, a contradiction since 1 is not prime. Since p is not divisible by any prime, it must itself be prime, thus contradicting the assumption that all primes had been listed. □

Many of the more difficult and sophisticated (i.e., nonelementary) direct proofs of existence are based on fundamental axioms asserting existence that have been adopted as a part of the foundations of modern mathematics.

One such axiom is the *least upper bound axiom for R*, stated in Exercise 10. Another axiom is the *well-ordering principle* for the set **N** of all positive integers. This axiom asserts that every nonempty subset of **N** has a smallest element. One interesting and nontrivial application of the well-ordering principle is the proof that any pair of integers m and n, not both zero, have a *greatest common divisor*.

EXAMPLE 10   An integer d is called a *greatest common divisor* of integers m and n if and only if (i) $d \geq 0$, (ii) $d|m$ and $d|n$, and (iii) for all $c \in \mathbf{Z}$, if $c|m$ and $c|n$, then $c|d$. Prove that if m and n are integers, not both zero, then a greatest common divisor of m and n exists.

Solution   Consider the set S consisting of all integers of the form $mx + ny$, where x and y are integers. Clearly S must contain some positive integers and so, by the well-ordering principle, must contain a smallest positive integer, let us call it d. Since $d \in S$, then $d = mx_1 + ny_1$ for some integers x_1 and y_1. Our claim is that d satisfies conditions (i), (ii), and (iii) of the definition of greatest common divisor of m and n.

Now property (i) is true by definition of d and (iii) is proved easily as follows. If $c|m$ and $c|n$, then $c|mx_1$ and $c|ny_1$ so that $c|(mx_1 + ny_1) = d$, thus $c|d$ (recall the results of Example 2 and Exercise 2, Article 6.1). Property (ii) is the most difficult to prove, since its proof depends on the well-known *division algorithm* for the set **Z** of integers (which states "given any integers m and d with $d > 0$, there exist unique integers q and r such that $m = dq + r$, with $0 \leq r < d$.") To prove that $d|m$, apply this theorem to the integers m and d at hand to get integers q and r such that $m = dq + r$, $0 \leq r < d$. But then $m = (mx_1 + ny_1)q + r$, so that $r = m(1 - x_1q) + n(-qy_1)$, which is the appropriate form for membership in S. Hence $r \in S$; but $0 \leq r < d$ and d is the smallest positive element of S, so that $r = 0$. Hence $m = dq$ so that $d|m$, as desired. An identical argument establishes that $d|n$.

We conclude that this d, constructed from the set S by means of the well-ordering principle, is a greatest common divisor of m and n.   □

In Exercise 9 you are asked to show that the greatest common divisor of two integers is unique. If m and n are integers, not both zero, this unique positive integer corresponding to m and n is usually denoted by the symbol (m, n).

Study the proof in Example 10 carefully. The proof is, on the one hand, direct [i.e., (m, n) is derived directly from m and n, without recourse to any argument by indirect method] and yet is abstract, in that an actual greatest common divisor for the given m and n is not produced explicitly [i.e., the proof does not tell us how to calculate the value of (m, n) for given specific values of m and n.]. The crux of the proof is the idea of considering the set S and applying the well-ordering principle to it. Keep this approach in mind when doing exercises such as 9(d), 10(a), and 11(a).

The distinction between the types of existence proof given in Examples 9 and 10 (existence of an object proved, but no rule provided in the proof telling us how to calculate the object in particular cases) and those in Examples 7 and 8 is the basis of a famous controversy in mathematics that peaked in the early part of this century, but has recently reemerged. In brief, an existence proof in which we produce the object in question explicitly (we omit a detailed discussion of exactly what this means) is said to be a *constructive* proof. A school of mathematicians known as *intuitionists*, founded by the Dutch mathematician L. E. J. Brouwer (1881–1966), promulgated the belief that the only allowable proofs of existence should be constructive proofs. In particular, proofs by contradiction and proofs relying on such axioms as the well-ordering principle (cf., Examples 9 and 10) should not be regarded as legitimate. The intuitionist point of view failed to gain the influence held by the *formalist* school, led by the great German mathematician David Hilbert (1862–1943), whose program provided the framework in which most of modern mathematics has developed. The debate still rages however, as you can discover for yourself by consulting the January 1985 issue of the *College Mathematics Journal*. In that issue, a forum led by Dr. Stephen B. Maurer and entitled "The algorithmic way of life is best" provides ample evidence not only that mathematics is not a "closed book," but also that it is a developing field about whose major directions reasonable and well-informed people can disagree strongly.

Exercises

1. *(a)* Prove that there exists a unique negative real number x satisfying the equation $4\sqrt{(x^2 - 9)} = 2$.

(b) Prove that there does not exist a real number x satisfying the equation $\sqrt{(x - 3)} + \sqrt{(x + 5)} = 4$.

★*(c)* Prove that the equation $\sqrt{(4x + 36)} = x + 8$ has a unique real solution.

(d) Prove that the equation $\sqrt{(2x + 45)} = x + 5$ has a unique real solution.

2. *(a)* Recall from Example 3 the definition of *a complement* of a set. Prove that every set has at least one complement. Conclude from Example 3 that every set has a unique complement.

(b) Given sets A and B from a universal set U, a subset C of U is called a *complement of A relative to B* (or a *relative complement of A in B*) if and only if $A \cup C = A \cup B$ and $A \cap C = \varnothing$. Prove that, given any sets A and B, A has a unique relative complement in B.

3. *(a)* It is an axiom (*additive identity axiom*) for the real number system that there exists a real number, denoted 0, having the property that $x + 0 = 0 + x = x$ for all $x \in \mathbf{R}$. Prove that zero is the only real number y having the property that $x + y = y + x = x$ for each real number x.

(b) Another axiom for $\mathbf{R}$ (*multiplicative identity axiom*) asserts the existence of a real number, denoted 1, such that $x \cdot 1 = 1 \cdot x = x$ for all $x \in \mathbf{R}$. Prove that 1 is the only real number having this property.

(c)   The *additive inverse axiom* for **R** states that, corresponding to every $x \in$ **R**, there is a real number y such that $x + y = y + x = 0$. Prove that this y is uniquely determined by x. (Use the fact that, for any real numbers a, b, and c, if $a = b$, then $c + a = c + b$.) We denote this unique value of y by $-x$.

(d)   The *multiplicative inverse axiom* for **R** states that, corresponding to any nonzero $x \in$ **R**, there is a real number y such that $xy = yx = 1$. Prove that this y is uniquely determined by the given nonzero x. (Use the fact that, for any real numbers a, b, and c, if $a = b$, then $ca = cb$.) We denote this unique value of y by x^{-1}.

4. (a)   Prove that 0 is the only real number x satisfying the statement $ax = x$ for all $a \in$ **R**. [Assume the theorem $a \cdot 0 = 0$ for all $a \in$ **R**. (*Hint:* Use specialization.)]

★(b)   Prove that $\varnothing$ is the only subset X of a universal set U satisfying the statement $A \cap X = X$ for all sets $A \subseteq U$. (Assume that $A \cap \varnothing = \varnothing$ for all sets $A \subseteq U$.)

(c)   Prove that $\varnothing$ is the only subset X of a universal set U satisfying the statement $A \cup X = A$ for all sets $A \subseteq U$. (Assume that $A \cup \varnothing = A$ for all sets $A \subseteq U$.)

5. (a)   In Example 3, Article 6.1, we defined invertibility for an $n \times n$ matrix A. Show that if an $n \times n$ matrix A is invertible, then an associated matrix B such that $AB = BA = I_n$ is unique. We denote this uniquely determined matrix by A^{-1}.

(b)   Prove that if $A = (a_{ij})_{2 \times 2}$ has $a_{11}a_{22} - a_{12}a_{21} \neq 0$, then A is invertible.

(c)   Prove that the 2×2 matrix $\begin{pmatrix} 2 & 5 \\ 6 & 15 \end{pmatrix}$ is not invertible.

6. (a)   Give an indirect proof of the uniqueness of $\lim_{x \to a} f(x)$, where f is defined in an open interval containing a. That is, prove that if L_1 satisfies the epsilon-delta definition of $L = \lim_{x \to a} f(x)$, and $L_2 \neq L_1$, then L_2 cannot satisfy this definition.

(b)   Recall from Example 5, Article 6.1 the definition of $x = \lim_{n \to \infty} x_n$. Mimic the proof given in Example 5 to show that a limit of a convergent sequence is unique.

★(c)   Recall from Exercise 21, Article 6.1, the definition of *cluster point* of a sequence. Prove that if the sequence $\{x_n\}$ converges to the real number x, then this x is the unique cluster point of the sequence.

7. (a)   Prove that the set $\{1/n \mid n = 1, 2, 3, \ldots\}$ is bounded above in **R**. (cf., Example 7).

(b)   A subset S of **R** is said to be *bounded below* in **R** if and only if there exists a real number L such that $L \leq x$ for all $x \in S$. Prove that if S is bounded above in **R**, then the set $-S = \{x \in \mathbf{R} \mid -x \in S\}$ is bounded below in **R**.

★(c)   Prove that if S_1 and S_2 are both bounded above in **R**, then $S_1 \cup S_2$ is bounded above in **R**.

(d)   A subset S of **R** is said to be *bounded in* **R** if and only if there exists $M > 0$ such that $|x| \leq M$ for all $x \in S$. Prove that S is bounded in **R** if and only if S is bounded above <u>and</u> bounded below in **R**.

(e)   Prove that if $\{x_n\}$ is a convergent sequence of real numbers, then the set $\{x_1, x_2, \ldots\}$ is a bounded set.

8. (a)   Let $f(x) = \sin x$ and $A = [-\pi/4, \pi/4]$. Prove that $\frac{1}{2} \in f(A)$.

(b) Let f be a function that maps real numbers to real numbers, and let A and B be subsets of the domain of f. Prove that $f(A \cap B) \subseteq f(A) \cap f(B)$: Give an example to show that the reverse inclusion need not hold.

(c) Under the assumptions of (b), prove that $f(A \cup B) = f(A) \cup f(B)$.

(d) Under the assumptions of (b), prove that if $A \subseteq B$, then $f(A) \subseteq f(B)$.

9. In Example 10 the well-ordering principle for the set $\mathbf{N}$ of all positive integers was introduced and used to prove the existence of a greatest common divisor (m, n) for any integers m and n, not both zero.

(a) Prove that if m and n are integers, not both zero, then they have a unique greatest common divisor.

(b) Use the proof in Example 10 to show that if $d = (m, n)$, then there exist integers x and y such that $d = mx + ny$.

(c) Use the result of (b) to show that if a, b, and c are integers such that $a | bc$ and $(a, b) = 1$, then $a | c$ (recall Exercise 2, Article 6.2 and Exercise 2, Article 6.1).

(d) Use the well-ordering principle to prove that if S is a subset of the set $\mathbf{N}$ of all positive integers satisfying these two properties: (i) $1 \in S$ and (ii) for all $m \in \mathbf{N}$, if $m \in S$, then $m + 1 \in S$; then $S = \mathbf{N}$. This is known as the *principle of mathematical induction* (recall Article 5.4). (*Hint:* if $S \neq \mathbf{N}$, then S is a proper subset of $\mathbf{N}$ so that $\mathbf{N} - S$ is a nonempty subset of $\mathbf{N}$.)

10. One of the basic properties of the real number system is the *least upper bound axiom*: Every nonempty subset of $\mathbf{R}$ that is bounded above in $\mathbf{R}$ has a least upper bound in $\mathbf{R}$ (cf., Examples 4 and 7). We will see in Article 9.3 that this axiom is one of the basic distinguishing features between the real and rational number systems; that is, $\mathbf{Q}$ fails to satisfy this axiom.

★(a) Use the least upper bound axiom to derive the *Archimedean property*: If a and b are any positive real numbers, there exists a positive integer n such that $b < na$. (*Hint:* Suppose the conclusion is false and consider the set $S = \{na \,|\, n \in \mathbf{N}\}$.)

(b) Use the result in (a) to prove that the sequence $\{1/n\}$ converges to zero. (*Note:* This result has previously been assumed in exercises such as Exercise 20, Article 6.1.)

(c) Use the result in (a) to prove that the set $\mathbf{N}$ of all positive integers is not bounded above in $\mathbf{R}$.

(d) Use the least upper bound axiom and ideas suggested by Exercise 7(b) to prove that a nonempty set of real numbers that is bounded below in $\mathbf{R}$ has a *greatest lower bound* in $\mathbf{R}$. (First formulate, on the basis of the definition of "least upper bound," in Example 4, an appropriate definition of "greatest lower bound.")

★(e) Recall from Exercise 9, Article 6.1, the definition of "point of accumulation of a set S." Show that if $u = \text{lub } S$ and $u \notin S$, then u is a point of accumulation of S. Give an example to show that lub S need not in general be a point of accumulation of S.

11. A basic theorem of mathematical analysis asserts that if f is a function that is continuous on a closed and bounded interval $[a, b]$, then f attains both an absolute maximum and minimum value on that interval. The first of these means that there exists $m \in [a, b]$ such that $f(m) \geq f(x)$ for all $x \in [a, b]$. You should formulate the second definition.

(a)   Use this theorem, together with the result of Exercise 8, Article 6.2, to prove *Rolle's theorem*: If f is continuous on $[a, b]$, differentiable on (a, b), and if $f(a) = f(b) = 0$, then there exists a point $c \in (a, b)$ such that $f'(c) = 0$.

(b)   Consider the polynomial function $f(x) = x^4 + 3x + 1$. Use Rolle's theorem to prove that the equation $f(x) = 0$ has at most one real root between $a = -2$ and $b = -1$. What theorem of elementary calculus guarantees that this equation has at least one root between the given values of a and b?

(c)   Use Rolle's theorem to prove the *mean value theorem*: If f is continuous on $[a, b]$ and differentiable on (a, b), then there exists a point $c \in (a, b)$ such that $f'(c) = (f(b) - f(a))/(b - a)$. [*Hint*: Apply Rolle's theorem to the function $F(x) = f(x) - G(x)$, where $G(x)$ is the linear function determined by the points $(a, f(a))$ and $(b, f(b))$. First, draw a picture and find the specific defining rule for $G(x)$.]

12. (Continuation of Exercise 11) (a)   Use the mean value theorem to prove that if f' is identically zero on an interval I, then f is constant on I.

(b)   Use the result in (a) to prove that if $f' = g'$ on an interval I, then there exists a constant c such that $f = g + c$ on I.

(c)   Use the mean value theorem to prove that if f' exists on an open interval (a, b) and if f' is bounded on that interval [i.e., there exists $M > 0$ such that $|f'(x)| \le M$ for all $x \in (a, b)$], then f is uniformly continuous on (a, b) (recall Exercise 7, Article 4.3).

13. Frequently in mathematics, rather than proving that a certain set of properties is satisfied uniquely by a given object, the best we can do is prove that the objects satisfying the given conditions fall into certain very specific categories. Theorems of this type are usually called *classification theorems*. One example of a classification theorem from elementary calculus involves the notion of antiderivative, or indefinite integral. Recall that F is an antiderivative, or indefinite integral, of a function f on an interval I, denoted $F = \int f(x) \, dx$, if and only if $F'(x) = f(x)$ for all $x \in I$.

(a)   Prove that if F and G are both indefinite integrals of a function f on an interval I, then F and G differ by some constant on I.

(b)   Prove that if $y = f(x)$ satisfies the differential equation $y' + ay = 0$ for all $x \in \mathbf{R}$, then $y = y(x) = ce^{-ax}$ for some constant c. (*Hint*: Multiply the given equation by e^{ax}.)

(c)   Prove that there exists a unique function $y = f(x)$ satisfying both the differential equation $y' - 3y = 0$ on $\mathbf{R}$ and the *initial condition* $y(0) = 5$.

The subject of *differential equations*, from which (b) and (c) are simple examples, is an area of mathematics in which the dual themes of existence and uniqueness are particularly prominent.

6.4   Preview of Additional Advanced Methods of Proof (Optional)

In the first part of this text we have attempted systematically to lay a foundation by which you might more easily and quickly be able to obtain a measure of competence in reading and writing proofs, an important aspect of the mathematician's craft. In all likelihood, if you are thoroughly acquainted with, and well practiced in, the methods of proof covered thus far, you are well along the way to a command of basic proof-writing skills.

Several other advanced methods of proof are not covered in detail in this text. These methods, including *counting* arguments, *compactness* arguments, and arguments using various *transfinite processes*, are general in the sense that they have application to a wide variety of topics, yet are more specialized and less basic than the methods of proof on which we've focused. Their applications are found primarily at the senior and graduate levels, and their very introduction requires, for proper illustration, mathematical background material that is a normal part of the junior-senior curriculum and is, in any case, outside the domain of this text. In the remainder of this article, however, we will preview these methods briefly. It is not intended that you attempt, much less master, such proofs at this point. Rather the purpose of this section is to heighten your awareness that more advanced methods of proof exist and to indicate stages of future study where such methods are likely to be encountered.

The following introduction is divided into two major categories: proofs involving finiteness and methods based on transfinite processes.

PROOFS INVOLVING FINITENESS

Counting arguments. Proofs involving counting methods are especially prominent in relation to finite algebraic structures, particularly finite groups and rings. You will encounter, in almost any introductory abstract algebra course, results such as Lagrange's theorem ("the order of any subgroup of a finite group divides the order of the group"), the theorem asserting that "any finite integral domain is a field"; the third Sylow theorem of group theory (whose rather technical statement we omit); and the theorem asserting that "the set of nonzero elements of the ring of integers modulo n that are not divisors of zero forms a group under multiplication modulo n," whose proofs employ counting methods. A basic counting principle that has relevance for several of the preceding proofs is the so-called *pigeonhole principle*: If m objects are distributed among n places, where $m > n$, then at least one place must receive more than one object.

Compactness arguments. Just as counting arguments occur primarily in relation to algebra, compactness arguments occur in the domain of analysis and topology. A student is likely to encounter the notion of compactness for the first time in a course in advanced calculus, in the form of the *Heine-Borel theorem*. This theorem, in its application to the real line, asserts that any closed and bounded interval J in **R** has the following property, known as *compactness*: "Any collection of open intervals that *cover* J has a finite subcollection that also covers J." This admittedly technical property is the theoretical basis for the proofs of a pair of theorems whose statements may already be familiar to you: "A continuous function on a closed and bounded interval is bounded on that interval" (which has as a corollary the result that a continuous function on a closed and bounded interval attains an absolute maximum and minimum value on that interval), and "a continuous function on a closed and bounded interval is *uniformly continuous* on that interval."

TRANSFINITE PROCESSES

There exists, among the axioms of set theory that constitute what is usually called the *foundations* of modern mathematics, a collection of equivalent statements that, because of their logical equivalence, constitute a single axiom of set theory. This axiom, known in its various equivalent forms as the *axiom of choice*, the *principle of transfinite induction*, the *Hausdorff maximal principle*, *Tukey's lemma*, and perhaps most commonly, *Zorn's lemma*, is widely used in existence proofs, where the goal is to prove the existence of a "maximal" structure of some kind. Students are likely to encounter applications of this axiom for the first time at the senior or beginning graduate level. At a rather advanced stage of an introductory topology course, Zorn's lemma is employed in the proof of the famous theorem of Tychonoff, concerning the product of compact spaces. In abstract algebra a Zorn's lemma argument is used to show that every field has an algebraically closed extension field, while in linear algebra, the existence of a *Hamel basis* for any vector space is proved by using the same general approach. We note for your information the statement of Zorn's lemma: "A partially ordered set S having the property that every chain in S is bounded above in S has at least one maximal element." We mention also that this text provides an introduction to partially ordered sets in Article 7.4 and a brief consideration of the axiom of choice at the conclusion of Article 8.4.

Those of you who are motivated by the preceding discussion to pursue at this stage one or more of the topics alluded to should consult, as appropriate, any of a number of introductory texts in abstract algebra, topology, and mathematical analysis.

BOOK TWO

Bridging Topics: Relations, Functions, and Number Systems

Relations, Part I: Equivalence Relations and Partial Orderings
CHAPTER 7

In the next two chapters we study three related, yet diverse, mathematical concepts. *Equivalence relations* and *partial orderings* are studied in the present chapter, while the topic *functions/mappings* is covered in Chapter 8. You have undoubtedly had considerable experience with functions, but the terms "equivalence relation" and "partial ordering" are likely to be unfamiliar. In spite of this, most of you will probably feel more "at home" with the latter two concepts than you might anticipate, while feeling less familiar than expected with the approach to functions and mappings in Chapter 8. An abstract treatment of functions/mappings, although dealing with a familiar concept, has a strikingly different emphasis from that seen in precalculus and elementary calculus courses. On the other hand, equivalence relations and partial orderings, even though probably new to you as concepts, generalize familiar mathematical relationships.

The most basic example of an equivalence relation is the relationship "equals." The relationships of equality between numbers, equality between sets, and indeed equality between any kinds of objects, are all examples of equivalence relations. More generally, equivalence relations are the mathematician's way of describing situations in which two objects can, in some sense, be considered and treated as "the same." Viewing different objects as indistinguishable, from some specific vantage point, is common, both within and outside mathematics. As one example, high school geometry students with no knowledge of equivalence relations find it natural to regard two congruent triangles as identical in the context of Euclidean plane geometry. At even more elementary levels, students are trained to regard pairs of fractions such as $\frac{1}{4}$ and $\frac{6}{24}$ as the same for purposes of calculation. In a nonmathematical sphere everyone is familiar with the idea that two coins minted for circulation are the same if and only if they are of the same denomination, for example, both pennies, both quarters, and so on, and "different" otherwise. Hence, although two dimes are different as physical entities (and may, e.g., be different when viewed through the eyes of a coin collector), they are the same with respect to their value as money, the criterion we normally have in mind when dealing with coins. This fact, in turn, affects our attitude toward coins; when dealing with coins purely as money, we care not about individual coins, but only about <u>classes</u> of coins (e.g., the class of nickels, the class of half-dollars, etc.). The primary role of an individual coin is that of arbitrary representative of the class containing it.

The mathematically rigorous reason that we can "identify" distinct objects in examples such as the preceding three is that there is an equivalence relation implicitly underlying each. Because we are able to regard distinct objects as indistinguishable by means of equivalence relations, it is possible to study sets of mathematical objects by dealing with subsets consisting of elements identified with one another by the relation, known as *equivalence classes*, rather than with individual elements. Sets of equivalence classes, in turn, are fundamental to some of the most important constructions in mathematics. In Chapter 10 we deal with the questions, "What are the rational numbers?" and "What are the real numbers?" using an approach based on equivalence classes.

The concept of partial ordering is a generalization of the relationship "less than or equal to" on the set of real numbers. Whenever a partial ordering on a set of objects has been defined, some idea of "relative size" of some or all of the objects in the set is implied. The notion of partial ordering is the foundation of a number of theories falling under the heading "ordered algebraic structures" in advanced mathematics. Our treatment gives a very brief introduction to such theories.

The common thread linking the concepts of equivalence relation, partial ordering, and function/mapping is the notion of *relation between two sets*. We begin by focusing on that concept.

7.1   Relations

The concept of relation from a set A to a set B is based on the concept of ordered pair (x, y) and, more specifically, the idea of the cartesian product $A \times B$ of two sets A and B. You may wish to reread some of the relevant material in Article 1.2 and recall Exercise 1, Article 5.2; Exercise 4, Article 6.1; and Exercise 1, Article 6.2. Leaving aside, as in Chapter 1, a formal definition of "ordered pair" (given in Exercise 10, Article 4.1), we recall here the criteria for equality of ordered pairs and for membership of an object in the cartesian product of two sets.

DEFINITION 1

(a) We say that two ordered pairs of objects (a, b) and (y, z) are **equal**, denoted $(a, b) = (y, z)$, if and only if $a = y$ and $b = z$.

(b) Given sets A and B, we say that an object x is an element of the cartesian product $A \times B$ if and only if there exist $a \in A$ and $b \in B$ such that $x = (a, b)$.

In the following theorems we gather properties of cartesian product, some of which were listed as exercises earlier in the text, and provide proofs in selected cases.

THEOREM 1

Let W, X, Y, and Z be arbitrary sets. Then:

(a) $(X \cup Y) \times Z = (X \times Z) \cup (Y \times Z)$

(b) $(X \cap Y) \times Z = (X \times Z) \cap (Y \times Z)$

(c) $(X - Y) \times Z = (X \times Z) - (Y \times Z)$

(d) $(W \times X) \cap (Y \times Z) = (W \cap Y) \times (X \cap Z)$

(e) $(W \times X) \cup (Y \times Z) = (W \cup Y) \times (X \cup Z)$

(f) If $W \subseteq X$ and $Y \subseteq Z$, then $W \times Y \subseteq X \times Z$.

Partial proof   All except (f) are statements of set equality and so may be proved by a mutual inclusion approach. In some cases, such as (a) and (b), it is possible to write a string of valid biconditional statements (as in Example 10, Article 4.1). We will take the latter approach to prove (a).

(a)   An object a is an element of $(X \cup Y) \times Z$ $\Leftrightarrow$

$a = (x, z)$ for some objects $x \in X \cup Y$ and $z \in Z$ $\Leftrightarrow$

$a = (x, z)$ where either $x \in X$ or $x \in Y$, and $z \in Z$ $\Leftrightarrow$

$a = (x, z)$ where either $x \in X$ and $z \in Z$, or $x \in Y$ and $z \in Z$ $\Leftrightarrow$

either $a \in X \times Z$ or $a \in Y \times Z$ $\Leftrightarrow$

$a \in (X \times Z) \cup (Y \times Z)$

(c)   We will prove that $(X \times Z) - (Y \times Z) \subseteq (X - Y) \times Z$, leaving the reverse inclusion to you. Suppose $a \in (X \times Z) - (Y \times Z)$. Since $a \in X \times Z$, then $a = (x, z)$ where $x \in X$ and $z \in Z$. To show $a \in (X - Y) \times Z$, we need show only that $x \in X - Y$. We proceed indirectly. If $x \notin X - Y$, then since $x \in X$, we would have $x \in X \cap Y$, due to the theorem $X = (X \cap Y) \cup (X \cap Y') = (X \cap Y) \cup (X - Y)$, so that $x \in Y$. But then $x \in Y$ and $z \in Z$ so that $a = (x, z) \in Y \times Z$. But this contradicts the assumption $a \in (X \times Z) - (Y \times Z)$. $\square$

THEOREM 2

Let A, B, and C be arbitrary sets. Then:

(a) $A \times \varnothing = \varnothing \times A = \varnothing$

(b) If $A \times B = A \times C$ and $A \neq \varnothing$, then $B = C$.

(c)   If $A \times B = B \times A$, $A \neq \emptyset$, $B \neq \emptyset$, then $A = B$

(d)   If $A \times B = \emptyset$, then either $A = \emptyset$ or $B = \emptyset$

Proof   (a)   Suppose $x \in A \times \emptyset$. Then there exist objects $a \in A$ and $b \in \emptyset$ such that $x = (a, b)$. But the statement "there exists $b \in \emptyset$" is false, so we have arrived at a contradiction.

(b)   Recall Example 9, Article 5.2.

(c)   To prove $A \subseteq B$, let $x \in A$; we must prove $x \in B$. Since $B \neq \emptyset$, there must exist $y \in B$. Since $x \in A$ and $y \in B$, then $(x, y) \in A \times B$. Since $A \times B = B \times A$, then $(x, y) \in B \times A$. But this implies, among other things, that $x \in B$, as desired. The proof is completed by proving $B \subseteq A$ in an analogous fashion.

(d)   Suppose the conclusion is false; that is, suppose $A \neq \emptyset$ and $B \neq \emptyset$. Then there exist $a \in A$ and $b \in B$. But then $(a, b) \in A \times B$, contradicting the hypothesis $A \times B = \emptyset$.   □

Note that (a) and (d) of Theorem 2 are converses of each other. Part (b) may be thought of as a cancellation property; (c) states that the cartesian product is a highly noncommutative operation.

DEFINITION 2

Let A and B be sets. A **relation from A to B** is any subset R of $A \times B$. If $A = B$, we say that R is a relation on A.

The concept "relation" is extraordinarily general. Examples of relations are very easy to come by. On the other hand, we should not expect, in the absence of any assumptions about specific properties of a relation, that many general statements, that is, theorems, can be proved about relations. As we will soon see, it is only when we look at specific types of relations that any mathematically interesting theory begins to develop. Since a relation is among other things a set, specific relations may be described by either the roster method or the rule method. As was the case in describing general sets, a rule describing a relation must have the property that, given an ordered pair (x, y), we must be able to determine, by the rule, whether or not (x, y) lies in the relation. Relations having infinitely many ordered pairs must, of course, be described by the rule method. A number of relations are presented in the following examples.

EXAMPLE 1   Let $A = \{1, 2, 3\}$ and $B = \{w, x, y, z\}$. Then $R_1 = \{(1, x),$ $(2, y), (3, z)\}$, $R_2 = \{(2, w), (2, x), (2, y), (2, z)\}$, and $R_3 = \{(1, z), (2, z),$ $(3, z)\}$ are relations from A to B. The set $R_4 = \{(x, 1), (x, 3)\}$ is a relation from B to A. The entire set $A \times B$ is itself a relation from A to B, as is the empty set $\emptyset$. The relation R_2 may be described by the rule method, namely, $R_2 = \{(2, b) \mid b \in B\}$ or $R_2 = \{(a, b) \mid a = 2 \text{ and } b \in B\}$. You should write a description of R_3, by using the rule method.   □

EXAMPLE 2 Define a relation R_5 on **R** by $R_5 = \{(x, y) \in \mathbf{R} \times \mathbf{R} \mid 3 < x \le 8$, $-2 \le y < 4\}$. This relation may be pictured as a rectangle in the xy plane, open on the left and top, closed on the right and bottom, as pictured in Figure 7.1. You should draw a pictorial representation of the relation on **R**, $\{(x, y) \mid (x^2/9) + (y^2/49) \ge 1\}$. $\square$

EXAMPLE 3 Define relations R_6, R_7, and R_8 on the set H of all human beings living in the year 1987 by $R_6 = \{(x, y) \mid x$ is older than y or the same age as $y\}$, $R_7 = \{(x, y) \mid y$ is a biological parent of $x\}$, and $R_8 = \{(x, y) \mid x$ and y are both male or both female$\}$. $\square$

EXAMPLE 4 Define relations R_9, R_{10}, and R_{11} on **Z** by the rules $R_9 = \{(m, n) \mid m$ and n are both even or both odd$\}$, $R_{10} = \{(m, n) \mid m$ and n are both nonnegative$\}$, and $R_{11} = \{(m, n) \mid m$ is less than or equal to $n\}$. $\square$

EXAMPLE 5 Define relations R_{12}, R_{13}, and R_{14} on **Z** by the rules $R_{12} = \{(m, n) \mid m$ divides $n\}$ (recall the paragraph preceding Example 7, Article 5.4), $R_{13} = \{(m, n) \mid 5$ divides the difference $m - n$ of m and $n\}$, and $R_{14} = \{(m, n) \mid m$ equals $n\}$. $\square$

EXAMPLE 6 Let X be any finite set and let $A = \mathscr{P}(X)$. Define relations R_{15}, R_{16}, and R_{17} on A by $R_{15} = \{(M, N) \mid M$ is a subset of $N\}$, $R_{16} = \{(M, N) \mid M$ and N are disjoint$\}$, and $R_{17} = \{(M, N) \mid M$ and N have the same number of elements$\}$. $\square$

A common way of viewing a relation is from a dynamic, rather than a static, point of view. Frequently, we think of a relation not primarily as a set of ordered pairs, but rather, as a relationship, where the relationship exists between precisely those pairs of objects that occur together in an

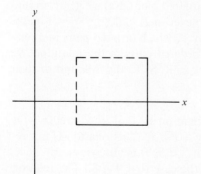

Figure 7.1 *Graphic representation of the relation $R_5 = \{(x, y) \mid 3 < x \le 8$, $-2 \le y < 4\}$.*

ordered pair contained in the relation. Using this approach, we might refer to R_{15} as the *subset relation on the set A*. We might agree to name this relation by the symbol $\subseteq$ and write $M \subseteq N$ instead of $(M, N) \in R_{15}$ to symbolize that the sets M and N are related by the relation. R_{13} is usually called the relation *congruence modulo 5 on* **Z**, and we customarily write $13 \equiv 18$ mod 5, rather than $(13, 18) \in R_{13}$. More generally, we often deal with a generic relation R by using the notation $x \, R \, y$, rather than $(x, y) \in R$. Also, it is common to identify a generic relation by some symbol, such as $\sim$, rather than by a letter, so that $x \sim y$ means the same thing as $(x, y) \in R$. The relation "equality" on any set X (as in R_{14}) can be described by either the symbol $=$ or by the notation $I_X = \{(x, x) \mid x \in X\}$. This relation is often referred to as the *identity relation on X*.

We next consider four properties that a given relation may, or may fail to, possess. These properties are fundamental to the definitions of equivalence relation and partial ordering, as we will see in Articles 7.2 and 7.4.

DEFINITION 3
Let A be a set and R a relation on A. We say that:

(a) R is **reflexive on A** if and only if $x \, R \, x$ for all $x \in A$ [in symbols, $(\forall x \in A)((x, x) \in R)$].

(b) R is **symmetric** if and only if, for every $x, y \in A$, if $x \, R \, y$, then $y \, R \, x$ [in symbols, $(\forall x \in A)(\forall y \in A)((x, y) \in R \rightarrow (y, x) \in R)$].

(c) R is **transitive** if and only if, for every x, y, and z in A, if $x \, R \, y$ and $y \, R \, z$, then $x \, R \, z$.

(d) R is **antisymmetric** if and only if, for every $x, y, \in A$, if $x \, R \, y$ and $y \, R \, x$, then $x = y$.

From the point of view of a relation R as a set of ordered pairs, the reflexive property means that R contains all pairs (x, x) where x ranges over all the elements of A. Dynamically, the reflexive property means "every element of A is related to itself." Symmetry means that whenever we "flip over" an ordered pair in R, the resulting ordered pair is also in R. On the other hand, antisymmetry says that the ordered pair (y, x) we get from flipping over an ordered pair (x, y) in R is <u>never</u> in R, unless $x = y$. Finally, transitivity may be regarded as a property by which ordered pairs in a relation are "linked together" to form new ordered pairs in the relation. We will occasionally refer to these properties as R, S, T, and AS, and to their negations as NR, NS, NT, and NAS.

EXAMPLE 7   Consider the relation *less than* on **R**; that is, a pair (x, y) is an element of this relation if and only if $x < y$. This relation is <u>not reflexive</u> since, for instance, it is false that $5 < 5$. It is <u>not symmetric</u> since, for example, $8 < 9$, whereas it is not the case that $9 < 8$. The relation clearly <u>is transitive</u> since if $x < y$ and $y < z$, then $x < z$ for any real numbers x, y, and z. The relation is <u>antisymmetric</u>, although only by means of a logical technicality. The question is whether the statement "for all $x, y \in \mathbf{R}$, if $x < y$ and $y < x$, then $x = y$" is true. The answer is "yes" since the premise "$x < y$ and $y < x$" is false for any x and y. $\square$

EXAMPLE 8   Let $A = \{1, 2, 3, 4\}$. Let R be a relation on A defined by $R = \{(1, 1), (2, 2), (3, 3), (4, 4), (1, 2), (1, 3), (1, 4), (2, 4)\}$. You should check, by dealing with all possible cases, that R is reflexive, antisymmetric, and transitive, and is <u>not</u> symmetric. $\square$

The four properties in Definition 3 are dealt with further in the exercises that follow, as well as throughout the remainder of this chapter.

DEFINITION 4

Let R be a relation from a set A to a set B. We define the **domain of R** to be the set dom $R = \{x \in A \mid x\,R\,y \text{ for some } y \in B\}$ and the **range of R** by the rule rng $R = \{y \in B \mid x\,R\,y \text{ for some } x \in A\}$.

Clearly whenever R is a relation from A to B, dom R is a subset of A and rng R is a subset of B. In fact, dom R consists of those elements of A that are first elements of ordered pairs in R, whereas rng R comprises the elements of B that are second elements of ordered pairs in R.

EXAMPLE 9   Using the sets and relations defined in Example 1, we note that dom $R_1 = \{1, 2, 3\} = A$, whereas rng $R_1 = \{x, y, z\} \subseteq B$. Also, dom $R_2 = \{2\}$, whereas rng $R_2 = B$. Borrowing from Example 3, we observe that dom $R_7 = H$ (since everyone has biological parents), but rng $R_7 \subset H$ (since not everyone <u>is</u> a parent). $\square$

DEFINITION 5

Let R be a relation from a set A to a set B. We define the relation **R inverse**, denoted R^{-1}, by the rule $R^{-1} = \{(y, x) \mid (x, y) \in R\}$.

Clearly R^{-1} is a relation from B to A; it is gotten from R by flipping over all the ordered pairs in R. We gather together other properties of R^{-1} in the next theorem.

THEOREM 3

Let R be a nonempty relation from A to B. Then:

(a)   dom (R^{-1}) = rng R

(b)   rng (R^{-1}) = dom R

(c) $R = (R^{-1})^{-1}$

(d) $R = R^{-1}$ if and only if $A = B$ and R is symmetric

(e) $R \cap R^{-1} = I_A$ if and only if $A = B$ and R is antisymmetric

Partial proof   We consider the "only if" part of (e). Suppose $R \cap R^{-1} = I_A$. To prove $A = B$, let $x \in A$ be given. Then $(x, x) \in I_A$. Since $I_A = R \cap R^{-1}$, then $(x, x) \in R$. Since R is a relation from A to B, we must have $x \in B$. Thus $A \subseteq B$. The fact that $B \subseteq A$ can be proved in an identical manner. To show that R is antisymmetric, suppose that $(x, y) \in R$ and $(y, x) \in R$, we claim $x = y$. Since $(y, x) \in R$, then $(x, y) \in R^{-1}$, so that $(x, y) \in R \cap R^{-1} = I_A$. Hence, by definition of I_A, we conclude $x = y$, as desired.

Proving the remaining properties is left to you in Exercises 9 and 10.   □

Exercises

1. (a)   Prove that the cross product distributes over intersection [Theorem 1(b)].
(b)   Prove that $(X - Y) \times Z \subseteq (X \times Z) - (Y \times Z)$ for any three sets X, Y, and Z.
(c)   Prove parts (d), (e), and (f) of Theorem 1.

2. Write down five specific ordered pairs in each of the following relations from Example 2 through 6 of the text:

★(a) R_5 (b) R_8
(c) R_9, R_{10}, and R_{11} (d) R_{12}, R_{13}, and R_{14}
(e) R_{15}, R_{16}, and R_{17} (Let $X = \{1, 2, \ldots, 10\}$ in Example 6.)

3. ★(a)   Write symbolically, using quantifiers and ordered pair notation, the definitions of <u>R is transitive</u> and <u>R is antisymmetric</u>. [*Hint:* See (a) and (b) of Definition 3.]
★(b)   Write symbolically, using quantifiers and ordered pair notation, the <u>negation of</u> each of the four parts of Definition 3. (e.g., What is the precise meaning of "R is not reflexive"?)

4. Determine which of the four properties; reflexive, symmetric, antisymmetric, and transitive, are possessed by each of the relations R_1 through R_{17} in Examples 1 through 6.

5. Determine which of the four properties from Exercise 4 are satisfied by each of the following relations on the set $\mathbf{R}$ of all real numbers:

★(a) $R_{18} = \{(x, y) \,|\, y = 1/x\}$ (b) $R_{19} = \{(x, y) \,|\, x^2 = y^2\}$
★(c) $R_{20} = \{(x, y) \,|\, |x - y| \le 1\}$ (d) $R_{21} = \{(x, y) \,|\, x \ne y\}$

6. (a)   Show that if A is a nonempty set, then the relation $R = \varnothing$ on A is symmetric and transitive, but not reflexive.
(b)   Give an example of a relation $R \ne \varnothing$ on a set A which is symmetric and transitive, but not reflexive.
(c)   Find a flaw in the following argument, which purports to prove "a relation $R \ne \varnothing$ on a set A, which is symmetric and transitive, is necessarily reflexive."

"Proof"   Let $x \in A$. We claim $(x, x) \in R$. Choose $y \in A$ such that $(x, y) \in R$. Since R is symmetric and $(x, y) \in R$, then $(y, x) \in R$. Since R is transitive, and since both (x, y) and (y, x) are in R, we conclude $(x, x) \in R$, as desired.

7. Find the domain and range of each of the following relations:

(a) R_3 and R_4, Example 1   (b) R_5, Example 2

(c) R_7 and R_8, Example 3   (d) R_{10} and R_{11}, Example 4

(e) R_{15} and R_{16}, Example 6   (f) $R_{23} = \{(x, y) \in \mathbf{R} \times \mathbf{R} \,|\, y = \sqrt{x - 5}\}$

(g) $R_{22} = \{(1, 5), (1, 6), (2, 6), (2, 7), (3, 7), (3, 8), (4, 8), (4, 9), (5, 9), (5, 10)\}$

8. Find R^{-1} for each of the relations:

(a) R_2, Example 1   (b) R_5, Example 2

(c) R_7, Example 3   (d) R_{11}, Example 4

(e) R_{12} and R_{14}, Example 5

9. Prove (a), (b), and (c) of Theorem 3.

10. (a) Prove that a relation R on a nonempty set A is reflexive if and only if $I_A \subseteq R$.

(b) Prove that if a reflexive relation R on nonempty set A is both symmetric and antisymmetric, then $R = I_A$, the identity relation on A.

★(c) Prove that a relation R on a set A is symmetric if and only if $R = R^{-1}$.

(d) Prove that if a nonempty relation R on a set A is antisymmetric, then $R \cap R^{-1} = I_A$. [This is the unproved part of (e), Theorem 3.]

(e) Prove that if R is any nonempty relation on a set A, then the relations $R \cap R^{-1}$ and $R \cup R^{-1}$ are symmetric.

11. Given a relation R on a set A, define, for each $x \in A$, the set $[x]$ by the rule $[x] = \{y \in A \,|\, (x, y) \in R\}$. Note that $[x]$ consists of all elements of A to which x is related by the relation R. Notice also that $[x]$ is clearly a subset of A for each $x \in A$. Let $A = \{1, 2, 3, 4, 5\}$. Calculate $[1]$, $[2]$, $[3]$, $[4]$, and $[5]$ for each of the following relations on A:

(a) $R_{24} = \{(1, 1), (2, 2), (3, 3), (4, 4), (5, 5), (1, 2), (1, 3), (1, 4), (1, 5), (2, 3), (2, 4),$
     $(2, 5), (3, 4), (3, 5), (4, 5)\}$

(b) $R_{25} = \{(1, 1), (2, 2), (3, 3), (4, 4), (5, 5)\}$

★(c) $R_{26} = \{(1, 1), (2, 2), (3, 3), (1, 3), (3, 1), (2, 3), (3, 2), (4, 5), (5, 4)\}$

(d) $R_{27} = A \times A$

(e) $R_{28} = \{(1, 1), (2, 2), (3, 3), (4, 4), (5, 5), (2, 3), (3, 2), (4, 5), (5, 4)\}$

7.2 Equivalence Relations

An equivalence relation is a special kind of relation on a set; whenever two elements x and y of a set A are related by an equivalence relation on A, there is some property that x and y share in common, some point of view from which x and y can be regarded as indistinguishable.

EXAMPLE 1 (a) Consider the relation on $\mathbf{R}$, $R_{19} = \{(x, y) \,|\, x^2 = y^2\}$, from Exercise 5, Article 7.1. Two real numbers are related by R_{19} if and only if they have the <u>same absolute value</u>. We will soon see that R_{19} is an equivalence relation on $\mathbf{R}$.

(b)   Recall the relation R_{17} from Example 6, Article 7.1. Two subsets of a finite set X are related by R_{17} if and only if they have the same number of elements. R_{17} is an equivalence relation on $A = \mathscr{P}(X)$.

(c)   Define a relation R_{29} on the set S of all students in Math 197 in the fall semester by $R_{29} = \{(x, y) | x \text{ and } y \text{ achieve the same numerical grade on Test } \#1\}$. R_{29} is an equivalence relation on S.   □

We now proceed to the formal definition of *equivalence relation on a set A*. Our definition uses terminology introduced in Definition 3, Article 7.1.

DEFINITION   1

Let A be a set and E a relation on A. We say that E is an **equivalence relation on A** if and only if E is reflexive on A, symmetric, and transitive. (RST)

The most basic example of an equivalence relation on any set A is equality; that is, $E = \{(x, y) | x = y\}$, also denoted $I_A = \{(x, x) | x \in A\}$. To show that equality is an equivalence relation, we note that the reflexive property requires simply that every element of A equal itself, a true statement. Symmetry states that if $x = y$, then $y = x$ for any $x, y \in A$, again true. Transitivity means that if $x = y$ and $y = z$, then $x = z$ for any elements x, y, and z of A, which is also true.

At the other extreme, the whole cartesian product $A \times A$ is an equivalence relation on any set A (verify!). It is not a very useful one, however, since any two elements of A are related by it; certainly we will not often want to view all elements of a set A as indistinguishable from one another!

Returning to Example 1 and considering, for instance, part (b), we note that R_{17} is reflexive, since every subset of X surely has the same number of elements as itself. It is symmetric since if X and Y have the same number of elements, so do Y and X. It is transitive since if X and Y have the same number of elements, as do Y and Z, then certainly X and Z have the same number of elements. You should carry out similar verifications for parts (a) and (c).

For examples of relations that are not equivalence relations, you may refer to many of the examples R_1 through R_{28} in Article 7.1. Among these, only $R_8, R_9, R_{13}, R_{14}, R_{17}, R_{19}, R_{25}, R_{27}$, and R_{28} are equivalence relations. A relation fails to be an equivalence relation as soon as it fails to possess one of the three defining properties. The relation $\leq$ on $\mathbf{Z}$ (i.e., the example R_{11}) is reflexive on $\mathbf{Z}$ and transitive, but it is not symmetric (verify!), and so is not an equivalence relation on $\mathbf{Z}$.

EXAMPLE 2   Show that the relation E on $A = \mathbf{R} - \{0\}$ defined by $E = \{(x, y) | xy > 0\}$ is an equivalence relation on A, whereas the relation $N = \{(x, y) | xy < 0\}$ satisfies only symmetry.

Solution   To show E is reflexive, let $x \in A$ be given. Note that $(x, x) \in E$ means that $x^2 > 0$, clearly a true statement. For symmetry, suppose $x, y \in \mathbf{R}$ and $x \, E \, y$, so that $xy > 0$. Since $xy = yx$, we conclude $yx > 0$ so that $y \, E \, x$, as desired. As to transitivity, suppose $x, y, z \in \mathbf{R}$, that $x \, E \, y$ and $y \, E \, z$. To prove $x \, E \, z$, we need that $xz > 0$. We proceed by division into the cases $x > 0$ and $x < 0$. If $x > 0$, then since $xy > 0$, we have $y > 0$. Since $y > 0$ and $yz > 0$, then $z > 0$. Since $x > 0$ and $z > 0$, we conclude $xz > 0$, as desired. The argument for the case $x < 0$ is similar.

The relation N is clearly symmetric, since $yx = xy$, so that $xy < 0$ certainly implies $yx < 0$ for any $x, y \in A$. It is not reflexive because, for instance, $(5, 5) \notin N$, since $5^2 = 25$ is not less than 0. It is not transitive since $(5, -5) \in N$ (Why?) and $(-5, 7) \in N$, but $(5, 7) \notin N$. $\square$

EXAMPLE 3   Show that the relation "congruence modulo 5" (R_{13} from Example 5, Article 7.1) is an equivalence relation on $\mathbf{Z}$.

Solution   Integers m and n are related by this relation, denoted $m \equiv n$ mod 5, if and only if 5 divides the difference $m - n$. You may wish to recall Examples 2 and 7, as well as Exercise 2, from Article 6.1. For the reflexive property, if $m \in \mathbf{Z}$, then $m \equiv m$ mod 5, since $m - m = 0$ and $5 \,|\, 0$, by (e) of Exercise 2 (Article 6.1). For symmetry, assume $m, n \in \mathbf{Z}$ and $m \equiv n$ mod 5; thus 5 divides $m - n$. Since $n - m = -(m - n)$, and since 5 divides $-(m - n)$ by (h) of the aforementioned Exercise 2, then 5 divides $n - m$, so that $n \equiv m$ mod 5, as desired. To prove transitivity, suppose $m, n, p \in \mathbf{Z}$, that $5 \,|\, (m - n)$ and $5 \,|\, (n - p)$. We must prove $5 \,|\, (m - p)$. But $m - p = (m - n) + (n - p)$, and 5 divides the latter sum, by Example 7, Article 6.1. $\square$

At first glance, the relation "congruence modulo 5" seems to be an exception to our earlier statement that objects related by an equivalence relation share something in common. The fact that -2 is congruent to 13, modulo 5, seems to be saying something only about *the difference* of the two numbers, not about any property that the numbers might have in common. It can be proved, however, that two integers m and n are congruent modulo 5 if and only if both yield *the same remainder* upon division by 5, in accordance with the conditions of the *division algorithm for* $\mathbf{Z}$ (see Exercise 4).

It was observed earlier that a majority of the examples R_1 through R_{28} in Article 7.1 are not equivalence relations. For each such relation, either zero, one, or two of the three conditions RST are satisfied. An interesting exercise is to find examples of relations corresponding to the eight possible combinations of the three properties (e.g., R, NS, T or NR, NS, T, etc.).

EXAMPLE 4   Give two examples, one by means of listing ordered pairs, the other described by a rule, of relations that are reflexive, symmetric, and not transitive.

Solution   Let $A = \{1, 2, 3\}$ and define R_{30} on A by $R_{30} = \{(1, 1), (2, 2),$ $(3, 3), (1, 2), (2, 1), (1, 3), (3, 1)\}$. R_{30} is clearly reflexive on A (due to the presence of the first three ordered pairs) and symmetric. But R_{30} is not transitive; for example, $(2, 1)$ and $(1, 3)$ are in R_{30}, but $(2, 3)$ is not.

For our second example, let $A = \mathbf{R}$ and recall from Exercise 5(c), Article 7.1, the relation $R_{20} = \{(x, y) \in \mathbf{R} \times \mathbf{R} \mid |x - y| \leq 1\}$. For any $x \in \mathbf{R}$, $|x - x| = 0 \leq 1$, so R_{20} is reflexive. If $x, y \in \mathbf{R}$ with $|x - y| \leq 1$, then $|y - x| = |x - y| \leq 1$, so that R_{20} is symmetric. R_{20} is not transitive since, for example, $(\frac{1}{4}, \frac{1}{2}) \in R_{20}$ and $(\frac{1}{2}, \frac{11}{8}) \in R_{20}$, but $(\frac{1}{4}, \frac{11}{8}) \notin R_{20}$.   □

Discovering relations similar to those in Example 4, involving the other combinations of R, S, and T is the goal of Exercise 8.

The most important fact to understand about equivalence relations is that each equivalence relation on a set A generates a unique *partition* of A, and vice versa. This correspondence is the topic of the next article. In the following definition, based on Exercise 11, Article 7.1, we take a first step toward this correspondence.

DEFINITION 2
Given a relation R on a set A, define for each $x \in A$ the set $[x]$ by the rule $[x] = \{y \in A \mid (x, y) \in R\}$. The set $[x]$ is the subset of A consisting of all elements of A to which x is related. If R is an equivalence relation on A, we call $[x]$ the **equivalence class determined by x** and denote by the symbol A/R the set $\{[x] \mid x \in A\}$ of all equivalence classes.

EXAMPLE 5   (a)   The relations $R_{31} = \{(1, 1), (2, 2), (3, 3), (4, 4), (1, 2), (2, 3),$ $(3, 2), (1, 3), (3, 1), (4, 5), (5, 4)\}$ and $R_{32} = \{(2, 2), (3, 3), (4, 4), (5, 5), (3, 4),$ $(4, 3), (3, 5), (5, 3), (4, 5), (5, 4)\}$ are not equivalence relations on $A = \{1, 2, 3, 4, 5\}$. Calculate $[1], [2], [3], [4],$ and $[5]$ for both relations.
   (b)   The relation $R_{33} = \{(1, 1), (2, 2), (3, 3), (4, 4), (5, 5), (2, 5), (5, 2),$ $(3, 5), (5, 3), (2, 3), (3, 2)\}$ is an equivalence relation on $A = \{1, 2, 3, 4, 5\}$. Calculate A/R_{33}.

Solution   (a)   For R_{31}, $[1] = \{1, 2, 3\}$, $[2] = \{2, 3\}$, $[3] = \{1, 2, 3\}$, $[4] = \{4, 5\}$, and $[5] = \{4\}$. For R_{32}, we have $[1] = \emptyset$, $[2] = \{2\}$, $[3] = \{3, 4, 5\}$, $[4] = \{3, 4, 5\}$, and $[5] = \{3, 4, 5\}$.
   (b)   For the equivalence relation R_{33}, $[1] = \{1\}$, $[4] = \{4\}$, and $[2] = [3] = [5] = \{2, 3, 5\}$. Thus $A/R_{33} = \{\{1\}, \{4\}, \{2, 3, 5\}\}$.   □

Note the qualitative difference between the results in (a) and those in (b) of Example 5. The subsets generated in (b) present a much "tidier" picture than those in (a). Specifically, the sets $[m]$ in (b) have the properties that all are nonempty, any two of them are either identical or disjoint, and each element of A is contained in at least one of them. The collections generated by R_{31} and R_{32} both fail to have at least one of these three properties. The ideas in Example 5 are the basis for both Exercise 10 and for our work in the next article.

Exercises

1. Prove that the relations R_{19} and R_{29}, from parts (a) and (c) of Example 1, are equivalence relations.

2. Let A be the set of all people living in the year 1987. For each of the following relations $S_1, \ldots, S_5$, interpret the three properties RST, and verify that each of the five is an equivalence relation (in some cases, on a specified <u>subset</u> of A):

(a) $S_1 = \{(x, y) | x$ and y are of the same sex$\}$

★(b) $S_2 = \{(x, y) | x$ and y have the same biological parents$\}$

(c) $S_3 = \{(x, y) | x$ and y are the same weight (measured to the nearest pound)$\}$

(d) $S_4 = \{(x, y) | x$ and y have the same grade point average$\}$, where S_4 is defined on the set of all college seniors graduating during 1987.

(e) $S_5 = \{(x, y) | x$ and y had the same number of home runs during the 1986 season$\}$, where S_5 is defined on the set of all major league baseball players during 1986.

3. Show that the relation $R_{34} = \{(x, y) \in \mathbf{R} \times \mathbf{R} | xy \geq 0\}$ <u>is not</u> an equivalence relation on $\mathbf{R}$.

4. The division algorithm for $\mathbf{Z}$ states that, given any two integers m and d, where $d > 0$, there exist unique integers q and r such that $m = qd + r$ and $0 \leq r < d$. The integer q is called the *quotient* and r is called the *remainder*.

(a)   Find q and r for:

  ★(i) $m = 17, d = 4$ (ii) $m = 3, d = 5$

  (iii) $m = 0, d = 5$ ★(iv) $m = -17, d = 5$

(b)   Check that the integers -3 and 27 are congruent modulo 5. Given $m_1 = -3$ and $d = 5$, find q_1 and r_1. Given $m_2 = 27$ and $d = 5$, find q_2 and r_2.

★(c)   Mimic (b), letting $m_1 = 13, m_2 = -17$, and $d = 5$, noting that $13 \approx -17$ mod 5.

★(d)   Mimic (b), letting $m_1 = 8, m_2 = -3$, and $d = 5$, noting that 8 is not congruent to -3 modulo 5.

(e)   What conclusion do the results in (b), (c), and (d) seem to suggest?

5. (a)   Define a relation *congruence modulo 9* (denoted $\equiv_9$) on the set $\mathbf{Z}$ in a manner analogous to the definition of congruence modulo 5 (recall Example 5, Article 7.1). Prove that $\equiv_9$ is an equivalence relation on $\mathbf{Z}$.

(b)   Define a relation $\sim$ on $\mathbf{R}$ by the rule $x \sim y$ if and only if $x - y$ is an integer. Prove that $\sim$ is an equivalence relation on $\mathbf{R}$.

(c)   Define a relation $\approx$ on $\mathbf{R}$ by the rule $x \approx y$ if and only if $x - y$ is a rational number. Prove that $\approx$ is an equivalence relation on R. (*Note:* Use the facts that the sum of two rational numbers is rational and the negative of a rational number is rational.)

6. (a)   Let f be a real-valued function having domain $\mathbf{R}$. Define a relation $\sim_f$ on $\mathbf{R}$ by the rule $x \sim_f y$ if and only if $f(x) = f(y)$. Prove that $\sim_f$ is an equivalence relation on $\mathbf{R}$.

(b) Let F be the set of all real-valued functions having domain **R**. Define a relation $\sim$ on F by the rule $f \sim g$ if and only if $\{x \mid f(x) \neq g(x)\}$ is finite. Prove that $\sim$ is an equivalence relation on F. (*Hint:* Recall Exercise 7, Article 6.2.)

★**7.** Define a relation $\sim$ on the set $Q = \mathbf{Z} \times (\mathbf{Z} - \{0\})$ by the rule $(m, n) \sim (p, q)$ if and only if $mq = np$. Prove that $\sim$ is an equivalence relation on Q.

8. Give two examples, one by listing ordered pairs, the other described by a rule (as in Example 4), of relations which are:

(a) NR, NS, T   *(b)* R, NS, T
(c) NR, S, T   ★*(d)* R, NS, NT
(e) NR, S, NT   *(f)* NR, NS, T

9. Determine which of the three properties R, S, and T are possessed by each of the following relations:

(a) $L = $ the set of all lines in 3-space. Line l is related to line m if and only if
    (i) l equals m or l is parallel to m *(ii)* l is perpendicular to m
    (iii) l and m are coplanar   *(iv)* l and m are skew
  ★*(v)* l and m intersect in a point
(b) $D = $ the set of all triangles in a plane. Triangle X is related to triangle Y if and only if
    (i) X and Y are congruent   *(ii)* X and Y are similar

10. Calculate all equivalence classes $[n]$, where the integer n ranges from $n = -9$ to $n = 10$, corresponding to the equivalence relation, congruence modulo 5. Describe the set $Z/\equiv_5$ of all equivalence classes.

7.3 Equivalence Classes and Partitions

In Example 5(b) of the previous article we observed that the collection of subsets $[x]$ corresponding to a particular <u>equivalence relation</u> had a form different from that associated with the relations from part (a) of the example (which were <u>not</u> equivalence relations). In particular, we noted that the collection A/R_{33} satisfies three properties, but neither of the collections from (a) satisfies all these three properties. The next definition highlights the three properties.

DEFINITION 1
Let A be a set. A collection $\mathfrak{P}$ of subsets of A is said to be a **partition of A** if and only if:

(i) $S \neq \varnothing$ for each $S \in \mathfrak{P}$.
(ii) If $S_1, S_2 \in \mathfrak{P}$, then either $S_1 = S_2$ or $S_1 \cap S_2 = \varnothing$.
(iii) For each $a \in A$, there is some $S \in \mathfrak{P}$ such that $a \in S$. In symbols, $\cup (S \mid S \in \mathfrak{P}) = A$.

The elements of $\mathfrak{P}$ are often referred to as **cells** of the partition.

Condition (i) states that each cell is nonempty. Condition (ii) asserts that any two cells are either identical or disjoint (or equivalently that any two distinct cells are disjoint; recall from Chapter 2 that $p \vee q$ and $\sim p \to q$ are equivalent). Condition (iii) requires that every element of A fall within at least one of the cells. The division of the real numbers into positive and negative numbers and zero is an example of a "three-celled" partition of $\mathbf{R}$. Cells consisting of all rational and all irrational numbers provide a two-celled partition of $\mathbf{R}$, whereas the odd and even integers yield a two-celled partition of $\mathbf{Z}$. Any set A can be partitioned into a collection of singleton cells by $\mathfrak{P} = \{\{x\} \mid x \in A\}$. If A is infinite, the latter will constitute a partition with infinitely many cells. Another example of a partition having infinitely many cells is the partition $\mathfrak{P}_1 = \{\{0\}, \{-1, 1\}, \{-2, 2\}, \ldots\}$ of $\mathbf{Z}$. Even small sets, such as $A = \{1, 2, 3, 4, 5\}$, have a large number of partitions, for example, $\{\{1, 5\}, \{3, 4\}, \{2\}\}$ and $\{\{1, 2, 3, 5\}, \{4\}\}$. Determining the number of partitions of an n-element set is a difficult counting problem.

One connection between partitions and equivalence relations lies in the fact that any partition $\mathfrak{P}$ of a set A yields, in a canonical (i.e., standard) way, a corresponding equivalence relation.

THEOREM 1

Let A be a nonempty set and $\mathfrak{P}$ a partition of A. Define a relation $\sim$ on A by the rule $x \sim y$ if and only if there exists a cell $X \in \mathfrak{P}$ such that $x \in X$ and $y \in X$. Then $\sim$ is an equivalence relation on A.

Proof   We must prove that $\sim$ is reflexive, symmetric, and transitive.

   (R)   Let $x \in A$ be given. By (iii) of Definition 1, x lies in some cell of the partition. Clearly x lies in the same cell as itself so that $x \sim x$.

   (S)   Given $x, y \in A$, suppose $x \sim y$ so that x and y lie in some cell of $\mathfrak{P}$. Clearly then y and x lie in that same cell of $\mathfrak{P}$, so that $y \sim x$, as desired.

   (T)   Given $x, y, z \in A$, suppose that $x \sim y$ and $y \sim z$. To prove $x \sim z$, we must show that there is some cell $X \in \mathfrak{P}$ such that $x \in X$ and $z \in X$. Now since $x \sim y$, then there is a cell X_1 of $\mathfrak{P}$ such that both x and y are elements of X_1. Since $y \sim z$, there is a cell X_2 containing both y and z. Since $y \in X_1 \cap X_2$, then $X_1 = X_2$, by (ii) of Definition 1. Let X be this set $X_1 \, (= X_2)$ and note that x and z lie in X, as desired. $\square$

Because the equivalence relation $\sim$ of Theorem 1 is derived from a given partition $\mathfrak{P}$ of A in a canonical way, we label it by the symbol $A/\mathfrak{P}$, and call it the *equivalence relation determined by the partition* $\mathfrak{P}$.

EXAMPLE 1   Given the partition $\mathfrak{P} = \{\{2\}, \{1, 3, 4\}, \{5\}\}$ of the set $A = \{1, 2, 3, 4, 5\}$, list explicitly the ordered pairs in the corresponding equivalence relation $A/\mathfrak{P}$.

Solution

$$A/\mathfrak{P} = \{(2,2), (1,1), (3,3), (4,4), (1,3), (3,1), (1,4), (4,1), (3,4), (4,3), (5,5)\}.$$

$\square$

We have just seen that any partition of a set A leads automatically to a corresponding equivalence relation on A. A perhaps more surprising fact is that any equivalence relation on a set leads to a corresponding partition, whose cells are precisely the equivalence classes. [This fact, although possibly not predicted, should not be entirely unanticipated; recall Example 5(b) of the preceding article.] A first step toward this result is provided in the following lemma.

LEMMA

Let $\sim$ be an equivalence relation on a nonempty set A. For each $x \in A$, let $[x] = \{y \in A \,|\, x \sim y\}$, the equivalence class of x. Then:

(a) $[x] \neq \emptyset$ for each $x \in A$
(b) If $x, y \in A$, then either $[x] = [y]$ or $[x] \cap [y] = \emptyset$
(c) $\cup ([x] \,|\, x \in A) = A$

Proof   (a)   Given $x \in A$, we note that $x \sim x$, since $\sim$ is reflexive. Hence $x \in [x]$, which is thereby nonempty.

(b)   This is the most interesting result of the three and hardest to prove. It asserts that two equivalence classes generated by an equivalence relation are either identical or disjoint. To conclude "either $[x] = [y]$ or $[x] \cap [y] = \emptyset$," we recall the approach of Article 6.2 (particularly Examples 1 and 2); assume the negation of one of these conclusions and try to derive the other. Specifically, suppose $[x] \cap [y] \neq \emptyset$, so that there exists $z \in [x] \cap [y]$. We claim $[x] = [y]$; we will prove this by proving mutual inclusion. To show $[x] \subseteq [y]$, suppose $w \in [x]$. To conclude $w \in [y]$, we must prove $y \sim w$. Now since $z \in [x]$, we have $x \sim z$. Since $z \in [y]$ and $w \in [x]$, we have $y \sim z$ and $x \sim w$, respectively. How can we piece together the three known equivalences to arrive at the desired one? We have $y \sim z$, $x \sim z$, and $x \sim w$; we want $y \sim w$. Note first that since $x \sim z$, then by symmetry, $z \sim x$. Then since $y \sim z$ and $z \sim x$, we have $y \sim x$ by transitivity. Finally, since $y \sim x$ and $x \sim w$, we have, by transitivity, $y \sim w$, our desired result. Hence $[x] \subseteq [y]$. The reverse inclusion follows by an identical argument.

(c)   Clearly $\cup ([x] \,|\, x \in A) \subseteq A$, since each equivalence class $[x]$ is a subset of A. Conversely, if $y \in A$, then $y \in [y]$, as noted in (a), so that $y \in [x]$ for some $x \in A$ and therefore $y \in \cup ([x] \,|\, x \in A)$, as desired. $\square$

Comparison of (a), (b), and (c) of Lemma 1 with requirements (i), (ii), and (iii) of Definition 1, leads immediately to the following theorem.

THEOREM 2

Let E be an equivalence relation on a set A. Then the collection $A/E = \{[x] \,|\, x \in A\}$ of equivalence classes generated by E is a partition of A.

Additional properties of equivalence classes may be found in Exercise 4.

Consider the equivalence relation on $A = \{1, 2, 3, 4, 5\}$ given by $E = \{(1, 1), (2, 2), (3, 3), (4, 4), (5, 5), (1, 3), (3, 1), (1, 4), (4, 1), (3, 4), (4, 3), (2, 5), (5, 2)\}$. Since $[1] = [3] = [4] = \{1, 3, 4\}$ and $[2] = [5] = \{2, 5\}$, the set of equivalence classes (which is necessarily a partition of A, by Theorem 2) equals $\{\{1, 3, 4\}, \{2, 5\}\}$. Suppose now we apply Theorem 1 to A/E and compute the corresponding equivalence relation $A/(A/E)$. The result, which you may easily verify, is precisely the original equivalence relation E. On the other hand, suppose we start with a partition $\mathfrak{P} = \{\{1\}, \{2, 3\}, \{4\}, \{5\}\}$ of the same A. We calculate easily that $A/\mathfrak{P} = \{(1, 1), (2, 2), (3, 3), (4, 4), (5, 5), (2, 3), (3, 2)\}$. Then since $[1] = \{1\}, [2] = [3] = \{2, 3\}, [4] = \{4\}$, and $[5] = \{5\}$, we conclude that $A/(A/\mathfrak{P}) = \{\{1\}, \{2, 3\}, \{4\}, \{5\}\} = \mathfrak{P}$.

The upshot of the two preceding examples is that the two canonical processes by which we go from equivalence relation E to partition A/E (A/E is the set of equivalence classes generated by E) and from partition $\mathfrak{P}$ to equivalence relation $A/\mathfrak{P}$ (two elements of A are related by $A/\mathfrak{P}$ if and only if they are contained in some cell of $\mathfrak{P}$) are <u>inverse processes</u>. This means that by carrying out these two processes consecutively, we proceed <u>either</u> $E \to (A/E) \to E$ <u>or</u> $\mathfrak{P} \to (A/\mathfrak{P}) \to \mathfrak{P}$. The next theorem formalizes these facts.

THEOREM 3

(a) Let E be an equivalence relation on a set A. Then $A/(A/E) = E$.
(b) Let $\mathfrak{P}$ be a partition of a set A. Then $A/(A/\mathfrak{P}) = \mathfrak{P}$.

Proof We prove (a), leaving (b) as Exercise 5. We must show $A/(A/E) \subseteq E$ and $E \subseteq A/(A/E)$. Since E is an equivalence relation on A, then A/E is a partition of A (by Theorem 2) and so $A/(A/E)$ is an equivalence relation on A (by Theorem 1). Let $(x, y) \in A/(A/E)$. Then there exists a cell X of the partition A/E such that $x \in X$ and $y \in X$. But the cells of A/E are precisely the equivalence classes generated by E. Since X is therefore an equivalence class generated by E and since X contains both x and y, it follows from Exercise 4 that $[x] = X = [y]$ so that $x \, E \, y$ or $(x, y) \in E$, as desired. Thus $A/(A/E) \subseteq E$.

Conversely, suppose $(x, y) \in E$. To show $(x, y) \in A/(A/E)$, we must prove that there exists a cell X of the partition A/E that contains both x and y. Now since $x \, E \, y$, then $[x] = [y]$, by Exercise 4(c). Letting $X = [x] \, (= [y])$, we note that X is a cell of A/E and contains both x and y, as desired. Hence $(x, y) \in A/(A/E)$ and $E \subseteq A/(A/E)$, as we wished to prove. $\square$

You may have already discovered (using Exercise 10, Article 7.2) that the set of equivalence classes corresponding to the equivalence relation $\equiv_5$ on $\mathbf{Z}$ looks like $\{\{\ldots, -15, -10, -5, 0, 5, 10, 15, \ldots\}, \{\ldots, -14, -9, -4, 1, 6, 11, 16, \ldots\}, \{\ldots, -13, -8, -3, 2, 7, 12, 17, \ldots\}, \{\ldots, -12,$

$-7, -2, 3, 8, 13, 18, \ldots\}, \{\ldots, -11, -6, -1, 4, 9, 14, 19, \ldots\}\}$, a collection of subsets of $\mathbf{Z}$, which we may now recognize as a five-celled partition
of $\mathbf{Z}$, where each cell is infinite. This may be abbreviated to $\mathbf{Z}/\equiv_5 = \{[0],$
$[1], [2], [3], [4]\}$, where you will note that $[2]$, for instance, consists precisely of those integers that yield a remainder of 2 when divided by 5, in
accordance with the division algorithm theorem (recall Exercise 4, Article
7.2). In Chapter 9 where we study certain algebraic structures, we will see
that many sets of equivalence classes such as $\mathbf{Z}/\equiv_5$ may be equipped with
algebraic operations resembling, or based on, ordinary addition and multiplication of real numbers. The resulting mathematical structures, often
called *quotient structures*, are the basis for many important mathematical
constructions. Included among these is the theory of quotient groups and
rings (topics from the area of abstract algebra), the development of the
rational number system from the integers, and the development of the real
number system from the rationals. We will get a taste of the latter two
topics in Chapter 10.

Exercises

1. Describe the partition of the set $A = \{a, b, c, d, e, f\}$ corresponding to the equivalence relations:

(a) $E_1 = \{(a, a), (b, b), (c, c), (d, d), (e, e), (f, f), (a, d), (d, a), (d, f), (f, d), (a, f),$
      $(f, a)\}$
(b) $E_2 = \{(a, a), (b, b), (c, c), (d, d), (e, e), (f, f)\}$
★(c) $E_3 = \{(a, a), (b, b), (c, c), (d, d), (e, e), (f, f), (a, b), (b, a), (c, e), (e, c), (d, f), (f, d)\}$
(d) $E_4 = A \times A$
(e) $E_5 = \{(a, a), (b, b), (c, c), (d, d), (e, e), (f, f), (c, d), (d, c), (c, e), (e, c), (c, f), (f, c),$
      $(d, e), (e, d), (d, f), (f, d), (e, f), (f, e)\}$

2. Describe, by listing all ordered pairs, the equivalence relation on the set $A =$
$\{a, b, c, d, e, f\}$ corresponding to the partitions:

(a) $\mathfrak{P}_1 = \{\{a, c, e\}, \{b, d, f\}\}$ ★(b) $\mathfrak{P}_2 = \{\{a\}, \{b\}, \{c, d, f\}, \{e\}\}$
(c) $\mathfrak{P}_3 = \{\{a, b, c, d, e, f\}\}$ (d) $\mathfrak{P}_4 = \{\{a, c\}, \{e, f\}, \{b\}, \{d\}\}$
(e) $\mathfrak{P}_5 = \{\{a\}, \{b\}, \{c\}, \{d\}, \{e\}, \{f\}\}$

3. Referring to the equivalence relations defined in Articles 7.1, 7.2, and 7.3 of the
text, describe the partition of the appropriate set A determined by each of the
following equivalence relations. When possible, determine explicitly the number of
cells in each partition:

(a) $R_8 = \{(x, y) \mid x$ and y are both male or both female$\}$, $A =$ set of all people living
      in 1987
★(b) $R_9 = \{(m, n) \mid m$ and n are both even or both odd$\}$, $A = \mathbf{Z}$
(c) $R_{14} = \{(m, n) \mid m = n\}$, $A = \mathbf{Z}$
(d) $R_{17} = \{(M, N) \mid n(M) = n(N)\}$, $A = \mathscr{P}(X)$, where $X = \{1, 2, \ldots, 9, 10\}$
(e) $R_{19} = \{(x, y) \mid x^2 = y^2\}$, $A = \mathbf{R}$
(f)   The relation "*congruence modulo 9*" on $\mathbf{Z}$, from Exercise 5(a), Article 7.2

(g)   The equivalence relation $\sim$ on **R** defined in Exercise 5(b), Article 7.2
(h)   The equivalence relation $\approx$ on **R** defined in Exercise 5(c), Article 7.2
(i)   The equivalence relation $\sim_f$ on **R** defined in Exercise 6(a), Article 7.2
★(j)   The equivalence relation $\sim$ on F (where F is the set of all real-valued functions with domain **R**) defined in Exercise 6(b), Article 7.2
(k)   The equivalence relation $\sim$ on $\mathbf{Z} \times (\mathbf{Z} - \{0\})$ defined in Exercise 7, Article 7.2

4. Let E be an equivalence relation on a set A. For each $x \in A$, let $[x]$ represent the equivalence class determined by x; that is, $[x] = \{y \in A \mid x \, E \, y\}$. Prove:

(a) $x \in [x]$ for all $x \in A$
(b)   For all $x, y \in A$, $y \in [x] \Leftrightarrow x \, E \, y$
★(c)   For all $x, y \in A$, $[x] = [y] \Leftrightarrow x \, E \, y$

5. Prove (b) of Theorem 3: If $\mathscr{P}$ is a partition of a set A, then $A/(A/\mathscr{P}) = \mathscr{P}$.

6. Prove that if E_1 and E_2 are both equivalence relations on a set A, then $E_1 \cap E_2$ is an equivalence relation on A. How is the partition $A/(E_1 \cap E_2)$ related to the partitions A/E_1 and A/E_2? Is the <u>union</u> $E_1 \cup E_2$ of two equivalence relations on A necessarily an equivalence relation on A?

7.4   Partial Orderings

The notion of *partial ordering* on a set A is a generalization of the relation "less than or equal to" on real numbers. You should review your answer to Exercise 4, Article 7.1, in reference to the relation $R_{11} = \{(m, n) \mid m \leq n\}$ on **Z**. On that basis, the following definition should come as no surprise.

DEFINITION 1
Let A be a set and R a relation on A. We say that R is a **partial ordering on A** if and only if R is reflexive on A, antisymmetric, and transitive. A nonempty set A, together with a partial ordering R on A, is often referred to as a **partially ordered set** or **poset**.

Clearly $\leq$ is an example of a partial ordering on **R**. It is reflexive since every real number is less than or equal to itself. It is antisymmetric since the only way we can have both $x \leq y$ and $y \leq x$ is if $x = y$. It is transitive since, for any real numbers x, y, and z, if $x \leq y$ and $y \leq z$, then $x \leq z$.
   Since $\leq$ is the prototype for a partial ordering, it is not uncommon to denote generic partial orderings by the symbol $\leq$ rather than by a letter. We will often follow that convention and will sometimes use symbols $\leq_1$, $\leq_2$, and so on to denote specific examples of partial orderings.
   A poset consists of two things, a nonempty set A <u>and</u> a partial ordering $\leq$ on A. Often we will identify a poset by notation such as $(A, \leq)$. Occasionally, when there is no danger of confusion about the partial ordering, we may refer simply to the poset A.

EXAMPLE 1   Let S be any set and let $A = \mathscr{P}(S)$. Let $\leq_1$ represent the *subset relation* on A; that is, $M \leq_1 N$ if and only if $M \subseteq N$ (recall the relation R_{15} from Example 6, Article 7.1). Note the interpretations of the three properties R, AS, T in this example. <u>Reflexive</u>: Every set is a subset of itself [true by Fact 1(2), Article 1.4]. <u>Antisymmetric</u>: for any sets M and N, if $M \subseteq N$ and $N \subseteq M$, then $M = N$ [Fact 1(4), Article 1.4]. <u>Transitive</u>: for any sets L, M, and N, if $L \subseteq M$ and $M \subseteq N$, then $L \subseteq N$ [Fact 1(6), Article 1.4].

   Hence $(\mathscr{P}(S), \subseteq)$ is a partially ordered set for any set S. It is often said that the set $\mathscr{P}(S)$ is *ordered by inclusion*.   □

EXAMPLE 2   Let A be the set $\mathbf{N} \cup \{0\}$ of all nonnegative integers and let $\leq_2$ represent the relation *divides*; that is, given $m, n \in A$, $m \leq_2 n$ if and only if m divides n (also commonly denoted $m | n$; recall Example 5, Article 7.1, and the paragraph preceding Example 7, Article 5.4). To show that $\leq_2$ is a partial ordering on A, we note first that every integer divides itself [Exercise 2(c), Article 6.1]. Second, if $m | n$ and $n | m$, then (since m and n are nonnegative) we may conclude $m = n$. [Exercise 2(c), Article 6.1]. Third, if $m | n$ and $n | p$, then $m | p$ [Exercise 2(a), Article 6.1] for any $m, n, p \in A$, so that $\leq_2$ is transitive.   □

Note that the relation $\leq_2$ of Example 2 is a <u>different</u> partial ordering on $\mathbf{N} \cup \{0\}$ from the ordinary "less than or equal to" on that set. For example, $2 \leq 5$, but it is <u>not the case</u> that $2 \leq_2 5$ since 2 does not divide 5.

DEFINITION 2

Let $(A, \leq)$ be a partially ordered set and let X be a subset of A. We say that an element L of A is a **lower bound** for X if and only if $L \leq x$ for all $x \in X$. X is said to be **bounded below in A** if X has a lower bound in A. An element U of A is said to be an **upper bound** for X if and only if $x \leq U$ for all $x \in X$. X is **bounded above in A** if and only if X has an upper bound in A. Finally, X is said to be **bounded in A** if and only if X is both bounded above and bounded below in A, and **unbounded in A** if and only if it is not bounded.

In the poset $(\mathbf{R}, \leq)$, where $\leq$ represents ordinary "less than or equal to," the subsets $\mathbf{N}$, $\mathbf{Z}$, and $\mathbf{Q}$ are all unbounded subsets, although $\mathbf{N}$ <u>is</u> bounded below. The subset $\{ \ldots, -6, -3, 0, 3\}$ is bounded above (by 3, or 15, or π, e.g.) in $\mathbf{R}$, but not below. The interval $(5, \infty)$ is bounded below and not above, but the interval $(-3, 8)$ is bounded. Boundedness depends on the poset as well as on the subset. For example, the interval $(0, 1]$ is bounded below as a subset of $(\mathbf{R}, \leq)$, but not as a subset of $(\mathbf{R}^+, \leq)$, where $\mathbf{R}^+$ represents the set of all positive real numbers.

   A lower or upper bound for a subset X of a partially ordered set A may or may not be contained in X. For example, in $(\mathbf{R}, \leq)$, 2 is a lower bound both for $[2, 3]$ and for $(2, 3]$. If a lower bound L for X is also an element of X, we say that L is a *least element of X*. Analogously, an upper bound U of a subset X of a poset $(A, \leq)$ is said to be a *greatest element of X* if $U \in X$. By definition, a greatest element is an upper bound and a least element is a lower bound. However, a subset of a poset that is bounded above may or may not have a greatest element. In $(\mathbf{R}, \leq)$, $(-\infty, 7]$ and $\{\ldots, -9, -6, -3, 0, 3, 6\}$ both have a greatest element (7 and 6, respectively), but $[4, 7)$ and $\{1 - (1/n) | n \in \mathbf{N}\}$ do not, even though the latter two sets are both bounded above in $\mathbf{R}$.

It is clear from a number of the preceding examples that upper and lower bounds of subsets of posets are not unique. Uniqueness does occur, however, in the situation covered by the next theorem.

THEOREM 1

Let $(A, \leq)$ be a poset and $X \subseteq A$. If X has a greatest (respectively, least) element, then that element is unique.

Proof   To prove uniqueness, we proceed, as in Article 6.3, by letting u_1 and u_2 be greatest elements of X. We claim that $u_1 = u_2$. Since u_1 is an upper bound for X and $u_2 \in X$, then $u_2 \leq u_1$. Reversing the roles of u_1 and u_2, we deduce $u_1 \leq u_2$. By antisymmetry, we conclude $u_1 = u_2$, as desired. The proof of uniqueness for least elements is analogous. $\square$

EXAMPLE 3   Let S be any infinite set and let $A = \mathscr{P}(S)$, the collection of all subsets of S. Order A by inclusion, as in Example 1. Let X be the collection of all <u>finite</u> subsets of S; clearly X is a subset of A. Note first that X is bounded above in A, namely, S itself is "greater than or equal to" every finite subset of S. But X has no greatest element, since there is no single finite subset of S that is a superset of each finite subset of S. On the other hand, X is bounded below in A <u>and</u> has a least element, namely, $\varnothing$. $\square$

The poset $(\mathbf{N} \cup \{0\}, \leq_2)$ of Example 2 has both a greatest and a least element. You should use Exercise 2 ((d), (e)), Article 6.1, to determine these.

DEFINITION 3

Let $(A, \leq)$ be a partially ordered set, and let X be a subset of A. An element U of A is said to be the **least upper bound** of X, denoted $U = \text{lub } X$ or $U = \text{sup } X$, if U is the least element of the set of all upper bounds of X in A. An element $L \in A$ is said to be the **greatest lower bound** of X, denoted $L = \text{glb } X$ or $L = \text{inf } X$, if L is the greatest element of the set of all lower bounds of X.

The expressions *sup* and *inf* are abbreviations for the Latin *supremum* and *infimum*, respectively. The subset $X = (0, 1)$ of the poset $(\mathbf{R}, \leq)$ has $[1, \infty)$ as its set of upper bounds. Since 1 is clearly the least element of $[1, \infty)$, then $1 = \text{lub } X$. The set $Y = (0, 1]$ also has $[1, \infty)$ as its set of upper bounds, so that $1 = \text{lub } Y$, also. Note that, in the first case, lub $X \notin X$, whereas lub $Y \in Y$ in the second case.

By Theorem 1, a lub or glb, if it exists, is unique. But a subset of a poset may fail to have a lub and/or a glb. For one thing, the subset may not be bounded above, in which case its set of all upper bounds is empty and so has no least element. Another possibility is that the subset might be bounded above, but its set of all upper bounds may fail to have a least element. This situation is illustrated in the following two examples.

EXAMPLE 4   Consider the poset $(\mathbf{Q}, \leq)$ and let $X = \{r \in \mathbf{Q} \mid r^2 \leq 2\}$. X is clearly bounded above in $\mathbf{Q}$ (by 2, e.g.), but it can be proved that X has no least upper bound in $\mathbf{Q}$ (see Example 3, Article 9.3, for the details of a closely related example). Note that the least upper bound of X, considered as a subset of the poset $(\mathbf{R}, \leq)$, is $\sqrt{2}$, an irrational number.   □

EXAMPLE 5   Let A be the collection of all subsets of $\mathbf{N}$ that are either finite or whose complement is finite, ordered by inclusion. Let X be the subset $\{\{2\}, \{4\}, \{6\}, \ldots\}$ of A. Then X is bounded above in A, for example, $\{2, 3, 4, 5, \ldots\}$, $\{2, 4, 5, 6, 7, \ldots\}$ and A itself are all upper bounds for X. But it can be shown that the collections of all upper bounds of X in A has no least element, so that X has no lub in A.   □

The definition of *lub X* may be rephrased in accordance with the following two-part formulation. Under the assumptions in Definition 3, we say $u = \text{lub } X$ if and only if:

(i) $x \leq u$ for all $x \in X$ (i.e., u is an upper bound for X), and
(ii)   for each $y \in A$, if $x \leq y$ for all $x \in X$, then $u \leq y$ (i.e., u is "less than or equal to" any other upper bound of X).

A similar reformulation of the definition of glb is left to you.

When working in the abstract setting of an arbitrary partially ordered set, we can err by relying too closely on properties of the most familiar partial ordering, "less than or equal to, on $\mathbf{R}$." For example, when working with this poset, we never write an expression such as "$x \nleq y$." The reason is that we may write instead $y \leq x$, and indeed the stronger statement $y < x$, to convey this idea. We do not have this luxury in every poset, however. In $(\mathscr{P}(\mathbf{N}), \subseteq)$, letting $X = \{1, 2, 3\}$ and $Y = \{2, 3, 4\}$, we note that neither $X \subseteq Y$ nor $Y \subseteq X$ is true. Note then that the statement $X \nsubseteq Y$ cannot be translated into $Y \subseteq X$. The same is true of the example $(\mathbf{N} \cup \{0\}, \leq_2)$ of Example 2. The falsity of $5 \leq_2 2$ does not translate into $2 \leq_2 5$. In fact, neither of the two integers 2 and 5 divides the other. The issue involved in these examples is the focus of the following definition.

DEFINITION 4
The partially ordered set $(A, \leq)$ is said to be **totally ordered** (or **linearly ordered** or **a chain**) if and only if, for any elements $x, y \in A$, either $x \leq y$ or $y \leq x$.

Two elements x and y of a poset $(A, \leq)$ are said to be *comparable* if and only if either $x \leq y$ or $y \leq x$. The integers 2 and 5 are not comparable in the poset $(\mathbf{N} \cup \{0\}, \leq_2)$, whereas 6 and 18 are comparable in this poset. The sets $\{1, 2\}$ and $\{1, 2, 4\}$ are comparable in $(\mathscr{P}(\mathbf{N}), \subseteq)$, whereas $\{2, 3\}$ and $\{3, 4\}$ are not. We may rephrase Definition 4 by noting that a poset is a chain if and only if every two elements in it are comparable. Observe then that $(A, \leq)$, where A is any subset of $\mathbf{R}$ and $\leq$ is ordinary "less than or equal to," is a totally ordered set, whereas both $(\mathscr{P}(S), \subseteq)$, S any set, and $(\mathbf{N} \cup \{0\}, \leq_2)$ are not totally ordered.

If x and y are elements of a poset $(A, \leq)$, we denote by $x \vee y$ the element lub $\{x, y\}$, if it exists, while glb $\{x, y\}$, when it exists, is denoted by $x \wedge y$. These are called, respectively, the *join* and the *meet* of x and y. This situation is not very interesting if A is totally ordered; in that case $x \vee y$ is simply the "larger," whereas $x \wedge y$ is the "smaller" of x and y. But, in general, $x \vee y$ and $x \wedge y$ may be elements of A other than either x or y. In several of the exercises you should pursue these ideas further, and in particular, calculate certain meets and joins for the posets discussed earlier in the article.

Exercises

1. Consider the poset $(\mathbf{N} \cup \{0\}, \leq_2)$, where $\leq_2$ is the relation *divides* of Example 2.

(a) Find the greatest and least elements of this poset, if they exist.
(b) Find upper and lower bounds for the set $\{4, 8, 16\}$.
★(c) Find upper and lower bounds for the set $\{4, 6, 10\}$.
(d) Find upper and lower bounds for the set $\{3, 5, 7\}$.
(e) Find the greatest and least elements, when they exist, for the sets in (b), (c), and (d).
(f) Give an example of an unbounded subset of this poset, if any exists.
(g) Give a general description of $m \vee n$ and $m \wedge n$, where m and n are any nonnegative integers.

2. Answer (a) through (g) of Exercise 1 for the poset $(\mathbf{N} \cup \{0\}, \leq)$, where $\leq$ is ordinary "less than or equal to."

3. Consider the poset (X, R) where $X = \{1, 2, 3, \ldots, 9, 10\}$ and $R = \{(x, x) \mid x \in X\} \cup \{(1, x) \mid x \in X\} \cup \{(x, 10) \mid x \in X\} \cup \{(1, 3), (1, 5), (1, 7), (1, 9), (3, 5), (3, 7), (3, 9), (5, 7), (5, 9), (7, 9)\}$. Determine (when they exist):

(a) lub $\{1, 3, 5\}$ (b) lub $\{2, 4, 6\}$
(c) glb $\{2, 4, 6\}$ (d) the least element of $\{2, 4, 6\}$
(e) an upper bound for the set $\{3, 4, 5, 6, 8\}$

4. Let A be a poset. Let M and N be subsets of A such that lub M and lub N both exist. Prove that if $M \subseteq N$, then lub $M \leq$ lub N and glb $M \geq$ glb N.

5. (a) Let M and N be subsets of an arbitrary set S. Clearly $M \subseteq M \cup N$ and $N \subseteq M \cup N$. Prove that if X is any subset of S such that $M \subseteq X$ and $N \subseteq X$, then $M \cup N \subseteq X$.

(b) Let M and N be subsets of an arbitrary set S. Clearly $M \cap N \subseteq M$ and $M \cap N \subseteq N$. Prove that if X is any subset of S such that $X \subseteq M$ and $X \subseteq N$, then $X \subseteq M \cap N$.

6. *(a)* Let $A = \mathscr{P}(S)$, S any set, and order A by inclusion. Let M and N be any elements of A (i.e., M and N are subsets of S)

★*(i)* Describe $M \vee N$, the <u>join</u> of M and N in the poset $(A, \subseteq)$.

(ii) Describe $M \wedge N$, the <u>meet</u> of M and N in A.

(Recall $M \vee N = \text{lub } \{M, N\}$ and $M \wedge N = \text{glb } \{M, N\}$.)

(b) Assume S is infinite and let $C = \{M_1, M_2, \ldots\}$ be an infinite collection of subsets of S, indexed by $\mathbf{N}$. Note that C is a subset of $A = \mathscr{P}(S)$. Order the latter by inclusion, as in (a). Describe lub C and glb C in the poset $(A, \subseteq)$.

7. *(a)* Let $A = \mathscr{P}(\mathbf{N})$ be ordered by inclusion. Find lub C and glb C for each of the following subsets C of A:

(i) $C_1 = \{\{1\}, \{3\}, \{5\}, \ldots\}$

(ii) $C_2 = \{\{1\}, \{1, 3\}, \{1, 3, 5\}, \ldots\}$

★*(iii)* $C_3 = \{\{1, 3, 5, 7, \ldots\}, \{3, 5, 7, 9, \ldots\}, \{5, 7, 9, 11, \ldots\}, \ldots\}$

(b) The subset $C = \{\{2\}, \{4\}, \{6\}, \ldots\}$ of the poset in (a) has lub $C = \{2, 4, 6, \ldots\}$. Explain why $\{2, 4, 6, \ldots\}$ is not the lub of C in the poset of Example 5. Explain informally why C has no lub in that poset.

8. *(a)* Let S be any finite set and let $A = \mathscr{P}(S)$. Define a relation R on A by the rule $(M, N) \in R$ if and only if $n(M) \leq n(N)$, for any subsets M and N of S. Is R a partial ordering on A?

(b) Recall the equivalence relation R_{17} on $A = \mathscr{P}(S)$ (Example 6, Article 7.1) that identifies any two subsets of S having the same number of elements. Let $X = A/R_{17}$, noting that the elements of X are equivalence classes $[M]$ of subsets of S, where two subsets M and N of S are in the same equivalence class if and only if $n(M) = n(N)$. Define a relation $\leq$ on X by the rule $[M] \leq [N]$ if and only if $n(M) \leq n(N)$.

★*(i)* Prove that this relation is *well defined*; that is, verify that if $[M_1] = [M_2]$ and $[N_1] = [N_2]$, then $[M_1] \leq [N_1] \Leftrightarrow [M_2] \leq [N_2]$.

(ii) Prove that $\leq$ is a partial ordering on X.

(iii) Prove that $\leq$ is a total ordering on X.

9. Let $(X, \leq)$ be a poset. An element $m \in X$ is said to be a *maximal element* of X if and only if, for any $y \in X$, if $m \leq y$, then $m = y$.

(a) Formulate an analogous definition of *minimal element* of a poset.

(b) Prove that if a poset $(X, \leq)$ has a greatest element u, then u is the unique maximal element of X. State the analogous result for minimal elements.

(c) Let $S = \{1, 2, \ldots, 10\}$ and let $X = \mathscr{P}(S) - \{\varnothing, S\}$; that is, X consists of all nonempty proper subsets of S. Order X by inclusion; that is, consider the poset $(X, \subseteq)$. Find five maximal elements and five minimal elements of this poset.

(d) Consider the set $X = \mathbf{N} - \{1\}$. Order this set by "divisibility" (cf., Example 5, Article 7.1). How many minimal elements are contained in this poset? maximal elements? Answer the same question if $X = \mathbf{N} \cup \{0\}$.

(e) Prove that if a poset $(X, \leq)$ is totally ordered, then any maximal element is the greatest element of X, whereas every minimal element is the least element.

10. *(a)* *(i)* Calculate the set of all equivalence relations on the set $S = \{1, 2, 3, 4\}$.

   (ii) Calculate the set of all partitions of S.

(b) *(i)* Let S be any finite set and denote by ER the set of all equivalence relations on S. Define a relation $\leq$ on ER by the rule $E_1 \leq E_2$ if and only if $E_1 \subseteq E_2$, where E_1 and E_2 are arbitrary elements of ER. (We often say that E_1 is *stronger* than E_2 in this case.) Show that $\leq$ is a partial ordering on ER and describe the strongest and weakest elements of the poset $(ER, \leq)$.

   (ii) Let S be any finite set and denote by PAR the set of all partitions of S. Define a relation $\leq$ on PAR by the rule $P_1 \leq P_2$ if and only if every cell in P_1 is a subset of some cell in P_2. (We often say P_1 is a *refinement* of P_2 in that case.) Show that $\leq$ is a partial ordering on PAR and describe the smallest and largest elements of the poset $(PAR, \leq)$.

   (iii) Find a relationship between the statements $E_1 \leq E_2$ [from (i)] and $(S/E_1) \leq (S/E_2)$ [from (ii)].

11. Let F be the set of all real-valued functions with domain a subset of $\mathbf{R}$. Define a relation $\leq$ on F by the rule, $f \leq g$ if and only if $\operatorname{dom} f \subseteq \operatorname{dom} g$ and $f(x) \leq g(x)$ for all $x \in \operatorname{dom} f$, where f and g are arbitrary elements of F. (*Note:* Two functions are to be regarded as equal if and only if they have the same domain and the same function values over their common domain.)

(a) Prove that $\leq$ is a partial ordering on F.

(b) Prove that $\leq$ is not a total ordering on F.

(c) Given functions $f, g \in F$, describe the function h that serves as $f \vee g$ in the poset $(F, \leq)$. Describe $f \wedge g$.

Relations, Part II: Functions and Mappings
CHAPTER 8

At this point you may have some preconceived ideas about functions, relating especially to the mechanics of working with functions and to various purposes for which functions are used. Precalculus and calculus-level treatment of functions, however, provide little clue to some of their uses in higher-level mathematics (e.g., cardinality of sets, discussed in Article 8.3). Furthermore, introductory-level coverage is often so imprecise that many students do not have a clear idea of what a function is, even though they may know a lot about functions and, in particular, have the ability to "know one when they see one." In this chapter we attempt to fill some gaps in this area, and lay the groundwork for important areas of advanced mathematics. The material covered here is fundamental to courses such as abstract algebra, advanced calculus, and elementary topology.

We deal first with basic issues, including a precise definition of function. Next, we take a second look at familiar ideas such as *one-to-one function*, *composition* of functions, and *inverse function*. Then we launch into new material, including the concepts of *onto* mapping and *one-to-one correspondence* between sets, and the ideas of *image* and *inverse image* of a set under a mapping. We conclude the chapter with an introduction to *cardinality of sets* and a brief consideration of *arbitrary collections* of sets.

8.1 Functions and Mappings

A function can be defined as a certain kind of relation. Thus a function is, first of all, a set. More specifically, it is a set consisting of ordered pairs of objects. The additional property that distinguishes functions, among all relations, is specified in the following definition.

DEFINITION 1

A **function** is a relation R having the property that if $(x, y) \in R$ and $(x, z) \in R$, then $y = z$.

Following custom, we will most often use lower-case letters f, g, h, and so on, rather than R, to denote relations that are functions. If R is any relation, then by Definition 4, Article 7.1, for each $x \in$ dom R, there exists at least one object $y \in$ rng R such that $(x, y) \in R$. If f is a function, then by Definition 1 for each $x \in$ dom f, there exists at most one object $y \in$ rng f such that $(x, y) \in f$. In other words, every element x in the domain of a function f has a unique corresponding y in the range of f such that $(x, y) \in f$.

Like any other relation, and more generally like any other set, a function f may be described by the roster method, that is, by listing all the ordered pairs, or by the rule method. The former, of course, is applicable only when f has finitely many ordered pairs; indeed, it is practical only when f has a relatively small number of ordered pairs. Sometimes, the "pattern" approach to describing a set may be used to define functions having a finite, but large, number of ordered pairs.

EXAMPLE 1   The   relations $f_1 = \{(2, 3), (3, 5), (4, 7), (5, 9)\}$, $f_2 = \{(a, z),$ $(b, y), \ldots, (y, b), (z, a)\}$, $f_3 = \{(1, 1), (2, 2), \ldots, (100, 100)\}$ are   functions, whereas $R_1 = \{(1, a), (1, b), \ldots, (1, z)\}$ and $R_2 = \{(1, 1), (1, -1), (4, 2),$ $(4, -2), (9, 3), (9, -3)\}$ are not functions.   □

A relation described by listing all its ordered pairs is a function if and only if no two distinct ordered pairs in the list have the same first element. This criterion could be used in general as a somewhat less precise definition of the function concept. You should determine the domain and range of each of the relations in Example 1 [Exercise 1(a)]. Also, you should examine each of the relations in Example 1, Article 7.1, to determine which are functions [Exercise 1(b)].

If f is a function, then each $x \in$ dom f can be viewed as determining a unique corresponding $y \in$ rng f. For this reason we often refer to this y as *the value of the function f* at x, or simply "f of x," and write $y = f(x)$, rather than $(x, y) \in f$ or $x f y$. In addition, when f is a function, the set rng f is sometimes referred to as the *image* of f, denoted im f.

When the rule method is used to describe a function, the rule is usually one that specifies a relationship between each $x \in$ dom f and its corresponding y, such as $y = f(x) = x^3$, $y = g(x) = \sin^{-1} x$, or "y is the biological father of x." Thus functions are most often described by designating the domain and specifying such a rule, often called the *rule of correspondence*. When a function is defined by a rule of correspondence $y = f(x)$, the latter is often referred to as *functional notation*, in contrast to ordered pair notation. We can express in these terms what is meant by *equality of functions*; two functions f and g are *equal* if and only if (1) dom $f =$ dom g and

(2) $f(x) = g(x)$ for all x in the common domain. You are asked to prove this fact in Exercise 2(a). The following example provides several functions defined in the manner just described.

EXAMPLE 2   (a)   Define g_1 by dom $g_1 = \{x \in \mathbf{R} \,|\, x \geq 0\}$ and $g_1(x) = x^2$.
(b)   Define g_2 by dom $g_2 = \mathbf{R}$ and $g_2(x) = (x^3 + 5)^{1/3}$.
(c)   Define g_3 by dom $g_3 = [4, \infty)$ and $g_3(x) = \sqrt{(x - 4)}$, where $\sqrt{x}$ represents the unique positive square root of x. □

The relations g_1, g_2, and g_3 in Example 2 are all functions, whereas the relation R defined by the (inappropriate, but common) notation $R(x) = \pm\sqrt{x}$, dom $R = [0, \infty)$, is <u>not a function</u> (Why?).
A common practice, in cases where the domain of a function f is a subset of the reals, is to describe the function by stating the rule only, with the understanding that the domain is the set of all real numbers for which the rule makes sense. With this understanding, specification of the domain in (b) and (c) of Example 2 is superfluous. On the other hand, part (a) of Example 2 requires that the domain be given explicitly, since the "squaring function" is otherwise assumed to have domain $\mathbf{R}$, that is, g_1 is a different function from the function we designate simply as $f(x) = x^2$.
Because of the convention discussed in the preceding paragraph, it is common <u>to think of the rule</u> describing a function <u>as the function</u>. This interpretation can lead to difficulties, especially since it is possible to have a function without an explicit rule (see, e.g., Example 4, Article 8.3), but is consistent with the widespread and very useful practice of considering functions from a dynamic, rather than a static, point of view. In this context, emphasis is placed on the transformation of an *independent variable* (x, representing elements in the domain) into a *dependent variable* [y, given by the formula $y = f(x)$, representing elements of the range]. It is important that you be able to pass comfortably between the ordered pair approach and various other ways of interpreting what a function is, so that, for example, the function described by $g(x) = x^3$ or "the cubing function" or "the function that sends (or maps) x to x^3" or the function described by the graph in Figure 8.1, can be recognized as $\{(x, x^3) \,|\, x \in R\}$.
In the context of real-valued functions of a real variable certain categories of function are determined with respect to the form of the defining rule. An *algebraic* function is defined by an equation in variables x and y involving a finite number of algebraic operations, that is, sums, differences, products, quotients, nth powers, and nth roots. An example is provided by the function $y = [(x^3 - 5x^2 + 3x + 7)/(x^4 - 3x + 2)]^{3/5}$. A function such as $f(x) = \sin(x)$ or $g(x) = 2^x$, which can be shown to be nonalgebraic, is said to be *transcendental*. Important subcategories of algebraic functions, listed in order of decreasing generality, are *rational* functions, *polynomial* functions, *linear* functions, and the *identity* function. You should already be familiar with these categories and able to give examples of functions of

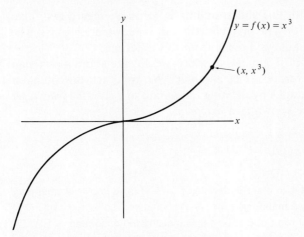

Figure 8.1 *Graph of the "cubing function."*

the type described in Exercise 3(b). It should be noted also that the identity function and constant functions may be considered in much wider contexts than that of the real numbers as domain and range. If A is any set, the *identity function on* A, denoted I_A, is defined by the rule $I_A(x) = x$ for all $x \in A$. If A is any set and $c \in A$, the *constant function* C is defined by $C(x) = c$ for all $x \in A$.

The alert reader may have noticed an inconsistency between our discussion thus far of the function concept and the definition of relation, given earlier. If, as Definition 1 states, a function f is a particular type of relation, then according to Definition 2, Article 7.1, there must be an underlying cartesian product $A \times B$ containing f as a subset, where we necessarily have dom $f \subseteq A$ and rng $f \subseteq B$. Technically, this is true, with the result that, strictly speaking, we should not be able to define a function simply by giving a rule (or even by listing a set of ordered pairs), but rather, should also have to specify sets A and B. This situation has the rather disturbing consequence that the result in Exercise 2(a) becomes false. A set of ordered pairs satisfying the condition in Definition 1, possibly determined by a given domain and rule of correspondence, could correspond to many different functions, as we vary the sets A and B. It is a fact of mathematical life that we often wish to specify a function simply by giving a domain and rule or a rule with the domain understood, or by describing explicitly a set of ordered pairs, and do not wish to be entangled in a cartesian product. Indeed, we have proceeded this way in Examples 1 and 2. Let us agree, then, that we may view a function as being properly defined by the various methods exhibited in Examples 1 and 2, even though the underlying cartesian product may not be identified explicitly. When this is done, the understanding is that an appropriate cartesian product exists but is irrelevant to our current application, so that in essence we don't care what it is. Furthermore, with this understanding in force, we regard two functions as equal if and only if they contain the same ordered pairs. The result in Exercise 2(a) follows directly from this criterion.

There are mathematical contexts in which we <u>do care</u> about a cartesian product containing a function f as a subset. We approach this situation in the following paragraphs by defining the notion of a *function from a set A to a set B*, otherwise known as a *mapping*.

MAPPINGS

DEFINITION 2

A **function from a set *A* to a set *B***, denoted $f: A \rightarrow B$ (also known as **mapping from *A* to *B***, or simply a **mapping**) consists of a function f, satisfying dom $f = A$, and a set B such that rng $f \subseteq B$. The set B is called the **codomain** of f.

The notation $f: A \rightarrow B$ from Definition 2 is usually read "f is a mapping from the set A to the set B," or "f is a function that maps the set A to the set B." In view of the discussion preceding Definition 2, the concept of "function from A to B" or "mapping (from A to B)" differs in a subtle way from that of function; a mapping consists of a function plus something more. In order to define a mapping, we must specify along with the function f (whose definition already determines the sets dom f and rng f) a set B such that rng $f \subseteq B$. As an example, we might consider a constant mapping of $\mathbf{R}$ into $\mathbf{R}$, given by $C: \mathbf{R} \rightarrow \mathbf{R}$, where $C(x) = c$, $c \in \mathbf{R}$; the codomain $\mathbf{R}$ contains the range $\{c\}$, as required by the definition of mapping. Or, a mapping could be defined by $g: \mathbf{R} \rightarrow [1, \infty)$, where $g(x) = \cosh x$. In this case the codomain $[1, \infty)$ not only contains the range of g as a subset, but in fact equals rng g. Most particularly, it is possible to have two distinct mappings, both of which involve the same function. The mappings $k: \mathbf{R} \rightarrow \mathbf{R}$ and $k: \mathbf{R} \rightarrow [0, \infty)$, where $k(x) = x^4$, illustrate this situation. We say that mappings $f: A \rightarrow B$ and $g: C \rightarrow D$ are *equal* if and only if $f = g$ (which implies automatically that $A = C$ <u>and</u> $B = D$).

The notion of mapping may be used to amplify concepts encountered earlier in the text. As one example, an infinite collection of sets $\{A_1, A_2, \ldots\}$ indexed by $\mathbf{N}$ (recall Article 4.2) may be viewed as a mapping of $\mathbf{N}$ into any set containing each of the sets in the collection as an element, such as $\mathscr{P}(\bigcup_{i=1}^{\infty} A_i)$. More generally, any infinite sequence is a mapping of $\mathbf{N}$ into some codomain (such as $\mathbf{R}$ or $\mathbf{C}$).

ONE-TO-ONE MAPPINGS

At various earlier stages of the text (and surely at several points in your prior mathematical training), the notion of a *one-to-one* function has come into play (see, in particular, Exercise 6, Article 5.2). There are various ways of characterizing "one-to-oneness," in addition to the definition "$f(x_1) =$

$f(x_2)$ implies $x_1 = x_2$ for all $x_1, x_2 \in \operatorname{dom} f$." For example, the contra-positive of the definition states "for all x_1 and x_2, if $x_1 \neq x_2$, then $f(x_1) \neq f(x_2)$." A translation of this condition into plain English yields the requirement that distinct x values have distinct corresponding y values. As we saw earlier, a set of ordered pairs is a function if and only if no two distinct ordered pairs have the same <u>first</u> element. Analogously, a function, viewed as a set of ordered pairs, is one to one if and only if no two distinct ordered pairs have the same <u>second</u> element. For if (x_1, y) and (x_2, y) are both in f, for some pair of distinct objects x_1 and x_2, then we have $y = f(x_1)$ and $y = f(x_2)$ so that $f(x_1) = f(x_2)$, but $x_1 \neq x_2$, contradicting the definition of one to one. For real-valued functions of a real variable, the property of one to one is equivalent to the requirement "each <u>horizontal</u> line $y = k$ intersects the graph of f in at most one point." (Why? Note also, in this context, that the definition of function requires that each <u>vertical</u> line meet the graph in at most one point.) These considerations lead to the following definition.

DEFINITION 3

A mapping $f: A \to B$ is said to be **one to one**, or **injective**, if and only if the function f is a one-to-one function; that is, whenever $x_1, x_2 \in A$ with $f(x_1) = f(x_2)$, then $x_1 = x_2$. Such a mapping is also said to be an **injection** of A into B.

The mapping $k: \mathbf{R} \to \mathbf{R}$ defined by $k(x) = x^4$ is not injective since $16 = k(2) = k(-2)$, but any linear mapping $f: \mathbf{R} \to \mathbf{R}$, $f(x) = Mx + B$, is an injection provided $M \neq 0$. The one-to-one property of a mapping depends entirely on the "ordered pair part" of the mapping, that is, it is not affected by the choice of codomain. The same is not true of the companion concept of *onto mapping*, which is discussed in the next article.

NEW FUNCTIONS FROM OLD ONES

From precalculus courses you are probably familiar with various methods of constructing functions from given functions. If f and g both map a subset of $\mathbf{R}$ into $\mathbf{R}$, then the functions $f + g$, $f - g$, fg, and f/g also map subsets of $\mathbf{R}$ into $\mathbf{R}$. The first three have domain equal to $\operatorname{dom} f \cap \operatorname{dom} g$, while $\operatorname{dom} (f/g) = \operatorname{dom} f \cap \operatorname{dom} g \cap \{x \in \mathbf{R} \,|\, g(x) \neq 0\}$. The defining rule for fg, for example, is $(fg)(x) = f(x)g(x)$ for all $x \in \operatorname{dom} f \cap \operatorname{dom} g$, with the defining rules for $f + g$, $f - g$, and f/g given similarly. If k is a real number, kf is defined by $(kf)(x) = kf(x)$, with $\operatorname{dom} (kf) = \operatorname{dom} f$. The sum, difference, product, and quotient of functions are often referred to as *operations* on functions.

We now wish to consider three other methods of constructing new functions and mappings from old ones, that is, three other operations on functions. Unlike the operations of the previous paragraph, which are dependent for their effectiveness on our ability to add, multiply (and so on) real numbers, these operations are so general as to be applicable to any mappings. The operations are *inverse, restriction,* and *composition* of functions and mappings.

The *inverse* of a function f is simply the inverse $f^{-1} = \{(y, x) \mid y = f(x)\}$ of f regarded as a relation, as defined in Article 7.1, Definition 5. As examples, if $f = \{(3, 5), (5, 8), (7, 11), (9, 14), (11, 17)\}$, then $f^{-1} = \{(5, 3), (8, 5), (11, 7), (14, 9), (17, 11)\}$. If $g = \{(x, 4x - 7) \mid x \in \mathbf{R}\}$, then $g^{-1} = \{(4x - 7, x) \mid x \in \mathbf{R}\}$, which, as you should verify, is the same as $\{(y, y/4 - 7/4) \mid y \in \mathbf{R}\}$, or $\{(x, x/4 - \frac{7}{4}) \mid x \in \mathbf{R}\}$. The properties $\mathrm{dom}\,(f^{-1}) = \mathrm{rng}\,f$, $\mathrm{rng}\,(f^{-1}) = \mathrm{dom}\,f$, and $(f^{-1})^{-1} = f$, listed in Theorem 3, Article 7.1, are, of course, true in the special case of a relation that happens to be a function.

If f maps $\mathbf{R}$ into $\mathbf{R}$, then the graph of f^{-1} is simply the "mirror image" of the graph of f across the line $y = x$ (see Figure 8.2). Familiar examples from your calculus experience are the logarithm and exponential functions to various bases, the nth power and nth root functions, and the trigonometric and hyperbolic functions together with their inverses. The function $f(x) = 1/x$ provides us with an unusual situation; this function is its own inverse as shown in Figure 8.3.

The key question concerning inverse functions is: "Under what circumstance(s) is the inverse of a function itself a function?" In order for f^{-1} to be a function, it must be the case that no two distinct ordered pairs of elements in f^{-1} have the same first element. This means that, back in

Figure 8.2   *There is a specific relationship between the graph of a function and the graph of its inverse. The graphs of f and f^{-1} are symmetric with respect to the line $y = x$.*

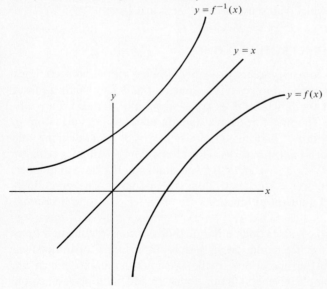

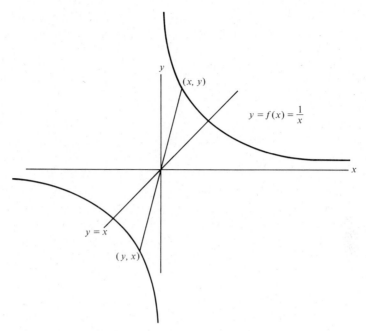

Figure 8.3 *Graph of a function that is its own inverse. Each point*
(x, y) on the graph of the function y = 1/x has its corresponding
point (y, x) also lying on the curve.

f, it must have happened that no two distinct ordered pairs had the same
second element. The next theorem formalizes this relationship.

THEOREM 1

Let f be a function. Then the inverse relation f^{-1} is a function if and only if
f is one to one.

Proof   Assume that f^{-1} is a function. To prove f is one to one, choose
$x_1, x_2 \in \text{dom } f$ and assume $f(x_1) = f(x_2)$; we must prove $x_1 = x_2$. Letting $y = f(x_1) = f(x_2)$, we have that the ordered pairs (y, x_1) and (y, x_2)
are both in f^{-1} (why?). Since f^{-1} is a function, we conclude $x_1 = x_2$,
as desired. The converse is left as an exercise [Exercise 5(a)]. □

Many authors express this theorem as "if f is a function, then f^{-1} exists
(or f has an inverse) if and only if f is one to one." Since f^{-1} always
exists as a relation, such a formulation is, strictly speaking, inaccurate.
What is meant by this, of course, is that f^{-1} exists as a function precisely
when f is one to one. We say that f is *invertible* in this case.
    A second general method of creating a function from a given function
is suggested by the difficulties that are faced in defining the inverse trigonometric functions. As you know, functions such as sin, cos, and tan, are

highly non-one to one and so "do not have inverses" (i.e., their inverse relations are not functions). The functions we know as $\sin^{-1}$, $\tan^{-1}$, and so on, then, are not actually the inverses of sin and tan, respectively, but rather are, inverses of *restrictions* of those functions to certain convenient subsets of their domains.

DEFINITION 4

Let $f\colon A \to B$ be a mapping and let $X \subseteq A$. We define a new mapping, the **restriction** of f to X, denoted $f|_X$, by $f|_X\colon X \to B$ where $f|_X(x) = f(x)$ for all $x \in X$.

Note that, given $f\colon A \to B$ and a subset X of A, a mapping $g\colon X \to B$ equals $f|_X$ if and only if $g(x) = f(x)$ for all $x \in X$. As one example, the function $g(x) = \sqrt{x}$ is not the inverse of $f(x) = x^2$, but rather, of the restriction $f|_X$, where $X = [0, \infty)$. Similarly, $\tan^{-1}$ is the inverse of $\tan/_{(-\pi/2,\pi/2)}$, while $\cosh^{-1}$ is the inverse of $\cosh/_{[0,\infty]}$.

An important special case of restriction is the *inclusion mapping*. If A is any set and X is a subset of A, we define the mapping i_X by $i_X = (I_A)/_X$; that is, $i_X\colon X \to A$ with $i_X(x) = x$ for all $x \in X$.

In addition to its usefulness in the definitions of certain inverse functions, the notion of "restriction" provides mathematicians with a notational convenience that proves valuable in a variety of settings in higher-level mathematics.

COMPOSITION

Unlike inverse and restriction, composition of functions and mappings is a binary operation. You have encountered this operation in both precalculus and elementary calculus classes and will probably recall, for instance, warnings from instructors to understand the difference between functions such as $f(x) = (\sin x)e^x$, a product of functions, and $g(x) = \sin(e^x)$, a composition of the sine function with the exponential function. You will also recall from elementary calculus that the *chain rule* is a rule for calculating the derivative of a composition of two functions. We now give a definition of composition from the "ordered pair" point of view.

DEFINITION 5

Let f and g be functions. Consider the relation $h = \{(x, z)\,|\,\text{there exists } y \text{ such that } (x, y) \in f \text{ and } (y, z) \in g\}$. The relation h is called the **composite** of f and g, or simply **g composition f**, and is denoted $h = g \circ f$.

EXAMPLE 3   Let $f = \{(1, 3), (2, 7), (3, 10), (4, 17), (5, 20)\}$, $g = \{(2, 6), (3, 4), (7, 10), (17, 10), (20, 10)\}$, and $k = \{(4, 3), (6, 5), (10, 20)\}$. Calculate $f \circ k$, $g \circ k$, and $k \circ g$.

Solution   Note first that $f \circ k$ may have at most 15 ordered pairs, since it is clearly a subset of $(\text{dom } k) \times (\text{rng } f)$. But, due to the fact that f and k are both functions, together with the condition "there exists $y \ldots$" in Definition 5, it clearly has far fewer ordered pairs. For example, we may ask whether $(6, 17)$ is an element of $f \circ k$. Since $(6, 5) \in k$, we would need $(5, 17) \in f$ in order to have $(6, 17) \in f \circ k$. Since $(5, 17) \notin f$, the answer to our question is "no." We may quickly list the ordered pairs in $f \circ k$, in fact, by "splicing together" ordered pairs in k and f. Since $(4, 3) \in k$ and $(3, 10) \in f$, then $(4, 10) \in f \circ k$. Since $(6, 5) \in k$ and $(5, 20) \in f$, then $(6, 20) \in f \circ k$. Now $(10, 20) \in k$, but $20 \notin \text{dom } f$, so that this ordered pair from k does not lead to an ordered pair in $f \circ k$. In fact, $f \circ k = \{(4, 10), (6, 20)\}$ so that, for instance, $(f \circ k)(4) = 10$. Similarly, $g \circ k = \{(4, 4), (10, 10)\}$, while $k \circ g = \{(2, 5), (3, 3), (7, 20), (17, 20), (20, 20)\}$. □

You should calculate $k \circ f$, $f \circ g$, and $g \circ f$ in the preceding example. Also, noting that f and k are one-to-one functions, so that f^{-1} and k^{-1} are functions, you should calculate $f \circ f^{-1}$, $f^{-1} \circ f$, $k \circ k^{-1}$, and $k^{-1} \circ k$. General conclusions from these calculations are contained in Exercise 9. Finally, you should calculate and compare $f \circ (k \circ g)$ and $(f \circ k) \circ g$.

The definition of composition, together with the results from Example 3, suggest a number of observations about function composition. For instance, using standard functional notation, we see that $z = (g \circ f)(x)$ if and only if $y = f(x)$ and $z = g(y)$ for some y. If such a y exists, we then have $z = g(y) = g(f(x))$. The equation $z = g(f(x))$ is the formula commonly used to calculate the rule of correspondence for $g \circ f$, given rules for g and for f. Thus if $f(x) = 3x - 4$ and $g(x) = e^x$, then $(g \circ f)(x) = g(f(x)) = g(3x - 4) = e^{3x-4}$ for each $x \in \mathbf{R}$.

Second, we note that dom $(g \circ f)$ is clearly contained as a subset in dom f. That is, in order to be in dom $(g \circ f)$, an object x must first be in dom f. Furthermore, for each such x, the object $f(x)$ (i.e., y) must be in dom g. Indeed, $x \in \text{dom } (g \circ f)$ if and only if both these conditions are satisfied, so that dom $(g \circ f) = \{x \mid x \in \text{dom } f \text{ and } f(x) \in \text{dom } g\}$ [see Exercise 8(a)].

Third, the results of the calculations of $g \circ k$ and $k \circ g$ indicate that composition of functions is a <u>noncommutative</u> operation; that is, it is not the case that $f \circ g = g \circ f$ for all functions f and g; indeed, this relationship seldom holds (see Exercise 3).

Fourth, our results in Example 3 suggest the following fact.

THEOREM 2

If f and g are functions, then the composite $g \circ f$ is a function.

Proof   To prove that $g \circ f$ is a function, assume that the ordered pairs (x, z_1) and (x, z_2) are in $g \circ f$. Our claim is that $z_1 = z_2$. By Definition 5, there exists objects y_1 and y_2 such that $(x, y_1) \in f$, $(y_1, z_1) \in g$, $(x, y_2) \in f$, and $(y_2, z_2) \in g$. Since f is a function, we conclude $y_1 = y_2$. Let us denote this common value by y. Since g is a function and since both (y, z_1) and (y, z_2) are elements of g, we conclude $z_1 = z_2$, as desired. □

In view of Theorem 2, we will dispense henceforth with ordered pair notation in discussing the composition of two functions, using functional notation instead.

The final property of function composition suggested by the calculations from Example 3 is *associativity*, with the following precise statement:

THEOREM 3

If f, g, and h are functions, then $f \circ (g \circ h) = (f \circ g) \circ h$.

Proof By Exercise 2, we may prove two functions equal by showing that (1) their domains are equal and (2) their values are the same at each point in the common domain.

1. Let x be an element of dom $[(f \circ g) \circ h]$. Then $x \in$ dom h and $h(x) \in$ dom $(f \circ g)$. The latter property means that $h(x) \in$ dom g and $g(h(x)) \in$ dom f. But since $x \in$ dom h and $h(x) \in$ dom g, then $x \in$ dom $(g \circ h)$. Since $x \in$ dom $(g \circ h)$ and $(g \circ h)(x) \in$ dom f, then $x \in$ dom $[f \circ (g \circ h)]$, as desired. Hence dom $[(f \circ g) \circ h] \subseteq$ dom $[f \circ (g \circ h)]$. The proof of the reverse inclusion is completely analogous.

2. Let $x \in$ dom $[(f \circ g) \circ h]$ $(=$dom $[f \circ (g \circ h)])$. Then $[(f \circ g) \circ h](x) = ((f \circ g)(h(x))) = f(g(h(x))) = f((g \circ h)(x)) = [f \circ (g \circ h)](x)$. Since $[(f \circ g) \circ h](x) = [f \circ (g \circ h)](x)$ for any value of x in the common domain of the two functions $f \circ (g \circ h)$ and $(f \circ g) \circ h$, we conclude that these two functions are actually the same, as desired. $\square$

Suppose now that $f: A \to B$ and $g: B \to C$ are mappings, where we make explicit note of the assumption that the codomain of the first mapping equals the domain of the second. Due to this assumption, we have that for any $x \in A =$ dom f, $f(x) \in B =$ dom g. From this, we may easily conclude that the function $g \circ f$ has the domain A and a range that is a subset of C. Therefore it is meaningful to refer to the mapping $g \circ f: A \to C$ whenever we are given mappings $f: A \to B$ and $g: B \to C$. By common agreement among mathematicians, this is the only circumstance in which we consider the composition of two mappings [see, however, Exercise 10(e)]. This situation is often pictured by diagrams such as the one in Figure 8.4.

There are other fairly standard ways of creating new mappings from old ones, in addition to inverse, restriction, and composition. Several examples are provided in Exercises 11, 12, and 13.

Figure 8.4 *A diagrammatic view of the composition of mappings.*

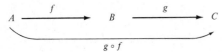

We conclude this article with a rather abstract result that relates the concept of one to one to the composition of mappings. This theorem, which states that one-to-one mappings are precisely those mappings having a sort of "left-cancellation" property, is typical of a number of statements that can be proved about mappings and on which we focus in the next article. For our purposes, the proofs of these theorems are as important as the results themselves. We will try to strike a balance between proofs detailed in the text and others left as exercises. You should pay particular attention to these proofs.

THEOREM 4

Let $f: X \to Y$ be a mapping. Then f is injective if and only if for any set W and for any mappings $g: W \to X$ and $h: W \to X$ such that $f \circ g = f \circ h$, we have $g = h$.

Sketch of proof $\Rightarrow$ Assume f is one to one; let W be a set, and let $g: W \to X$ and $h: W \to X$ be mappings such that $f \circ g = f \circ h$. We claim that $g = h$. Since g and h both have domain W, we need only show $g(w) = h(w)$ for all $w \in W$. So let $w \in W$ be given. Now, by assumption, $f \circ g = f \circ h$ so that, in particular, $(f \circ g)(w) = (f \circ h)(w)$. Hence $f(g(w)) = f(h(w))$. Since f is one to one, we conclude $g(w) = h(w)$, as desired.
   $\Leftarrow$ The proof in this direction is more difficult. We have a hypothesis whose form is quite complicated and a relatively simple desired conclusion, namely, "f is injective." In Article 6.2 we noted that, in such circumstances, it is often best to try a proof by contrapositive. In such a proof we must begin by assuming f is not one to one. If we are to prove the negation of the hypothesis, we must note carefully what that negation says. It states that there exists a set W and mappings $g: W \to X$ and $h: W \to X$ such that $f \circ g = f \circ h$, but $g \neq h$. We give several hints from here, and leave the completion of the proof as an exercise. Since f is not one to one, there exist <u>distinct</u> elements $x_1, x_2 \in X$ such that $f(x_1) = f(x_2)$. Our job is to produce a set W and <u>distinct</u> mappings g and h of W into X such that $f \circ g = f \circ h$. Our key hint is this: Let $W = \{x_1, x_2\}$. In Exercise 10(a) you are to produce the required mappings g and h.   □

Exercises

1. *(a)*   Find the domain and range of each of the relations in Example 1.
(b)   Determine which of the relations in Example 1, Article 7.1, are functions.
(c)   Show that each of the following relations is not a function:

  (i) $r_1 = \{(x, y) \in \mathbf{R} \times \mathbf{R} \,|\, 4x^2 + 9y^2 = 108\}$
★*(ii)* $r_2 = \{(x, y) \in \mathbf{R} \times \mathbf{R} \,|\, x^3 y + xy^3 = 0\}$
  (iii) $r_3 = \{(x, y) \in \mathbf{R} \times \mathbf{R} \,|\, y = x \pm 3\}$
  (iv) $r_4 = \{(x, y) \in \mathbf{R} \times \mathbf{R} \,|\, x = |y|\}$

(d)   Find all functions having the set $\{1, 2, 3\}$ as domain and the set $\{w, z\}$ as range.

2. *(a)*   Prove that two functions f and g are equal (i.e., contain precisely the same ordered pairs) if and only if dom f = dom g and $f(x) = g(x)$ for all x in the common domain.

(b)   Use (a) to show that the functions $f(x) = x + 4$ and $g(x) = (x^2 - 16)/(x - 4)$ are distinct.

3. *(a)*   Determine the domain and range of each of the following functions:

(i)	$y = x^2 + 5$	*(ii)*	$y = 2x^2 - 8x + 5$
(iii)	$y = \sqrt{(x + 7)}$	*(iv)*	$y = \sqrt{(25 - x^2)}$
(v)	$y = -3/x$	*(vi)*	$y = 3 + \cos x$
(vii)	$y = (x - 2)/(2 - x)$	*(viii)*	$y = 3/(x - 5)$
(ix)	$y = (x/(1 - x))^{1/2}$	*(x)*	$y = |x - 3| + 2$

(b)   Give an example of a real-valued function of a real variable for each of the following categories:

(i)   Transcendental

(ii)   Algebraic, but not rational

(iii)   Rational, not a polynomial. Is your example an algebraic function?

(iv)   A polynomial. Is your example a rational function? an algebraic function?

4. Establish whether each of the following functions is or is not one to one:

(a) $f(x) = -14x + 243$ *(b)* $C(x) = 46$

(c) $g(x) = x^4 + 5x^2$ *(d)* $h(x) = x^4 + 5x^2$, dom $h = [0, \infty)$

★*(e)* $j(x) = x^3 - x$ *(f)* $k(x) = 1/(x^2 + 2)$

(g) $m(x) = x^3 + x$ [*Hint:* If x_1 and x_2 have different signs, so do $m(x_1)$ and $m(x_2)$.]

5. *(a)*   Prove that if f is a one-to-one function, then the relation f^{-1} is a function.

(b)   Prove that if $f: A \to B$ is a one-to-one mapping, then $f^{-1}:$ rng $f \to A$ is also a one-to-one mapping. [*Note:* From (a), we know that f^{-1} is a function. You must prove that dom f^{-1} = rng f, rng $f^{-1} \subseteq A$, and f^{-1} is one to one.]

6. *(a)*   Let A be any set and $X \subseteq A$. Prove that the inclusion mapping $i_X: X \to A$ is injective.

(b)   Let $f: A \to B$ be an injective mapping and let $X \subseteq A$. Prove that the restriction $f/_X: X \to B$ is also injective.

7. In each of the following examples, compute $f \circ g$ and $g \circ f$, either by listing all the ordered pairs or by specifying domain and rule of correspondence, as appropriate:

(a) $f = \{(2, 4), (3, 6), (4, 8), (5, 10)\}$, $g = \{(4, 16), (6, 36), (8, 64), (10, 100)\}$

(b) $f = \{(7, 12), (5, 2), (3, 11), (8, 8), (1, 2)\}$, $g = \{(12, 7), (2, 5), (11, 3), (8, 8), (2, 1)\}$

(c) $f = \{(1, 1), (2, 2), (3, 3)\}$, $g = \{(1, 5), (3, 11), (4, 12)\}$

(d) $f(x) = \sqrt{(x - 3)}$, $g(x) = e^x$

(e) $f(x) = \sin x$, $g(x) = x^3 - 5x$

(f) $f = \{(1, 2), (2, 3), (3, 4), (4, 5), (5, 6), (6, 7)\}$, $g = \{(2, 4), (3, 5), (4, 6), (5, 7), (7, 2)\}$

8. *(a)*   Prove formally from Definition 5 that if f and g are functions, then $x \in$ dom $(g \circ f)$ if and only if $x \in$ dom f and $f(x) \in$ dom g.

(b)   *(i)*   Give an example of two functions f and g such that $f \circ g \neq g \circ f$.

(ii)   Give an example of two functions k and h such that $k \circ h \neq h \circ k$.

(c)   Prove that if f and g are linear mappings of **R** into **R**, that is $f(x) = Mx + B$ and $g(x) = Nx + C$, then $f \circ g$ and $g \circ f$ are both linear mappings with slope MN.

(d)   [Continuation of (c)] Determine conditions on M, N, B, and C such that $f \circ g = g \circ f$. Give a specific example of linear mappings f and g such that $f \circ g = g \circ f$.

(e)   Consider two functions f and g, where $f \neq \varnothing$ and $g \neq \varnothing$. Find a condition involving domains and ranges of these functions that guarantees that $g \circ f = \varnothing$.

9. Let $f \colon A \to B$ be any mapping, let I_A and I_B be the identity mappings on A and B, respectively. Prove:

(a) $f \circ I_A = I_B \circ f = f$

(b)   If f is injective, then $f^{-1} \circ f = I_A$.

★(c)   If $X \subseteq A$, then $f \circ i_X = f|_X$, where i_X is the inclusion mapping of X into A.

10. (a)   Complete the proof of the "if" part of Theorem 4.

(b)   Prove that if $f \colon A \to B$ and $g \colon B \to C$ are injections, the $g \circ f \colon A \to C$ is an injection.

(c)   Prove that if $f \colon A \to B$ and $g \colon B \to C$ are mappings such that $g \circ f \colon A \to C$ is an injection, then f is an injection.

(d)   In each of the following two cases, give examples of two mappings $f \colon A \to B$ and $g \colon B \to C$ such that:

(i) $g \circ f \colon A \to C$ is an injection, but g is not an injection (*Note:* What must be true of f in any such example?)

(ii) f is injective, but $g \circ f$ is not injective (*Note:* What must be true of g in any such example?)

★(e)   Suppose that $f \colon A \to B$ and $g \colon C \to D$ are mappings and assume $\operatorname{rng} f \subseteq C$. Prove that $\operatorname{dom}(g \circ f) = A$ and $\operatorname{rng}(g \circ f) \subseteq D$.

11. Let f and g be mappings of **R** into **R**. Define new mappings $f \vee g$ and $f \wedge g$ from **R** into **R** by $(f \vee g)(x) = \max\{f(x), g(x)\}$ and $(f \wedge g)(x) = \min\{f(x), g(x)\}$ for each $x \in$ **R**. Give examples to show that $f \vee g$ and $f \wedge g$ can fail to be one to one, even when f and g are both one to one.

12. Let $f \colon A \to B$ and $g \colon C \to D$ be mappings:

(a)   Prove that if $A \cap C = \varnothing$, then the relation $f \cup g$ (the set theoretic union of f and g, regarded as sets of ordered pairs) is a mapping of $A \cup C$ into $B \cup D$.

(b)   Prove that if $A \cap C = B \cap D = \varnothing$ and if f and g are injective, then $f \cup g$ is injective.

(c)   Prove that if $A \cap C = \varnothing$, then $(f \cup g)|_A = f$ and $(f \cup g)|_C = g$.

13. Let $f \colon A \to B$ be a mapping. A mapping $g \colon C \to B$ is said to be an *extension of* f if and only if $f \subseteq g$.

★(a)   Prove that if $g \colon C \to B$ is an extension of $f \colon A \to B$, then $A \subseteq C$.

(b)   Prove that if $f \colon A \to B$ and $g \colon C \to D$ are mappings with $A \cap C = \varnothing$, then $f \cup g \colon A \cup C \to B \cup D$ is an extension of both f and g.

(c)   Prove that if $g \colon C \to B$ is an extension of $f \colon A \to B$, then $g|_A = f$.

(d)   Find an extension of the mapping $f(x) = (x^2 - 25)/(x + 5)$ of $\mathbf{R} - \{-5\}$ into **R**, whose domain is **R** and that is continuous on **R**.

(e)   Show that the mapping $g \colon \mathbf{C} \to \mathbf{C}$ defined by $g(z) = e^x(\cos y + i \sin y)$, where $z = x + yi$, is an extension of the mapping $f \colon \mathbf{R} \to \mathbf{C}$ given by $f(x) = e^x$.

8.2   More on Functions and Mappings— Surjections, Bijections, Image, and Inverse Image

In the preceding article we saw that the definition of mapping (or, synonymously, function from one set to another) provides for the specification of a codomain, possibly distinct from the range (or image) of the associated function. If $f: A \to B$, then the general relationship between the codomain B and rng f is rng $f \subseteq B$. In general, we say that f maps A *into* B. In the special case, such as $f: \mathbf{R} \to [0, \infty)$, $f(x) = x^2$, where rng f equals B, we say that f maps A *onto* B. We formalize this condition in the following definition.

DEFINITION   1

The mapping $f: A \to B$ is said to be **onto**, or **a function that maps A onto B**, in case rng $f = B$. We also say that such a mapping is **surjective**, or a **surjection**.

In view of the definition of rng f, we may characterize the *onto* property as follows. The mapping $f: A \to B$ is onto if and only if, for every $y \in B$, there exists $x \in A$ such that $f(x) = y$ [see Exercise 1(a)]. Unlike the one-to-one property, which depends only on the function part of a mapping, the onto property depends in a crucial way on the choice of codomain. In fact, given various mappings built on the same function, at most one of them can be onto. As one example, if $f: \mathbf{R} \to B$, $f(x) = \sin x$, where $[-1, 1] \subseteq B \subseteq \mathbf{R}$, f is onto if and only if $B = [-1, 1]$. In Exercise 2 you are asked to determine whether or not various given mappings are surjective.

We suggested earlier that the injective and surjective properties of a mapping are, in a sense, companion properties. This fact may not be evident from a comparison of their definitions, but consider the following. A mapping $f: A \to B$ is one to one if and only if each $y \in B$ has at most one $x \in A$ such that $f(x) = y$, and onto if and only if each $y \in B$ has at least one $x \in A$ such that $f(x) = y$. For mappings of $\mathbf{R}$ into $\mathbf{R}$, the one-to-one property dictates that every horizontal line meet the graph in at most one point; the onto property requires that every horizontal line intersect the graph in at least one point. Recalling Theorem 4 of Article 8.1, we see another analogy between the injective and surjective properties in the following result.

THEOREM   1

Let X be a nonempty set and let $f: X \to Y$ be a mapping. Then f is surjective if and only if for any set Z and for any mappings $g: Y \to Z$ and $h: y \to Z$ such that $g \circ f = h \circ f$, we have $g = h$.

Proof $\Rightarrow$ Assume f maps X onto Y, let Z be a set, and let g and h be mappings of Y into Z such that $g \circ f = h \circ f$. To prove $g = h$, let y be an arbitrary element of Y. We must prove that $g(y) = h(y)$. Since f is surjective, there exists $x \in X$ such that $f(x) = y$. Since $g \circ f = h \circ f$, by assumption, then $(g \circ f)(x) = (h \circ f)(x)$ so that $g(f(x)) = h(f(x))$. Since $y = f(x)$, we conclude $g(y) = h(y)$, as desired. We may express the latter argument in the form of a proof by transitivity by the string $g(y) = g(f(x)) = (g \circ f)(x) = (h \circ f)(x) = h(f(x)) = h(y)$.

$\Leftarrow$ As in the "if" part of the proof of Theorem 4, Article 8.1, we are motivated by the relatively complex form of the hypothesis to attempt an indirect proof. Suppose f is not surjective. Our goal is to contradict the hypothesis by producing a set Z and distinct mappings g and h of Y into Z such that $g \circ f = h \circ f$. Now since f is not onto, there exists $y_0 \in Y$ such that $y_0 \notin \mathrm{rng}\, f$. Let $x_0 \in X$ (which we have assumed to be nonempty) and note that $y_0 \neq f(x_0)$, since $y_0 \notin \mathrm{rng}\, f$. It is now time that we define Z, g, and h. Let $Z = Y$, let $g\colon Y \to Z$ be the identity mapping, and let $h\colon Y \to Z$ be defined by the rule $h(y) = y$ if $y \neq y_0$ and $h(y) = f(x_0)$ if $y = y_0$. Since $y_0 \neq f(x_0)$, then g and h are clearly <u>distinct</u> mappings from Y to Z. Finally, if x is any element of X, we have $(g \circ f)(x) = g(f(x)) = f(x) = h(f(x)) = (h \circ f)(x)$, so that the mappings $g \circ f$ and $h \circ f$ are identical, as required. $\square$

In the string of equations at the conclusion of the proof of Theorem 1, the key assertion $f(x) = h(f(x))$ is valid because h is the identity mapping except at y_0. By our construction, we know $f(x)$ does not equal y_0 for any $x \in X$ so that our conclusion $h(f(x)) = f(x)$ is warranted.

Theorem 1 asserts that onto mappings are precisely the mappings with a sort of "right-cancellation" property, analogous to the left-cancellation property of one-to-one mappings derived in Theorem 4 of Article 8.1.

In the following theorem we combine several results relating the injective and surjective properties to composition of mappings. As we will see, it is possible to view the proofs of these properties as applications of Theorem 1 and Theorem 4, Article 8.1.

THEOREM 2
Let $f\colon X \to Y$ and $g\colon Y \to Z$, so that $g \circ f\colon X \to Z$. Then:

(a) If f and g are injective, $g \circ f$ is injective.
(b) If f and g are surjective, $g \circ f$ is surjective.
(c) If $g \circ f$ is injective, then f is injective.
(d) If $g \circ f$ is surjective, then g is surjective.

Partial proof   Each of these results may be proved directly from the definitions involved. Let us consider (d). To prove g is surjective, let $z \in Z$ be given. We must show there exists $y \in Y$ such that $g(y) = z$. Now since $g \circ f$ maps X onto Z, by hypothesis, then corresponding to this z (using specialization), there is an element $x \in X$ such that $z = (g \circ f)(x)$. Since $(g \circ f)(x) = g(f(x))$ and since $f(x) \in Y$, our choice of the desired y is now clear. Let $y = f(x)$. We reiterate that $y \in Y$ and note that $g(y) = g(f(x)) = z$, as desired. The proof of (d) is complete.

Each of the remaining results (a), (b), and (c) can be proved in a similar direct manner. You, in fact, may already have proved (a) and (c) in Exercise 10, Article 8.1. You are asked to provide a similar elementary (i.e., direct from the definitions involved) proof of (b) in Exercise 3(a). An alternative, and far more sophisticated, approach to each of the four results may be taken by employing our two theorems on right and left cancellation. The former, Theorem 1, relating to the surjective property, is useful for (b) and (d). The latter, Theorem 4 of Article 8.1, concerning injectivity, may be employed to prove (a) and (c). Let us see how such an argument would go by proving (c).

Given that $g \circ f$ is injective, we use the condition in Theorem 4, Article 8.1, to prove f is injective. To set up such a proof, we let W be a set and let h and k be mappings of W into X such that $f \circ h = f \circ k$. We must prove that $h = k$. Now since $f \circ h = f \circ k$, then $g \circ (f \circ h) = g \circ (f \circ k)$, where both these mappings send W to Z, as shown in Figure 8.5. By associativity of composition (Theorem 3, Article 8.1), we may deduce $(g \circ f) \circ h = (g \circ f) \circ k$. Since $g \circ f$ is injective, then by Theorem 4, Article 8.1, we may "cancel" $g \circ f$ on the left to conclude $h = k$, as desired. $\square$

Exercise 5 requires you to give similar proofs of (a), (b), and (d) of Theorem 2.

We next consider possible combinations of the one-to-one and onto properties. If $f(x) = x^2$, then $f: \mathbf{R} \to \mathbf{R}$ is neither one to one nor onto, whereas $f: \mathbf{R} \to [0, \infty)$ is onto, but is not one to one. On the other hand, if $g(x) = e^x$, then $g: \mathbf{R} \to \mathbf{R}$ is one to one, but is not onto. Finally, mappings from $\mathbf{R}$ to $\mathbf{R}$ such as $y = Mx + B \ (M \neq 0)$, $y = \sinh x$, and $y = x^3$

Figure 8.5   *A diagram helps to keep track of the sets between which various mappings operate.*

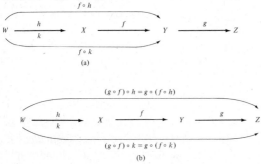

are both one to one and onto. The latter combination is of sufficient importance to warrant special designation:

DEFINITION 2
A mapping $f: A \to B$ is called a **one-to-one correspondence**, or a **bijection**, between A and B if and only if it is both one to one and onto.

The two parts of the next result follow from Theorem 2.

COROLLARY
Let $f: X \to Y$ and $g: Y \to Z$ so that $g \circ f: X \to Z$.

(a) If f and g are bijections, then $g \circ f$ is a bijection.
(b) If $g \circ f$ is a bijection, then f is injective and g is surjective.

Formal verification of (a) and (b) are left to you [Exercise 4(a)], as are the simple proofs of parts (a) and (b) of the next theorem.

THEOREM 3
Given sets A and B.

(a) The identity mapping $I_A: A \to A$ on A is a bijection.
(b) If $f: A \to B$ is a bijection, so is $f^{-1}: B \to A$.
(c) If $f: A \to B$ is a bijection, then $f^{-1} \circ f = I_A$ and $f \circ f^{-1} = I_B$.

Proof of (c)   Since f is a one-to-one mapping of A onto B, then by (b), f^{-1} is a bijection from B to A. Hence by (a) of the corollary to Theorem 2, $f^{-1} \circ f$ is a bijection from A to A, while $f \circ f^{-1}$ is a bijection from B to B. To show $f^{-1} \circ f = I_A$, let $x \in A$; we need only show that $(f^{-1} \circ f)(x) = x$; that is, $f^{-1}(f(x)) = x$, or the ordered pair $(f(x), x) \in f^{-1}$, which is equivalent to $(x, f(x)) \in f$, evidently a true statement. To show $f \circ f^{-1} = I_B$, let $y \in B$. We claim that $f(f^{-1}(y)) = y$. For this, we need only that $(f^{-1}(y), y) \in f$. The latter is true since $(y, f^{-1}(y)) \in f^{-1}$. The proofs of parts (a) and (b) are the content of Exercise 6(a). □

The idea of a one-to-one correspondence between sets is the basis of the theory of cardinal numbers, a study of the "relative size" of sets. As we will see in Article 8.3, this theory is of primary interest in relation to infinite sets, providing as it does a means of distinguishing between "relatively small" and "relatively large" infinite sets. The starting point in our brief glimpse at cardinality of sets will be the concept of *numerical equivalence* of sets; in brief, two sets A and B are said to be *numerically equivalent* if and only if there exists a bijection from one to the other. In preparation for Article 8.3, let us take an informal look at possibilities for injections, surjections, and bijections between pairs of finite sets.

Suppose A and B are finite sets with $n(A) = m$ and $n(B) = n$. Suppose there exists an injection f from A to B; What can we can say about the relationship between m and n? Every element of A is mapped to an element of B and there is no "doubling up." Hence B must have at least as many elements as A; that is, $m \le n$. On the other hand, if there exists a surjection from A to B, then every element of B is mapped into by at least one element of A. Since again, there is no "doubling up" (the definition of function forbids it) in this direction, A must have at least as many elements as B. We conclude $m \ge n$ in this case. Finally, suppose there is a bijection f between A and B. Since f is injective, we have $m \le n$. Since f is surjective, $m \ge n$. The result of our informal considerations is the conclusion $m = n$. Two finite sets having m and n elements are in one-to-one correspondence if and only if $m = n$.

IMAGE AND INVERSE IMAGE

DEFINITION 3

Let $f: A \rightarrow B$ be a mapping, and let $M \subseteq A$ and $N \subseteq B$. Then we define

(a)   The **image $f(M)$ of M under f** by $f(M) = \{f(m) \mid m \in M\}$
(b)   The **inverse image $f^{-1}(N)$ of N under f** by $f^{-1}(N) = \{x \in A \mid f(x) \in N\}$

Image and inverse image are useful tools for expressing many ideas in advanced mathematics; we provide several examples of their uses in the exercises (e.g., Exercise 15). But our primary goal now is to introduce you to the two concepts and to study a number of their elementary properties.

Let us begin with some basic facts. Note first that $f(M)$ and $f^{-1}(N)$ are sets; $f(M)$ is a subset of B, whereas $f^{-1}(N)$ is a subset of A. Note also that $f^{-1}(N)$ is a separate entity from the inverse relation f^{-1} and, in particular, is always defined, even when the relation f^{-1} is not a function.

Here is an important and useful fact about $f(M)$. An element $y \in B$ is contained in $f(M)$ if and only if $y = f(m)$ for some $m \in M$. Hence proofs of theorems about $f(M)$ usually involve the techniques studied in Article 6.1. It is generally easier to prove theorems whose conclusion involves inverse image. If $x \in A$, we may prove $x \in f^{-1}(N)$ simply by proving $f(x) \in N$.

A few other elementary properties of image and inverse image are combined in the following result, most of whose proof is left to you in Exercise 8(a).

THEOREM 4

Let $f: A \rightarrow B$. Then:

(a) $f(\emptyset) = \emptyset$
(b) $f^{-1}(\emptyset) = \emptyset$

(c) $A = f^{-1}(B)$

(d)   rng $f = f(A)$

(e)   If $M_1, M_2 \subseteq A$ with $M_1 \subseteq M_2$, then $f(M_1) \subseteq f(M_2)$

(f)   If $N_1, N_2 \subseteq B$ with $N_1 \subseteq N_2$, then $f^{-1}(N_1) \subseteq f^{-1}(N_2)$

Partial proof   (a)   To prove $f(\varnothing) = \varnothing$, we recall the approach of Examples 11 and 12, Article 4.1, and assume $y \in f(\varnothing)$. By definition of image, we may then assert there exists $m \in \varnothing$ such that $y = f(m)$. But the statement "$\exists m \in \varnothing$" is a contradiction.

(f)   Let N_1 and N_2 be subsets of B with $N_1 \subseteq N_2$. To prove $f^{-1}(N_1) \subseteq f^{-1}(N_2)$, suppose $x \in f^{-1}(N_1)$. To show $x \in f^{-1}(N_2)$, we need only show $f(x) \in N_2$. Now since $x \in f^{-1}(N_1)$, we have $f(x) \in N_1$. Since $N_1 \subseteq N_2$, we conclude $f(x) \in N_2$, as desired. $\square$

Let us next consider an example. If $f(x) = x^2$ maps $\mathbf{R}$ to $\mathbf{R}$, then $f([-1, 1]) = [0, 1]$, whereas $f^{-1}([0, 4]) = [-2, 2]$. Also, $f^{-1}(\{9\}) = \{-3, 3\}$, whereas $f^{-1}(\{-9\}) = \varnothing$. Furthermore, $f(\mathbf{R}) = [0, \infty)$, the range of f.

Let us compute $f^{-1}(f([0, 1]))$. Now $f([0, 1]) = [0, 1]$, so $f^{-1}(f([0, 1])) = f^{-1}([0, 1]) = [-1, 1]$. Note that letting $M = [0, 1]$, we have that $f^{-1}(f(M)) = [-1, 1] \supset [0, 1] = M$ in this example. On the other hand, $f(f^{-1}([-1, 1])) = f([-1, 1]) = [0, 1]$. Letting $N = [-1, 1]$, we note that $f(f^{-1}(N)) = [0, 1] \subset [-1, 1] = N$ in this example.

The results of several parts of the preceding example are suggestive of part of the next result.

THEOREM 5

Given a mapping $f: A \to B$.

(a) $M \subseteq f^{-1}(f(M))$ for any subset M of A

(b) $f(f^{-1}(N)) \subseteq N$ for any subset N of B

(c) $M = f^{-1}(f(M))$ for each subset M of A if and only if f is injective

(d) $f(f^{-1}(N)) = N$ for each subset N of B if and only if f is surjective

Proof   (a)   Let $x \in M$. To prove $x \in f^{-1}(f(M))$, we need only show $f(x) \in f(M)$. Since $x \in M$, the latter statement is true.

(b)   Let $y \in f(f^{-1}(N))$. We claim $y \in N$. Now we know there exists $x \in f^{-1}(N)$ such that $y = f(x)$. Since $x \in f^{-1}(N)$, then $f(x) \in N$. Since $y = f(x)$, we conclude $y \in N$, as desired.

(c)   Suppose $M = f^{-1}(f(M))$ for every subset M of A. To prove f injective, let $x_1, x_2 \in A$ and suppose $f(x_1) = f(x_2)$. We claim $x_1 = x_2$. Letting $M = \{x_1\}$, we note that $f^{-1}(f(M)) \subseteq M$ for this particular set M, because of our hypothesis. But $f(x_2) = f(x_1) \in f(M)$ so $x_2 \in f^{-1}(f(M))$. Since $f^{-1}(f(M)) \subseteq M = \{x_1\}$, we have $x_2 \in \{x_1\}$, so that $x_2 = x_1$, as desired. Conversely, suppose f is injective. Let $M \subseteq A$ and recall from (a) that $M \subseteq f^{-1}(f(M))$. To prove equality, we need only show

$f^{-1}(f(M)) \subseteq M$. Let $x \in f^{-1}(f(M))$. Then $f(x) \in f(M)$ so that $f(x) = f(m)$ for some $m \in M$. Since f is one to one, we conclude $x = m$. Since $m \in M$ and $x = m$, we conclude $x \in M$, as desired.

(d) This is left as an exercise for you [Exercise 8(c)]. □

In the example preceding Theorem 5 we noted that M is a proper subset of $f^{-1}(f(M))$, while $f(f^{-1}(N))$ is a proper subset of N. In view of (c) and (d) of Theorem 5, these conclusions are consistent with the evident fact that the mapping in that example is neither one to one nor onto. Also, in attempting the proof of the "only if" part of (d), you should keep in mind that the "only if" part of the proof of (c) employed a clever application of the specialization technique, namely, an appropriate choice $M = \{x_1\}$ of a set M.

In our next theorem we consider how image and inverse image interact with the set operations of union and intersection. As we will see, inverse image is slightly "better behaved" than image.

THEOREM 6

Let $f: A \to B$. Then:

(a) $f^{-1}(N_1 \cup N_2) = f^{-1}(N_1) \cup f^{-1}(N_2)$ and $f^{-1}(N_1 \cap N_2) = f^{-1}(N_1) \cap f^{-1}(N_2)$ for any subsets N_1 and N_2 of B.

(b) $f(M_1 \cup M_2) = f(M_1) \cup f(M_2)$ for any subsets M_1 and M_2 of A.

(c) $f(M_1 \cap M_2) \subseteq f(M_1) \cap f(M_2)$ for any subsets M_1 and M_2 of A.

(d) $f(M_1 \cap M_2) = f(M_1) \cap f(M_2)$ for any subsets M_1 and M_2 of A if and only if f is injective.

Partial proof   Let us consider (c) and the "if" part of (d). The remaining parts are left to you in Exercise 9. For (c), let M_1 and M_2 be subsets of A and let $y \in f(M_1 \cap M_2)$. Then $y = f(m)$ for some $m \in M_1 \cap M_2$. Since $m \in M_1$, then $y \in f(M_1)$. Since $m \in M_2$, then $y \in f(M_2)$. Hence $y \in f(M_1) \cap f(M_2)$, as desired.

As for (d), assume f is one to one and let $y \in f(M_1) \cap f(M_2)$. To show $y \in f(M_1 \cap M_2)$, we must show there exists $m \in M_1 \cap M_2$ such that $y = f(m)$. Now since $y \in f(M_1)$, then $y = f(m_1)$ for some $m_1 \in M_1$. Since $y \in f(M_2)$, then $y = f(m_2)$ for some $m_2 \in M_2$. Since $f(m_1) = y = f(m_2)$ and since f is one to one, we may conclude $m_1 = m_2$. Let the desired m equal the common value of m_1 and m_2, noting that $y = f(m)$ and $m \in M_1 \cap M_2$ (since $m = m_1 \in M_1$ and $m = m_2 \in M_2$), as desired. □

In view of (d) of Theorem 6, a mapping for which the containment in (c) is proper cannot be injective. You should supply an example of f, M_1, and M_2 to illustrate this case. The results in (a) through (c) of Theorem 6 may be generalized to any finite number of sets, using an induction argument (Exercise 10) and also to infinite collections of sets indexed by $\mathbf{N}$ (Exercise 11).

Exercises

1. Use Definition 1 and the definition of rng f (Definition 4, Article 7.1) to prove that a mapping $f: A \to B$ is a surjection if and only if, for each $y \in B$, there exists $x \in A$ such that $y = f(x)$.

2. Determine whether each of the following mappings is (i) a surjection, (ii) an injection, (iii) a bijection:

(a) $f: \mathbf{R} - \{0\} \to \{-1, 1\}$, $f(x) = x/|x|$

★(b) $f: \mathbf{R} - \{4\} \to \mathbf{R}$, $f(x) = (x^2 - x - 12)/(x - 4)$

(c) $f: \mathbf{R} \to (-\infty, 11]$ $f(x) = -3x^2 - 12x - 1$

(d) $f: \mathbf{R} \to \mathbf{R}$, $f(x) = \begin{cases} x^2 + 1, & x \geq 0 \\ -x^2 - 1, & x < 0 \end{cases}$

(e) $f: \{1, 2, 3, 4, 5\} \to \{a, b, c, d, e\}$, $f = \{(1, a), (2, a), (3, b), (4, c), (5, e)\}$

(f) $f: \{a, b, c, d, e\} \to \{A, B, C, D, E\}$, $f = \{(a, A), (b, B), (c, C), (d, D), (e, E)\}$

(g) $f: \{1, 2, 3, 4\} \to \{a, b, c, d, e\}$, $f = \{(1, a), (2, b), (3, d), (4, e)\}$

(h) $f: \mathbf{R} \to \mathbf{R}$, $f(x) = \sin x$

(i) $f: \mathbf{R} \to [-1, 1]$, $f(x) = \sin x$

(j) $f: [-\pi, \pi] \to [-1, 1]$, $f(x) = \sin x$

★(k) $f: \mathbf{R} \to [-\pi/2, \pi/2]$, $f(x) = \tan^{-1} x$

3. (a) Use the definition of onto mapping to prove that if f maps X onto Y and g maps Y onto Z, then $g \circ f$ maps X into Z [(b) of Theorem 2].

(b) In each of the following three cases, give examples of two mappings $f: A \to B$ and $g: B \to C$ such that:

(i) $g \circ f: A \to C$ is a surjection, but f is not surjective. (What must be true of g in any such example?)

(ii) g is surjective, but $g \circ f$ is not surjective. (What must be true of f in any such example?)

(iii) f is surjective, but $g \circ f$ is not surjective. (What must be true of g in any such example?)

★(c) Prove that if $f: X \to Y$ is surjective and $g: Y \to Z$, then $g \circ f: X \to Z$ is a surjection if and only if g is surjective.

(d) State and prove a result analogous to (c) for injective mappings.

4. (a) Prove the corollary to Theorem 2. That is, prove that if $f: X \to Y$ and $g: Y \to Z$ so that $g \circ f: X \to Z$, then:

(i) If f and g are bijections, then $g \circ f$ is a bijection.

(ii) If $g \circ f$ is a bijection, then f is injective and g is surjective.

(b) In each of the following three cases, give example of mappings: $f: X \to Y$ and $g: Y \to Z$ such that:

(i) $g \circ f: X \to Z$ is a bijection, but f is not onto and g is not one to one

★(ii) f is bijective, but $g \circ f$ is not bijective

(iii) g is bijective, but $g \circ f$ is not bijective

5. (a) Use the result of Theorem 1 to give a proof of (b) of Theorem 2, different from the proof in Exercise 3(a). [Recall the proof of (c) Theorem 2, given in the text.]

(b) Use Theorem 1 to give a proof of (d) of Theorem 2, different from the proof given in the text.

(c)   Use the result of Theorem 4, Article 8.1, to give a proof of (a) of Theorem 2, different from the proof in Exercise 10(b), Article 8.1.

6. (a)   Prove parts (a) and (b) of Theorem 3: that is, prove that, given sets A and B:

(i)   The identity mapping $I_A: A \to A$ on A is a bijection.

(ii)   If $f: A \to B$ is a bijection, then $f^{-1}: B \to A$ is a bijection.

(b)   Prove that if $f: A \to B$ and $g: B \to C$ are bijections, then:

(i) $(g \circ f)^{-1}$ is a bijection from C to A

(ii) $f^{-1} \circ g^{-1}$ is a bijection from C to A

(iii) $(g \circ f)^{-1} = f^{-1} \circ g^{-1}$

(c)   According to the text (see the paragraph after the proof of Theorem 3), two sets A and B are numerically equivalent if and only if there exists a bijection from one to the other. Use previously proved results in this chapter to prove that the relation of numerical equivalence is an equivalence relation on the collection of all subsets of any given universal set U.

7. (a)   Given $f: \mathbf{R} \to \mathbf{R}$, $f(x) = 3x - 7$, calculate:

(i) $f^{-1}(\{3\})$ ⎟   (ii) $f(\{5\})$

★(iii) $f^{-1}([-7, 2])$ ⎟   (iv) $f(\{0\})$

(v) $f(\varnothing)$ ⎟   (vi) $f^{-1}([3, 5] \cup [8, 10])$

(b)   Given $f: \{A, B, C, D, E, F, G, H\} \to \{a, e, i, o, u\}$,   where $f = \{(A, e), (B, u),$ $(C, o), (D, o), (E, e), (F, a), (G, e), (H, e)\}$, calculate:

(i) $f(\{A, C, D, E, G, H\})$ ⎟   (ii) $f(\{A, C\})$

(iii) $f^{-1}(\{e\})$ ⎟   ★(iv) $f^{-1}(\{e, o\})$

(v) $f^{-1}(f(\{A, C\}))$ ⎟   (vi) $f^{-1}(\{i\})$

(vii) $f^{-1}(\{e, i\})$ ⎟   (viii) $f(f^{-1}(\{e, i\}))$

(ix) $f(\{A, B\}) \cap f(\{E, F\})$ ⎟   (x) $f(\{A, B\} \cap \{E, F\})$

(c)   Given $f: \mathbf{R} \to \mathbf{R}$, $f(x) = (x + 1)^2$, calculate:

(i) $f(\{-1\})$ ⎟   (ii) $f^{-1}([0, 1])$

★(iii) $f^{-1}([-1, 1])$ ⎟   (iv) $f^{-1}([-3, 5])$

(v) $f(f^{-1}([-3, -1]))$ ⎟   (vi) $f(f^{-1}([-1, 1]))$

8. (a)   Prove parts (b) through (e) of Theorem 4; that is, if $f: A \to B$, then:

(i) $f^{-1}(\varnothing) = \varnothing$ ⎟   (ii) $A = f^{-1}(B)$

(iii)   rng $f = f(A)$

(iv)   If $M_1, M_2 \subseteq A$ and $M_1 \subseteq M_2$, then $f(M_1) \subseteq f(M_2)$

(b)   (i)   Give an example of a mapping $f: A \to B$ and subsets M_1, and M_2 of A such that $M_1 \subset M_2$, but $f(M_1) = f(M_2)$.

(ii)   Prove that if $f: A \to B$ is one to one, then for any subsets M_1 and M_2 of A, if $f(M_1) = f(M_2)$, we may conclude $M_1 = M_2$.

(c)   Prove (d) of Theorem 5; that is, given a mapping $f: A \to B$, $f(f^{-1}(N)) = N$ for each subset N of B if and only if f is an onto mapping.

9. (a)   Prove (a) of Theorem 6; that is, if $f: A \to B$, then:

★(i) $f^{-1}(N_1 \cup N_2) = f^{-1}(N_1) \cup f^{-1}(N_2)$ for any subsets N_1 and N_2 of B

(ii) $f^{-1}(N_1 \cap N_2) = f^{-1}(N_1) \cap f^{-1}(N_2)$ for any subsets N_1 and N_2 of B

(b)   Prove (b) of Theorem 6; that is, if $f: A \to B$, then $f(M_1 \cup M_2) = f(M_1) \cup f(M_2)$ for any subsets M_1 and M_2 of A.

(c)   Prove the "only if" part of (d) of Theorem 6; that is, if $f: A \to B$ has the property that $f(M_1 \cap M_2) = f(M_1) \cap f(M_2)$ for any subsets M_1 and M_2 of A, then f is injective.

10. Let $f: A \to B$, let k be a positive integer. Let $M_1, M_2, \ldots, M_k$ and $N_1, N_2, \ldots, N_k$ be k subsets of A and B, respectively. Use induction (recall Example 6, Article 5.4) to prove:

(a) $f^{-1}(N_1 \cap N_2 \cap \cdots \cap N_k) = f^{-1}(N_1) \cap f^{-1}(N_2) \cap \cdots \cap f^{-1}(N_k)$
(b) $f^{-1}(N_1 \cup N_2 \cup \cdots \cup N_k) = f^{-1}(N_1) \cup f^{-1}(N_2) \cup \cdots \cup f^{-1}(N_k)$
(c) $f(M_1 \cap M_2 \cap \cdots \cap M_k) \subseteq f(M_1) \cap f(M_2) \cap \cdots \cap f(M_k)$
(d) $f(M_1 \cup M_2 \cup \cdots \cup M_k) = f(M_1) \cup f(M_2) \cup \cdots \cup f(M_k)$

11. Let $f: A \to B$. Let $\{M_k | k = 1, 2, 3, \ldots\}$ and $\{N_k | k = 1, 2, 3, \ldots\}$ be infinite collections, indexed by $\mathbf{N}$, of subsets of A and B, respectively (recall Article 4.2). Prove:

(a) $f^{-1}(\bigcap_{k=1}^{\infty} N_k) = \bigcap_{k=1}^{\infty} f^{-1}(N_k)$ (b) $f^{-1}(\bigcup_{k=1}^{\infty} N_k) = \bigcup_{k=1}^{\infty} f^{-1}(N_k)$
(c) $f(\bigcup_{k=1}^{\infty} M_k) = \bigcup_{k=1}^{\infty} f(M_k)$ (d) $f(\bigcap_{k=1}^{\infty} M_k) \subseteq \bigcap_{k=1}^{\infty} f(M_k)$

12. Let $f: A \to B$, $X \subseteq A$, and $Y \subseteq B$. Prove that:

★(a) $f(f^{-1}(Y)) = Y$ if and only if $Y \subseteq \text{rng } f$. Is this result consistent with the result in (d) of Theorem 5?

(b) $f^{-1}(f(X)) = X$ if and only if the restriction of f to the subset $f^{-1}(f(X))$ of A is one to one. Is this result consistent with the result in (c) of Theorem 5?

13. Let $f: A \to B$, let $M \subseteq A$, and $N \subseteq B$. Prove:

(a) $f^{-1}(B - N) = A - f^{-1}(N)$
(b) $f(M) \subseteq N$ if and only if $M \subseteq f^{-1}(N)$
(c)   If f is a bijection, then $f(M) = N$ if and only if $M = f^{-1}(N)$

14. Let $f: A \to B$, let $M_1, M_2 \subseteq A$, and $N_1, N_2 \subseteq B$. Prove:

(a) $f^{-1}(N_1 - N_2) = f^{-1}(N_1) - f^{-1}(N_2)$
(b) $f(M_1) - f(M_2) \subseteq f(M_1 - M_2)$
★(c)   If f is one to one, then $f(M_1) - f(M_2) = f(M_1 - M_2)$.

15. (a)   Prove that if f and g are functions, then $\text{dom } (g \circ f) = \text{dom } f \cap f^{-1}(\text{dom } g)$ [recall Exercise 8(a), Article 8.1].

(b)   Prove that if $f: \mathbf{R} \to \mathbf{R}$, if $a, L \in \mathbf{R}$, and if $\lim_{x \to a} f(x) = L$, then to every $\varepsilon > 0$, there corresponds $\delta > 0$ such that $(a - \delta, a + \delta) - \{a\} \subseteq f^{-1}((L - \varepsilon, L + \varepsilon))$.

(c)   Suppose $f: \mathbf{R} \to \mathbf{R}$ and that f is continuous at $a \in \mathbf{R}$. Prove that the inverse image of every ε neighborhood $(f(a) - \varepsilon, f(a) + \varepsilon)$ of $f(a)$ contains as a subset some δ neighborhood $(a - \delta, a + \delta)$ of a.

16. Image and inverse image of sets under a mapping can be used to define the so-called *induced set functions.* Suppose $f: A \to B$. We define the function from $\mathscr{P}(A)$ to $\mathscr{P}(B)$, $S_f: \mathscr{P}(A) \to \mathscr{P}(B)$, by the rule $S_f(X) = f(X)$, where X is any subset of A; that is, X is any element of $\mathscr{P}(A)$. We define the mapping $S_{f^{-1}}: \mathscr{P}(B) \to \mathscr{P}(A)$ by the rule $S_{f^{-1}}(Y) = f^{-1}(Y)$, for any subset Y of B.

(a)   Prove that $S_{f^{-1}}$ is a function, even if f is not one to one (i.e., even if the relation f^{-1} is not a function).

(b)   Prove that if f is one to one, then S_f is one to one [recall Exercise 8(b)(ii)].

(c)   Prove that if f is onto, then S_f is onto [recall Exercise 8(c)].

(d)   Prove that if f is onto, then $S_{f^{-1}}$ is one to one.

(e)   Prove that if f is one to one, then $S_{f^{-1}}$ is onto [recall (c) of Theorem 5].

(f)   Conclude from (b) through (e) that if f is a bijection, then S_f and $S_{f^{-1}}$ are both bijections and $(S_f)^{-1} = S_{f^{-1}}$.

(g)   Suppose $f: A \to B$ and $g: A \to B$ satisfy $S_f = S_g$. Prove that $f = g$.

17. Let A and B be sets and let R be a relation from A to B; that is, $R \subseteq A \times B$. Define mappings $p_1: R \to A$ and $p_2: R \to B$ by $p_1(a, b) = a$ and $p_2(a, b) = b$ for all $a \in A$, $b \in B$. The mappings p_1 and p_2 are called the *projections* of R onto A and B, respectively.

(a)   Give examples to show that:

   (i)   Neither p_1 nor p_2 need be one to one

   (ii)   Neither p_1 nor p_2 need be onto

(b)   Find a condition on R that guarantees that p_1 is one to one. Prove your assertion.

(c)   Find a condition on R that guarantees that p_1 and p_2 are both one to one. Prove your assertion.

(d)   Find a condition on R that guarantees that p_1 is onto. Prove your assertion.

(e)   Find a condition on R that guarantees that p_2 is onto. Prove your assertion.

18. (This exercise anticipates the proof of the Schroeder-Bernstein theorem in the next article.) Consider the sets $A = \mathbf{N}$ and $B = \{5, 10, 15, 19, 22, 25, 28, 31, 34, \ldots\}$. Define mappings $f: A \to B$ and $g: B \to A$ by $f(1) = 5$, $f(2) = 10$, $f(3) = 15$, $g(5) = 3$,

$$g(10) = 2, \quad g(15) = 1, \quad \text{and} \quad f(a) = \begin{cases} 6a + 10, & a \text{ even}, & a \neq 2 \\ 3a + 4, & a \text{ odd}, & a \neq 1, a \neq 3 \end{cases}, \quad \text{with}$$

$$g(b) = \begin{cases} (b + 2)/3, & b \text{ even}, & b \neq 10 \\ (b - 4)/3, & b \text{ odd}, & b \neq 5, b \neq 15 \end{cases}$$

(a)   Prove f is a one-to-one mapping of A into, but not onto B, and that g is a one-to-one mapping of B into, but not onto, A.

(b)   The following process is called *tracing the ancestry* of an element of B. Consider the element 70 of B. We illustrate the process by tracing the ancestry of 70. We begin by looking for an element a of A such that $70 = f(a)$. We note that 10 does the job; that is, $f(10) = 70$. We continue by focusing now on the element 10 of A and seeking an element $b \in B$ such that $10 = g(b)$. This time, $b = 28$ is chosen since $10 = g(28)$. We attempt to continue the process by looking at the element 28 of B, but at this point, our attempt fails since $28 \notin \operatorname{im} f$. Thus the process of tracing the ancestry of the element 70 of B terminates, and we say that 70 has an <u>even number of ancestors</u> (*two*, to be exact, 10 and 28). We may trace the ancestry of an element of A in a similar manner. You should trace the ancestry of the element 14 of A.

(c)   (i)   Find three elements of A having an odd number of ancestors and three having an even number of ancestors.

   (ii)   Find three elements of B having an odd number of ancestors and three having an even number of ancestors.

   (iii)   Find an element of A for which the process of tracing the ancestry never terminates. We say that such an element has *infinite ancestry*. Find such an element in B.

(d) Suppose $a \in A - \text{im } g$ or $b \in B - \text{im } f$. What is the appropriate conclusion about ancestry in both these cases?

(e) Suppose an element $a \in A$ has an odd number of ancestors. What must be true of the element $f(a)$ of B? Formulate three additional analogous statements.

(f) Use the preceding mappings f and g to create a bijection between A and B.

8.3 Cardinal Number of a Set

This article might be considered an extension of Chapter 1, especially Article 1.5, because we return to the topic of sets and, in particular, to questions related to the size of a set. As you will soon see, however, the flavor of the material in this article differs greatly from that in Chapter 1 for two principal reasons: (1) Unlike the earlier treatment, we set down in this article rigorous definitions of finite set and infinite set. (2) Then we focus on the infinite set category. You may recall that, in Article 1.5, we developed formulas for counting the elements of finite sets. Implicit in this study was the understanding that two finite sets can, in many cases, be distinguished from each other (i.e., can be established to be different sets) purely on the basis of their differing number of elements. Any thought you may have given at that stage to infinite sets was probably with an equally certain, although again only implicit, assumption that there is no way of differentiating the sizes of infinite sets. This assumption is incorrect! Indeed, *the single most important idea of this article is that relative sizes of infinite sets can be distinguished in a mathematically satisfying and useful way.* As one example, we will see that the familiar sets $\mathbf{N}$, $\mathbf{Z}$, and $\mathbf{Q}$ can be distinguished from $\mathbf{R}$ and $\mathbf{C}$ with respect to "size," but $\mathbf{N}$ and $\mathbf{Q}$, for instance, cannot be so differentiated! The existence of different levels of infinity rests on the theory of infinite cardinal numbers, the creation of which (by Georg Cantor) inspired the development of much of modern set theory and formal logic.

The theory of infinite cardinal numbers is not only a fundamental tool in modern mathematics at the graduate and research levels, but since its creation in the late nineteenth century, has been widely celebrated as both an example of the creative genius of the human mind and a prime example of the aesthetic appeal of mathematics at its finest! Much of the theory is beyond both the level and intent of this text; hence our objective is limited to giving you some idea about the theory, and providing in the process a foundation for possible further study.

NUMERICAL EQUIVALENCE OF SETS

We begin our consideration of cardinality of sets by restating formally a definition alluded to in Article 8.2.

DEFINITION 1

Let A and B be sets. We say that A and B are **numerically equivalent**, denoted $A \cong B$, if and only if there exists a one-to-one mapping $f: A \to B$ of A onto B.

Justification for the name "numerical equivalence" is provided by the following result.

THEOREM 1

$\cong$ is an equivalence relation on the collection of all subsets of any given universal set U.

Proof   (Reflexive) Let A be any set. Clearly $A \cong A$, since $I_A: A \to A$ is one to one and onto, by Exercise 6(a)(i), Article 8.2.

(Symmetric) Assume that A and B are sets with $A \cong B$. Let $f: A \to B$ be a bijection. Then $f^{-1}: B \to A$ is a bijection, by Exercise 6(a)(ii), Article 8.2, so that $B \cong A$.

(Transitive) Suppose A, B, and C are sets with $A \cong B$ and $B \cong C$. Let $f: A \to B$ and $g: B \to C$ be bijections. We must provide a bijection $h: A \to C$. Let $h = g \circ f$. By (a) of the corollary to Theorem 2, Article 8.2, h is a bijection. Hence $A \cong C$, as desired. $\square$

In view of Theorem 1, we know from Article 7.3 that any collection of sets is partitioned into equivalence classes, with any two sets in the same class numerically equivalent and two sets in different classes numerically nonequivalent. Let us agree to say that two numerically equivalent sets have the *same cardinal number*. In subsequent paragraphs we will see that a cardinal number is essentially a symbol associated with sets in an equivalence class of numerically equivalent sets. Before developing this idea, let us look at some examples to illustrate numerical equivalence.

EXAMPLE 1   Let $A = \{1, 2, 3, 4\}$ and $X = \{a, b, c, d\}$. The mapping $f: A \to X$ given by $f(1) = c, f(2) = a, f(3) = d, f(4) = b$, is clearly a bijection between A and X, so that $A \cong X$. $\square$

Note that the function f in Example 1 is by no means the only bijection between A and X; in fact (recalling the topic of permutations from Article 1.5), there are as many bijections between A and X as there are arrangements of the letters $a, b, c,$ and d; that is, $P(4, 4) = 4! = 24$.

EXAMPLE 2   Let $B = \{1, 2, 3\}$ and $X = \{a, b, c, d\}$. Then there are precisely $P(4, 3) = 4! = 24$ one-to-one mappings of B into X. One example is $f(1) = a, f(2) = b, f(3) = c$. Clearly none of these mappings is onto. No bijection exists between B and X, so that $B \not\cong X$. $\square$

You should verify (by an indirect argument) that the sets A and B in the preceding examples are not numerically equivalent. (What conclusion could we derive if it were true that $B \cong A$?) This result is satisfying to our intuition since B, after all, is a proper subset of A and, surely, it would seem, no set should be in one-to-one correspondence with a proper subset of itself. If you agree with the statement following "surely" you will be enlightened, although perhaps slightly disoriented, by the next result.

EXAMPLE 3　Prove that the set **N** of all positive integers is in one-to-one correspondence with 2**N**, the set of all positive even integers.

Solution　The mapping $f\colon \mathbf{N} \to 2\mathbf{N}$ given by $f(n) = 2n$ is clearly a bijection between **N** and 2**N**. First, f is one to one, because if $f(n_1) = f(n_2)$, then $2n_1 = 2n_2$ so that $n_1 = n_2$. Second, f is onto, because if m is an arbitrary element of 2**N**, then m is an even integer so that $m = 2n$ for some $n \in \mathbf{N}$. Clearly $m = 2n = f(n)$, so that $m \in \operatorname{rng} f$. Since m was arbitrarily chosen from 2**N**, we conclude $\operatorname{rng} f = 2\mathbf{N}$, as desired.　□

Example 3 shows that a set <u>can be in one-to-one correspondence with a proper subset of itself</u>. Focusing for the moment on this phenomenon, we notice that the example in which it occurred was one in which both sets involved were infinite, unlike the sets in Examples 1 and 2. In fact, the underlined property can be taken as the formal definition of an infinite set.

DEFINITION　2

A set A is said to be **infinite** if and only if there exists a proper subset B of A such that $B \cong A$. A set that is not infinite is said to be **finite**.

It can be proved (we do not do so in this text) that a nonempty set A is finite if and only if A is numerically equivalent to the set $F_n = \{1, 2, 3, \ldots, n\}$ for some positive integer n. It is easy to show that $\varnothing$ is finite, and you are asked to do so in Exercise 2(a). It can be proved furthermore that, for positive integers m and n, $F_m \cong F_n$ if and only if $m = n$. Thus we may associate with each finite set A a unique nonnegative integer $n(A)$, called the number of elements in A. If $n(A) = k$, we say that A has *finite cardinal number* k. We usually denote a generic finite set A having k elements by such notation as $A = \{a_1, a_2, \ldots, a_k\}$.

In Examples 1 and 2, A and X were both sets with four elements and <u>were</u> numerically equivalent. All sets in the equivalence class they share have cardinal number 4. The set B from Example 2 lies in a different equivalence class from A and X and has the cardinal number 3. Once again, the cardinal number of a finite set is simply the number of elements in that set, in the usual sense. Two finite sets with same number of elements, in the usual sense, have the same cardinal number; two finite sets with different numbers of elements, in the usual sense, have different cardinal numbers.

As seen thus far, the relation of numerical equivalence between sets is applicable to any two sets, finite or infinite, and in addition, agrees with the familiar "same number of elements as" relation in the finite case. Let us reflect for a moment on why this relation "seems right" as a measure of the comparative sizes of infinite sets. Why, to begin with, is it difficult to measure the size of an infinite set? The answer lies in a realization of what we actually do when counting the elements of a finite set S. Using the set **N** as our point of reference, we associate with each element of S a unique positive integer, starting with 1 and ending with some n. We then designate n by a symbol such as $n(S)$ or $\#(S)$ and call it the number of elements in S. For a finite set T, we might go through the same process and arrive at a positive integer m. We then answer the question whether S and T are the same size by asking whether n equals m.

The problem, of course, in dealing with infinite sets is that we never exhaust the elements; there is no positive integer m we can associate with such a set. So how can we reasonably compare the size of two such sets? The answer lies in considering how the sizes of finite sets might be compared if no set N is available. Imagine living in a situation, be it a primitive culture today or perhaps in a prehistoric time, in which systems of naming (possibly any but the smallest) counting numbers do not exist. How could we then determine, for instance, whether we have more pegs or more holes in a Peg-Board? With luck, the most intelligent or creative among us might think of putting pegs into holes until the supply of one or the other is exhausted. In so doing, we are clearly setting up a one-to-one mapping between pegs and holes. Only if both pegs and holes run out simultaneously, could that mapping be onto and would we then judge the two sets to be of the same size, that is, numerically equivalent. We would not, at this stage, have in mind any measure of the common size of the two sets (with counting numbers unavailable); rather, we would have only the knowledge that the two sets are the same size.

The genius of Cantor consisted partially in his realization that this approach does not depend on exhausting the elements in the set for its effectiveness. Given any two sets, both infinite, one finite and one infinite, or both finite, we can ask whether they are numerically equivalent, that is, can we discover a one-to-one correspondence between them or prove that none exists? This is not to say that the question will be easy to answer in all cases, or that we won't run into surprises and challenges to our intuition once this genie is out of the bottle. One such surprise is the possibility of a one-to-one correspondence between a set S and one of its proper subsets P. This is (by our formal definition as well as by intuition) out of the question in the finite case. In that case, as we try to match elements in P with those in S, we will clearly run out of elements in P, so that our mapping is doomed to fail to be onto. This "running out of elements" is precisely what will not happen in the infinite case. Clearly the inclusion mapping $i_p: P \to S$ is not the desired one-to-one correspondence (never onto when P is a proper subset of S), but some other mapping may be. Realizing this possibility, we must rise above the limitations on our intuition imposed by overexposure to the simplest and most familiar case, that is, finite sets.

Returning to Example 3, we find a more bizarre situation than this example suggests. You should verify that the sets $S = \{n^2 \mid n \in N\} = \{1, 4, 9, 16, 25, \ldots\}$ (of all perfect squares) and $M = 10^6\, N = \{10^6, 2 \times 10^6, 3 \times 10^6, \ldots\}$ (of all integral multiples of "one million") are in one-to-one correspondence with N. As sparsely distributed as these sets may be within

N, they have just as many elements as **N**! In fact, it can be proved that **N** is numerically equivalent to <u>any</u> infinite subset of itself. More surprises are in store in the following theorems. When Cantor established the cardinality relationships between **N** and **Q** (the same cardinal number) and between **N** and **R** (different cardinal numbers), so unexpected were these types of conclusions and so innovative was his approach that his results did not immediately win wide acceptance among mathematicians. Yet his extraordinarily clever arguments are not really that difficult to follow. In addition, the arguments in Theorems 3 and 4 illustrate the possibilities for both aesthetic appeal and monumental power that are inherent in the method of proof by contradiction.

THEOREM 2

N is numerically equivalent to **Q**, in symbols **N** $\cong$ **Q**.

Proof   We wish to define a one-to-one mapping of **N** onto **Q**. To define a bijection between **N** and any set X, it is sufficient to create a scheme in which we "line up" the elements of X in such a manner that every element of X is accounted for. We then associate with each element of X the positive integer corresponding to its place on the list, noting that the place of any given element of X can be determined (if in no simpler way) by "counting" through the list until we arrive at that element (thus our use of the term *countably infinite*, see Definition 3).

The problem then for a given set X we believe to be equivalent to **N** is to find such a scheme. In the case $X = \mathbf{Q}$ an ingenious scheme was developed by Cantor. We first show that **N** is equivalent to $\mathbf{Q}^+$, the positive rationals, by lining up the positive rationals according to the sum of their numerator and denominator. One picture (or actually two) is worth a thousand words at this stage. Note that repeats clearly occur in the array in Figure 8.6a. In counting through the array of positive

Figure 8.6   *The idea behind the proof that* **Q** *is countable is a systematic "lining up" of the positive rationals, as pictured.*

$$\frac{1}{1} \quad \frac{1}{2} \quad \frac{1}{3} \quad \frac{1}{4} \quad \frac{1}{5} \cdots$$

$$\frac{2}{1} \quad \frac{2}{2} \quad \frac{2}{3} \quad \frac{2}{4} \quad \frac{2}{5} \cdots$$

$$\frac{3}{1} \quad \frac{3}{2} \quad \frac{3}{3} \quad \frac{3}{4} \quad \frac{3}{5} \cdots$$

(a)

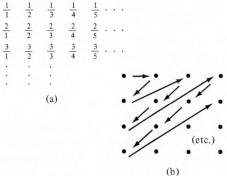

(etc.)

(b)

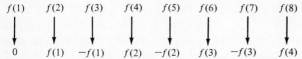

Figure 8.7 *Write down an explicit rule defining the correspondence pictured here.*

rationals, lined up as in Figure 8.6*a*, we simply skip over any quotient of integers corresponding to a rational number that has already been accounted for. Thus we have $f(1) = 1, f(2) = \frac{1}{2}, f(3) = 2, f(4) = \frac{1}{3}, f(5) = 3, f(6) = \frac{1}{4}$, and so on. Note that we have skipped over $\frac{2}{2}$ in defining $f(5)$, since $\frac{2}{2} = 1$, and 1 has already been accounted for, having been first in the array.

With the equivalence of **N** and $\mathbf{Q}^+$ established, we may conclude $\mathbf{N} \cong \mathbf{Q}$ by showing $\mathbf{Q}^+ \cong \mathbf{Q}$ (What property of $\cong$ is the key to this conclusion?). This we may do as follows. Let $\mathbf{Q}^+ = \{f(1), f(2), f(3), \ldots\}$ and let us set up the correspondence in Figure 8.7. This mapping is clearly onto since every nonzero rational number is either equal to or is the negative of a positive rational number.   □

At this point, you may think you have figured out all there is to know about the equivalence classes induced by numerical equivalence. First, we know already that there are equivalence classes (consisting of all the *n* element subsets of *U*) corresponding to each positive integer *n*. We should represent each such class by the appropriate *n* and call *n* the cardinal number of any set in its class. Second, based on Theorem 2, you may be ready to conclude that any two infinite sets are numerically equivalent, and in particular, are equivalent to **N**, as we have just witnessed for **Q**. We might then say that all such sets have cardinal number ∞ and be done with it, secure in the belief that the list $1, 2, 3, \ldots, \infty$ accounts for all possible equivalence classes of numerically equivalent sets, or in other words, all possible cardinal numbers. Those who believe all of this are only half-right. The statements about finite sets are correct, as we had seen earlier; everything else ("Second, you may . . .") is a gross oversimplification. Assuming *U* is sufficiently large, there are infinite sets in *U* with cardinality different from that of **N**. A familiar example of such a set is provided in our next result.

THEOREM 3
The open unit interval (0, 1) is not numerically equivalent to **N**.

Proof   (Cantor) In fact, we will show that every one-to-one mapping of **N** into (0, 1) must fail to be onto; that is, every listing of the elements of (0, 1) must leave out some element of (0, 1). It is a known fact that every element x in $(0, 1)$ can be represented by a decimal expansion, say, $x = d_1 d_2 d_3 \ldots$. We can guarantee that each such expansion is uniquely determined by x if we agree to dispense with the usual convention involving infinite strings of nines. It is normally understood that any terminating decimal (like .168) is also represented by a decimal involving an infinite string of nines $(.167999 \ldots$ in this case), thus providing a situation in which two different decimal expansions correspond to the same number. We hereby, and for the course of the current proof, disallow that understanding by outlawing the use of decimals ending in an infinite string of nines.

So, let us assume that the elements of $(0, 1)$ have been listed in sequence $x_1, x_2, x_3, \ldots$, where

$$x_1 = .a_{11}a_{12}a_{13} \ldots$$

$$x_2 = .a_{21}a_{22}a_{23} \ldots$$

$$x_3 = .a_{31}a_{32}a_{33} \ldots$$

We now proceed to construct a decimal corresponding to a real number between 0 and 1 that cannot possibly be on the list. Let us denote this number $y = .b_1 b_2 b_3 \ldots$, where $b_1 = 4$, if $a_{11} \neq 4$ and $b_1 = 7$, if $a_{11} = 4$. Clearly $y \neq x_1$, because the decimal expansion of y differs from that of x_1 in the first place. In general, let $b_i = 4$, if $a_{ii} \neq 4$ and $b_i = 7$, if $a_{ii} = 4$. Note that, for each $i = 1, 2, 3, \ldots$, we have $y \neq x_i$, because the decimal expansion of y differs from that of x_i in the ith place. We have constructed a new decimal, different from any of those listed, contradicting the assumption that a listing of all such decimals is possible. $\square$

And so we see that there are at least two levels of infinite cardinality, or two infinite cardinal numbers. It can be proved (see Exercise 1) that $(0, 1) \cong \mathbf{R}$, so that the "level of infinity" uncovered in Theorem 3 is actually that of the real number system. Following convention, let us now agree to denote the cardinal number of $\mathbf{N}$ (and of $\mathbf{Z}$, $\mathbf{Q}^+$, and $\mathbf{Q}$) by the symbol $\aleph_0$ (pronounced "aleph-null"; "aleph" is the first letter of the Hebrew alphabet). The cardinal number of $\mathbf{R}$ [and of $(0, 1)$ and $\mathbf{C}$] is denoted by c and is called the *cardinal number of the continuum*. We introduce some standard terminology in the following definition.

DEFINITION 3

A set that is numerically equivalent to **N** is said to be **countably infinite** or **denumerable**. Any set that is either finite or countably infinite is said to be **countable**. An infinite set that is not countable is said to be **uncountable**.

The sets $\{1, 2, 3, \ldots, 100\}$, $\mathbf{N}$, $\mathbf{Z}$, $\mathbf{Q}^+$, and $\mathbf{Q}$ are all countable sets; the latter four are countably infinite. The sets $\mathbf{R}$, $\mathbf{C}$, and $(0, 1)$, and indeed any interval on the real line (see Exercise 1) are uncountable, and in fact have the cardinal number c.

There are two remaining questions about cardinality that we wish to address in some detail. First, is there any relationship of *order* between the two infinite cardinal numbers $\aleph_0$ and c, similar to the relation $\leq$ existing between any two finite cardinal numbers? We have seen that $\mathbf{N}$ and $(0, 1)$ have different cardinal numbers, $\aleph_0$ and c, respectively. Is one of these sets of a "higher" or "larger" level of infinity than the other? The answer is not totally clear if we rely solely on our intuition. $\mathbf{N}$ seems larger in the sense that it is unbounded, whereas $(0, 1)$ is bounded. On the other hand, between any two elements of $(0, 1)$ lies another element of $(0, 1)$, a statement not true for $\mathbf{N}$. In this sense $(0, 1)$ seems larger. To "muddy the waters" further, keep in mind that $\mathbf{Q} \cong \mathbf{N}$ and $\mathbf{Q} \ncong (0, 1)$, even though $\mathbf{Q}$ differs from $\mathbf{N}$ and resembles $(0, 1)$ in containing, between any two of its members, another of its members. Clearly this problem calls for some clear and rigorous thinking.

Second, we wish to ask whether there are other infinite cardinal numbers besides $\aleph_0$ and c. Our starting point in dealing with both these problems is the following definition.

DEFINITION 4

(a) Let A and B be sets. We write $A \preceq B$ and say the **cardinal number of A is less than or equal to the cardinal number of B**, if and only if there exists a one-to-one mapping $f: A \to B$.

(b) We write $A \prec B$ if and only if $A \preceq B$, but $A \ncong B$. In this case we say that the **cardinal number of A is (strictly) less than the cardinal number of B**.

Note that $A \preceq B$ if and only if A is numerically equivalent to a subset of B (namely, im f), including possibly B itself. Stated differently, the relationship $A \preceq B$ between two sets leaves open the possibility that $A \cong B$, analogous to the connection between the relations $\leq$ and $=$ on the real numbers. On the other hand, $A \prec B$ means that there exists a one-to-one mapping of A <u>into</u> B, but no such mapping of A <u>onto</u> B.

Only (b) of Definition 4 is needed to settle the question whether $\aleph_0$ and c are the only infinite cardinal numbers. An immediate consequence of the following result is that there are infinitely many infinite cardinal numbers.

THEOREM 4 (Cantor's theorem)
Let S be any set. Then $S \prec \mathscr{P}(S)$.

Proof First, the mapping $x \to \{x\}$ is clearly a one-to-one mapping of S into $\mathscr{P}(S)$, so that $S \preceq \mathscr{P}(S)$. We must still show that there is no one-to-one mapping of S onto $\mathscr{P}(S)$. For suppose $f: S \to \mathscr{P}(S)$ were such a mapping. Now, for each $x \in S$, $f(x) \in \mathscr{P}(S)$, so that $f(x) \subseteq S$. Thus for each $x \in S$, we may consider whether $x \in f(x)$. Surely we may say that either $x \in f(x)$ or $x \notin f(x)$ for each $x \in S$. Consider the set $N = \{x \in S \mid x \notin f(x)\}$. Clearly $N \subseteq S$ so $N \in \mathscr{P}(S)$. Since f is assumed to be onto, there exists $x_0 \in S$ such that $f(x_0) = N$. Now either $x_0 \in N$ or $x_0 \notin N$. If $x_0 \in N$, then $x_0 \notin f(x_0) = N$, so $x_0 \notin N$, a contradiction. If $x_0 \notin N$, then $x_0 \in f(x_0) = N$, again a contradiction. Our assumption of the existence of a one-to-one mapping of S onto $\mathscr{P}(S)$ leads to a contradiction, so that no such mapping exists, and our desired conclusion $S \prec \mathscr{P}(S)$ is established. $\square$

Note that $\mathbf{N} \prec \mathscr{P}(\mathbf{N}) \prec \mathscr{P}(\mathscr{P}(\mathbf{N})) \prec \cdots$ and so forth. The same can be said of $\mathbf{R}$, $\mathscr{P}(\mathbf{R})$, $\mathscr{P}(\mathscr{P}(\mathbf{R}))$, and so on. The existence of infinitely many distinct infinite cardinal numbers is established.

We now wish to get at the relationship between $\aleph_0$ and c. Our first result (Theorem 5) will probably come as no surprise to you; first, we prove a more general fact, from which our theorem follows immediately.

LEMMA
If A and B are sets with $A \subseteq B$, then $A \preceq B$.

Proof   Clearly the inclusion mapping $i_A: A \to B$ is a one-to-one mapping of A into B. $\square$

THEOREM   5
$\mathbf{N} \preceq \mathbf{R}$.

Since $\mathbf{R} \cong (0, 1)$, we may conclude from Theorem 5 [by way of Exercise 6(c)] that $\mathbf{N} \preceq (0, 1)$ also. Viewing the relation $\preceq$ between sets as a relation between the cardinal numbers of those sets, we may rephrase Theorem 5 as $\aleph_0 \preceq c$ [again, see Exercise 6(c)].

Actually, there is much more we can say about the relationship between $\aleph_0$ and c. First, as a result of Theorems 3 and 5, we may conclude $\aleph_0 \prec c$. Second, and quite remarkably, we can prove that $\mathscr{P}(\mathbf{N}) \cong \mathbf{R}$, a result often expressed in terms of cardinal numbers by the equation $2^{\aleph_0} = c$. (*Note:* If A and B are sets with cardinal numbers α and β, we denote by α^β the cardinal number of the set of all mappings from B into A. Hence $2^{\aleph_0}$ is the cardinal number of the set of all mappings of $\mathbf{N}$ into $\{0, 1\}$, clearly numerically equivalent to the collection of all subsets of $\mathbf{N}$.) An important tool in the derivation of this result is a theorem that is both very famous and highly important in its own right. The Schroeder-Bernstein theorem states essentially that $\preceq$ is an antisymmetric relation between cardinal numbers.

THEOREM   6   (Schroeder-Bernstein)
Given sets A and B, if $A \preceq B$ and $B \preceq A$, then $A \cong B$.

Proof   Our hypotheses yield the existence of injections $f: A \to B$ and $g: B \to A$. We must use these mappings somehow to produce a bijection $h: A \to B$. The technique is more complicated than you might suspect (although if you worked through Exercise 18, Article 8.2, you should find it familiar). Consider an element $a \in A$. This element may be, or may fail to be, in the image of g. If it is, let b be the element of B such that $a = g(b)$. Now focus on this b, in connection with the injection f. Again, we may have either $b \in \operatorname{im} f$ or $b \notin \operatorname{im} f$. If the former, let $a_1 \in A$ have the property that $b = f(a_1)$. Note then that $a = g(b) = g(f(a_1))$. If we continue this process (a process often referred to as "tracing the ancestry" of a), we find that one of three mutually exclusive possibilities must occur:

1. The process terminates with either no ancestor for a or an ancestor of a lying in A which is not in the image of g, that is, with an even number of ancestors for a. Let us say that $a \in A_A$ in this case.
2. The process terminates with an ancestor of a lying in B which is not in the image of f, so that a has an odd number of ancestors. Let us say that $a \in A_B$ in this case.
3. The process does not terminate; we denote this circumstance of infinite ancestry for a by writing $a \in A_\infty$.

Clearly the sets A_A, A_B, and A_∞ are mutually disjoint subsets of A whose union equals A; that is, the sets constitute a partition of A having at most three cells. Also, we can partition B in a totally analogous manner, into subsets B_A, B_B, and B_∞ (an element $b \in B_A$, e.g., has an odd number of ancestors). Note now that f maps A_A onto B_A and A_∞ onto B_∞ in a one-to-one fashion, while g restricted to B_B is a bijection onto A_B [see Exercise 7(b)]. Hence we may arrive at the desired bijection h in the following manner:

$$h(a) = \begin{cases} f(a), & a \in A_A \quad \text{or} \quad a \in A_\infty \\ g^{-1}(a), & a \in A_B \end{cases} \qquad \square$$

Again, for readers familiar with Article 7.4, the results of Exercise 6(a), combined with Theorem 6, enable us to conclude that $\preceq$ is a partial-ordering relation between cardinal numbers.

The Schroeder-Bernstein theorem is extremely useful for proving numerical equivalence of sets. As one example, suppose it is known that any open interval (a, b) in $\mathbf{R}$ is numerically equivalent to $\mathbf{R}$ (see Exercise 1). We may prove easily, using Schroeder-Bernstein, that any subset X of $\mathbf{R}$ containing an open interval is also numerically equivalent to $\mathbf{R}$ [note Exercise 7(a)], no matter how complicated the structure of X might be.

Let us now apply the Schroeder-Bernstein theorem to the problem stated immediately before Theorem 6.

THEOREM 7
$\mathbf{R}$ is numerically equivalent to the power set of $\mathbf{N}$. In terms of cardinal numbers, we have $2^{\aleph_0} = c$.

Proof   Since $(0, 1) \cong \mathbf{R}$, by Exercise 1, we may just as well prove that $(0, 1) \cong \mathscr{P}(\mathbf{N})$. We will show that $(0, 1) \preceq \mathscr{P}(\mathbf{N})$ and $\mathscr{P}(\mathbf{N}) \preceq (0, 1)$ and appeal to Schroeder-Bernstein. To define a one-to-one mapping f of $(0, 1)$ into $\mathscr{P}(\mathbf{N})$, let $.b_1 b_2 b_3 \ldots$ be the binary expansion of a given $x \in (0, 1)$, so that each b_i is either 0 or 1. As before; that is, in the proof of Theorem 3, we outlaw the use of an infinite string of 1's in a binary representation, in order to guarantee uniqueness. Now define f by the rule $f(x) = \{n \in \mathbf{N} \mid b_n = 1\}$. By the uniqueness of binary representation, we conclude that f is a one-to-one mapping of $(0, 1)$ into $\mathscr{P}(\mathbf{N})$. To prove $\mathscr{P}(\mathbf{N}) \preceq (0, 1)$, let $A \subseteq \mathbf{N}$. We must associate with A in a one-to-one fashion an element of $(0, 1)$. Using standard decimal representation of numbers in $(0, 1)$, with the (by now familiar) eschewing of infinite strings of nines, we decree that $g(A) = .x_1 x_2 x_3 \ldots$, where $x_i = 4$ if $i \in A$ and $x_i = 7$ if $i \notin A$. Clearly g maps $\mathscr{P}(\mathbf{N})$ into $(0, 1)$. Furthermore, by uniqueness of decimal representation, if $g(A) = g(B)$, where $g(B) = .y_1 y_2 y_3 \ldots$, then $x_i = y_i = $ either 4 or 7 for all $i \in \mathbf{N}$, so that $i \in A$ if and only if $i \in B$; that is, $A = B$. Hence g is one to one and the proof is complete. $\square$

Before concluding our coverage of cardinality of sets, we allude briefly to one of the most famous (and, until recently, unsolved) problems in modern mathematics. In the *continuum hypothesis* Cantor conjectured that there is no infinite cardinal number properly between $\aleph_0$ and c; that is, no set X exists such that $\mathbf{N} \prec X \prec \mathscr{P}(\mathbf{N})$. Only in 1963 was it proved by the logician Paul Cohen that this proposition is *undecidable* on the basis of the usual axioms of formal set theory; that is, the proposition can neither be proved nor disproved in that context. This may give you some idea of the kinds of research problems Cantor's theory has led to in modern times, as well as indicating the level of difficulty involved in dealing with those problems. Actually, there are many other, relatively elementary, questions on cardinality of sets whose answers are known, but whose solutions (i.e., proofs) we choose not to deal with in this text. We conclude this article, presenting, without proof and with only brief commentary, a list of additional theorems about cardinality.

1.   Results about finite and infinite sets (several of these may be proved by mathematical induction):

   (a)   A set X is finite if and only if $X \cong F_n$ for some $n \in \mathbf{N}$.
   (b) $F_m \cong F_n$ if and only if $m = n$, for any $m, n \in \mathbf{N}$.
   (c) $F_m \preceq F_n$ if and only if $m \leq n$, for any $m, n \in \mathbf{N}$.
   (d)   Every subset of a finite set is finite.
   (e)   If A and B are finite sets, then $A \cup B$ is finite.
   (f)   If $A_1, A_2, \ldots, A_n$ are finite sets, then $\bigcup_{i=1}^{n} A_i$ is finite.
   (g)   If A is infinite and B is finite, then $A - B$ is infinite.

2.   Results about countably infinite sets:

   (a)   If $n \in \mathbf{N}$, then $n \prec \aleph_0$.
   (b)   If A is a countably infinite set and $B \subseteq A$, then B is countable.
   (c) $\aleph_0$ is the smallest infinite cardinal number; that is, if A is an infinite set such that $A \preceq \mathbf{N}$, then $A \cong \mathbf{N}$, so that A is countably infinite.
   (d)   If $\{A_\lambda \,|\, \lambda \in I\}$ is a collection of countably infinite sets, indexed by a countably infinite set I (such as $I = \mathbf{N}$), then $\bigcup_{\lambda \in I} A_\lambda$ is countably infinite (notation discussed in Article 8.4).
   (e)   If A and B are nonempty sets with A countable and $f\colon A \to B$ a mapping of A onto B, then B is countable.
   (f)   If A and B are countable sets, then $A \times B$ is countable.
   (g)   If $A_1, A_2, \ldots, A_n$ are countable sets (where $n \in \mathbf{N}$), then $A_1 \times A_2 \times \cdots \times A_n$ is countable.

3.   The proofs of these results depend on the *axiom of choice* (axiom discussed in Article 8.4):

   (a)   Any two cardinal numbers are comparable (recall Definition 4, Article 7.4), that is, given two sets A and B, either $A \preceq B$ or $B \preceq A$.
   (b)   Any infinite set has a countably infinite subset.

Exercises

1. Use Definition 1, that is, the definiton of *numerical equivalence*, to prove:

(a) $\mathbf{R} \cong (0, \infty)$
(b) $(-\pi/2, \pi/2) \cong \mathbf{R}$
★(c) $(0, 1) \cong (7, 13)$
(d) $(a, b) \cong (c, d)$, where a, b, c, and d are real with $a \neq b$ and $c \neq d$
(e) $(0, 1) \cong \mathbf{R}$
(f) $(a, b) \cong \mathbf{R}$, where $a, b \in \mathbf{R}$ and $a \neq b$
(g) $(0, 1] \cong [1, \infty)$.

2. ★(a)   Use Definition 2 to prove that $\varnothing$ is a finite set.
(b)   Use Definition 2 to prove that if S is any infinite set and $S \subseteq T$, then T is infinite.
(c)   Conclude from (b) that any subset of a finite set is finite.
(d)   Conclude from (b) that if A and B are infinite sets, then $A \cup B$ is infinite.
(e)   Prove that if A is an infinite set and B is a set satisfying $B \cong A$, then B is infinite.
(f)   Prove by mathematical induction that the set $F_n = \{1, 2, 3, \ldots, n\}$ is finite, for any positive integer n.

3. (a)   Prove that if A is finite and $x \notin A$, then $A \cup \{x\}$ is finite.
(b)   Conclude from (a) that if A is infinite and $x \in A$, then $A - \{x\}$ is infinite.
(c)   Prove by induction that if A is finite and $x_1, x_2, \ldots, x_n$ are all not elements of A (where $n \in \mathbf{N}$), then $A \cup \{x_1, x_2, \ldots, x_n\}$ is finite.

4. *(a)* Prove that the set $\mathbf{Z}$ of all integers is countably infinite (recall Figure 8.7).
(b) Prove that $\mathbf{N} \times \mathbf{N}$ is a countably infinite set (recall Figure 8.6).
(c) Prove that if S is any countably infinite set, then $S \times S$ is countably infinite.
(d) Prove by induction that if $\{S_1, S_2, \ldots, S_n\}$ (where $n \in \mathbf{N}$) is a collection of n countably infinite sets, then $S_1 \times S_2 \times \cdots \times S_n$ is countably infinite.

5. *(a)* Prove that if A_1 and A_2 are countably infinite sets, then $A_1 \cup A_2$ is countably infinite. (*Hint:* Using notation such as $A_1 = \{a_{11}, a_{12}, a_{13}, \ldots\}$ and $A_2 = \{a_{21}, a_{22}, a_{23}, \ldots\}$, develop a scheme for listing the elements of $A_1 \cup A_2$ systematically.)
(b) Prove that if $\{A_i \,|\, i = 1, 2, 3, \ldots\}$ is a countable collection of sets, each of which is countably infinite, then $\bigcup_{i=1}^{\infty} A_i$ is countably infinite. (This result is usually paraphrased "a countable union of countable sets is countable.")

6. *(a)* Prove that the relation $\preceq$, from Definition 4(a), is a reflexive and transitive relation on the collection of all subsets of any given universal set U. Is $\preceq$ an antisymmetric relation on this collection?
(b) Prove that the relation $\prec$, from Definition 4(b), is transitive and not reflexive.
★*(c)* Prove that if A_1, A_2, B_1, and B_2 are sets satisfying $A_1 \preceq B_1$, $A_2 \cong A_1$, and $B_2 \cong B_1$, then $A_2 \preceq B_2$. Explain the significance of this result, relative to the two paragraphs immediately following Theorem 5. In particular, explain in exactly what sense $\preceq$ can be regarded as an antisymmetric relation, in view of the Schroeder-Bernstein theorem.

7. *(a)* Use the Schroeder-Bernstein theorem to prove that if $a, b, c, d \in \mathbf{R}$ with $a \neq b$ and $c \neq d$, then $(a, b) \cong [c, d]$.
(b) Verify the following details from the proof of the Schroeder-Bernstein theorem:

   (i) The three sets A_A, A_B, and A_∞ are pairwise disjoint and have union A.
   (ii) The mapping f/A_A is a one-to-one mapping of A_A onto B_A.
   (iii) The mapping f/A_∞ is a one-to-one mapping of A_∞ onto B_∞.
   (iv) The mapping g/B_B is a one-to-one mapping of B_B onto A_B.
   (v) The mapping h, defined in the proof, is a bijection between A and B.

(c) Prove that if a subset S of $\mathbf{R}$ contains a nonempty open interval as a subset, then $s \cong \mathbf{R}$.

8.4 Arbitrary Collections of Sets

We now return briefly to infinite collections of sets. Recall the treatment, in Article 4.2, of infinite collections indexed by $\mathbf{N}$, including the union and intersection of such collections. After studying cardinal numbers, we now have a different way of characterizing the condition "indexed by $\mathbf{N}$." First, recall the role of $\mathbf{N}$ as an indexing set. It essentially provides a means of labeling the sets in the collection, of keeping track of and, in a sense, counting them. Now if each set in an infinite collection can be matched in a one-to-one fashion with a positive integer, then the collection must contain only a countable number of sets. Thus the collections of sets considered in Article 4.2 were *countably infinite collections* only. Consider, however, the collection consisting of all intervals of the form $[r, \infty)$, where r is an arbitrary real number. Since **R** is uncountable, this collection clearly contains an uncountable number of sets and so represents for us a mathematical object different from (although conceptually similar to) those studied in Article 4.2. All circumstances involving an infinite collection of sets indexed by a set of unknown cardinality (possibly $\aleph_0$, c, 2^c, or any other infinite cardinal number) are encapsulated under the heading *arbitrary collections of sets*, or *collections of sets indexed by an arbitrary indexing set*.

DEFINITION 1
Let *I* be an arbitrary set. The collection of sets $\mathscr{A} = \{A_\lambda \mid \lambda \in I\}$, containing a set A_λ corresponding to each element $\lambda \in I$ (where some universal set U contains each set A_λ in the collection) is called a **family** (or **collection**) of sets indexed by *I*.

An arbitrary collection of sets may also be viewed as a mapping $f: I \to U$, where $f(\lambda) = A_\lambda$ for each $\lambda \in I$, and where U is a set containing each A_λ as an element. Clearly, countably infinite collections of sets are a special case of arbitrary collections. As with all generalizations, you must be careful in dealing with arbitrary collections not to attribute to them characteristics that are particular to the special (i.e., countable) case. For example, we cannot in general talk about "increasing" or "decreasing" families of sets [recall Example 1(b, c), Article 4.2], since there may be no notion of "less than" in the indexing set. On the other hand, the idea of "pairwise disjoint" [Example 1(a), Article 4.2] does carry over to arbitrary collections (Exercise 3); as do the concepts of union and intersection.

DEFINITION 2
If $\mathscr{A} = \{A_\lambda \mid \lambda \in I\}$ is a collection of sets indexed by the arbitrary set *I*, we define:

(a) The **union of the collection** $\mathscr{A}$, denoted $\bigcup_{\lambda \in I} A_\lambda$ (also denoted $\bigcup \{A_\lambda \mid \lambda \in I\}$), to be the set, $\{x \mid x \in A_\lambda \text{ for some } \lambda \in I\}$; that is, $\{x \mid \exists \lambda \in I \text{ such that } x \in A_\lambda\}$.

(b) The **intersection of the collection** $\mathscr{A}$, denoted $\bigcap_{\lambda \in I} A_\lambda$ (also denoted $\bigcap \{A_\lambda \mid \lambda \in I\}$), to be the set, $\{x \mid x \in A_\lambda \text{ for every } \lambda \in I\}$; that is, $\{x \mid x \in A_\lambda \forall \lambda \in I\}$.

With reference to terminology introduced earlier in this article, note that we dealt in Article 4.2 with *countable unions* and *countable intersections*, the preceding definition introduces *arbitrary unions* and *arbitrary intersections*.

From the point of view of the undergraduate student of mathematics, the primary importance of arbitrary collections, including arbitrary unions and intersections, lies in the formulation of statements and execution of proofs of theorems involving arbitrary collections. The main difficulty for most students is adapting to the notational requirements of arbitrary collections, and especially, avoiding the temptation to represent all collections of sets as if they were countable collections.

EXAMPLE 1   Let $f: X \rightarrow Y$. Prove that the image under f of the intersection of any collection of subsets of X is a subset of the intersection of the images under f of the sets in the collection.

Solution   Our first problem is to formulate in symbols the statement to be proved. Let $\mathscr{A}$ represent the given collection of subsets of X. An incorrect approach is to write $\mathscr{A} = \{A_1, A_2, A_3, \ldots\}$ and to represent the desired conclusion $f(\bigcap_{i=1}^{\infty} A_i) \subseteq \bigcap_{i=1}^{\infty} f(A_i)$; this notation assumes the collection to be countably infinite, which it may or may not be. Instead, we write $\mathscr{A} = \{A_\lambda | \lambda \in I\}$, where I is an arbitrary set. We must prove $f(\bigcap_{\lambda \in I} A_\lambda) \subseteq \bigcap_{\lambda \in I} f(A_\lambda)$. Let $y \in f(\bigcap_{\lambda \in I} A_\lambda)$. Then $y = f(x)$ for some $x \in \bigcap_{\lambda \in I} A_\lambda$. Since $y = f(x)$ and $x \in A_\lambda$ for all $\lambda \in I$, then $y \in f(A_\lambda)$ for all $\lambda \in I$; that is, $y \in \bigcap_{\lambda \in I} f(A_\lambda)$, as desired. $\square$

Another important definition involving arbitrary collections of sets is a generalization of the notion of the cartesian product of a finite number of sets.

DEFINITION 3
Let $\{A_\lambda | \lambda \in I\}$ be an arbitrary collection of sets. We define the **direct product** $\prod_{\lambda \in I} A_\lambda$ of the sets in the collection to be the set of all mappings $f: I \rightarrow \bigcup_{\lambda \in I} A_\lambda$ such that $f(\lambda) \in A_\lambda$ for each $\lambda \in I$.

If I is a finite set, say, $I = \{1, 2, \ldots, n\}$, then each element of the direct product is essentially an n tuple $(a_1, a_2, \ldots, a_n)$, where each $a_i \in A_i$, corresponding to the familiar cartesian product in that special case. Each function of the type noted in Definition 3 is called a *choice function*, since defining it amounts to "choosing" an element from each of the sets A_λ in the collection. Clearly if one of the sets in the collection is empty, no choice function exists. It may seem self-evident that a choice function always exists for an arbitrary collection of nonempty sets, but in fact this statement, like the continuum hypothesis, can neither be proved nor disproved on the basis of the usual axioms of set theory. It is common (although not uncontroversial) in modern-day mathematics to assume it as an axiom; the proofs of many important theorems at the graduate and research levels depend on this so-called *axiom of choice*. To recapitulate, the axiom of choice states that if $\{A_\lambda | \lambda \in I\}$ is a family of nonempty sets, then $\prod_{\lambda \in I} A_\lambda$ is nonempty. Stated differently, there exists a choice function, that is, a mapping f from I into $\bigcup_{\lambda \in I} A_\lambda$ such that $f(\lambda) \in A_\lambda$ for each $\lambda \in I$.

Exercises

1. Let $\mathscr{A} = \{A_\lambda | \lambda \in I\}$ be a collection of subsets of a set X and let $B \subseteq X$. Prove:

(a) $\bigcup_{\lambda \in I} A_\lambda' = (\bigcap_{\lambda \in I} A_\lambda)'$

(b) $\bigcap_{\lambda \in I} A_\lambda' = (\bigcup_{\lambda \in I} A_\lambda)'$.

★(c) $B \cap (\bigcup_{\lambda \in I} A_\lambda) = \bigcup_{\lambda \in I} (B \cap A_\lambda)$

(d) $B \cup (\bigcap_{\lambda \in I} A_\lambda) = \bigcap_{\lambda \in I} (B \cup A_\lambda)$

2. Suppose $\mathscr{A} = \{A_\lambda | \lambda \in I\}$ is a collection of sets and $J \subseteq I$. Prove:

(a) $\bigcap_{\lambda \in I} A_\lambda \subseteq \bigcap_{\lambda \in J} A_\lambda$ (b) $\bigcup_{\lambda \in J} A_\lambda \subseteq \bigcup_{\lambda \in I} A_\lambda$

3. Suppose $\mathscr{A} = \{A_\lambda | \lambda \in I\}$ is a pairwise disjoint collection of sets; that is, for any $\lambda, \mu \in I$ with $\lambda \neq \mu$, we have $A_\lambda \cap A_\mu = \varnothing$. Prove that $\bigcap_{\lambda \in I} A_\lambda = \varnothing$.

4. Let $f : X \to Y$ be a mapping. Let $\mathscr{A} = \{A_\lambda | \lambda \in I\}$ and $\mathscr{B} = \{B_\mu | \mu \in J\}$ be collections of subsets of X and Y, respectively. Prove:

(a) $f(\bigcup_{\lambda \in I} A_\lambda) = \bigcup_{\lambda \in I} f(A_\lambda)$ $\star$(b) $f^{-1}(\bigcap_{\mu \in J} B_\mu) = \bigcap_{\mu \in J} f^{-1}(B_\mu)$

(c) $f^{-1}(\bigcup_{\mu \in J} B_\mu) = \bigcup_{\mu \in J} f^{-1}(B_\mu)$

5. Let $\mathscr{A} = \{A_\lambda | \lambda \in I\}$ be a collection of subsets of a set X. Suppose the indexing set I is empty. Prove, in this case, that:

(a) $\bigcap_{\lambda \in I} A_\lambda = X$ (b) $\bigcup_{\lambda \in I} A_\lambda = \varnothing$

Properties of the Number Systems of Undergraduate Mathematics
CHAPTER 9

Throughout most precalculus and elementary calculus courses, as well as in several earlier portions of this text, a basic assumption is that a mathematical object called the *real numbers* is familiar to students. Indeed, we would guess that most students would respond "somewhat familiar," if not "very familiar," to a multiple-choice question asking for a rating of their familiarity with the real number system **R**. If this guess is accurate, before reading further you might engage in an interesting exercise by trying to write an explanation of why **R** is familiar. In fact, you should at this point pause to write down all that you actually know about **R**.

Assuming you have spent some time on this exercise, let us speculate on your answers. Various algebraic properties of **R** probably came to mind, such as "anything times zero equals zero, ... the product of a positive with a negative real number is negative, ... and ... a nonzero factor can be canceled from both sides of an equation." On another level, you may have focused on the representation of **R** as the set of points on a line. Theorems such as "between any two real numbers lies a third real number ... and ... there is no largest real number" suggest themselves in this context. Or else, you may have alluded to the role of the rational numbers within **R** and the existence of real numbers, such as $\sqrt{2}$, that are not rational.

Any number of other responses are, of course, possible and of equal value to those just suggested. But consider the following: How many of these responses, as well as the ones you gave, apply equally well to the question,

"Write down what you know about the rational number system, . . . the integers, . . . the complex numbers"? As one example, the three algebraic properties listed previously are just as true, when applied to **Z** or **Q**, as they are about **R**. The question that begins to arise when we begin to list descriptive properties of **R** is, "What properties characterize **R**?" Stated differently, "What description can we give of **R** that, among other things, distinguishes it from its familiar subsets **N**, **Z**, and **Q** and its superset **C**?" Answering that question is the goal of this chapter. In the course of developing this answer we will justify the use of the real numbers, as opposed to, say, the rationals, as the "universal set" for calculus of a single variable, by showing that properties specific to **R** are crucial for the proofs of certain basic theorems of calculus.

A more direct, and more open-ended question, in line with the preceding paragraph, is, "What are the real numbers?" In this text we provide two types of answer. As indicated, the material in this chapter provides a descriptive answer. In Chapter 10 we will give a *constructive* answer. With the positive integers as our starting point, we "build" first the integers, then the rationals, then the reals, using a process based on equivalence relations and equivalence classes, a process of considerable importance in a number of areas of upper-level mathematics.

9.1   Fields

We can answer descriptively the question, "What are the real numbers?" in just a few sentences. To do so, however, we must use terms that require the better part of this chapter for their definition and elaboration. An important theorem of advanced mathematics states that there is at most one *complete ordered field*. Accepting the truth of that theorem (whose proof is beyond the scope of this text), and assuming the existence of a "complete ordered field," we give it the name "the real numbers." *The real numbers* are the unique complete ordered field! Now we only need to answer the questions: "What is a field? What is an ordered field? What does it mean for an ordered field to be complete?" This article is dedicated to answering the first question.

The definition of field requires first that we define *binary operation* on a set.

DEFINITION 1
Given a nonempty set S, we define a **binary operation** $*$ **on** S to be any mapping of $S \times S$ into S. We denote by $a * b$ the value of the function $*$ at the ordered pair (a, b).

EXAMPLE 1   Familiar operations include addition and multiplication on the set **Z** of integers, union and intersection on the collection of all subsets of any given universal set U, addition of n-dimensional vectors,

*	a	b	c
a	a	b	c
b	b	c	a
c	c	a	b

Figure 9.1 *Typical table used to specify a particular finite algebraic structure. What is the relationship between this table and a table in Figure 9.2a?*

multiplication of $n \times n$ matrices, and composition of mappings from a given set X into itself. An operation may be defined on a finite set; this is customarily done by means of a finite "multiplication table" such as the one in Figure 9.1. □

A set, having one or more (usually one or two) operations, constitutes what is known as an *algebraic structure*. A *field* is an algebraic structure with two operations.

DEFINITION 2

A **field** $(F, +, \cdot)$ consists of a nonempty set F, together with two binary operations on F, denoted by the symbols "$+$" (plus) and "$\cdot$" (times), satisfying the following 11 axioms:

1. If $a, b \in F$, then $a + b \in F$ (additive **closure**)
2. If $a, b, c \in F$, then
    $(a + b) + c = a + (b + c)$ (addition is **associative**)
3. If $a, b, \in F$, then $a + b = b + a$ (addition is **commutative**)
4. There exists an element in F,
    denoted "0" and called
    the *zero*, or *zero element*,
    of the field, satisfying
    $a + 0 = 0 + a = a$,
    for all $a \in F$ (**additive identity axiom**)
5. To each $a \in F$, there corresponds an
    element $b \in F$ having the property that
    $a + b = b + a = 0$. The element b,
    which can be shown to be uniquely
    determined by a (see Theorem 1), is
    denoted $-a$ and called *minus a*   (**additive inverse axiom**)
6. If $a, b \in F$, then $ab \in F$ (multiplicative **closure**)
         (Note the convention of
    writing ab for $a \cdot b$.)
7. If $a, b, c, \in F$, then $(ab)c = a(bc)$ (multiplication is **associative**)
8. If $a, b \in F$, then $ab = ba$ (multiplication is **commutative**)
9. There exists a nonzero element in F
    denoted "1" and called the *unity* of

the field, satisfying $1 \cdot a = a$ for all $a \in F$ **(multiplicative identity axiom)**

10. To each $a \in F$, there corresponds an an element $b \in F$ having the property that $ab = ba = 1$. The element b, which can be shown to be uniquely determined by a (see Theorem 1), is denoted a^{-1} and called the *reciprocal of a*

11. If $a, b, c \in F$, then $a(b + c) = ab + ac$ **(multiplicative inverse axiom)** (multiplication **distributes** over addition)

Since $1 \neq 0$ in a field, any field must contain at least two elements. Also, Axioms 1 and 6 are, strictly speaking, not necessary, due to the definition of binary operation (Definition 1), which already forces closure. We include them, nonetheless, for the sake of emphasis.

The set of real numbers, with the usual operations of addition and multiplication, constitutes a field, by its definition as the (unique) complete ordered field and our assumption in this chapter that such an object exists. Therefore the fact that addition and multiplication of real numbers satisfy the field axioms, a fact that is familiar to any high school algebra student, is dictated by the definition of **R**; in particular, it is not something that has to (or can) be proved. All other familiar properties of **R** are either additional axioms involved in the definition of "complete ordered field" (to be studied later in the chapter) or are theorems that can be proved from the axioms for a complete ordered field. **R** is often thought of as the prototypical field, and the borrowing of real number notation, for example, $+, \cdot, 0, 1, -a$, and so on, to denote aspects of general fields, bears this out. But the concept of abstract, or generic, field is much more general than just the real numbers, as the following examples show.

EXAMPLE 2 $(\mathbf{Q}, +, \cdot)$ and $(\mathbf{C}, +, \cdot)$ are both fields. Looking at some key axioms, we note that the rational numbers $0/1$ and $1/1$ are the additive and multiplicative identities in **Q**, whereas $0 + 0i$ and $1 + 0i$ play those roles, respectively, in **C**. If a/b is a nonzero rational, then b/a is its multiplicative inverse; if $a + bi$ is a nonzero complex number, then $(a - bi)/(a^2 + b^2)$ is its multiplicative inverse. Since **Q** is a subset of **R** and is itself a field under the two operations "inherited" from **R**, **Q** is said to be a *subfield* of **R**. Properties of **Q** and **C** will be discussed in some detail later, **C** in Article 9.4 and **Q** in Chapter 10. $\square$

EXAMPLE 3   The substructures $(\mathbf{N}, +, \cdot)$ and $(\mathbf{Z}, +, \cdot)$ of the real number field fail to be fields. For example, **N** fails to satisfy Axiom 4, among others, whereas **Z** violates Axiom 10. You should determine which of the field axioms are satisfied by these two algebraic structures. $\square$

EXAMPLE 4   For those familiar with a little matrix theory, the set of all
2×2 matrices, with operations of ordinary matrix addition and multiplication, provides us with an algebraic structure satisfying a number
of the field axioms. The additive part of this structure, in fact, satisfies
field axioms 1 through 5, with $\begin{pmatrix} 0 & 0 \\ 0 & 0 \end{pmatrix}$ being the additive identity and
$\begin{pmatrix} -a & -b \\ -c & -d \end{pmatrix}$ the additive inverse of the matrix $\begin{pmatrix} a & b \\ c & d \end{pmatrix}$. Furthermore,
matrix multiplication distributes over addition, is associative, and has
an identity, namely, $\begin{pmatrix} 1 & 0 \\ 0 & 1 \end{pmatrix}$. The structure fails to be a field on two
counts: Matrix multiplication is noncommutative and not every 2×2
matrix has a multiplicative inverse. In fact, the matrices having inverses
are precisely those with nonzero determinant $ad - bc$.   □

EXAMPLE 5   For any positive integer m, denote by $\mathbf{Z}_m$ the set of symbols
$\{0, 1, 2, \ldots, m - 1\}$. We define operations "plus" and "times" on such
sets as follows: if $a, b \in \mathbf{Z}_m$, we calculate the "sum" $a + b$, in $\mathbf{Z}_m$, by computing the ordinary sum of a and b; that is, their sum in $\mathbf{Z}$, and writing
down the remainder (necessarily an integer between 0 and $m - 1$, inclusive. Recall the "division algorithm for $\mathbf{Z}$," stated in the solution to
Example 10, Article 6.3) upon division of that ordinary sum by m. Thus
in $\mathbf{Z}_8$, $7 + 7 = 6$, $2 + 7 = 1$, and $4 + 4 = 0$. The calculation of the
"product" in $\mathbf{Z}_m$ is totally analogous, replacing "ordinary sum" by
"ordinary product." Thus, in $\mathbf{Z}_8$, we have $7 \cdot 7 = 1$, $2 \cdot 7 = 6$, and $4 \cdot 4 =$
0. You should construct the complete "addition" and "multiplication"
tables for $\mathbf{Z}_8$ and use them to check the various field axioms. We recommend special attention to the associative, identity, and inverse axioms,
as well as distributivity of multiplication over addition (the fact that
the latter works in all cases is rather remarkable). In the course of doing
this you should discover that $(\mathbf{Z}_8, +, \cdot)$ is <u>not</u> a field.
   We list in Figure 9.2 complete addition and multiplication tables for
$(\mathbf{Z}_3, +, \cdot)$ and $(\mathbf{Z}_4, +, \cdot)$. Both structures satisfy all field axioms except
possibly Axiom 10, the multiplicative inverse axiom. Now $(\mathbf{Z}_3, +, \cdot)$
satisfies Axiom 10 also, and so is a field. The criterion determining
whether a structure $(\mathbf{Z}_m, +, \cdot)$ is a field is suggested by Exercise 2, Article
6.2. Such a structure satisfies Axiom 10, and so is a field, if and only if
m is prime. Structures $(\mathbf{Z}_m, +, \cdot)$ are called the *integers modulo m*.   □

EXAMPLE 6   Consider the set of those real numbers having the form
$a + b\sqrt{2}$, where a and b are rational. Let us denote this subset of $\mathbf{R}$
(and superset of $\mathbf{Q}$ (Why?)) by $\mathbf{Q}(\sqrt{2})$. Exercise 11 calls for you to provide portions of the proof that $\mathbf{Q}(\sqrt{2})$ is a field, under the ordinary
addition and multiplication it inherits from $\mathbf{R}$.   □

+	0	1	2
0	0	1	2
1	1	2	0
2	2	0	1

·	0	1	2
0	0	0	0
1	0	1	2
2	0	2	1

(a)

+	0	1	2	3
0	0	1	2	3
1	1	2	3	0
2	2	3	0	1
3	3	0	1	2

·	0	1	2	3
0	0	0	0	0
1	0	1	2	3
2	0	2	0	2
3	0	3	2	1

(b)

Figure 9.2 *(a) Tables defining the field of integers modulo 3; (b) tables defining the algebraic structure, the integers modulo 4.*

EXAMPLE 7 Denote by $\mathbf{R}[x]$ the set of all polynomials in a single variable x having real coefficients. Endow $\mathbf{R}[x]$ with the operations of ordinary polynomial addition and multiplication. It can be shown that $(\mathbf{R}[x], +, \cdot)$ fails to be a field only in that it violates Axiom 10. Furthermore, there is a field associated with $\mathbf{R}[x]$ in a canonical way (actually a field that can be constructed from $\mathbf{R}[x]$, by means of standard type of construction that we will study in Chapter 10). This associated field is denoted $\mathbf{R}(x)$ and may be thought of as consisting of the rational functions, that is, quotients of polynomials with real coefficients. $\square$

Here is an important distinction between the role of $\mathbf{R}$ in this chapter and that of the structures presented in Examples 2 through 7. Under our approach here, where we assume a complete ordered field exists, $\mathbf{R}$ is defined to be a field. Hence the 11 field properties are axioms for $\mathbf{R}$, in particular, there is no question in this chapter of proving or verifying any of these properties for $\mathbf{R}$. On the other hand, each of these structures is defined independently of the field concept. The fact that each is or is not a field is a theorem, that is, each of the field axioms must be verified or demonstrated to be false for each of those examples. In Chapter 10, where we drop the aforementioned existence assumption and outline a proof of the existence of a complete ordered field, the approach is to construct a mathematical object and prove it is a complete ordered field. In that approach the role of **R** is analogous to that of our other examples of fields now; in particular, we must verify (i.e., prove) the 11 field properties for **R** in that approach.

We now wish to prove some elementary theorems about fields. Any theorem we can prove about fields in general is, of course, true in any of the specific examples of fields considered in Examples 1 through 7. On the other hand, there are familiar properties of the real number field that do not appear in our list of general field theorems, and indeed, are not true in an arbitrary field. Several such results are found in Articles 9.2 and 9.3. An analysis of their proofs reveals that they depend for their validity on properties of **R** other than pure field properties, and so are true in less generality than the theorems we are about to state. In particular, some may fail to hold in our various specific examples of fields.

Throughout the following discussion we use freely the basic principles "equals added to (respectively, multiplied by) equals yield equals." In symbols, if $(F, +, \cdot)$ is a field with x, y, $z \in F$ and if $x = y$, then $x + z = y + z$ and $xz = yz$. An easy consequence of Axiom 4 and this property is *additive cancellation*, namely, if a, b, $c \in F$ and $a + b = a + c$, then $b = c$ (see Exercise 1).

THEOREM 1
Let $(F, +, \cdot)$ be a field. Then the additive and multiplicative identities of F are unique. The additive and multiplicative inverses of a given element $x \in F$ ($x \neq 0$ in the multiplicative case) are uniquely determined by x.

Proof   First, suppose 0 and $0'$ are both additive identities for F. Then $0 = 0 + 0' = 0'$, where the first equation uses the fact that $0'$ is an additive identity, with the second using that property in reference to 0. Thus $0 = 0'$ and the uniqueness of the additive identity is established. Second, suppose y and z are both additive inverses for a given $x \in F$. Then $y = 0 + y = (y + x) + y = (z + x) + y = z + (x + y) = z + 0 = z$, so that $y = z$, and the uniqueness of additive inverses is proved. The key step $(y + x) + y = (z + x) + y$ in the preceding sequence follows from the assumption $y + x = 0 = z + x$.

The arguments in the multiplicative case are identical to those just given and are left as an exercise (Exercise 2).   □

THEOREM 2
Let $(F, +, \cdot)$ be a field and $x \in F$. Then $x \cdot 0 = 0 \cdot x = 0$.

Proof   We claim first that $x \cdot 0 + x \cdot 0 = x \cdot 0 + 0$. This follows from the sequence of steps $x \cdot 0 + 0 = x \cdot 0 = x \cdot (0 + 0) = x \cdot 0 + x \cdot 0$. By additive cancellation, we conclude $0 = x \cdot 0$. The equation $0 = 0 \cdot x$ follows immediately from Axiom 8.   □

THEOREM 3
Let $(F, +, \cdot)$ be a field and $x \in F$. Then $(-1)x = -x$.

Proof By the uniqueness of the additive inverse $-x$ of a field element x (Theorem 1), we need only show that $(-1)x$ behaves as $-x$ is defined to behave, namely, $x + (-1)x = 0$. But

$$x + (-1)x = 1(x) + (-1)x \qquad \text{(Axiom 9)}$$
$$= [1 + (-1)]x \qquad \text{(Axiom 11)}$$
$$= 0 \cdot x \qquad \text{(Axiom 5)}$$
$$= 0 \qquad \text{(Theorem 2)} \quad \square$$

A result such as Theorem 3, in a general field, is not so mundane or unremarkable as our familiarity with its application to **R** would have us believe. Let us apply this rèsult in the field $\mathbf{Z}_7$ of integers modulo 7. The theorem says that, in any field, the product of the additive inverse of the multiplicative identity with any element equals the additive inverse of that element. Let $x = 5$ in $\mathbf{Z}_7$. Note that in $\mathbf{Z}_7$, $-5 = 2$ and $-1 = 6$. Hence our theorem boils down to the equation $(6) \cdot (5) = 2$. A quick check of the $\mathbf{Z}_7$ multiplication table indicates that this equation is true, as Theorem 3 predicts.

COROLLARY
Let $(F, +, \cdot)$ be a field with $x, y \in F$. Then:

(a) $x(-y) = -(xy) = (-x)y$
(b) $-(-x) = x$
(c) $(-x)(-y) = xy$

Proof (a) Using Theorem 3, we note the equations $x(-y) = x[(-1)y] = [(x)(-1)]y = (-1)(xy) = -(xy)$. We may prove $-(xy) = (-x)y$ in a similar manner.

(b) Our claim is that x is the additive inverse of $-x$. By uniqueness of the additive inverse (Theorem 1), we need show only that $(-x) + x = 0$. But this holds since $-x$ is the additive inverse of x.

(c) $(-x)(-y) = -[(x)(-y)] = -[-(xy)] = xy$. The first two equalities follow from (a), the third from (b). $\square$

Theorem 2 stated that, in a field, the product of any element with the additive identity zero equals zero. The following result indicates that the only way a product of two field elements can be zero is if one of the elements is zero.

THEOREM 4
Let $(F, +, \cdot)$ be a field with $x, y \in F$. If $xy = 0$, then either $x = 0$ or $y = 0$.

Proof We have seen both our general approach to this proof and this specific proof earlier in the text (recall Example 1, Article 6.2). Given $xy = 0$, suppose $x \neq 0$. We will try to conclude on this basis that $y = 0$. Since $x \neq 0$, then x^{-1} exists, by Axiom 10. Hence $y = 1(y) = (x^{-1}x)y = x^{-1}(xy) = x^{-1}(0) = 0$, as desired. $\square$

Analogs to the familiar subtraction and division operations from **R** exist in an arbitrary field.

DEFINITION 3

Let $(F, +, \cdot)$ be a field with $x, y, \in F$. We define:

(a) The **difference** $x - y$ (x minus y) by the rule $x - y = x + (-y)$
(b) The **quotient** x/y (x divided by y) by the rule $x/y = xy^{-1}$, where $y \neq 0$

The restriction "division by nonzero divisors only" results from the fact that 0^{-1} does not exist in any field (a consequence of Theorem 2, see Exercise 3). Subtraction and division in a field have properties that are familiar from experience with real numbers. Several such properties are grouped together in the following theorem.

THEOREM 5

Let $(F, +, \cdot)$ be a field with $w, x, y, z \in F$. Then:

(a) If $w \neq 0$, then $w^{-1} = 1/w$
(b) If $x \neq 0$, then $(w/x)^{-1} = x/w$
(c) $x = y$ if and only if $x - y = 0$
(d) $x/y = 1$ if and only if $x = y$ and $y \neq 0$
(e) $w - (x - y) = (w - x) + y$
(f) $-w - x = -(w + x)$
(g) If $x \neq 0$ and $y \neq 0$, then $xw/xy = w/y$
(h) If $x \neq 0$ and $z \neq 0$, then $(w/x) + (y/z) = (wz + xy)/(xz)$
(i) If $x \neq 0$ and $z \neq 0$, then $(w/x) \cdot (y/z) = wy/xz$

Partial proof (g) By the definition of a quotient, $xw/xy = (xw)(xy)^{-1} = (xw)(x^{-1}y^{-1}) = (xx^{-1})(wy^{-1}) = wy^{-1} = w/y$. The step $(xw)(xy)^{-1} = (xw)(x^{-1}y^{-1})$ follows from Exercise 6(a).

(h) By (g), $(w/x) + (y/z) = (wz/xz) + (xy/xz) = (wz + xy)/(xz)$. The final equality follows from Exercise 8(a). The remaining parts of the proof are left as exercises. $\square$

Part (c) of Theorem 5 can be combined with Theorem 4 to provide a proof of the multiplicative cancellation property of a field. This proof is left as an exercise [Exercise 8(d)].

THEOREM 6

If $(F, +, \cdot)$ is a field, if $x, y, z \in F$ with $xy = xz$ and $x \neq 0$, then $y = z$.

Let us test parts of Theorem 5, using the field $\mathbf{Z}_7$. In (b), let $w = 3$ and $x = 4$. Then $x^{-1} = 2$, whereas $w^{-1} = 5$. Hence $w/x = wx^{-1} = (3)(2) = 6$, so that $(w/x)^{-1} = (6)^{-1} = 6$. On the other hand, $x/w = xw^{-1} = (4)(5) = 6$. Hence $(w/x)^{-1} = 6 = x/w$, as predicted by (b) of Theorem 5. In (e), let $w = 1$, $x = 5$, and $y = 6$. Then $x - y = x + (-y) = 5 + (-6) = 5 + 1 = 6$, so

$w - (x - y) = 1 - 6 = 1 + (-6) = 1 + 1 = 2$. On the other hand, $w - x = w + (-x) = 1 + (-5) = 1 + 2 = 3$, so $(w - x) + y = 3 + 6 = 2$. Again, the result predicted by a part of Theorem 5 is borne out in the example $\mathbf{Z}_7$, as $w - (x - y) = 2 = (w - x) + y$ when $w = 1$, $x = 5$, and $y = 6$.

A brief look at the nonfield $\mathbf{Z}_6$ shows that Axiom 10 (the multiplicative inverse axiom; the only field axiom that $\mathbf{Z}_6$ fails to satisfy) must be crucial for the proof of both Theorems 4 and 6. In $\mathbf{Z}_6$, $3 \cdot 2 = 0$, whereas neither 3 nor 2 equals 0. Hence the conclusion of Theorem 4 fails in $\mathbf{Z}_6$. Of course, there is no inconsistency, since the hypothesis of Theorem 4 also fails in $\mathbf{Z}_6$. Also, in $\mathbf{Z}_6$, we have $2 \cdot 4 = 2 \cdot 1$ (both equal 2), but $4 \neq 1$. Cancellation of nonzero factors, the subject of Theorem 6, does not work in the nonfield $\mathbf{Z}_6$.

> DEFINITION 4
>
> Let F be a field and $x \in F$. If n is a positive integer, we define x^n recursively by $x^1 = x$ and $x^n = (x^{n-1})x$. If $n = 0$, we define $x^n = x^0 = 1$. If $x \neq 0$ and n is a negative integer, we define $x^n = (x^{-1})^{-n}$.

Earlier in the text (e.g., Remark 2, Article 1.5), we avoided recursive definition, and would have defined x^n ($n \in \mathbf{N}$) informally as "x times x times $x \cdots$ (n times)." By now, you should be mathematically mature enough to prefer a precise and formal approach. Recursive definition is discussed in detail in Article 10.1.

Properties such as $x^m x^n = x^{m+n}$, $x^m y^m = (xy)^m$, and $x^{-m} = (x^m)^{-1}$, where m and n are positive integers and x and y are elements of an arbitrary field, familiar from high school algebra as laws of exponents in the real number system, are valid in the context of an arbitrary field as well.

Exercises

1. Verify the additive cancellation property of a field; that is, if $x, y, z \in F$ (F a field), if $x + z = y + z$, then $x = y$.

2. *(a)* Prove that the multiplicative identity (i.e., unity) 1 of a field is unique.
★*(b)* Prove that the multiplicative inverse x^{-1} of an element x in a field F is uniquely determined by x.

3. Prove that the zero element of a field necessarily has no multiplicative inverse. (*Note:* Axiom 10 allows only as how 0 <u>need not</u> have a multiplicative inverse.)

4. *(a)* *(i)* Construction addition and multiplication tables for the structure $\mathbf{Z}_8$ of integers modulo 8.
  (ii) Verify five instances of the distributive law (multiplication over addition, as in Axiom 11 of the definition of field) in $\mathbf{Z}_8$. How many possible instances of distributivity are there for $\mathbf{Z}_8$?
  (iii) Show that $\mathbf{Z}_8$ fails to satisfy Axiom 10 of the definition of field.
  (iv) Show that the equation $(-1)a = -a$ is valid for each $a \in \mathbf{Z}_8$, even though $\mathbf{Z}_8$ is not a field. Is there any inconsistency between this conclusion and the result of Theorem 3?

(b) *(i)* Construct addition and multiplication tables for the field $\mathbf{Z}_7$ of integers modulo 7.

(ii) Find all solutions in $\mathbf{Z}_7$ of the equation $x^3 + x^2 - 2x = 0$.

5. *(a)* Prove that the zero and unity elements in a field equal their own additive and multiplicative inverses, respectively. That is, prove that $-0 = 0$ and $1^{-1} = 1$.

★*(b)* Prove or disprove: In any field F, if $x \in F$ and $x = x^{-1}$, then $x = 1$.

★*(c)* Prove or disprove: In any field F, if $x \in F$ and $x = -x$, then $x = 0$.

(d) Let m be a positive integer. Give an example of a field F and an element $x \in F$ such that $mx = 0$ (where we define mx recursively by $1 \cdot x = x$ and $mx = (m - 1)x + x$ if $m > 1$; recall Definition 4) but $x \neq 0$.

6. *(a)* Prove that if F is a field and if x and y are nonzero elements of F (so that $xy \neq 0$; recall Theorem 4), then $(xy)^{-1} = x^{-1}y^{-1}$.

(b) Prove that if x is a nonzero element of a field F, then $(x^{-1})^{-1} = x$.

7. *(a)* Prove that if F is a field and $x \in F$ satisfies $x^2 = x$, then either $x = 0$ or $x = 1$.

(b) Prove that if F is a field and $x \in F$ satisfies $x^2 = 1$, then $x = \pm 1$. Does this result hold true in the structure $\mathbf{Z}_8$?

8. *(a)* Prove that if $x, y, z \in F$ (F a field) with $z \neq 0$, then $(x/z) + (y/z) = (x + y)/z$.

(b) Show that if $a, b, c,$ and d are elements of F (F a field), then $(a + b)(c + d) = ac + ad + bc + bd$.

(c) Prove parts (a) through (f) and (i) of Theorem 5.

(d) Prove Theorem 6.

9. *(a)* Prove, in a field F, if $a, b, c, x \in F$ and $a \neq 0$, then $ax + b = c$ if and only if $x = (c - b)a^{-1}$. Hence a linear equation in one variable with coefficients in a field F has a unique solution in F.

(b) Prove that if F is a field and $a, b \in F$, then $a^2 = b^2$ if and only if $a = b$ or $a = -b$.

(c) Give an example in the structure $\mathbf{Z}_8$ of a linear equation $ax + b = c$ that has:

(i) no solution x in $\mathbf{Z}_8$ *(ii)* more than one solution in $\mathbf{Z}_8$

(d) Find an example of elements $a, b \in \mathbf{Z}_8$ such that $a^2 = b^2$, but $a \neq b$ and $a \neq -b$.

10. Prove or disprove, in an arbitrary field F:

★*(a)* If $a \in F$, then there corresponds $x \in F$ such that $x^2 = a$ (such an element x would be called a *square root* of the field element a).

(b) If $x, y \in F$ and $x^2 + y^2 = 0$, then $x = y = 0$.

11. Verify field axioms 7, 10, and 11 for the field $\mathbf{Q}[\sqrt{2}]$.

9.2 ORDERED FIELDS

We saw in Article 9.1 that $\mathbf{R}$ is a field and is thereby distinguishable from its subsets $\mathbf{N}$ and $\mathbf{Z}$. But the theory of general fields fails to provide a means of differentiating between $\mathbf{R}$ and either $\mathbf{Q}$ or $\mathbf{C}$. Like the reals, the rational and complex number systems are themselves fields.

In the previous article, there was a lack of any reference to ordering of elements in an arbitrary field. The familiar fact that any two distinct real numbers a and b satisfy either $a < b$ or $a > b$ is the basis of substantial portions of the algebra of the real numbers that we learn in high school. As we will soon see, this part of the theory of the real number field does not carry over to an arbitrary field, but only to a class of fields known as *ordered fields*. The theory of ordered fields will provide a way of distinguishing **R**, as well as **Q**, from **C**.

DEFINITION 1

An **ordered field** $(F, \mathscr{P})$ consists of a field $(F, +, \cdot)$, together with a nonempty subset $\mathscr{P}$ of F satisfying:

(a)   For all $x, y \in F$, if $x, y \in \mathscr{P}$, then $x + y \in \mathscr{P}$
(b)   For all $x, y \in F$, if $x, y \in \mathscr{P}$, then $xy \in \mathscr{P}$
(c)   For any $x \in F$, one and only one of the following three statements is true:
    (i) $x \in \mathscr{P}$
    (ii) $-x \in \mathscr{P}$
    (iii) $x = 0$

The subset $\mathscr{P}$ is called the **positive part** of the ordered field $(F, \mathscr{P})$, and an element $x \in \mathscr{P}$ is called a **positive element** of F. If $-x \in \mathscr{P}$, x is said to be a **negative element** of $(F, \mathscr{P})$.

Conditions (a) and (b) state that $\mathscr{P}$ is closed under the addition and multiplication operations of the field F. Condition (c) is called *trichotomy*. When there is no danger of ambiguity, we sometimes refer simply to the ordered field F, rather than the ordered field $(F, \mathscr{P})$.

Our first theorem about ordered fields is not only important in its own right, but contains all that is needed to show that the complex number field does not admit an ordering, that is, cannot possibly be ordered. Remember, **R** is, by definition, an ordered field.

THEOREM 1

Let $(F, \mathscr{P})$ be an ordered field. Then:

(a) $1 \in \mathscr{P}$
(b)   If $x \in \mathscr{P}$, then $x^{-1} \in \mathscr{P}$
(c)   If $x \in F$ and $x \neq 0$, then $x^2 \in \mathscr{P}$

Proof   (a)   Since $1 \neq 0$, then either $1 \in \mathscr{P}$ or $-1 \in \mathscr{P}$, by (c) of Definition 1. Suppose $-1 \in \mathscr{P}$ and let $a \in \mathscr{P}$. Then $(-1)a \in \mathscr{P}$ by (b) of Definition 1. But $(-1)a = -a$ by Theorem 3, Article 9.1, so that $-a \in \mathscr{P}$. But $a \in \mathscr{P}$ and $-a \in \mathscr{P}$ contradicts (c) of Definition 1.
    (b)   Assume $x \in \mathscr{P}$ so that $x \neq 0$ and $x^{-1} \neq 0$. If $x^{-1} \notin \mathscr{P}$, then $-x^{-1} \in \mathscr{P}$ by (c) of Definition 1. But then, $(x)(-x^{-1}) = -(xx^{-1}) = -1 \in \mathscr{P}$, a contradiction since $1 \in \mathscr{P}$, by (a).

(c) Let x be a nonzero element of the ordered field F. Then either $x \in \mathscr{P}$ or $-x \in \mathscr{P}$. If $x \in \mathscr{P}$, then $x^2 = (x)(x) \in \mathscr{P}$ by (b) of Definition 1. If $-x \in \mathscr{P}$ then, for the same reason, $(-x)(-x) \in \mathscr{P}$. But $(-x)(-x) = x^2$, by the corollary to Theorem 3, Article 9.1, so that, again, $x^2 \in \mathscr{P}$, as desired. $\square$

Only slight knowledge of algebraic properties of **C** (which we won't cover in detail until Article 9.4) is required to observe now that no ordering of **C** is possible. For if **C** were ordered, with positive part $\mathscr{P}$, we would necessarily have $i^2 \in \mathscr{P}$, by (c) of Theorem 1. But $i^2 = -1$ and $-1 \in \mathscr{P}$ contradicts (a) of Theorem 1. The following result is established.

COROLLARY
The field **C** of complex numbers does not admit an ordering.

Other examples of fields from Article 9.1 also prove to be nonorderable. It is impossible, for instance, to order $\mathbf{Z}_7$, because if $\mathscr{P}$ is the positive part of $\mathbf{Z}_7$, then $1 \in \mathscr{P}$ so that $1 + 1 + \cdots + 1$ (7 times) $= 0 \in \mathscr{P}$, as well. But $0 \in \mathscr{P}$ contradicts (c) of Definition 1 [see Exercise 1(c)].

On the other hand, in addition to the ordered fields **R** and **Q**, the field described in Example 6, Article 9.1, is ordered by the ordering inherited from **R**. Also, we may order the field in Example 7, Article 9.1, by an ordering based on the sign of the lead coefficient of a polynomial (see Example 1, Article 10.3 for details).

We next show that the ordering in an ordered field gives rise to a total ordering of the elements of that field, in the sense of Definition 4, Article 7.4.

DEFINITION 2
Let F be an ordered field with positive part $\mathscr{P}$. We define a relation "less than," denoted $<$, on F by the rule $x < y$ (x is **less than** y, or x is **strictly less than** y) if and only if $y - x \in \mathscr{P}$, for any $x, y \in F$. We also write $y > x$ in case $x < y$.

THEOREM 2
In an ordered field $(F, \mathscr{P})$:

(a) $x < x$ is false for any $x \in F$.
(b) If $x < y$ and $y < z$, then $x < z$, for any $x, y, z \in F$.
(c) $x > 0$ if and only if $x \in \mathscr{P}$, whereas $x < 0$ if and only if $-x \in \mathscr{P}$.
(d) Given any $x \in F$, precisely one of the three possibilities, $x > 0$, $x < 0$, or $x = 0$ obtains.
(e) Given any $x, y \in F$, precisely one of the three possibilities, $x > y$, $x < y$, or $x = y$ obtains.

Partial proof We leave (a) and (e) as exercises (see Exercise 2). For (b), assume $x < y$ and $y < z$; to show $x < z$, we must prove $z - x \in \mathscr{P}$. Now, by our assumptions, we have $y - x \in \mathscr{P}$ and $z - y \in \mathscr{P}$. By (a) of

Definition 1, $(z - y) + (y - x) \in \mathscr{P}$. But $(z - y) + (y - x) =$ $z + (-y + y) - x = z - x$, so $z - x \in \mathscr{P}$, as desired.

For (c) and (d), we note, by Definition 2 (using specialization), $0 < x$ if and only if $x - 0 \in \mathscr{P}$, that is, $x \in \mathscr{P}$. Similarly, $x < 0$ if and only if $0 - x \in \mathscr{P}$; that is, $-x \in \mathscr{P}$. Hence (d) follows directly from (c) of Definition 1. □

Part (c) of Theorem 2 confirms that the positive part of the real number field corresponds to our usual notion of positive real number, that is, a number greater than zero, or graphically, a number to the right of zero on the real number line.

The relation "less than," in an ordered field, leads in a natural way, to an associated partial ordering relation on F.

DEFINITION 3

Let F be an ordered field. We define a relation "less than or equal to," denoted $\leq$, by the rule $x \leq y$ (x is **less than or equal to** y) if and only if either $x < y$ or $x = y$.

THEOREM 3

In an ordered field F:

(a) $\leq$ is a partial ordering on F, so that $(F, \leq)$ is a poset.
(b) $\leq$ is a total ordering on F.

Proof   (a)   Clearly $x \leq x$ for any $x \in F$, since $x = x$, so that the relation $\leq$ is reflexive. For antisymmetry, assume $x, y \in F$ with $x \leq y$ and $y \leq x$. If $x \neq y$, then $x < y$ and $y < x$. But this contradicts (e) of Theorem 2. Hence $\leq$ is antisymmetric. Finally, if $x, y, z \in F$ with $x \leq y$ and $y \leq z$, an analysis of all the logical possibilities for cases [e.g., $x = y$ and $y < z$; you should determine how many cases there are and verify each one, see Exercise 3(a)] leads to the desired conclusion $x \leq z$, so that $\leq$ is transitive.

(b)   Let $x, y \in F$ be given. We must prove that either $x \leq y$ or $y \leq x$. Suppose $x \leq y$ is false. Then it is not the case that either $x < y$ or $x = y$; that is, x is not less than y and x is not equal to y. By (e) of Theorem 2, we have $y < x$, which implies $y \leq x$. □

The proof of the transitivity of $\leq$ in (a) of Theorem 3 suggests a fact that is worth noting. By the definition of $\leq$ in an ordered field, many properties of that relation are best proved by arguments involving division into cases [e.g., Exercise 3(b)(iii)]. (Recall Article 5.3.)

A number of properties that are familiar from the algebra of inequalities involving real numbers carry over to an arbitrary ordered field.

THEOREM 4

Let a, b, x, and y be elements of an ordered field F:

(a) If $x < y$, then $a + x < a + y$
(b) If $a < b$ and $x < y$, then $a + x < b + y$
(c) If $x < y$ and $a > 0$, then $ax < ay$
(d) If $x < y$ and $a < 0$, then $ax > ay$

Partial proof   We leave (a) and (c) as exercises [see Exercise 3(b)]. For (b), assume $a < b$ and $x < y$. To prove $a + x < b + y$, we must show that $(b + y) - (a + x) \in \mathscr{P}$. Now, by assumption, $b - a \in \mathscr{P}$ and $y - x \in \mathscr{P}$. Hence $(b - a) + (y - x) \in \mathscr{P}$ by (a) of Definition 1. But we have the equation $(b - a) + (y - x) = (b + y) - (a + x)$ (Verify!) so that the latter element of F is in $\mathscr{P}$, as desired.

To prove (d), suppose $x < y$ and $a < 0$. To prove $ax > ay$, we must show that $ax - ay \in \mathscr{P}$. By assumption, $y - x \in \mathscr{P}$ and $-a \in \mathscr{P}$. Hence $(-a)(y - x) \in \mathscr{P}$ by (a) of Definition 1. But $(-a)(y - x) = ax - ay$ (Verify!) so that the latter is contained in $\mathscr{P}$, as we wished to show. $\square$

We next consider extensions of the notion of absolute value of a real number and distance between two real numbers to the context of an arbitrary ordered field.

DEFINITION 4

Let F be an ordered field. If $x \in F$, we define the **absolute value** of x, denoted $|x|$, by the rule

$$|x| = \begin{cases} x, & x \geq 0 \\ -x, & x < 0 \end{cases}$$

We issue the usual caveat that in a general ordered field, as in the familiar ordered field $\mathbf{R}$, we must be careful to avoid false conclusions such as "$-x$ is negative for any $x \in F$" and "$|-x| = x$ for any $x \in F$." A number of properties of absolute value are contained in the exercises (see Exercise 6); several that are especially familiar are listed in the following theorem.

THEOREM 5

Let F be an ordered field with x, $y \in F$. Then:

(a) $|x| \geq 0$ for any $x \in F$; $|x| = 0$ if and only if $x = 0$
(b) $|x||y| = |xy|$
(c) $|x + y| \leq |x| + |y|$
(d) $|x| - |y| \leq |x - y|$

Proof   (a)   If $x > 0$, then $|x| = x > 0$. If $x < 0$, then $|x| = -x > 0$. If $x = 0$, then $|x| = x = 0$. If $x \neq 0$, then either $x > 0$ or $x < 0$ so that $|x| \neq 0$, from the first two sentences of this proof. Hence $|x| = 0$ implies $x = 0$, so that the conclusion "$|x| = 0 \Leftrightarrow x = 0$" is justified.

(b) There are six distinct cases to check. For example, if x is positive and y is negative, then xy is negative [Exercise 4(a)(ii)] so that $|xy| = (x)(-y) = -xy$. However $|x| = x$ and $|y| = -y$ so that $|x||y| = (x)(-y) = -(xy)$ also. Formulation and verification of the other five cases are left as an exercise [Exercise 4(a)(iii)].

(c) Our approach assumes the result of Exercise 4(b)(ii) and uses (b) of this theorem. Namely, we note

$$|x + y|^2 = |(x + y)^2| \qquad \text{[follows immediately from (b)]}$$
$$= (x + y)^2 \qquad \text{[from Theorem 1(c) and Definition 4]}$$
$$= x^2 + 2xy + y^2$$
$$\leq x^2 + 2|xy| + y^2 \qquad \text{[from Exercise 5(a)(iii)]}$$
$$= |x|^2 + 2|x||y| + |y|^2 \qquad \text{[from (b)]}$$
$$= (|x| + |y|)^2$$

Since $|x + y|^2 \leq (|x| + |y|)^2$, and since both $|x + y|$ and $|x| + |y|$ are nonnegative, we conclude, from Exercise 4(b)(ii), that $|x + y| \leq |x| + |y|$, as desired.

(d) $|x| = |y + (x - y)| \leq |y| + |x - y|$, where the inequality follows from (c). Hence $|x| - |y| \leq |x - y|$, as desired. $\square$

Note the following discussion about the proof of Theorem 5(c). In an arbitrary field we need to be careful when using the symbol "2" to represent $1 + 1$ (and $2x$ for $x + x$ for any $x \in F$, etc.), since it is possible that $1 + 1 = 0$. This is indeed the case in the field $\mathbf{Z}_2$. However, in an ordered field, $1 + 1$ cannot equal zero, so that $2 = 1 + 1$ must represent a nonzero, and, in fact, a positive field element. In particular, $\frac{1}{2} = 2^{-1}$ has got to exist in any ordered field (cf. Exercise 8).

The concept of absolute value in an arbitrary ordered field provides us with a notion of *distance* between field elements, in a manner totally analogous to the way we calculate distances between real numbers along a number line.

DEFINITION 5

Let F be an ordered field. If $x, y \in F$, we define the **distance** between x and y, denoted $d(x, y)$, by the rule $d(x, y) = |x - y|$.

Note that d is a mapping from $F \times F$ into F. It is easy to show, and it is left as an exercise to prove [see Exercise 7(a)], that d satisfies the properties listed in Theorem 6.

THEOREM 6

Let F be an ordered field with $x, y, z \in F$. Then:

(a) $d(x, y) \geq 0$; $d(x, y) = 0$ if and only if $x = y$
(b) $d(x, y) = d(y, x)$
(c) $d(x, z) \leq d(x, y) + d(y, z)$

We conclude this article with the reminder that the concept of ordered field has now given us the ability to distinguish between **R** and **C**. But **R** and **Q** are both ordered fields; what we need next is an abstract property of ordered fields that is satisfied by one, but not the other. *Completeness* in an ordered field, the subject of the next article, is just such a property.

Exercises

1. Suppose $(F, \mathscr{P})$ is an ordered field. Prove:

★(a)   If $x \in F$, $x \neq 0$, and $n \in \mathbf{N}$, then $x^{2n} \in \mathscr{P}$
 (b)   If $a, b \in \mathscr{P}$, then $a/b \in \mathscr{P}$
 (c)   If $x \in \mathscr{P}$ and $n \in \mathbf{N}$, then $nx \in \mathscr{P}$. (*Note:* If F is any field, if $x \in F$, and $n \in \mathbf{N}$, we define the quantity nx recursively by the rules $1 \cdot x = x$ and $nx = (n-1)x + x$ if $n > 1$.)

2. Suppose $(F, \mathscr{P})$ is an ordered field. Prove:

(a) $x < x$ is false for any $x \in F$ ($<$ is irreflexive)
(b) $x < y$ if and only if $y - x > 0$
(c)   Given any $x, y \in F$, precisely one of the three possibilities $x < y, x = y,$ or $x > y$ is true.

3. Suppose $(F, \mathscr{P})$ is an ordered field.

(a)   Prove that if $x, y, z \in F$ with $x \leq y$ and $y \leq z$, then $x \leq z$ [recall Theorem 3(a)].
(b)   Prove that if $a, x, y \in F$, then:
  (i) $x < y$ implies $a + x < a + y$ (ii) $x < y$ and $a > 0$ imply $ax < ay$
  (iii) $x \leq y$ implies $a + x \leq a + y$ (iv) $x \leq y$ and $a \geq 0$ imply $ax \leq ay$
  ★(v) $x \leq y$ and $a \leq 0$ imply $ax \geq ay$
(c)   Prove that if $a, b, x, y \in F$, then:
  (i) $a \leq x$ and $b < y$ imply $a + b < x + y$
  (ii) $a \leq x$ and $b \leq y$ imply $a + b \leq x + y$
  (iii) $0 \leq a < x$ and $0 \leq b < y$ imply $ab < xy$
  (iv) $0 \leq a \leq x$ and $0 \leq b < y$ imply $ab < xy$
  (v) $0 \leq a \leq x$ and $0 \leq b \leq y$ imply $ab \leq xy$

4. Let $(F, \mathscr{P})$ be an ordered field.

(a)   (i)   Prove that the product of two negative elements is positive.
       (ii)   Prove that the product of a positive and a negative element is negative.
       (iii)   Verify the remaining cases of the proof of Theorem 5.

(b) ★(i)   Prove that if $a, b \in F$ with $a \geq 0$ and $b \geq 0$, then $a < b$ if and only if $a^2 < b^2$.

(ii)   Prove that if $a, b \in F$ with $a \geq 0$ and $b \geq 0$, then $a \leq b$ if and only if $a^2 \leq b^2$.

5. (a)   Let F be an ordered field with $x \in F$. Prove:

(i) $|-x| = |x|$ ★(ii) $|x|^2 = x^2$

(iii) $-|x| \leq x \leq |x|$

(b)   Suppose F is an ordered field with $x, a \in F$.

(i)   Prove that if $a \geq 0$, then $|x| \leq a$ if and only if $-a \leq x \leq a$.

(ii)   Prove that if $a \geq 0$, $x \leq a$, and $-x \leq a$, then $|x| \leq a$.

6. (a)   Suppose F is an ordered field with $x, y \in F$:

(i)   Prove that $||x| - |y|| \leq |x - y|$ [*Hint:* Use (d) of Theorem 5 and (ii) of part (b) of Exercise 5.]

(ii)   Prove that if $y \neq 0$, then $|1/y| = 1/|y|$.

★(iii)   Prove that if $y \neq 0$, then $|x/y| = |x|/|y|$.

(iv)   Prove that $|x - y| \leq |x| + |y|$.

(b)   Suppose F is an ordered field, $n \in \mathbf{N}$, and $x_1, x_2, \ldots, x_n \in F$. Prove that $|x_1 + x_2 + \cdots + x_n| \leq |x_1| + |x_2| + \cdots + |x_n|$.

7. (a)   Prove Theorem 6.

(b)   Prove that if F is an ordered field with $x, y, z \in F$, then $d(x, y) = d(x - z, y - z)$.

8. (a)   Prove that if F is an ordered field, if $x, y \in F$ with $x < y$, then $\frac{1}{2}(x + y) \in F$ and $x < \frac{1}{2}(x + y) < y$.

(b)   Conclude from (a) that an ordered field must contain an infinite number of elements.

9.3   Completeness in an Ordered Field

Thus far, we have isolated **R** from **N**, **Z**, and **C** by means of abstract properties. It remains only for us to find a property by which the ordered fields **R** and **Q** can be distinguished from each other. Now any ordered field is infinite and has the property that between any two distinct elements there is a third element (recall Exercise 8, Article 9.2); indeed, it is a familiar fact that **R** and **Q** both have these properties. Thus rational numbers, like real numbers, occur arbitrarily close to one another. Yet, the key to the difference between the two fields is discovered by looking at them on a microscopic level. In particular, a difference between **R** and **Q** begins to surface when we consider an element of **R** − **Q** such as π. The infinite sequence 3.1, 3.14, 3.141, 3.1415, 3.14159, . . . , consisting of successive decimal approximations to π, has two properties of immediate interest: (1) Each member is strictly less than π. (2) For any positive integer n, the nth number in this sequence differs from π by less than 10^{-n}, so that any real number less than π, no matter how close to π, is less than some number in the sequence. Stated differently, π is the smallest real number greater than each number in the sequence.

Because of these two properties (to be formalized later in Definitions 1 and 3), we say that the real number π is the *least upper bound* in **R** of the given infinite set of real numbers. Note, however, a third significant property of the given sequence; each of its members is not only real, but rational as well. Now suppose we try to find a *rational* number that is the "least upper bound in **Q**" of this infinite set of rational numbers. Your intuition may suggest that no such rational number exists; indeed, none does (see Example 3, for a rigorous treatment of a similar example).

The preceding example is at the heart of the theoretical difference between **R** and **Q**. Let us begin now to take a more systematic approach.

DEFINITION 1

Let F be an ordered field. A subset S of F is said to be **bounded above in F** if and only if there exists an element $u \in F$ such that $x \le u$ for all $x \in S$. Any such field element u is called an **upper bound of S in F**.

In the ordered field **R** the interval $(0, 1)$ is bounded above by 1, as well as by any real number larger than 1. The same is true of the interval $[0, 1]$. In the ordered field **Q** the subset $S = \{x \in \mathbf{Q} \,|\, x^2 \le 3\}$ is bounded above by rational numbers such as 1.8, 1.74, and 1.733. The real number $\sqrt{3}$ is not an upper bound of S in **Q**, because $\sqrt{3} \notin \mathbf{Q}$. Clearly $\sqrt{3}$ is an upper bound in **R** for the subset $I = \{x \in \mathbf{R} \,|\, x^2 \le 3\}$ of **R**.

The concepts *bounded below* and *bounded* in an ordered field are defined in a manner analogous to Definition 1. Specifically, we have Definition 2.

DEFINITION 2

A subset S of an ordered field F is said to be **bounded below in F** if and only if there exists an element $l \in F$ such that $l \le x$ for all $x \in S$. Any such field element l is called a **lower bound of S in F**. S is said to be **bounded in F** if and only if there exists $b \in F$ such that $|x| \le b$ for all $x \in S$.

It is easy to show that a subset of an ordered field F is bounded in F if and only if it is bounded both above and below in F (see Exercise 2). The subset $(-5, \infty)$ of **R** is bounded below but not above in **R**, whereas $(-6, 17]$ is a bounded subset of the ordered field **R**.

There is, as you may have noticed, a similarity between Definition 1, above, and Definition 2 of Article 7.4. The relationship is that every ordered field is a partially ordered set, and indeed, a totally ordered set (recall Theorem 3, Article 9.2), so that the theory developed in Article 7.4 applies to ordered fields. The following definition is analogous to, and consistent with, Definition 3, Article 7.4. It is, however, designed to take more direct advantage of the additional knowledge we gain about a totally ordered set from the fact that it is also an ordered field.

DEFINITION 3

Let F be an ordered field and $S \subseteq F$. An element u of F is said to be a **least upper bound for S in F**, denoted $u = \text{lub}_F\, S$ (or most often $u = \text{lub}\, S$ when there is no possibility of confusion about the underlying ordered field) if and only if:

(a) $x \le u$ for all $x \in S$
(b)   For all $\varepsilon > 0$ (ε an element of F), there exists $x \in S$ such that $x > u - \varepsilon$

Condition (a) asserts that u is an upper bound of S in F, whereas (b) states that no element of F smaller than u is an upper bound of S. The concept of *greatest lower bound*, denoted $\text{glb}_F\, S$ or simply $\text{glb}\, S$, is defined in a similar manner. You are asked to write out this definition in Exercise 3(a). Also, it is easy to show that lub's and glb's, as defined in the context of an ordered field, are unique whenever they exist [see Exercise 3(b)], so that we may correctly refer to the lub and the glb of S (also known, incidentally, as sup S and inf S, respectively).

EXAMPLE 1   Use the definitions of lub and glb to show that the subset $S = \{n + (-1)^n/n \,|\, n \in \mathbf{N}\}$ of the ordered field $\mathbf{R}$ is not bounded above in $\mathbf{R}$, but is bounded below with $0 = \text{glb}\, S$.

Solution   For each positive integer n, we have $n - 1 \le n + (-1)^n/n$. Since the set $\{n - 1 \,|\, n \in \mathbf{N}\}$ is clearly not bounded above, we conclude the same for S, by Exercise 4(a). Also, 0 is clearly a lower bound for S, since $n + (-1)^n/n$ equals zero when $n = 1$ and is clearly greater than 1 if $n \ge 2$. Finally, 0 is the greatest lower bound of S, because for any $\varepsilon > 0$, there exists $x \in S$ such that $x < 0 + \varepsilon$, namely, take x equal to 0. □

EXAMPLE 2   Prove that $(-\infty, 2]$ has least upper bound in $\mathbf{R}$ equal to 2.

Solution   By definition, $S = (-\infty, 2] = \{x \in \mathbf{R} \,|\, x \le 2\}$. Since $x \le 2$ for all $x \in S$, then 2 is an upper bound for S. To show that 2 is the least upper bound of S, let $\varepsilon > 0$ be given. Then $x = 2 - (\varepsilon/2)$ is clearly an element of S, and furthermore, $x = 2 - (\varepsilon/2) > 2 - \varepsilon$. □

It is clear that, in an ordered field, any subset having a least upper bound in the field is bounded above in that field. Thus the set S in Example 1 has no least upper bound in $F = \mathbf{R}$. But what about the converse? That is, suppose we know that a nonempty subset S of an ordered field F is bounded above in F. Can we conclude that S has a least upper bound in F? In Example 2 that conclusion was warranted. Consider, however, the following example.

EXAMPLE 3   Show that the subset $S = \{x \in \mathbf{Q} \,|\, x^2 < 3\}$ of the ordered field $\mathbf{Q}$ has no least upper bound in $\mathbf{Q}$.

Solution   Suppose there is a rational number u such that $u = \mathrm{lub}_\mathbf{Q}\, S$. If u exists, then either $u^2 < 3$, $u^2 > 3$, or $u^2 = 3$. Now if $u^2 < 3$, the rational number $x = u + [(3 - u^2)/7]$ is clearly greater than u and [it can be proved—see Exercise 7(a)] satisfies $x^2 < 3$; thus $x \in S$. The facts $x \in S$ and $x > u$ contradict the assumption that u is an upper bound of S. Hence $u^2 < 3$ must be false. On the other hand, if $u^2 > 3$, we can prove that the rational number $y = (u^2 + 3)/2u$ is less than u and is an upper bound for S in $\mathbf{Q}$ [see Exercise 7(b)—prove this by showing $y^2 > 3$]. This contradicts the assumption that u is a <u>least</u> upper bound for S. Since it is false that either $u^2 < 3$ or $u^2 > 3$, we must conclude $u^2 = 3$. But it can be proved, in a manner analogous to the proof in Example 9, Article 6.2, that no rational number satisfies this equation. Our conclusion is that S, although nonempty and bounded above in $\mathbf{Q}$, has no least upper bound in $\mathbf{Q}$.   □

With the result of Example 3, we are on the verge of a precise formulation of the theoretical difference between $\mathbf{Q}$ and $\mathbf{R}$.

DEFINITION   4

An ordered field F is said to be **complete** if and only if every nonempty subset of F that is bounded above in F has a least upper bound in F. Otherwise F is said to be **incomplete**.

By its definition, the ordered field $\mathbf{R}$ is complete. By Example 3, $\mathbf{Q}$ is an incomplete ordered field.

Let us review once again the criteria by which we are now able to differentiate in an abstract way among the familiar structures $\mathbf{N}$, $\mathbf{Z}$, $\mathbf{Q}$, $\mathbf{R}$, and $\mathbf{C}$, where each is equipped with the operations of addition and multiplication. As we've repeatedly stressed, $(\mathbf{R}, +, \cdot)$ is, by definition, a complete ordered field (we now know what this means). At this point we <u>assume</u> that a complete ordered field exists (we pursue this matter further in Article 10.3) and remind you that at most one complete ordered field <u>can</u> exist. The structure $(\mathbf{Q}, +, \cdot)$ of rationals is an ordered field, but it is incomplete. The complex numbers $(\mathbf{C}, +, \cdot)$ constitute a field (see Article 9.4), but a field that cannot be ordered. The integers $(\mathbf{Z}, +, \cdot)$ and positive integers $(\mathbf{N}, +, \cdot)$ each violates one or more of the field axioms; that is, each fails to be a field.

SOME CONSEQUENCES OF THE COMPLETENESS PROPERTY OF R

A number of important theorems about the real numbers and about functions of a real variable depend on the completeness property of $\mathbf{R}$ for their validity. Such results are generally stated and used, but not proved, in elementary and intermediate calculus courses. The purpose of the material that follows is to expose you to the theoretical foundation of several familiar properties.

DEFINITION 5

An ordered field F is said to be **Archimedean ordered** if and only if for all $a \in F$ and $b > 0$, there exists a positive integer n such that $nb > a$.

In other words, if an ordered field is Archimedean ordered, then regardless of how small b is and how large a is, a sufficient number of repeated additions b to itself will exceed a. See Article 10.3, Example 1 for an example of a non-Archimedean ordered field.

THEOREM 1

A complete ordered field F is necessarily Archimedean ordered.

Proof   Let $a \in F$ and $b > 0$ be given. Proceeding indirectly, suppose that $nb \leq a$ for all positive integers n, and consider the subset $S = \{nb \mid n \in \mathbf{N}\}$ of F. Clearly S is nonempty, since $b \in S$, and S is bounded above, by a. Hence, by the completeness property, S has a least upper bound in F, call it u. Now $u - b$ is less than u, so $u - b$ is not an upper bound of S. Hence there is a positive integer n' such that $u - b < n'b$. Thus $(n' + 1) b > u$. Since $n' + 1 \in \mathbf{N}$, this contradicts the fact that u is an upper bound of S. Hence our initial assumption $nb \leq a$ for all $n \in \mathbf{N}$ must be incorrect; we are forced to accept the statement $nb > a$ for some $n \in \mathbf{N}$, the desired conclusion. $\square$

COROLLARY 1

The real number field is Archimedean ordered.

For those who are familiar with the notion of a convergent sequence of real numbers, note the following fact.

COROLLARY 2

The sequence $\{1/n \mid n = 1, 2, 3, \ldots\}$ converges to zero in **R**.

Proof   Let $\varepsilon > 0$ be given. We must show that there exists $n \in \mathbf{N}$ such that $1/n < \varepsilon$, that is, $1 < n\varepsilon$. Since **R** is Archimedean ordered, by Theorem 1, we may let $a = 1$ and $b = \varepsilon$ in Definition 5 to obtain the desired conclusion. $\square$

Thus we have a rigorous derivation of the fact that the familiar and important sequence $\{1/n\}$ tends to zero in **R**. When the topic of infinite sequences is covered in second or third semester calculus, this fact is generally taken for granted and then used as the basis for deriving convergence properties of a large number of other sequences. Thus Corollary 2 fills a significant gap in the calculus experience of most students.

The result of Corollary 2 can also be used to derive another familiar fact about **R**, namely between any two reals, there is a rational number. This property, which intuitively may seem inconsistent with our discovery, in Article 8.3, that **Q** has "fewer" elements than **R**, is often described by the statement "**Q** is dense in **R**." Its proof follows easily from Corollary 2 if we are willing to assume that any real number falls between two consecutive integers. We assume the latter property for now, justifying it rigorously in Chapter 10, where we study both the integers and the real numbers in greater detail.

T H E O R E M   2

If a and b are real numbers with $a < b$, then there exists a rational number q such that $a < q < b$.

Proof   Given $a, b \in \mathbf{R}$ with $a < b$, note that $b - a > 0$ so that, by Corollary 2, there exists a positive integer n such that $1/n < b - a$. By the assumed property of integers, there must exist an integer m such that $m - 1 \le an < m$, so that $(m - 1)/n \le a < m/n$. Hence we have that the rational number m/n is greater than a. Furthermore, since $(m - 1)/n \le a$, we have $m/n \le a + 1/n$. But $a + 1/n < b$ so we conclude $m/n < b$. Letting $q = m/n$, we note that q is rational and $a < q < b$, as desired. $\square$

THE INTERMEDIATE VALUE THEOREM

The following theorem is familiar to every student of elementary calculus.

T H E O R E M   3 (Intermediate Value Theorem)

If f is continuous on the closed and bounded interval $[a, b]$, with $f(a) < f(b)$ (so that $a \ne b$), and if y_0 is any real number with $f(a) < y_0 < f(b)$, then there exists $x_0 \in (a, b)$ such that $f(x_0) = y_0$.

This theorem states that the graph of a function continuous on a closed and bounded interval $[a, b]$ must pass through every horizontal line $y = y_0$, where $f(a) < y_0 < f(b)$, as opposed to possibly "jumping over" any such line. Perhaps more than any other property of continuity, and surely more than the formal definition, this result corresponds to our intuitive understanding of a continuous function as one whose graph has no "breaks" and no "missing points," as shown in Figure 9.3. (You may also want to review

Figure 9.3   *Graphic view of the intermediate value theorem. Since g is continuous on $[a, b]$, and $g(a) < y_0 < g(b)$, the line $y = y_0$ must intersect the graph of g.*

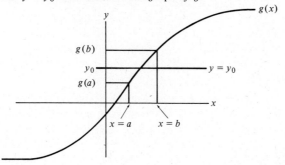

parts of Article 4.3 at this stage.) Furthermore, this theorem is the basis of important properties of the real number system, such as the existence of a real nth root of any positive real number a, where $n \in \mathbf{N}$ (see Exercise 9). The proof of the intermediate value theorem, however, may not be familiar to you. As we will soon see, the "IVT" is a consequence of the completeness of $\mathbf{R}$. In preparation for the proof, we state and prove the following lemma.

LEMMA

Suppose the function $y = f(x)$ is continuous on an interval I containing the real number x_0, and that c and d are real numbers such that $c < f(x_0) < d$. Then there exists a positive real number δ such that $c < f(x) < d$ for all $x \in (x_0 - \delta, x_0 + \delta) \cap I$.

Proof   [Recall Exercise 16(b), Article 6.1.] The proof uses the technique of specialization as well as the definition of continuity at a point. We separate the proof into two cases, according as x_0 either is or is not an endpoint of the interval I. Applying the definition of continuity at a point to the latter case, we have that, to any $\varepsilon > 0$, there corresponds $\delta > 0$ such that $f(x_0) - \varepsilon < f(x) < f(x_0) + \varepsilon$ when $x \in (x_0 - \delta, x_0 + \delta)$, where δ may be chosen so small that the interval $(x_0 - \delta, x_0 + \delta)$ is a subset of I. In particular, letting ε equal the smaller of $d - f(x_0)$ and $f(x_0) - c$, we may assert that a positive number δ exists such that $f(x_0) - (f(x_0) - c) < f(x_0) - \varepsilon < f(x) < f(x_0) + \varepsilon < f(x_0) + (d - f(x_0))$ for any x between $x_0 - \delta$ and $x_0 + \delta$. From this, we conclude that $c < f(x) < d$ whenever $x \in (x_0 - \delta, x_0 + \delta)$, as desired.

The cases in which x_0 is either a left- or right-hand endpoint of I are left to the reader in Exercise 10.   □

Proof of theorem   Define a subset S of $[a, b]$ by the rule $S = \{x \in [a, b] \mid f(x) < y_0\}$. Note that S is nonempty, since $a \in S$, and S is bounded above in $\mathbf{R}$, by b. Hence, by the completeness property of $\mathbf{R}$, S has a least upper bound in $\mathbf{R}$, call it x_0. Note that $x_0 \in [a, b]$ (Why?). We claim that $f(x_0) = y_0$; our approach is to prove that each of the other two possibilities $f(x_0) < y_0$ and $f(x_0) > y_0$ leads to a contradiction.

Now if $f(x_0) < y_0$, then necessarily $x_0 < b$ and we may conclude from the lemma that there exists $\delta > 0$ such that $x_0 + \delta < b$ and $f(x) < y_0$ for any $x \in [x_0, x_0 + \delta)$. In particular, there exists $x' \in (x_0, b]$ such that $f(x') < y_0$. Since $x' \in S$ (Why?) and $x' > x_0$, we have a contradiction of the fact that x_0 is an upper bound of S.

On the other hand, if $f(x_0) > y_0$, then x_0 cannot equal a and, again using the lemma, we note that a positive δ exists with $a < x_0 - \delta$ such that $f(x) > y_0$ for any $x \in (x_0 - \delta, x_0]$. In particular, there is no element of S greater than $x_0 - \delta$, a violation of condition (b) of Definition 3 and thus a contradiction of the fact that x_0 is the least upper bound of S.

Hence $f(x_0) = y_0$, as desired. Since $f(a) < y_0 < f(b)$, we have $x_0 \neq a$ and $x_0 \neq b$, so that $x_0 \in (a, b)$, as claimed.   □

The abstract definition of "interval" given earlier in the text (Definition 3, Article 1.1) makes possible a brief and rather nice proof that the image of an interval under a continuous function is again an interval. This consequence of the intermediate value theorem also provides us with a fairly typical example of the use of the concept of image, introduced in Article 8.2, in formulating a theorem.

COROLLARY
Suppose the function $y = f(x)$ is continuous on an interval I. Then $f(I)$ is an interval.

Proof If f is constant on I, then $f(I)$ is a singleton set, which is an interval. So assume f is not constant on I, and let $y_1, y_2 \in f(I)$ with $y_1 < y_2$. Let y_0 be given such that $y_1 < y_0 < y_2$; we must prove $y_0 \in f(I)$; that is, $y_0 = f(x_0)$ for some $x_0 \in I$. Now since $y_1, y_2 \in f(I)$, there must exist $x_1, x_2 \in I$ such that $y_1 = f(x_1)$ and $y_2 = f(x_2)$. Since $f(x_1) < y_0 < f(x_2)$ and f is continuous on the closed interval determined by x_1 and x_2, there must exist, by the intermediate value theorem, x_0 strictly between x_1 and x_2 such that $y_0 = f(x_0)$. Since $x_1, x_2 \in I$, since x_0 is between x_1 and x_2, and since I is an interval, we have $x_0 \in I$, as required. □

We indicated, just prior to Definition 4 of Article 1.1, that the intervals on the real line are precisely the subsets of **R** having one of nine possible forms (e.g., $[a, b], (-\infty, b)$, etc.). In Exercise 3(a), Article 5.2 you were asked to prove that any set having one of these forms satisfies the definition of interval. We propose now to prove the converse; that is, any subset of **R** satisfying the definition of interval must have one of these forms.

THEOREM 4
If a subset I of **R** is an interval, then I has one of the nine forms listed in Definition 3, Article 1.1; that is, I has one of the nine forms $[a, b], (a, b), [a, b)$, $(a, b], (-\infty, b), (-\infty, b], (a, \infty), [a, \infty)$, or $(-\infty, \infty)$.

Proof Assume $I \subseteq \mathbf{R}$ and I is an interval. Consider the four possibilities, I is bounded, I is bounded above only, I is bounded below only, and I is bounded neither above nor below. Clearly one and only one of these four possibilities is true for I. Suppose, for instance, that I is bounded above, but not below. By the completeness of **R**, we may let $b = \text{lub } I$ and take note of the fact that, necessarily, either $b \in I$ or $b \notin I$. Our claim is that $I = (-\infty, b]$ in the first case and $I = (-\infty, b)$ in the second. Suppose first that $b \in I$. To show that $I = (-\infty, b]$, we use a mutual inclusion approach and start by letting $x \in I$. Since b is an upper bound for I, then $x \le b$ so that $x \in (-\infty, b]$. Thus $I \subseteq (-\infty, b]$. Conversely, suppose $x \in (-\infty, b]$. If $x = b$, then $x \in I$ since we've assumed $b \in I$. If $x < b$, then since $b = \text{lub } I$, we may invoke condition (b) of the definition of least upper bound to produce $c \in I$ such that $x < c < b$.

Also, since I is not bounded below, there exists $d \in I$ such that $d < x$. Hence $d < x < c$, $d \in I$, and $c \in I$. Since I is an interval, we have $x \in I$, so that $(-\infty, b] \subseteq I$, and $(-\infty, b] = I$, as desired.

In Exercise 8 you should handle the subcase $b \notin I$, as well as the remaining three cases described at the start of the proof. $\square$

The preceding material should suffice to convince you of the importance of the completeness property of **R** and especially of its relevance to material encountered in previous calculus courses. The least upper bound property has additional important applications to calculus, the most familiar one probably being the so-called *extreme value theorem*: A function continuous on a closed and bounded interval attains an absolute maximum and minimum value on that interval. This result is the basis for part of the approach to applied "max-min" problems taught in most first-semester calculus courses. Its proof is based on a very technical property of **R** known as the Heine-Borel theorem. The latter, in turn, follows, in a nontrivial fashion, from the completeness property of **R**. The details, including the proof, of the Heine-Borel theorem and its consequences are a standard part of a course in advanced calculus; we omit them from this text.

Exercises

1. Use the definitions of lub and glb in the ordered field **R** to prove:

(a) $b = \text{lub } [a, b]$, where $a, b \in \mathbf{R}$, $a < b$
(b) $a = \text{glb } (a, \infty)$, where $a \in \mathbf{R}$
(c) $1 = \text{lub } \{1/n \mid n \in \mathbf{N}\}$; $0 = \text{glb } \{1/n \mid n \in \mathbf{N}\}$
(d) $1 = \text{glb } \mathbf{N}$
★(e) $3 = \text{glb } ((3, 4) \cup \{6\})$; $6 = \text{lub } ((3, 4) \cup \{6\})$

2. Prove that a subset S of an ordered field F is bounded in F if and only if it is bounded both above and below in F.

3. (a) Formulate a definition of $l = \text{glb}_F\, S$, analogous to Definition 3.
(b) Prove that a least upper bound of a subset of an ordered field F, if it exists, is unique.

4. (a) Suppose that a subset S of an ordered field F is not bounded above in F. Let T be a subset of F satisfying the property that, for each $x \in S$, there exists $y \in T$ such that $x \le y$. Prove that T is not bounded above in F.
(b) Suppose S and T are subsets of a complete ordered field F, both bounded above in F, satisfying the property that for all $x \in S$, there exists $y \in T$ such that $x \le y$. Prove $\text{lub } S \le \text{lub } T$.
★(c) Suppose S and T are subsets of a complete ordered field F, both bounded above in F, such that $S \subseteq T$. Prove that $\text{lub } S \le \text{lub } T$.

5. Let S be a subset of an ordered field F such that $u = \text{lub } S$.

(a) Prove that $-u = \text{glb } T$, where $T = \{-x,\ \ x \in S\}$.
(b) Prove that if $v \in F$ and v is an upper bound for S, then $u \le v$.

*6. Prove that, in a complete ordered field F, any nonempty subset S of F that is bounded below in F has a greatest lower bound in F.

7. Complete the solution to Example 3 by proving:

(a) If u is a real number such that $u^2 < 3$, then $(u + [(3 - u^2)/7])^2 < 3$.
(b) If u is a real number with $u^2 > 3$, then:
   (i) $(u^2 + 3)/2u < u$, and
   (ii) $[(u^2 + 3)/2u]^2 > 3$. Conclude that $(u^2 + 3)/2u$ is an upper bound in **Q** for the set S of Example 3.

8. Suppose a subset I of **R** is an interval. Prove:

(a) If I is bounded above, but not below, and if $b = \text{lub } I \notin I$, then $I = (-\infty, b)$.
(b) If I is bounded, then I has one of the forms (a, b), $[a, b)$, $(a, b]$, or $[a, b]$, for some $a, b \in \mathbf{R}$.
(c) If I is bounded below, but not above, then I has one of the forms $[a, \infty)$ or (a, ∞).
(d) If I is bounded neither above nor below, then $I = (-\infty, \infty)$.

9. Use the intermediate value theorem to prove that if y is a positive real number and $n \in \mathbf{N}$, then there exists a positive real number x such that $x^n = y$.

10. Verify the lemma following the statement of Theorem 3 for the cases:

(a) x_0 is the left endpoint of the interval I. [*Note:* The continuity of f on an interval having x_0 as its left endpoint means that the limit, as x approaches x_0 from the right, of $f(x)$, equals $f(x_0)$. In other words, to any $\varepsilon > 0$, there corresponds $\delta > 0$ such that $f(x_0) - \varepsilon < f(x) < f(x_0) + \varepsilon$ whenever $x \in [x_0, x_0 + \delta)$].
(b) x_0 is the right endpoint of the interval I.

9.4   Properties of the Complex Number Field

We conclude this chapter with a brief introduction to properties of the field **C** of complex numbers. This important mathematical structure is often cited as an example of an "invented number system." Such a description is historically accurate. We can trace the origin of complex numbers to distinguished "inventors," the German mathematician Karl Gauss (1777–1855) and the Irish mathematician and physicist William Hamilton (1805–1865). It is accurate in another sense as well, if we interpret the word "invented" to carry a meaning such as "contrived" or "concocted," as opposed to "occurring naturally." One way to view the complex numbers is as a product of the resourcefulness of man, a creation designed to solve a problem that, in the traditional context, has no solution. The problem we refer to is the quadratic equation $x^2 + 1 = 0$, and the "traditional context" is the real number system. As you undoubtedly know, the complex numbers $\pm i$ are solutions to this equation, whereas no real number satisfies it. Indeed, complex numbers enable us to solve easily any quadratic equation with real coefficients, and, in fact, enable us, in principle, to find a solution to any polynomial equation with complex coefficients (see Theorem 7).

We interject at this point only one discordant note into the rather "tidy" view, just presented, of the complex numbers as "cooked up," in contrast to the "more natural" real numbers. We will see in Chapter 10 that the various numbers systems studied throughout this chapter, including **Z**, **Q**, and **R**, can all be regarded as invented, in exactly the same mathematical sense as described earlier in reference to **C**. Once this fact is accepted, it becomes possible to regard complex numbers to be just as "real" as numbers in the system we designate by that name.

BASIC DEFINITIONS AND PROPERTIES

DEFINITION 1

The **complex number system** (**C**, $+$, $\cdot$) consists of a set **C**, comprising all ordered pairs of real numbers (x, y), together with two operations, $+$ and $\cdot$, where we specify:

(a) Two complex numbers (x_1, y_1), and (x_2, y_2) are **equal** if and only if $x_1 = x_2$ and $y_1 = y_2$.

(b) The **sum** of two complex numbers (x_1, y_1) and (x_2, y_2) is the complex number $(x_1 + x_2, y_1 + y_2)$.

(c) The **product** of two complex numbers (x_1, y_1) and (x_2, y_2) is the complex number $(x_1 x_2 - y_1 y_2, x_1 y_2 + y_1 x_2)$.

Complex numbers are most often denoted by the letters z and w, with subscripts as necessary. Furthermore, the notation $x + yi$ is customarily used in place of the ordered pair notation (x, y). Thus $-2 + 3i$ corresponds to $(-2, 3)$, $5 = 5 + 0i$ corresponds to $(5, 0)$, and $i = 0 + 1i$ corresponds to $(0, 1)$. According to (c) of Definition 1, the product of $(0, 1)$ with $(0, 1)$ equals $((0)(0) - (1)(1), (0)(1) + (1)(0)) = (-1, 0)$. In the alternative notation this translates to the equation $i^2 = -1$. This rule, in turn, can be used along with ordinary high school algebra to provide a practical method of multiplying complex numbers.

EXAMPLE 1   Calculate the product $z_1 z_2$, where $z_1 = 3 - 7i$ and $z_2 = -4 + 6i$.

Solution   The product $z_1 z_2 = (3 - 7i)(-4 + 6i)$ equals $(3)(-4) + (-7)(i)(6)(i) + (-7)(i)(-4) + (3)(6)(i) = (-12) + (-42i^2) + (28i) + (18i) = (-12 + 42) + (28 + 18)i = 30 + 46i$. $\square$

The equation $i^2 = -1$ can be rephrased $i = \sqrt{-1}$. We can calculate easily, using the methods of Example 1, that $(ri)^2 = r^2 i^2 = -r^2$ so that we have the equation $ri = \sqrt{-r^2}$ for any real number r. This equation provides us with the interpretation "complex roots" (no doubt familiar to you) of a negative value of the quadratic discriminant $b^2 - 4ac$, in applying the quadratic formula. The following example illustrates this.

EXAMPLE 2   Use the quadratic formula to find the solution(s) to the equation $5x^2 + 2x + 1 = 0$.

Solution   The quadratic formula yields roots $(\frac{1}{10})[-2 \pm \sqrt{(2^2) - (4)(5)(1)}]$, which simplifies to $(-\frac{1}{5}) \pm (\frac{1}{10})\sqrt{-16}$, which equals $(-\frac{1}{5}) \pm (\frac{2}{5})i$.   □

Recall that equation $i^2 = -1$ was our basis, in Article 9.2, for concluding that the complex number field cannot be ordered. In the next definition we resume our introduction of notation associated with **C**.

DEFINITION   2

Let $z = x + yi$ be a complex number. We call the real number x **the real part** of z, denoted Re(z), while the real number y is called **the imaginary part** of z, denoted Im (z).

Note that any complex number z can be expressed $z = \text{Re}(z) + \text{Im}(z)i$. Notice also that both the real and imaginary parts of a complex number z are real numbers. We can reexpress (a) and (b) of Definition 1 easily in terms of real and imaginary parts. For (a), two complex numbers are equal if and only if their respective real and imaginary parts are equal. For (b), the sum of two complex numbers is the complex number whose real (resp., imaginary) part is the sum of the real (resp., imaginary) parts of the given numbers. A complex number z such that Re $(z) = 0$ is said to be *purely imaginary* (or just *imaginary*). If Im $(z) = 0$, we say that the complex number z is real. It is left for you to verify (Exercise 6) that if the complex numbers z_1 and z_2 are real with real parts x_1 and x_2 respectively, then the sum and product of z_1 and z_2 in **C** equal the sum and product, respectively, of x_1 and x_2 in **R**. Thus complex numbers that are real, in the sense just defined, behave algebraically just like real numbers, so that we may regard **R** and the subset $\{z \in \mathbf{C} \mid \text{Im}(z) = 0\}$ of **C** as, for all intents and purposes, identical. It is in this precise sense that **R** may be thought of as a subset of **C**.

We now state the property of the complex number system that provides its closest link to the number systems **R** and **Q**.

THEOREM   1

The complex number system (**C**, $+, \cdot$) is a field.

Outline of proof   Verification of field axioms 1 through 3, 6 through 8, and 11 are left to you in Exercise 7(a). For Axioms 4 and 9, we note that the complex numbers $0 = 0 + 0i$ and $1 = 1 + 0i$ serve as additive and multiplicative identities, respectively. For example, if $z = x + yi \in \mathbf{C}$, then $z \cdot 1 = (x + yi)(1 + 0i) = ((x)(1) - (y)(0)) + ((y)(1) + (x)(0))(i) = x + yi = z$, as required. You may complete the formal verification of Axiom 4, as well as show that $-z = -x - yi$ is the additive inverse of $z = x + yi$, that is, Axiom 5. For Axiom 10, we note that if $z = x + yi \neq 0$, then the complex number $(x - yi)/(x^2 + y^2)$ serves as the multiplicative inverse of z, and so may be denoted z^{-1}. The details of this as well are left to you.

□

Because **C** satisfies the multiplicative inverse axiom, it is possible to define division by a nonzero complex number, namely, if z_1 and $z_2 \in$ **C** with $z_2 \neq 0$, we define z_1/z_2 to be $z_1 z_2^{-1}$. For example, if $z_1 = 2 - 3i$ and $z_2 = 5 + i$, then $z_1/z_2 = (2 - 3i)/(5 + i) = (2 - 3i)[(5 - i)/26] = (7 - 17i)/26 = \frac{7}{26} - (\frac{17}{26})i$. As a further example, if $z_1 = 1$ and $z_2 = i$, then $z_1/z_2 = 1/i = (1)(i)^{-1} = (1)(-i/1) = -i$. Note that i has the unusual property that its multiplicative and additive inverses are identical. Verification of various properties involving division of complex numbers is part of Exercise 7(b).

COMPLEX CONJUGATE AND MODULUS

The formula $z^{-1} = (x - yi)/(x^2 + y^2)$, for the multiplicative inverse of a nonzero complex number $z = x + yi$, contains two important quantities related to z. If $z = x + yi$ is represented by one arrow in Figure 9.4(a), the quantity $x - yi$ is represented by the other. Note the symmetry with respect to the y (or imaginary) axis. The real number $(x^2 + y^2)$ represents the square of the common length of both arrows [see Theorem 2(f), and Figure 9.4(b)]. These two quantities, which may be calculated for any complex number z, are of sufficient importance to warrant formal designation.

DEFINITION   3

Let $z = x + yi$ be a complex number. We define:

(a) The **complex conjugate** of z, denoted $z*$, by the rule $z* = x - yi$
(b) The **modulus** of z, denoted $|z|$, by the rule $|z| = (x^2 + y^2)^{1/2}$

Figure 9.4   *Complex conjugate and modulus of a complex number z.*

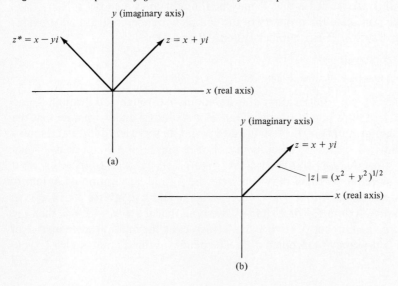

(a)

(b)

An immediate consequence of Definition 3 and the formula $(x + yi)^{-1} = (x - yi)/(x^2 + y^2)$ is the equation $z^{-1} = z^*/|z|^2$, for any nonzero complex number z. Since this implies $zz^*/|z|^2 = 1$, we have also $zz^* = |z|^2$ for any complex number z, so that, in particular, the product zz^* (a product of two complex numbers) is always a nonnegative <u>real</u> number. This fact is the basis of a familiar algebraic technique, illustrated in the following example.

EXAMPLE 3   Express $1/(6 + 8i)$ in the form $x + yi$.

Solution   The technique is multiplication by the complex conjugate of the denominator divided by itself. Specifically, we have that $1/(6 + 8i) = [1/(6 + 8i)][(6 - 8i)/(6 - 8i)] = (6 - 8i)/(36 + 64) = (3/50) - (2/25)i$. What are we actually doing when we apply this technique? The original problem could be rephrased, "find z^{-1}, where $z = 6 + 8i$." By the formulas developed following Definition 3, $z^{-1} = z^*/|z|^2 = z^*/zz^*$, a formula corresponding precisely to the algebraic technique.   □

We are now ready to state formally several properties involving Re (z), Im (z), z^*, and $|z|$.

THEOREM 2
Let z be a complex number. Then:

(a) $z + z^* = 2$ Re (z), so that Re $(z) = (\frac{1}{2})(z + z^*)$
(b) $z - z^* = 2i$ Im (z), so that Im $(z) = (i/2)(z^* - z)$
(c) $zz^* = |z|^2$
(d) $|z| \geq 0$; $|z| = 0$ if and only if $z = 0$
(e) $z^{**} = z$
(f) $|z^*| = |z|$
(g) $z = z^*$ if and only if z is real
(h) $-z = z^*$ if and only if z is imaginary
(i) Im $(iz) =$ Re (z)
(j) Re $(iz) = -$Im (z)

Partial proof   (a)   Let $z = x + yi$. Then $z + z^* = (x + yi) + (x - yi) = 2x = 2$ Re (z). The conclusion Re $(z) = (\frac{1}{2})(z + z^*)$ follows immediately.
(h)   Assume $z^* = -z$, where $z = x + yi$. This means that $x - yi = -x - yi$, so that $2x = 0$ and hence $x = 0$, thus proving that z is purely imaginary. The converse is left to you.
(i)   If $z = x + yi$, then $iz = xi + yi^2 = -y + xi$. Hence Im $(iz) = x =$ Re (z).
The remaining portions of the theorem are left as exercises (see Exercise 8).   □

THEOREM 3
Let z_1 and z_2 be complex numbers. Then:

(a) Re $(z_1 + z_2) =$ Re $(z_1) +$ Re (z_2)
(b) Im $(z_1 + z_2) =$ Im $(z_1) +$ Im (z_2)

(c) $(z_1 + z_2)^* = z_1^* + z_2^*$

(d) $(z_1 z_2)^* = z_1^* z_2^*$

(e) $(z_2^{-1})^* = (z_2^*)^{-1}$, if $z_2 \neq 0$

(f) $(z_1/z_2)^* = z_1^*/z_2^*$, if $z_2 \neq 0$

(g) $|z_1 z_2| = |z_1||z_2|$

(h) $|z_2^{-1}| = 1/|z_2|$, if $z_2 \neq 0$

(i) $|z_1/z_2| = |z_1|/|z_2|$, if $z_2 \neq 0$

(j) $|z_1 + z_2| \leq |z_1| + |z_2|$

Partial proof (e) If $z_2 = x + yi \neq 0$, then $z_2^{-1} = (x - yi)/(x^2 + y^2)$, so that $(z_2^{-1})^* = (x + yi)/(x^2 + y^2)$. On the other hand, $z_2^* = x - yi$, so that $(z_2^*)^{-1} = (x + yi)/(x^2 + y^2)$, as well. Hence we have $(z_2^{-1})^* = (x + yi)/(x^2 + y^2) = (z_2^*)^{-1}$, as desired.

(f) If $z_2 \neq 0$, then $(z_1/z_2)^* = (z_1 \cdot z_2^{-1})^* = $ [by (d)] $(z_1^*)(z_2^{-1})^* = $ [by (e)] $(z_1^*)(z_2^*)^{-1} = z_1^*/z_2^*$

(h) If $z_2 = x + yi \neq 0$, then $z_2^{-1} = (x - yi)/(x^2 + y^2)$, so that $|z_2^{-1}| = \{[x^2/(x^2 + y^2)^2] + [y^2/(x^2 + y^2)^2]\}^{1/2} = [(x^2 + y^2)/(x^2 + y^2)^2]^{1/2} = 1/(x^2 + y^2)^{1/2} = 1/|z_2|$.

The remaining portions of the proof are left to you in Exercise 9. □

POLAR FORM AND DEMOIVRE'S THEOREM

Let r and θ be polar coordinates of the ordered pair (x, y), where $x \neq 0$, $y \neq 0$, and $r > 0$. Then we may represent the complex number $x + yi$ in the form $r(\cos \theta + i \sin \theta)$. This representation is called a *polar form* of $x + yi$. Note that r is uniquely determined by x and y, and the stipulation that r be positive. Specifically, if $z = r(\cos \theta + i \sin \theta)$, then $|z| = (r^2 \cos^2 \theta + r^2 \sin^2 \theta)^{1/2} = [r^2(\cos^2 \theta + \sin^2 \theta)]^{1/2} = \sqrt{r^2} = r$; that is, r is simply the modulus of z. Unfortunately, the situation is not so simple for θ, as the following example indicates.

EXAMPLE 4 Describe all possible polar representations of $z = 2 + 2\sqrt{3}i$.

Solution Note first that $r = |z| = [(2)^2 + (2\sqrt{3})^2]^{1/2} = \sqrt{16} = 4$. Thus we may express z as $z = 4(\frac{1}{2} + i\sqrt{3}/2) = 4(\cos \pi/3 + i \sin \pi/3)$. Hence $r = 4$, $\theta = \pi/3$ provides one polar representation of z. The periodicity of cos and sin, both of period 2π, dictates that $r = 4$ and $\theta_k = \pi/3 + 2k\pi$, where k is any integer, provide infinitely many additional (and, in fact, all possible) polar representations of z. □

Given a nonzero complex number $z = x + yi$, any number θ such that $z = r \cos \theta + ir \sin \theta$ is called an *argument* of z, denoted arg z. Any nonzero complex number has infinitely many values of arg z. The unique value of arg z such that $-\pi < $ arg $z \leq \pi$ is called the *principal value* of arg z. Hence the principal value of arg z in Example 4 is $\pi/3$; some other values are $-5\pi/3$, $7\pi/3$, and $13\pi/3$.

The primary use of the polar form is in connection with multiplication of complex numbers. The reason this form is of value in complex multiplication is that we may calculate polar form of a product of two complex numbers, expressed in polar form, by adding the arguments (and multiplying the moduli). We approach this important fact and some of its consequences by using Definition 4.

DEFINITION 4

If z is any complex number $x + yi$, we define the **complex exponential** e^z by the rule $e^z = e^x(\cos y + i \sin y)$.

If z is purely imaginary, so that $x = 0$, e^z equals e^{iy} which has the value $\cos y + i \sin y$. Hence $e^{x+iy} = e^x(\cos y + i \sin y) = e^x e^{iy}$ for any $x, y \in \mathbf{R}$, a result consistent with a familiar property of the ordinary (real) exponential function. The complex-valued function $f(z) = e^z$ is an extension of the real exponential function, in that if the complex number z is real, then $e^z = e^x(\cos 0 + i \sin 0) = e^x$ (recall Exercise 13, Article 8.1). Other properties of the real exponential shared by e^z are listed in the next theorem.

THEOREM 4

The complex exponential e^z has these properties:

(a) If $z = 0$, then $e^z = 1$ (i.e., $e^0 = 1$)
(b) $e^{z+w} = e^z e^w$ for any $w, z \in \mathbf{C}$
(c) $(e^z)^n = e^{nz}$ for any $n \in \mathbf{N}$ and $z \in \mathbf{C}$
(d) $e^{-z} = 1/e^z$ for any $z \in \mathbf{C}$

The proof of Theorem 4, which should not be difficult, given the following result, is left as an exercise (Exercise 10).

LEMMA

If $x, y \in \mathbf{R}$, then $e^{i(x+y)} = e^{ix} e^{iy}$.

The special case e^{iy}, $y \in \mathbf{R}$, of the complex exponential, is the case of primary interest for our purposes, and this lemma focuses on its most important property. Note that any nonzero complex number can be expressed $z = re^{i\theta}$, where $r = |z| > 0$ and $|e^{i\theta}| = 1$.

Proof of lemma $e^{i(x+y)} = \cos(x+y) + i \sin(x+y) = (\cos x \cos y - \sin x \sin y) + i(\sin x \cos y + \cos x \sin y) = (\cos x + i \sin x)(\cos y + i \sin y) = e^{ix} e^{iy}$. $\square$

THEOREM 5

(a) If $z_1 = r_1 e^{i\theta_1}$ and $z_2 = r_2 e^{i\theta_2}$, then $z_1 z_2 = r_1 r_2 e^{i(\theta_1 + \theta_2)}$
(b) If $z = re^{i\theta}$ and $n \in \mathbf{N}$, then $z^n = r^n e^{in\theta}$

Proof   (a) $z_1 z_2 = (r_1 e^{i\theta_1})(r_2 e^{i\theta_2}) = r_1 r_2 e^{i\theta_1} e^{i\theta_2} = r_1 r_2 e^{i(\theta_1 + \theta_2)}$, where the last step follows from the lemma.

(b)   The proof proceeds by induction on n. The case $n = 1$ is evident. If the conclusion is true for m, then $z^{m+1} = z^m \cdot z = (r^m e^{im\theta})(re^{i\theta}) = r^{m+1}e^{i(m+1)\theta}$, as required. $\square$

The special case $r = 1$ of Theorem 5(b) is known as deMoivre's theorem. It has an important application; using it we can calculate the n complex nth roots of any given complex number.

THEOREM 6

If $z = re^{i\theta}$, then the n complex numbers $r^{1/n}e^{i[(\theta + 2k\pi)/n]}$, $k = 0, 1, \ldots, n - 1$, are the n distinct complex nth roots of z.

Proof   Let $w = r^{1/n}e^{i[(\theta + 2k\pi)/n]}$, for any $k = 0, 1, \ldots, n - 1$. Then $w^n = (r^{1/n})^n(e^{i[(\theta + 2k\pi)/n]})^n = re^{in[(\theta + 2k\pi)/n]} = re^{i(\theta + 2k\pi)} = re^{i\theta} = z$.   Hence   each such w is an nth root of z. The n values of w are clearly distinct, for if $e^{i[(\theta + 2k\pi)/n]} = e^{i[(\theta + 2h\pi)/n]}$, then $(\theta + 2k\pi)/n = (\theta + 2h\pi)/n + 2m\pi$, for some integer m. Hence $\theta + 2k\pi = \theta + 2h\pi + 2mn\pi$, so that $k - h = mn$. But $k - h$ cannot be an integral multiple of n since both are between 0 and $n - 1$, inclusive. Finally, all nth roots of z have this form. For if $w = se^{ix}$ satisfies $w^n = z = re^{i\theta}$, then $w^n = s^n e^{inx} = re^{i\theta}$. Hence $s = r^{1/n}$ and $e^{inx} = e^{i\theta}$ so that $nx = \theta + 2k\pi$ and $x = (\theta + 2k\pi)/n$. There are only n such roots because if $m \in \mathbf{N}$, we can express m, using the division algorithm, in the form $m = nq + r$, where $q, r \in \mathbf{N}$ and $0 \le r < n$. Then $e^{i[(\theta + 2m\pi)/n]} = e^{i[(\theta + 2(nq + r)\pi)/n]} = e^{i[(\theta/n) + (2nq\pi/n) + (2r\pi/n)]} = e^{i[(\theta + 2r\pi)/n]}$, where r is one of the integers $0, 1, 2, \ldots, n - 1$. $\square$

Theorem 6 is particularly useful, and relatively easy to apply, for computing nth roots of complex numbers that are either real or purely imaginary. In particular, if z is real, we may take $\arg z = 0$ if $z > 0$ and $\arg z = \pi$ if $z < 0$.

EXAMPLE 5   Find the four 4th roots of $z = 16$.

Solution   Express z in polar form with $r = 16$ and $\theta = 0$. Then $r^{1/4} = 2$ and the four 4th roots have the form $2e^{i[(\theta + 2k\pi)/4]}$, $k = 0, 1, 2, 3$, that is, $2e^0$, $2e^{i(\pi/2)}$, $2e^{i\pi}$, and $2e^{i(3\pi/2)}$, or in simplified form, 2, $2i$, -2, and $-2i$. Note from Figure 9.5 that the roots are equally spaced about a circle of radius 2 in the complex plane. $\square$

We conclude this article by stating formally a property of $\mathbf{C}$ alluded to earlier. The proof requires results from the area of complex analysis and is encountered in any introductory complex variables course.

THEOREM 7 (Fundamental Theorem of Algebra)

Any polynomial $c_0 + c_1 z + c_2 z^2 + \cdots + c_n z^n (c_i \in \mathbf{C}, c_n \ne 0)$ of degree n with complex coefficients has at least one zero (i.e., root) in $\mathbf{C}$.

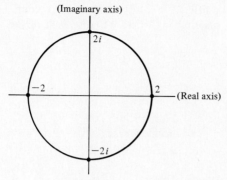

Figure 9.5 *Graphic view of the four complex 4th roots of z = 16.*

Exercises

1. Express each of the following complex numbers in the form $x + yi$:

(a) $6(4 - i) - 3(2 + 2i)$

(b) $-1/i$

(c) $(2 + i)(2 - i)$

(d) $(2 - i)/(2 + i)$

(e) $(1 - i)^4$

(f) $i^{16} + i^6 + i^5$

★(g) $(4/(4 - i)) - (4/(4 + i))$

2. Given $z_1 = 5 - 3i$, $z_2 = 4 + 5i$, and $z_3 = 2i$, calculate:

(a) $2z_1 + 3z_3$

(b) $z_1 z_2$

(c) z_2/z_3

(d) $z_3^* + z_3$

(e) $z_1^* z_2$

3. Find all $z \in \mathbf{C}$ satisfying the equation:

★(a) $(4 + 3i)z + (7 + 4i) = 6$

(b) $z + z^* = 4i$

(c) $z^* - z = 4i$

(d) $z + z^* = 12$

(e) $z + (4/z) = 0$

(f) $z^2 + 121 = 0$

(g) $z^2 - 4z + 13 = 0$

4. Use polar form $z = re^{i\theta}$ of a complex number $z = x + yi$ (and Theorem 5(a), in particular) to calculate the product $z_1 z_2$ and the quotient z_1/z_2, where $z_1 = 3 - 3i$ and $z_2 = 2\sqrt{3} + 2i$.

5. Use Theorem 6 and the method of Example 5 to find:

(a) The four complex 4th roots of $z = -16$

(b) The three complex cubed roots of $z = 8i$

6. Prove that if the complex numbers z_1 and z_2 are both real, then:

(a) $z_1 + z_2 = \text{Re}(z_1) + \text{Re}(z_2)$

★(b) $z_1 z_2 = \text{Re}(z_1) \, \text{Re}(z_2)$

7. *(a)*   Prove, in detail, that $(\mathbf{C}, +, \cdot)$ is a field.

(b)   Explain, on the basis of (a) and material in Article 9.1, why each of the following is a theorem in $\mathbf{C}$:

   (i) $z \cdot 0 = 0$ for any $z \in \mathbf{C}$

   (ii) $(-1)z = -z$ for any $z \in \mathbf{C}$

   (iii) $(z_1)(-z_2) = -(z_1 z_2)$ for any $z_1, z_2 \in \mathbf{C}$

   (iv) $(-z_1)(-z_2) = (z_1 z_2)$ for any $z_1, z_2 \in \mathbf{C}$

   (v)   If $z_1 z_2 = 0$, then either $z_1 = 0$ or $z_2 = 0$ for any $z_1, z_2 \in \mathbf{C}$

   (vi)   If $wz_1 = wz_2$ and $w \neq 0$, then $z_1 = z_2$ for any $w, z_1, z_2 \in \mathbf{C}$

   (vii) $1/(z_1 z_2) = (1/z_1)(1/z_2)$ for any $z_1, z_2 \in \mathbf{C}$, $z_1 \neq 0$ and $z_2 \neq 0$

   (viii) $1/(1/z) = z$ for any $z \in \mathbf{C}$, $z \neq 0$

8. Verify parts (b) through (g), and (j) of Theorem 2.

9. *(a)*   Verify parts (a) through (d), (g), and (i) of Theorem 3.

(b)   Prove part (j) of Theorem 3, the triangle inequality for complex numbers. [*Hint:* Prove that $|z_1 + z_2|^2 \leq (|z_1| + |z_2|)^2$ and use Exercise 4(b)(ii), Article 9.2, noting that Re $(z) \leq |z|$ for any $z \in \mathbf{C}$.]

10. *(a)*   Use the result of the lemma following the statement of Theorem 4 to verify parts (a) through (d) of that theorem.

(b)   Prove that $e^{i\pi} = -1$.

Construction of the Number Systems of Undergraduate Mathematics
CHAPTER 10

In Chapter 9 we studied the number systems **N**, **Z**, **Q**, **R**, and **C** from a descriptive point of view. For most applications requiring knowledge of elementary properties of the real numbers and associated number systems, the material in that chapter provides adequate information. There is, however, a totally different approach to the real numbers, a *constructive* approach, by which we literally build the real number system from more basic number systems. An in-depth study of this approach is a formidable and lengthy project, and is not necessarily appropriate for all sophomore and junior mathematics students. An understanding of the general structure and of a number of crucial details of this approach, though, probably is worthwhile and well within the capability of those who have successfully progressed through the preceding chapters of this text. We propose to present such a general outline in this final chapter.

For reasons philosophical and historical, as well as mathematical, every serious student of abstract mathematics should be at least generally familiar with an approach to constructing the reals. Whether one uses the approach of *Dedekind cuts* or (as we do) *Cauchy sequences* to pass from the rationals to the reals, the general approach is the same. The reals are constructed from the rationals, which, in turn, have been constructed from the integers, with the latter having been built from the positive integers. The starting point for all these constructions is an axiomatic description of the natural number system such as the axiomatization of Peano.

Philosophically, knowledge of this construction provides insight into the famous remark of Dedekind to the effect that the positive integers are a creation of God while all else is the work of man. It also provides background information to support the statement, in Article 9.4, that the complex numbers are no less "real" than the real numbers.

Historically, this construction emanates from a time, the late nineteenth century, when the modern idea of the real numbers as a concrete object (i.e., the unique complete ordered field) had not developed fully. The positive integers were generally regarded as the "base in reality" for mathematical analysis, and the prevalent view was that a number system such as the reals had to be built from them in an explicit way in order to be credited with "existence." Modern mathematics, of course, is perfectly happy to as-sume existence of the reals as an axiom (our approach in Chapter 9), as long as it is understood precisely how the system of real numbers is defined.

The construction of the reals, however, is not to be regarded by students purely as an historical curiosity. It involves a wealth of mathematical ideas that are important and useful for the study of mathematics today, many of which are probably new to you. Two main ideas are: (1) the role of the axiomatic approach in abstract mathematics (Article 1) and (2) the importance of equivalence classes (recall Chapter 7) in mathematical constructions (Articles 2 and 3), and thus the value of equivalence classes as a tool in existence proofs. Students taking courses in formal logic or non-Euclidean geometry will receive extensive exposure to (1), while students learning about quotient structures in an abstract algebra course will become familiar with several key examples of (2). Additional important topics arising in this chapter are *recursive definition*, the *well-ordering principle*, *well-definedness* of an algebraic operation, and *Cauchy sequence*, among others.

As indicated earlier, many of the proofs are omitted from this chapter. Students who are particularly interested in the ideas presented here may wish to "work through" the material, filling in missing proofs. Those who elect only to "read through" the chapter should find the experience profitable as well, due both to expanding their general knowledge about relationships among number systems and to exposure to the topics just mentioned.

10.1   An Axiomatization for the System of Positive Integers

In this article we take our first steps toward replacing the ad hoc axiom of Chapter 9, "a complete ordered field exists," with basic assumptions that are more intuitive and, in a sense, believable. We start with a two-part axiom, based on the celebrated five postulates of Guiseppe Peano, published in 1889. At first glance, this axiom appears to have bearing on the system of positive integers only, but as we will see in Articles 10.2 and 10.3, its assumption leads to the construction of the systems of integers and rationals and yields ultimately to the existence of a complete ordered field (ie., the reals) as a theorem.

As we begin this development, we should be mindful of what must be expected from any successful axiomatization of **N**; the 11 field axioms (recall Definition 2, Article 9.1) are a helpful guide in this direction. Of these axioms, the system of positive integers, as we know it intuitively, should satisfy all except three: the additive identity, the additive inverse, and the multiplicative inverse axioms (i.e., field axioms 4, 5, and 10). Thus our initial assumptions must be of a character that we are able to derive from them as theorems such familiar arithmetic properties as commutativity of addition and distributivity of multiplication over addition and, beyond these, properties such as multiplicative cancellation. There are also familiar properties of **N** involving *order* that must be derivable as theorems if our axiomatization is to be satisfactory.

As indicated earlier, our point of departure is a single two-part axiom.

AXIOM 1

There exists a set **N** and a mapping $\sigma: \mathbf{N} \to \mathbf{N}$ satisfying:

(a) σ is one to one, but not onto. In particular, there exists an element of **N**, which we denote by the symbol 1, such that $1 \notin \text{im}(\sigma)$.

(b) If S is a subset of **N** satisfying the properties:

(I) $1 \in S$, and

(II) for all $m \in \mathbf{N}$, if $m \in S$, then $\sigma(m) \in S$,

then $S = \mathbf{N}$.

The mapping $m \to \sigma(m)$ from (a) of the axiom is called a *successor function* and may be thought of (in the interest of developing a sense of familiarity with the set **N**) as sending any positive integer to "the next" positive integer; for this reason, the image $\sigma(m)$ of an element $m \in \mathbf{N}$ is called the *successor* of m. We refrain at this stage from writing $\sigma(m) = m + 1$, because there is not as yet any operation of addition available to us. Condition (b) of Axiom 1 is known as *the induction postulate* and should remind you of the principle of mathematical induction, the basis of our work in Article 5.4.

Let us begin by noting, for the record, several immediate consequences of Axiom 1. The set **N** is nonempty since $1 \in \mathbf{N}$; in fact, **N** must be infinite since σ is a one-to-one mapping of **N** into a proper subset of itself, namely, $\mathbf{N} - \{1\}$ (recall Definition 2, Article 8.3). The stipulation that σ is a one-to-one mapping means of course that if $m, n \in \mathbf{N}$ with $\sigma(m) = \sigma(n)$, then $m = n$. This was the fourth original postulate of Peano. The requirement that $1 \notin \text{im}(\sigma)$ means that 1 is not the successor of any element of **N**.

No doubt you have already noticed the absence of algebraic operations from the definition of **N**. Clearly a major obstacle to the plan to prove as theorems the familiar arithmetic properties of **N** is the need to create from

Axiom 1 the operations of addition and multiplication. The theorem by which we will bring these operations into being is indeed the most important and difficult in this article (see Theorems 3 and 4). Therefore, before tackling this problem, let us first get our bearings by proving a few preliminary results. An important aspect of "getting our bearings" in the current context is an early appreciation of the preponderance here of proof by induction. Considering what there is to work with at this stage, namely, parts (a) and (b) of Axiom 1, it should not be surprising that induction proofs are so prominent; yet it will probably take some time to get used to this fact.

THEOREM 1

$\sigma(n) \neq n$ for all $n \in \mathbf{N}$; that is, the mapping σ has no *fixed points*.

Proof   Let $S = \{n \in \mathbf{N} \mid \sigma(n) \neq n\}$. We will attempt to prove $S = \mathbf{N}$ by verifying (I) and (II) of (b) of Axiom 1. (I) Clearly $1 \in S$. We cannot have $1 = \sigma(1)$ since $1 \notin \text{im}(\sigma)$. (II) Assume $m \in S$; we claim $\sigma(m) \in S$; that is, $\sigma(m) \neq \sigma(\sigma(m))$. For if the latter equation were valid, then by the one-to-one property of the mapping σ, we could conclude $m = \sigma(m)$, contradicting the induction hypothesis. □

THEOREM 2

$\text{im}(\sigma) = \mathbf{N} - \{1\}$; that is, 1 is *the only* element of **N** that is not the successor of some element of **N**.

Proof   Our strategy is as follows. Let $S = \text{im}(\sigma) \cup \{1\}$. If we can prove $S = \mathbf{N}$, then by elementary set theory, we have $\mathbf{N} - \{1\} = S - \{1\} = (\text{im}(\sigma) \cup \{1\}) \cap \{1\}' = \text{im}(\sigma)$, as desired. Note that the last equality depends on the fact that $1 \notin \text{im}(\sigma)$. Hence we claim $S = \mathbf{N}$; we turn to (b) of Axiom 1 to support this claim. Clearly $1 \in S$, by our definition of S. So suppose $m \in S$; we claim $\sigma(m) \in S$. Now since $m \in S$, then either $m = 1$ or $m \in \text{im}(\sigma)$. If $m = 1$, then $\sigma(m) = \sigma(1) \in \text{im}(\sigma) \subseteq S$, so that $\sigma(m) \in S$, as desired, in this case. If $m \in \text{im}(\sigma)$, then $m = \sigma(m')$ for some $m' \in \mathbf{N}$. Hence $\sigma(m) = \sigma(\sigma(m'))$ so that $\sigma(m) \in \text{im}(\sigma)$, as desired. By (b) of Axiom 1, we conclude $S = \mathbf{N}$. The result now follows from the argument given at the outset. □

The next result is the centerpiece of the development of **N**, for in it we prove the existence and uniqueness of an operation on **N** corresponding to our intuitive idea of addition. As we will see, the definition of multiplication is formulated in an analogous fashion. Our problem is somehow to "get at" an operation of addition. Let us first stop to realize what kind of mathematical object addition is; addition on the positive integers is a *mapping s* (for sum) of $\mathbf{N} \times \mathbf{N}$ into **N**, satisfying certain properties. For the sake of simplicity, let us fix a positive integer m and try to create a mapping in one independent variable. Such a mapping might be denoted $s_m \colon \mathbf{N} \to \mathbf{N}$

and called "addition to m." Intuitively, our goal is that $s_m(n)$ should equal $m + n$ for any $n \in \mathbf{N}$, but, of course, $+$ is exactly what we're trying to define. We have no tools at our disposal by which to define $s_m(n)$ explicitly. What we <u>do</u> have is a successor function and an induction property; the proposed solution is to define $s_m(n)$ *inductively* (or *recursively*). What this means is that we define $s_m(n)$ explicitly for $n = 1$; then, assuming that $s_m(n)$ has been defined for an arbitrary $n \in \mathbf{N}$, we define $s_m(\sigma(n))$ in terms of $s_m(n)$. We must do two things to carry out this program successfully: (1) come up with rea- sonable definitions of $s_m(1)$ and $s_m(\sigma(n))$, the latter assuming that $s_m(n)$ has been defined and (2) prove existence and uniqueness of a mapping satisfying the properties specified in our definition. Let us deal with the first problem immediately. Experience tells us that we want $s_m(1)$ to equal $m + 1$. For- tunately, we can formulate this idea in language available to us, namely, $s_m(1) = \sigma(m)$. Now suppose that $s_m(n)$ has been defined; for familiarity sake, let us denote its value by $m + n$. How then should we define $s_m(\sigma(n))$? That is, what is the value of $m + (n + 1)$? Why not $(m + n) + 1$? That is, $s_m(\sigma(n)) = \sigma(s_m(n))$. These definitions are used in the following important theorem.

THEOREM 3

If $m \in \mathbf{N}$, then there exists a unique mapping $s_m \colon \mathbf{N} \to \mathbf{N}$ satisfying

(i) $s_m(1) = \sigma(m)$, and
(ii) $s_m(\sigma(n)) = \sigma(s_m(n))$ for each $n \in \mathbf{N}$.

Proof (Existence)   The proof is quite abstract and makes use, at several stages, of the induction postulate. Let m be an arbitrary positive inte- ger. We begin by considering the collection of all subsets r_m of $\mathbf{N} \times \mathbf{N}$ satisfying the properties (i)$'$ $(1, \sigma(m)) \in r_m$, and (ii)$'$ $(n, p) \in r_m$ implies $(\sigma(n), \sigma(p)) \in r_m$ for each $n, p \in \mathbf{N}$. Note that (i)$'$ and (ii)$'$ are simply (i) and (ii), with functional notation replaced by the more general ordered pair notation, appropriate for a relation that may not be a function. Note also that this collection is nonempty, since $\mathbf{N} \times \mathbf{N}$ itself satisfies (i)$'$ and (ii)$'$. Let s_m equal the set theoretic intersection of all relations on $\mathbf{N}$ satisfying (i)$'$ and (ii)$'$. It is easy to show [with verification left to you in Exercise 2(a)] that s_m satisfies (i)$'$ and (ii)$'$, and furthermore, is a subset of any relation on $\mathbf{N}$ satisfying (i)$'$ and (ii)$'$. For the latter reason, we say that s_m is the *smallest* relation on $\mathbf{N}$ satisfying (i)$'$ and (ii)$'$; this prop- erty of s_m will be a key later in the proof. We claim now that this s_m is the desired mapping of $\mathbf{N}$ into $\mathbf{N}$. Since s_m is known to satisfy (i)$'$ and (ii)$'$, we need only verify that s_m actually is a mapping on $\mathbf{N}$. In other words, we must verify:

(a)   dom $(s_m) = \mathbf{N}$; that is, for any $n \in \mathbf{N}$, there exists $p \in \mathbf{N}$ such that $(n, p) \in s_m$, and
(b) s_m is a function; that is, if $n, p, q \in \mathbf{N}$ with $(n, p) \in s_m$ and $(n, q) \in s_m$, then $p = q$.

We channel our efforts now toward verifying (a) and (b), relying heavily on the induction postulate in both proofs.

(a) Let $X = \{n \in \mathbf{N} \mid (n, p) \in s_m \text{ for some } p \in \mathbf{N}\}$. We claim $X = \mathbf{N}$:

(I) $1 \in X$, since $(1, \sigma(m)) \in s_m$, by (i)$'$.

(II) If $n \in X$, then $(n, p) \in s_m$ for some $p \in \mathbf{N}$, so that $(\sigma(n), \sigma(p)) \in s_m$, by (ii)$'$, and so $\sigma(n) \in X$. By the induction postulate, we conclude $X = \mathbf{N}$, as desired.

(b) Let $Y = \{n \in \mathbf{N} \mid (n, q_1) \in s_m \text{ and } (n, q_2) \in s_m \text{ together imply } q_1 = q_2\}$. We claim that $Y = \mathbf{N}$:

(I) We first show $1 \in Y$. We know that $(1, \sigma(m)) \in s_m$. Now suppose $(1, p) \in s_m$, where $p \in \mathbf{N}$. If $p \neq \sigma(m)$, then the set $s_m - \{(1, p)\}$ is a proper subset of s_m containing the ordered pair $(1, \sigma(m))$; that is, satisfying (i)$'$. Furthermore, if $(n, q) \in s_m - \{(1, p)\}$, then $(n, q) \in s_m$ and so $(\sigma(n), \sigma(q)) \in s_m$. Also, $(\sigma(n), \sigma(q)) \neq (1, p)$, since $1 \notin \text{im}(\sigma)$. Hence $(\sigma(n), \sigma(q)) \in s_m - \{(1, p)\}$. Thus $s_m - \{(1, p)\}$, a proper subset of s_m, is a subset of $\mathbf{N} \times \mathbf{N}$ satisfying both (i)$'$ and (ii)$'$, contradicting the fact that s_m is the <u>smallest</u> such subset. We conclude $p = \sigma(m)$.

(II) We next suppose that $n \in Y$, where n is an arbitrary element of $\mathbf{N}$. We must prove that $\sigma(n) \in Y$. By the result in (a), we know that $(n, y) \in s_m$ for some $y \in \mathbf{N}$. Hence our assumption $n \in Y$ means that $(n, y) \in s_m$ for exactly one $y \in \mathbf{N}$. Now from (ii)$'$ and the assumption $(n, y) \in s_m$ follows the fact that $(\sigma(n), \sigma(y)) \in s_m$. Hence we must prove only that if $(\sigma(n), t) \in s_m$ for some $t \in \mathbf{N}$, then $t = \sigma(y)$. To do this, let us suppose there is an element $t \in \mathbf{N}$, $t \neq \sigma(y)$, such that $(\sigma(n), t) \in s_m$. As in the proof of (a), consider the set $s_m - \{(\sigma(n), t)\}$. Again, as in (a), note that since $1 \notin \text{im}(\sigma)$, then $\sigma(n) \neq 1$ so that $s_m - \{(\sigma(n), t)\}$ is a proper subset of s_m containing the ordered pair $(1, \sigma(m))$, so that (i)$'$ is satisfied by $s_m - \{(\sigma(n), t)\}$. To verify that $s_m - \{(\sigma(n), t)\}$ satisfies (ii)$'$, suppose that $p \in \mathbf{N}$ and that $(p, x) \in s_m - \{(\sigma(n), t)\}$; we must show that $(\sigma(p), \sigma(x)) \in s_m - \{(\sigma(n), t)\}$. Since $(\sigma(p), \sigma(x)) \in s_m$ by (ii)$'$, the only issue is whether $(\sigma(p), \sigma(x))$ equals $(\sigma(n), t)$; we claim, of course, that it does not. There are two cases to consider, $p = n$ and $p \neq n$. In the first case the desired inequality is valid, since there is only one $y \in \mathbf{N}$ such that $(n, y) \in s_m$. For this y, $(\sigma(n), \sigma(y)) \in s_m$, by (ii)$'$, and does not equal $(\sigma(n), t)$, since $t \neq \sigma(y)$. As to the second case, if $p \neq n$, then $(\sigma(p), \sigma(x)) \in s_m$ and $\sigma(p) \neq \sigma(n)$, since σ is one to one. Hence $(\sigma(p), \sigma(x)) \neq (\sigma(n), t)$ and so $(\sigma(p), \sigma(x)) \in s_m - \{(\sigma(n), t)\}$, again, as desired. Therefore $s_m - \{(\sigma(n), t)\}$ satisfies (ii)$'$, and again, we have a contradiction of the fact that s_m is the smallest subset of $\mathbf{N} \times \mathbf{N}$ satisfying both (i)′ and (ii)′. Thus the inductive step (II) is proved and we conclude, by induction, that $Y = \mathbf{N}$; that is, s_m is a function. With this, existence is established.

(Uniqueness) Suppose r_m is any mapping from $\mathbf{N}$ to $\mathbf{N}$ satisfying properties (i) and (ii). Since r_m is a relation on $\mathbf{N}$ satisfying (i) and (ii) and since s_m is the intersection of all such relations, then necessarily s_m is a subset of r_m. We claim that, in fact, r_m is a subset of s_m, so that s_m equals r_m. Let $(x, y) \in r_m$. Since $x \in \mathbf{N}$ and dom $(s_m) = \mathbf{N}$, there exists $z \in \mathbf{N}$ such that $(x, z) \in s_m$. Since $s_m \subseteq r_m$, then $(x, z) \in r_m$. Since $(x, y) \in r_m, (x, z) \in r_m$, and r_m is a function, we may conclude $y = z$, so that $(x, y) = (x, z)$ and $(x, y) \in s_m$, as required. □

With a mapping $s_m: \mathbf{N} \to \mathbf{N}$ determined uniquely by each positive integer m, we are now in a position to define the desired "sum function" s.

DEFINITION 1

If $m, n \in \mathbf{N}$, we define the sum $s(m, n)$ of m and n by the rule $s(m, n) = s_m(n)$. Following normal usage, we frequently denote $s(m, n)$ by the symbol $m + n$.

By Theorem 3, each function s_m is uniquely determined by a given $m \in \mathbf{N}$ and properties (i) and (ii) of that theorem. For a given m, the value $s_m(n)$ is uniquely determined by $n \in \mathbf{N}$, since each s_m is a function. Hence each pair (m, n) of positive integers determines uniquely a corresponding number $s(m, n)$. Furthermore, it is clear that each such value $s(m, n)$ is contained in $\mathbf{N}$. The following statement summarizes these two properties.

COROLLARY

(a) $+$ is a function on $\mathbf{N} \times \mathbf{N}$ and so constitutes a well-defined operation on $\mathbf{N}$; that is, if $a, a', b, b' \in \mathbf{N}$ with $a = a'$ and $b = b'$, then $a + b = a' + b'$.

(b) $\mathbf{N}$ is closed under the operation $+$; that is, if $a, b \in \mathbf{N}$, then $a + b \in \mathbf{N}$.

Part (a) of the corollary is the assertion that "equals added to equals yield equals," a particular case of which is the result "$y = z$ implies $x + y = x + z$ for any $x, y, z \in \mathbf{N}$." The property in (b) is called *closure* under addition.

Before dealing with other properties of addition, let us first define the multiplication operation. Our approach will be to look closer at what we actually did in Theorem 3, when we formulated addition. It is not hard to see that Theorem 3 is a special case of the much more abstract-appearing result we are about to state. What is only slightly more difficult is the verification [left as an exercise in Exercise 2(b)] that a proof essentially identical to the proof of Theorem 3 works in this more general case as well.

THEOREM   4 (Principle of Inductive Definition)

Let $f: \mathbf{N} \to \mathbf{N}$ be an arbitrary mapping and let $a \in \mathbf{N}$ be given. Then there exists a mapping φ of $\mathbf{N}$ into $\mathbf{N}$, uniquely determined by f and a, such that:

(i) $\varphi(1) = a$, and
(ii) $\varphi(\sigma(n)) = f(\varphi(n))$ for all $n \in \mathbf{N}$

A function φ, defined as in Theorem 4, is said to have been defined *by induction* or *recursively*. As we suggested just before stating Theorem 4, the "sum to m" function s_m was defined by induction. In that case, for a given $m \in \mathbf{N}$, we had $a = \sigma(m)$ and $f(p) = \sigma(p)$ for each $p \in \mathbf{N}$. Other familiar functions with domain $\mathbf{N}$ may be defined formally in a recursive manner, among these *factorial*, *nth power*, and the *nth Fibonacci number* (see Exercise 1). The inductive definition of "product with m," denoted p_m, is most germane to our current considerations.

DEFINITION   2

For a fixed $m \in \mathbf{N}$, we defined the function "product with m," denoted p_m, inductively by the rules $p_m(1) = m$ and $p_m(\sigma(n)) = p_m(n) + m$, for any $n \in \mathbf{N}$. Given two positive integers m and n, we define their product $p(m, n)$ (usually denoted $m \cdot n$ or simply mn) by the rule $p(m, n) = p_m(n)$.

Note that multiplication by m is defined by applying Theorem 4 with $a = m$ and $f(p) = p + m$. You should formulate closure and well-definedness statements for the product, analogous to those stated for the sum in the corollary to Theorem 3.

With addition and multiplication now defined, we turn to properties of these operations. As we work toward these properties, it will prove useful to have at our disposal translations of the defining properties from functional to operational notation. For this purpose, we note that the addition and multiplication operations are defined by the equations (for all $m, n \in \mathbf{N}$):

$$m + 1 = \sigma(m) \tag{1}$$

$$m + (n + 1) = (m + n) + 1 \tag{2}$$

$$m \cdot 1 = m \tag{3}$$

$$m \cdot (n + 1) = mn + m \tag{4}$$

THEOREM   5

Let $n, p, q \in \mathbf{N}$. Then:

(a) $(n + p) + q = n + (p + q)$ (addition is associative)
(b) $n + p = p + n$ (addition is commutative)
(c) $n + p \neq n$ (there is no additive identity in $\mathbf{N}$)
(d)   If $n + q = p + q$, then $n = p$ (additive cancellation)

Partial proof (a) Given $n, p \in \mathbf{N}$, denote by S_{np} the set $\{q \in \mathbf{N} | (n + p) + q = n + (p + q)\}$. It is left to you [Exercise 2(a)] to verify conditions (I) and (II) of the induction postulate and conclude thereby that $S_{np} = \mathbf{N}$.

(b) This proof is more difficult than the proof of associativity. Recall that $\sigma(m) = m + 1$ for all $m \in \mathbf{N}$, by (1). We need as a lemma the fact the $\sigma(m) = 1 + m$ for any $m \in \mathbf{N}$; note that this is a special case of the desired result. Assuming that you have supplied the straightforward induction verification [Exercise 2(b)], we approach the desired result by using another induction. For $n \in \mathbf{N}$, let $S_n = \{p \in \mathbf{N} | n + p = p + n\}$. Using this lemma, we observe that $1 \in S_n$, since $n + 1 = \sigma(n) = 1 + n$. For (II), assume $p \in S_n$, so that $n + p = p + n$. We must prove $\sigma(p) = p + 1 \in S_n$; that is, $n + (p + 1) = (p + 1) + n$. Now

$$
\begin{aligned}
n + (p + 1) &= (n + p) + 1 && \text{[by (2)]} \\
&= (p + n) + 1 && \text{(by induction hypothesis and well-} \\
& && \text{definedness (wd) of “+”)} \\
&= p + (n + 1) && \text{[by (2)]} \\
&= p + (1 + n) && \text{(by the lemma)} \\
&= (p + 1) + n && \text{[by (2)]}
\end{aligned}
$$

(c) Given $p \in \mathbf{N}$, let $S_p = \{n \in \mathbf{N} | n + p \neq n\}$. Note first that $1 \in S_p$, since $1 + p = \sigma(p) \neq 1$, since $1 \notin \mathrm{im}\,(\sigma)$. Next, assume $n \in S_p$, so that $n + p \neq n$. To show $\sigma(n) = n + 1 \in S_p$, we must prove that $(n + 1) + p \neq n + 1$; that is, $\sigma(n) + p \neq \sigma(n)$. Now if $\sigma(n) + p = \sigma(n)$, then we would have $\sigma(n) = \sigma(n) + p = \sigma(n + p)$ and, by the one-to-one property of σ, $n = n + p$, a contradiction.

(d) Given $n, p \in \mathbf{N}$, let $S_{np} = \{q \in \mathbf{N} | n + q = p + q \text{ implies } n = p\}$. Note first that $1 \in S_{np}$ since if $n + 1 = p + 1$, then $\sigma(n) = \sigma(p)$ so that $n = p$, by the one-to-oneness of σ. Now suppose $q \in S_{np}$, so that $n = p$ whenever $n + q = p + q$. To show $\sigma(q) = q + 1 \in S_{np}$, assume that $n + (q + 1) = p + (q + 1)$. We must show that $n = p$. In that case we have $(n + q) + 1 = n + (q + 1) = p + (q + 1) = (p + q) + 1$, so that $\sigma(n + q) = \sigma(p + q)$. By the one-to-one property of σ, we have $n + q = p + q$. By the induction hypothesis, we conclude $n = p$, as desired. $\square$

Property (d) of Theorem 5 might be called "right-additive" cancellation. Note that combining (d) with (b), the commutative property of addition, yields easily a corresponding "left-additive" cancellation property [see Exercise 2(c)].

Our next goal is to begin to consider algebraic properties involving multiplication. We begin by giving a proof of the only field property that involves addition and multiplication together.

THEOREM 6

Let $n, p, q \in \mathbf{N}$. Then $n(p + q) = np + nq$.   (distributivity)

Proof   For $n, p \in \mathbf{N}$, let $S_{np} = \{q \in \mathbf{N} \,|\, n(p + q) = np + nq\}$. First, we have $1 \in S_{np}$, because

$$n(p + 1) = np + n \qquad [\text{by (4)}]$$
$$ = np + n \cdot 1 \qquad [\text{by (3) and wd of addition}]$$

Second, assume $q \in S_{np}$, so that $n(p + q) = np + nq$. We must prove $q + 1 \in S_{np}$; to do this, we need to show $n(p + (q + 1)) = np + n(q + 1)$. Now:

$$n(p + (q + 1)) = n((p + q) + 1)) \qquad [\text{by (2) and wd of multiplication}]$$
$$ = n(p + q) + n \qquad [\text{by (4)}]$$
$$ = (np + nq) + n \qquad (\text{by induction hypothesis and wd of addition})$$
$$ = np + (nq + n) \qquad [\text{by Theorem 5(a)}]$$
$$ = np + n(q + 1) \qquad [\text{by (4) and wd of addition}] \quad \square$$

We next consider properties of multiplication, some of which correspond to additive properties in Theorem 5.

THEOREM   7
Let $n, p, q \in \mathbf{N}$. Then:

(a) $(np)q = n(pq)$ (multiplication is associative)
(b) $n \cdot 1 = 1 \cdot n = n$ (multiplicative identity)
(c) $np = pn$ (multiplication is commutative)
(d)   If $p \neq 1$, then $pq \neq 1$ for all $q \in \mathbf{N}$ (positive integers $\neq 1$ do not have reciprocals in **N**)
(e)   If $nq = pq$, then $n = p$ (multiplicative cancellation)

Proof   Parts (b), (c) and (e) are left as exercises (see Exercise 4). We now consider the proof of (a). Given $n, p \in \mathbf{N}$; denote by S_{np} the set $\{q \in \mathbf{N} \,|\, (np)q = n(pq)\}$. Note first that $1 \in S_{np}$, since $(np) \cdot 1 = np = n(p \cdot 1)$, where the latter step follows from (3) and the well-definedness of the multiplication operation. Next, assume $q \in S_{np}$, so that $(np)q = n(pq)$. To prove $q + 1 \in S_{np}$, we must show that $(np)(q + 1) = n(p(q + 1))$. Now:

$$n(p(q + 1)) = n(pq + p) \qquad [\text{by (4) and wd of multiplication}]$$
$$ = n(pq) + np \qquad (\text{by Theorem 6})$$
$$ = (np)q + np \qquad (\text{by induction hypothesis and wd of addition})$$
$$ = (np)(q + 1) \qquad [\text{by (4)}]$$

As for (d), assume $p \in \mathbf{N}$ and $p \neq 1$, and let $S_p = \{q \in \mathbf{N} \,|\, pq \neq 1\}$. We prove $S_{np} = \mathbf{N}$ by induction. Namely, $1 \in S_p$, since $p \cdot 1 = p \neq 1$. Also, if we assume $q \in S_p$, so that $pq \neq 1$ then $pq = \sigma(x)$ for some $x \in \mathbf{N}$. We must show that $p(q + 1) \neq 1$. Now $p(q + 1) = pq + p = p + pq = p + \sigma(x) = \sigma(p + x)$, where $p + x \in \mathbf{N}$, by additive closure. Hence $p(q + 1) \in \text{im}(\sigma)$. Since $1 \notin \text{im}(\sigma)$, we conclude $1 \neq p(q + 1)$, as desired. $\square$

ORDERING PROPERTIES OF N

We now consider properties of $\mathbf{N}$ having to do with the *ordering* of positive integers. Our starting point is the following definition.

DEFINITION 3

Let $a, b \in \mathbf{N}$. We say that $a < b$ (a is *less than* b) if and only if there exists $c \in \mathbf{N}$ such that $a + c = b$.

A number of facts related to Definition 3 present themselves immediately. We collect some of them in the following theorem, whose proof is left to you in Exercise 5(a).

THEOREM 8

Let $a, b, c \in \mathbf{N}$. Then:

(a) $a < \sigma(a)$
(b) $a < a + b$
(c) If $a < b$ and $b < c$, then $a < c$ (transitivity)
(d) If $a < b$, then $a \neq b$
(e) If $a \neq 1$, then $1 < a$
(f) If $a < b$, then there exists a <u>unique</u> $x \in \mathbf{N}$ such that $a + x = b$
(g) If $a < b$, then $a + c < b + c$
(h) If $a < b$, then $ac < bc$

The uniqueness in part (f) of Theorem 8 is suggestive of the subtraction operation, as defined in Definition 4.

DEFINITION 4

If $a, b \in \mathbf{N}$ with $a < b$, we denote by $b - a$ (b *minus* a) the unique positive integer x such that $a + x = b$.

We emphasize that $b - a$ is defined in $\mathbf{N}$ if and only if $a < b$. We collect other properties in Theorem 9.

THEOREM 9

Let $a, b, c \in \mathbf{N}$ with $a < b < c$. Then:

(a) $a + (b - a) = b$
(b) $(c - b) + a = c - (b - a)$
(c) $(c + b) - a = c + (b - a)$
(d) $c(b - a) = cb - ca$

Partial proof   We prove (b), with the others for you to verify in Exercise 5(b). To prove that $(c - b) + a = c - (b - a)$, we need only show that $(c - b) + a$ added to $b - a$ yields c. Note that $[(c - b) + a] + (b - a) = (c - b) + [a + (b - a)] = (c - b) + b = b + (c - b) = c$, as desired.

$\square$

We conclude our discussion of the "less than" relation on **N** by proving the important *trichotomy* property.

THEOREM 10
Given $a, b \in$ **N**, exactly one of the three statements $a < b$, $a = b$, and $a > b$ is true.

Proof   Given $a \in$ **N**, let $S_a = \{b \in$ **N** $|$ either $a < b$ or $a = b$ or $a > b\}$. We first show that $S_a =$ **N** by induction; then we show that at most one of the three relationships holds for any pair of positive integers. For the induction proof, note first that $1 \in S_a$ since if $a \neq 1$, then $a = \sigma(x) = 1 + x$ for some $x \in$ **N**, so that $1 < a$. Second, assume $b \in S_a$ so that either $a < b$ or $a = b$ or $a > b$. We must prove that $\sigma(b) \in S_a$; that is, either $a < \sigma(b)$, $a = \sigma(b)$, or $a > \sigma(b)$. Now if $a < b$, then since $b < \sigma(b)$, we have (by the transitivity of $<$) that $a < \sigma(b)$. If $a = b$, then since $b < \sigma(b)$, we have $a < \sigma(b)$. If $a > b$, then either $a = \sigma(b)$ or $a \neq \sigma(b)$. In the first case the desired result follows immediately. If $a \neq \sigma(b)$, then $a = b + x$ for some $x \in$ **N**, $x \neq 1$. Since $x \neq 1$, then $x = \sigma(y)$ for some $y \in$ **N**. Hence $a = b + x = b + \sigma(y) = \sigma(b + y) = \sigma(b) + y$ so that $\sigma(b) < a$. Thus $S_a =$ **N** and we may be certain that at least one of the three relationships must be true for any $a, b \in$ **N**. We next show that at most one of the relationships may hold between a given a and b. Note first that if either $a < b$ or $b < a$, then $a \neq b$, by Theorem 8(d). Thus we have only the possibility "$a < b$ and $b < a$" to eliminate. If both relationships hold, then there exist $x, y \in$ **N** such that $a = b + x$ and $b = a + y$. Hence $a = b + x = (a + y) + x = a + (y + x) = a + z$, where $z = x + y \in$ **N**, by closure. This contradicts (c) of Theorem 5. $\square$

WELL-ORDERING OF N

In (e) of Theorem 8 we observed informally that 1 is the smallest element of **N** [see Exercise 7(g)]. In fact, **N** satisfies a stronger property involving the idea of a smallest element, the *well-ordering principle*. Note first that if $S \subseteq$ **N**, an element $a \in$ **N** is said to be a *smallest* (or *least*) element of S if and only if $a \in S$ and, for all $x \in$ **N**, $x \in S$ implies either $a = x$ or $a < x$. The well-ordering principle (WOP) for **N** states that every nonempty subset of **N** has a least element. This property is an extremely useful theoretical tool for proving existence; you may recall, for instance, Example 10, Article 6.3. It turns out that WOP is equivalent to the induction postulate. We prove this fact and, for good measure, introduce another form of the induction postulate in the next theorem.

THEOREM 11

The following three statements about the set **N** are equivalent:

(a) The induction postulate (IP)
(b) The well-ordering principle (WOP)
(c) The second induction principle (IP2). Any set S of positive integers satisfying (i) $1 \in S$ and (ii) for any $m \in \mathbf{N}$, $k \in S$ for each $k \in \{1, 2, \ldots, m\}$ implies $m + 1 \in S$, equals **N**.

Proof   (a) $\Rightarrow$ (b) If (b) is false, then there is a nonempty subset S of **N** having no smallest element. Hence if a positive integer m has the property that $m < s$ for all $s \in S$, we must have $m \notin S$. Let M be the set of all such positive integers (i.e., $M = \{m \in \mathbf{N} \mid m < s \ \forall \ s \in S\}$); clearly $M \cap S = \emptyset$. We claim that $M = \mathbf{N}$. In support of this claim, note first that $1 \in M$. Since 1 is the smallest element of **N** and $1 \notin S$ (otherwise 1 would be the smallest element of S), then surely $1 < s$ for all $s \in S$. Second, suppose $m \in M$, so that $m < s$ for all $s \in S$. Then $m + 1 \le s$ for all $s \in S$, by Exercise 7(f). If $m + 1 \in S$, then $m + 1$ would be the smallest element of S. Hence $m + 1 \notin S$ and we may assert $m + 1 < s$ for all $s \in S$. Hence $m + 1 \in M$, so that we may conclude $M = \mathbf{N}$. Since $M \cap S = \emptyset$ and $M = \mathbf{N}$, S must be empty, contradicting the initial assumption that S is nonempty.

(b) $\Rightarrow$ (c) Assume S satisfies (i) and (ii) of (c). If $S \ne \mathbf{N}$, then $\mathbf{N} - S$ is nonempty. By WOP, $\mathbf{N} - S$ has a smallest element , call it s_0. Note that $s_0 \ne 1$, by (i). For all positive integers k such that $k \le s_0 - 1$, we have $k \in S$. Hence $s_0 \in S$, by (ii), contradicting the fact that $s_0 \in \mathbf{N} - S$. Hence $\mathbf{N} - S$ is empty and $S = \mathbf{N}$, as desired.

(c) $\Rightarrow$ (a) Let S be a subset of **N** satisfying the properties $1 \in S$ and $m \in S$ implies $m + 1 \in S$ for all $m \in \mathbf{N}$. We must prove $S = \mathbf{N}$. Now suppose that for each $k \in \mathbf{N}$ such that $k \le m$, we have $k \in S$. Then surely $m \in S$ so that, by our assumption, $m + 1 \in S$. Hence S satisfies (ii) of (c). Since S satisfies (i) of (c), by our assumption, we may conclude, by (c), that $S = \mathbf{N}$. $\square$

Note that the induction postulate [(a) in Theorem 11 and (b) of Axiom 1] is the same as the principle of mathematical induction we used extensively in Article 5.4. (We now know that $\sigma(m)$ and $m + 1$ are synonymous.) Our approach in this article has been to assume this property as one of the axioms defining **N**. Theorem 11 shows, among other things, that the well-ordering principle could just as well be assumed as an axiom for **N**, in which case IP could be proved as a theorem. Many texts adopt this approach; in Exercise 8, you are asked to write a proof deriving IP directly from WOP.

The second induction principle IP2 [(c) of Theorem 11] is occasionally useful in writing a more streamlined induction proof than would be possible with only IP at our disposal [see Exercise 8(b)]. An example of this follows.

EXAMPLE 1   Given $n \in \mathbf{N}$, we define the nth Fibonacci number f_n by the rules $f_1 = f_2 = 1$ and $f_{n+2} = f_n + f_{n+1}$ when $n \geq 1$. Use IP2 to prove that $f_n \in \mathbf{N}$ for each $n \in \mathbf{N}$.

Solution   Let $S = \{n \in \mathbf{N} \,|\, f_n \in \mathbf{N}\}$. We claim $S = \mathbf{N}$, and will use IP2 to prove it. Clearly $1 \in S$ since $f_1 = 1 \in \mathbf{N}$. Suppose now that $m \in \mathbf{N}$ and that $k \in S$ for each $k = 1, 2, \ldots, m$. We claim $m + 1 \in S$; that is, $f_{m+1} \in \mathbf{N}$. But $f_{m+1} = f_{m-1} + f_m$, the sum of two positive integers by the induction hypothesis, and thus a positive integer, by closure.   □

Exercises

1. Give a formal definition by induction for each of the following quantities, defined informally here. In each case $n \in \mathbf{N}$.

(a) n factorial, denoted $n!$, equal to the product $n(n-1)(n-2)\cdots(3)(2)(1)$

★(b) nth power of x, where $x \in \mathbf{R}$, denoted x^0, equal to the product $(x)(x)\cdots(x)$, n times

(c)   The sum of n copies of a real number a, denoted na, equal to $a + a + \cdots + a$, n times

(d)   The union of n sets, $X_1, X_2, \ldots, X_n$, equal to $X_1 \cup X_2 \cup \cdots \cup X_n$

(e)   Composition of n functions with domain $\mathbf{R}$ and range a subset of $\mathbf{R}$, denoted $f_n \circ f_{n-1} \circ f_{n-2} \circ \cdots \circ f_2 \circ f_1$, where $(f_n \circ f_{n-1} \circ f_{n-2} \circ \cdots \circ f_2 \circ f_1)(x) = (f_n(f_{n-1}(f_{n-2}\cdots(f_2(f_1(x)))\cdots))$ for all $x \in \mathbf{R}$

(f)   The nth Fibonacci number f_n, where the first two Fibonacci numbers are defined to equal 1, and where all other Fibonacci numbers equal the sum of the two preceding such numbers.

2. (a)   (This exercise relates to the proof of Theorem 3.) Consider the collection $\mathfrak{C}$ of all relations r_m on $\mathbf{N}$ (i.e., each r_m is a subset of $\mathbf{N} \times \mathbf{N}$) satisfying (i)' $(1, \sigma(m)) \in r_m$, and (ii)' $(n, p) \in r_m$ implies $(\sigma(n), \sigma(p)) \in r_m$ for any $n, p \in \mathbf{N}$. Let $s_m = \cap \{r_m \,|\, r_m \in \mathfrak{C}\}$. Prove that

(i) s_m satisfies (i)' and (ii)'

(ii)   If $c \in \mathfrak{C}$, then $s_m \subseteq c$ [i.e., s_m is the "smallest" relation on $\mathbf{N}$ satisfying (i)', (ii)']

(b)   Prove Theorem 4. (Mimic the proof, given in the text, of Theorem 3.)

3. This exercise relates to the proof of Theorem 5.

(a)   Prove Theorem 5(a); that is, addition on $\mathbf{N}$ is associative.

★(b)   Prove that $\sigma(m) = 1 + m = s_1(m)$ for any $m \in \mathbf{N}$. [This is the lemma used in the proof of Theorem 5(b).]

(c)   Prove the "left-additive cancellation" property of $\mathbf{N}$, that is, prove that if $n, p, q \in \mathbf{N}$ with $q + n = q + p$, then $n = p$.

4. This exercise relates to the proof of Theorem 7.

(a) Prove Theorem 7(b); that is, $1 \cdot n = n \cdot 1 = n$ for all $n \in \mathbf{N}$.
(b) Prove Theorem 7(c); that is, multiplication on $\mathbf{N}$ is commutative.
(c) Prove Theorem 7(e); that is, multiplicative cancellation on $\mathbf{N}$.

5. *(a)*   Prove Theorem 8.
(b)   Prove Theorem 9, parts (a), (c), and (d).

6. Assume $a, b, c, d \in \mathbf{N}$. Prove:

★*(a)*   If $a + c < b + c$, then $a < b$
(b)   If $ac < bc$, then $a < b$. [*Note* the relationship between the results in (a) and (b) and parts (g) and (h) of Theorem 8. *Hint for the proof:* Use Theorem 10, that is, trichotomy.]
(c)   If $a < b$ and $c < d$, then $a + c < b + d$
(d)   If $a < b$ and $c < d$, then $ac < bd$

7. Define a relation $\leq$ on $\mathbf{N}$ by the rule $a \leq b$ if and only if either $a < b$ or $a = b$. Prove that, given $a, b \in \mathbf{N}$:

(a) $a \leq a$ (i.e., $\leq$ is a reflexive relation on $\mathbf{N}$)
(b) $a < b$ if and only if $a \leq b$ and $a \neq b$
(c)   If $a \leq b$ and $b \leq a$, then $a = b$ (i.e., $\leq$ is an antisymmetric relation on $\mathbf{N}$)
(d)   If $a \leq b$ and $b \leq c$, then $a \leq c$ (i.e., $\leq$ is a transitive relation on $\mathbf{N}$)
(e)   Either $a \leq b$ or $b \leq a$
(f)   If $b < a$, then $b + 1 \leq a$
(g)   1 is the least element of $\mathbf{N}$

[*Note:* If you have read Article 7.4, you will recognize that $(\mathbf{N}, \leq)$ is a partially ordered set, or poset, by parts (a), (c), and (d), and indeed is a totally ordered set, due to (e).]

8. ★*(a)*   Write a direct proof of the principle of mathematical induction (IP) from the well-ordering principle.
(b)   Use IP2 to prove that any set X of n real numbers has a smallest element.

10.2   Development of the Integers and Rational Numbers

THE INTEGERS

As noted in Article 10.1, the system $\mathbf{N}$ of positive integers satisfies all the field axioms except the additive identity, additive inverse, and multiplicative inverse properties. We will soon see that we can construct from $\mathbf{N}$, by means of equivalence classes, the number system $\mathbf{Z}$ of all integers, including negative integers and zero. If the mathematical object about to be constructed corresponds to the integers, as we know them intuitively, we should expect the additive deficiencies of $\mathbf{N}$ to be remedied in $\mathbf{Z}$.

As suggested earlier, it is at this point that equivalence classes begin to assume a crucial role. We begin our development by considering the set

N × **N** of all ordered pairs of positive integers. Define a relation $\sim$ on this set by the rule $(m, n) \sim (p, q)$ if and only if $m + q = n + p$. On an intuitive basis we are identifying any two ordered pairs in which the corresponding quantities "first component minus second component" are equal, but our definition is such that only arithmetic in **N** is involved. Our first task is to prove Theorem 1.

THEOREM 1
$\sim$ is an equivalence relation on **N** × **N**.

Proof   (Reflexive) Given $m, n \in$ **N**. Then $(m, n) \sim (m, n)$ since $m + n = n + m$.

(Symmetric) Assume $(m, n) \sim (p, q)$ so that $m + q = n + p$. The statement $(p, q) \sim (m, n)$ means $p + n = q + m$, obviously equivalent to the assumed property.

(Transitive) Assume $(m, n) \sim (p, q)$ and $(p, q) \sim (r, s)$. Then $m + q = n + p$ and $p + s = q + r$. To prove $(m, n) \sim (r, s)$, we must verify $m + s = n + r$. Adding the two assumed equations yields $(m + q) + (p + s) = (n + p) + (q + r)$, which may be rewritten in the form $(m + s) + (p + q) = (n + r) + (p + q)$. Using additive cancellation in **N** [recall Theorem 5(d), Article 10.1], we conclude $m + s = n + r$, as desired. $\square$

Denote by **Z** the set of all equivalence classes induced on **N** × **N** by the equivalence relation $\sim$. Note that the elements of **Z** are of the form $[(a, b)]$, where $(c, d) \in [(a, b)]$ if and only if $a + d = b + c$. For the sake of your intuition, we note that $[(7, 4)]$ will correspond to the integer 3, $[(5, 5)]$ to 0, and $[(3, 4)]$ to -1. We propose now to introduce algebraic structure on **Z** by defining operations of addition and multiplication.

DEFINITION 1
Given elements $[(m, n)]$ and $[(p, q)]$ of **Z**, we define:

(a) The *sum* $[(m, n)] + [(p, q)]$ to equal $[(m + p, n + q)]$, and
(b) The *product* $[(m, n)][(p, q)]$ to equal $[(mp + nq, np + mq)]$

Several examples should be checked to convince you that the preceding definitions are reasonable. For instance, the product of $[(7, 4)]$ with $[(5, 3)]$ equals $[(35 + 12, 20 + 21)] = [(47, 41)]$, corresponding to the fact that the product of 3 and 2 is 6. Having formulated these definitions of addition and multiplication of equivalence classes of ordered pairs, we now come face to face with an issue that will be quite familiar to you by the end of the chapter, namely, *well-definedness* of an algebraic operation. Suppose we wish to use Definition 1(a) to add two elements of **Z**, that is, to add two equivalence classes of ordered pairs of positive integers. According to the definition of addition, we should choose an arbitrary ordered pair (often referred to in this context as a *representative*) from each of the two classes, add those two ordered pairs by (a) of Definition 1, and then locate the equivalence class containing the resulting ordered pair. The problem now is this. Suppose I carry out the procedure just described and arrive at an answer. Suppose you come along and carry out the same procedure, select-ing, however, representatives different from the ones I used (which you are perfectly free to do!). Is the answer you obtain necessarily the same as mine, assuming, of course, that we both calculate correctly? Note, by the way, what it means for our answers to be "the same." We need not arrive at identical ordered pairs as the sum; rather, we need only arrive at ordered pairs that come from the same equivalence class, that is, equivalent ordered pairs. If the operation of addition on **Z**, as defined previously, is to "make sense," if it is to be well defined, the answer to the preceding question had better be "yes." Fortunately, such is the case, with the analogous fact for multiplication also holding true. We formalize these results in our next theorem.

THEOREM 2

Let a, b, c, d, a', b', c', and d' be elements of **N** with $(a, b) \sim (a', b')$ and $(c, d) \sim (c', d')$. Then:

(a) $(a + c, b + d) \sim (a' + c', b' + d')$
(b) $(ac + bd, ad + bc) \sim (a'c' + b'd', a'd' + b'c')$

Proof (a) To show that $(a + c, b + d) \sim (a' + c', b' + d')$, we need to prove that $(a + c) + (b' + d') = (b + d) + (a' + c')$. Our assumptions that $(a, b) \sim (a', b')$ and $(c, d) \sim (c', d')$ yield the equations $a + b' = b + a'$ and $c + d' = d + c'$. Adding these equations and regrouping, by using additive associativity and commutativity, we obtain the desired result.
  (b) Left to the reader (see Exercise 1). □

With the proof of Theorem 2, we now know that $+$ and $\cdot$ are "honest" operations on the set **Z**. The main questions now about the system $(\mathbf{Z}, +, \cdot)$ are: (1) What are its algebraic properties? and (2) How is it related to the system $(\mathbf{N}, +, \cdot)$, from which it was constructed? We will address question (2) first. Experience tells us we should expect **Z** to contain **N** as a proper subset. Let us examine the precise sense in which this turns out to be true.

Let $n \in \mathbf{N}$ and $[(p, q)] \in \mathbf{Z}$. Let us agree to say that n is *associated with* $[(p, q)]$ if and only if $n + q = p$ (automatically implying that $p > q$). Sup-pose n is associated with $[(p, q)]$ and let (r, s) be an arbitrary element of $\mathbf{N} \times \mathbf{N}$. Then it is easy to verify that n is associated with the integer $[(r, s)]$ if and only if $(r, s) \in [(p, q)]$; that is, if and only if $(r, s) \sim (p, q)$. (*Proof*: Sup-pose $n + q = p$ and $n + s = r$. We claim that $(p, q) \sim (r, s)$; that is, $p + s = q + r$. But $p + n + s = n + q + r$ so, by additive cancellation, the desired result holds. Conversely, suppose that $n + q = p$ and $(p, q) \sim (r, s)$, so that $p + s = q + r$. We claim $n + s = r$. But $(n + q) + (p + s) = p + (q + r)$, so that, regrouping, we get $(n + s) + (q + p) = r + (q + p)$, so that $n + s = r$, as desired.) Noting that any positive integer n is surely associated with the integer $[(n + 1, 1)]$, we conclude that each $n \in \mathbf{N}$ is associated with a unique equivalence class in **Z**, a class we will denote by $[n]$, so that the mapping $n \to [n]$ of **N** into **Z** is well defined. Furthermore, this mapping is one to one (Verify!) and is <u>not onto</u>. In fact, an equivalence class $[(p, q)]$ in $\mathbf{Z}$ is in the image of this mapping if and only if $p > q$. Finally, this mapping *preserves the operations* of addition and multiplication, that is, $[n_1] + [n_2] = [n_1 + n_2]$ and $[n_1][n_2] = [n_1 n_2]$ for any positive integers n_1 and n_2. Stated differently, if n_1 is associated with $[(p_1, q_1)]$ and n_2 is associated with $[(p_2, q_2)]$, then $n_1 + n_2$ is associated with $[(p_1 + p_2, q_1 + q_2)]$ and $n_1 n_2$ is associated with $[(p_1 p_2 + q_1 q_2, p_1 q_2 + q_1 p_2)]$. The proofs of these facts are left to you in Exercise 2(c).

Thus we may think of $\mathbf{Z}$ as containing a proper subset; let us call it $\mathbf{Z}^+ = \{[(p, q)] \,|\, p \in \mathbf{N}, q \in \mathbf{N}, p > q\}$, which is, for all intents and purposes, identical to $\mathbf{N}$. (If you study abstract algebra later, you will come to recognize that we have established here an *isomorphism* between $\mathbf{N}$ and $\mathbf{Z}^+$.) It is in this technical sense that $\mathbf{N}$ may be regarded as a subset of the system $\mathbf{Z}$ that we have constructed.

As to properties of $\mathbf{Z}$, you should verify that a number of properties of $\mathbf{N}$, proved for $\mathbf{N}$ in Article 10.1 and listed in Exercise 3, "carry over" to $\mathbf{Z}$. In addition, $\mathbf{Z}$ has desirable properties that $\mathbf{N}$ fails to possess, including Theorem 3.

THEOREM 3

(a) There exists a unique integer a having the property that $x + a = a + x = x$ for all $x \in \mathbf{Z}$. We denote this integer by the symbol "0" and call it the *zero element* or *additive identity* of $\mathbf{Z}$.

(b) To each $x \in \mathbf{Z}$, there corresponds a uniquely determined $y \in \mathbf{Z}$ such that $x + y = y + x = 0$. We denote this integer by the symbol $-x$ and call it the *additive inverse* of x.

Proof (a) Let $a = [(1, 1)]$, and let $x = [(p, q)]$ be an arbitrary integer. Then $x + a = [(1 + p, 1 + q)]$, which clearly equals $[(p, q)]$, so that $x + a = x$, as desired. It is left to you to establish the facts that $a + x = x$ and that a is unique.

(b) Let $x = [(p, q)]$ be an arbitrary integer. Consider the integer $y = [(q, p)]$ and note that $x + y = [(p + q, q + p)] = [(1, 1)] = 0$. Again, you should verify that $y + x = 0$ and that this y is the only integer satisfying $x + y = y + x = 0$. $\square$

With Exercise 3 and Theorem 3, we see that the integers satisfy all but possibly one of the 11 field axioms. It is worth noting here that because $(\mathbf{Z}, +, \cdot)$ is an algebraic structure with two operations satisfying field axioms 1 through 7 and 11, it is an example of what algebraists call a *ring*. In fact, because $\mathbf{Z}$ satisfies Axiom 8, it is a *commutative ring*, and since it satisfies Axiom 9, it is a *ring with unity*. We will note an additional, and highly important, property of $\mathbf{Z}$, in Theorem 5(b). Also, we will address the question of Axiom 10, multiplicative inverses in $\mathbf{Z}$, following the proof of Theorem 6. You will recall that, given $a, b \in \mathbf{N}$, the equation $a + x = b$ does not need to have a solution in **N**. In fact, a solution exists in **N** if and only if $a < b$. This situation is improved upon in **Z**.

THEOREM 4

Let $a, b \in \mathbf{Z}$. Then there exists a unique integer x such that $a + x = b$. This x, which is given by the formula $x = b + (-a)$, is denoted $b - a$ and is called b minus a.

Proof   Note first that $a + x = a + (b + (-a)) = (a + (-a)) + b = 0 + b = b$. Hence $x = b + (-a)$ is a solution. Furthermore, if $b = a + x$, then $(-a) + b = -a + (a + x) = (-a + a) + x = 0 + x = x$, so that $b + (-a)$ is the only solution.   □

Note that the use of the symbol $b - a$ in Theorem 4 is consistent with its use for **N** in Article 10.1 (recall Definition 3). The difference, of course, is that $b - a$ exists in **Z** for any integers a and b, whereas in **N**, $b - a$ exists, for positive integers a and b, if and only if $a < b$. We describe this situation by saying that **Z** is *closed* under the operation of subtraction, whereas **N** fails to be closed under subtraction.

The integer 0, introduced in Theorem 3, has additional properties of interest, including Theorem 5.

THEOREM 5

(a)   For any $x \in \mathbf{Z}$, $x \cdot 0 = 0$

(b)   For any $x, y \in \mathbf{Z}$, if $xy = 0$, then either $x = 0$ or $y = 0$

(c)   For any $x, y, z \in \mathbf{Z}$, if $xy = xz$ and $x \neq 0$, then $y = z$

Proof   (a)   Let $x = [(p, q)]$ be an arbitrary element of **Z**. Recalling that $0 = [(1, 1)]$, we note that $x \cdot 0 = [(p, q)] \cdot [(1, 1)] = [(p + q, q + p)] = [(1, 1)] = 0$, as claimed.

(b)   Let $x = [(p, q)]$ and $y = [(r, s)]$ be integers and suppose $xy = 0$. That is, suppose $0 = [(1, 1)] = [(pr + qs, ps + qr)]$. Suppose furthermore that $x \neq 0$; that is, $p \neq q$. We claim $y = 0$; that is, $r = s$. Assume, with no loss of generality, that $p > q$. From $xy = 0$, we have $ps + qr = pr + qs$. Using algebraic properties of **N**, we arrive at the equation $(p - q)s = (p - q)r$. Since $p > q$, we have $p - q \in \mathbf{N}$ so that we may use multiplicative cancellation in **N** [recall Theorem 7(e), Article 10.1] to cancel $p - q$ and arrive at the desired conclusion $s = r$.

(c)   If $xy = xz$, then $xy - xz = 0$ [by Exercise 4(b)(ii)]. Hence $0 = xy - xz = x(y - z)$. Since $x \neq 0$, then by (b), we must have $y - z = 0$, or $y = z$.   □

A consequence of Theorem 5(a) is that 0 cannot possibly have a multiplicative inverse in **Z**. Because the ring **Z** satisfies the property in Theorem 5(b) (often referred to as "having no zero divisors"), **Z** is an example of what algebraists call an *integral domain*. We will soon see that all other integers except 1 and -1 also fail to have multiplicative inverses in **Z**. We next introduce an order relation in **Z**.

DEFINITION 2

Let $x = [(a, b)]$ and $y = [(c, d)]$ be integers. We say that $x < y$ in case $a + d < b + c$.

In Exercise 4(a) you are asked to verify that the relation $<$ is well defined. Our intuitive expectation of the inequality $[(a, b)] < [(c, d)]$ is that $a - b$ be less than $c - d$. The definition we have given amounts to the same thing, and furthermore, involves <u>positive</u> integers $a + d$ and $b + c$, so that we may take advantage of the "less than" relation already defined on **N**.

Note that if $x \in \mathbf{Z}$, $x = [(a, b)]$, then $x > 0$ if and only if $a > b$, $x = 0$ if and only if $a = b$, and $x < 0$ if and only if $a < b$. Furthermore, $x > 0$ if and only if $-x < 0$. Denoting again by $\mathbf{Z}^+$ the subset $\{[(p, q)] \mid p \in \mathbf{N}, q \in \mathbf{N}, p > q\}$ of **Z**, we can easily show that $\mathbf{Z}^+$ is closed under both addition and multiplication.

Once again, many properties of less than in **N** carry over to **Z**. A number of such properties are listed in Exercise 3. We have, in addition, a number of other properties of **Z** contained in Exercises 4 and 5, as well as in the following theorem.

THEOREM 6

Let $x, y, z \in \mathbf{Z}$:

(a) If $x < y$ and $z > 0$, then $xz < yz$
(b) If $x < y$ and $z < 0$, then $xz > yz$
(c) If $xz < yz$ and $z > 0$, then $x < y$
(d) If $xz < yz$ and $z < 0$, then $x > y$

Proof (a) Let $x = [(a, b)]$, $y = [(c, d)]$, $z = [(e, f)]$, where all variables in parentheses represent positive integers. By hypotheses, $a + d < b + c$ and $f < e$. To show $xz < yz$, we note that $xz = [(ae + bf, af + be)]$ and $yz = [(ce + df, cf + de)]$, so that the inequality $ae + bf + cf + de < af + be + ce + df$ must be derived. This inequality may be rewritten as $(b + c)f + (a + d)e < (b + c)e + (a + d)f$, which is equivalent to $(b + c)(f - e) + (a + d)(e - f) < 0$ or $[(b + c) - (a + d)](f - e) < 0$. But the latter inequality is true since $f - e < 0$ and $(b + c) - (a + d) > 0$.

The proofs of (b), (c), and (d) are similar and are left to you [Exercise 5(c)]. □

THE RATIONALS

In Theorem 7(d), Article 10.1, we showed that positive integers not equal to 1 do not have multiplicative inverses in **N**. A similar result can be established in **Z**. Suppose x is an integer not equal to ± 1. If $x = 0$, then x has no multiplicative inverse, by Theorem 5(a). If x is positive and y is an integer such that $xy = 1$, then y must be positive (since $1 > 0$) and we have a contradiction of Theorem 7(d). If x is negative and $xy = 1$ for some $y \in \mathbf{Z}$, then necessarily y is negative. But then $-x$ and $-y$ are both positive integers not equal to 1 and $(-x)(-y) = xy = 1$, again, contradicting Theorem 7(d). We conclude that the system $(\mathbf{Z}, +, \cdot)$ of integers fails to satisfy the multiplicative inverse property and, in fact, that all integers not equal to ± 1 fail to have multiplicative inverses. It is primarily for this reason that we wish to expand $\mathbf{Z}$ to a system $\mathbf{Q}$, the rationals, in which the favorable properties of $\mathbf{Z}$ are retained and the algebraic shortcoming just illustrated is remedied.

The construction of $\mathbf{Q}$ from $\mathbf{Z}$ is very similar to the construction of $\mathbf{Z}$ from $\mathbf{N}$, just accomplished. You will recall that the elements of $\mathbf{Z}$ are equivalence classes of ordered pairs of positive integers; elements of $\mathbf{Q}$ will soon be seen to be equivalence classes of certain ordered pairs of integers. Once constructed, $\mathbf{Z}$ was proved to contain a substructure $\mathbf{Z}^{+}$ "isomorphic to" $\mathbf{N}$ (so that, essentially, $\mathbf{N} \subseteq \mathbf{Z}$). We will see that $\mathbf{Q}$ contains a substructure isomorphic to $\mathbf{Z}$, so that, for all intents and purposes, $\mathbf{Z}$ is a subset of $\mathbf{Q}$. As indicated earlier, the primary advantage of $\mathbf{Z}$, compared to $\mathbf{N}$, is that it makes up for algebraic deficiencies of $\mathbf{N}$ (i.e., lack of additive identity and inverse properties). The corresponding primary advantage of $\mathbf{Q}$ is to make up for the lack of multiplicative inverses of most nonzero elements of $\mathbf{Z}$.

Because of all this familiarity, we will provide in the text only the bare outlines of the construction of $\mathbf{Q}$, leaving the details to you. To start, we consider the set of all ordered pairs of integers (x, y) such that $y \neq 0$, in symbols, $\mathbf{Z} \times (\mathbf{Z} - \{0\})$. For the sake of familiarity, you should think of (x, y) as the fraction x/y. Define a relation $\approx$ on this set by the rule $(x, y) \approx (w, z)$ if and only if $xz = yw$. It is easy to verify that $\approx$ is an equivalence relation on $\mathbf{Z} \times (\mathbf{Z} - \{0\})$. Denote by $\mathbf{Q}$ the set of all equivalence classes corresponding to $\approx$, denoting the equivalence class determined by an ordered pair (x, y) by the symbol $[[(x, y)]]$. Note that if $a, b, x, y \in \mathbf{Z}$ with $b \neq 0$ and $y \neq 0$, we have $(a, b) \in [[(x, y)]]$ if and only if $ay = bx$; as a specific example, we have $(1, 2) \in [[(7, 14)]]$.

Next, we define operations of addition and multiplication on $\mathbf{Q}$. Guided by familiar rules of arithmetic, we are led to formulate the following definition.

DEFINITION 3

Let $r = [[(w, x)]]$ and $s = [[(y, z)]]$ be elements of $\mathbf{Q}$. We define:

(a) The *sum* $r + s$ of r and s by the rule $r + s = [[(wz + xy, xz)]]$, and

(b) The *product* rs by $rs = [[(wy, xz)]]$

Clearly our goal at this stage should be to prove that the set $\mathbf{Q}$, endowed with the two operations just defined, satisfies a number of familiar algebraic properties. Of primary interest should be the multiplicative inverse axiom (Axiom 10 of the field axioms) if, as we expect, $\mathbf{Q}$ is to prove to be a field. But before attempting to prove any such properties, we must address an issue that must always be attended to whenever we define algebraic operations on a set whose elements are equivalence classes—prove that the operations are well defined. It is left to you to formulate the meaning of this statement (using Theorem 2 as a guide) and write out the proofs (Exercise 7).

Once it has been verified that addition and multiplication, as described in Definition 3, are legitimate operations, it remains to show that $(Q, +, \cdot)$ is a field. To do this, you should verify the 11 field axioms. It should be noted that $[[(0, 1)]]$ and $[[(1, 1)]]$ are additive and multiplicative identities for Q, respectively, while $[[(-a, b)]]$ and $[[(b, a)]]$ are, respectively, the additive and multiplicative inverses of a given $[[(a, b)]] \in Q$, with the assumption of a nonzero value of a made in the multiplicative case.

After verifying the 11 axioms, you might next look to Article 9.1, where number of general field properties are proved, for additional algebraic properties of Q.

Let us consider next how Z might be regarded as a subset of Q. Given integers x, a, and b, with $b \neq 0$, we say that x is associated with the rational number $[[(a, b)]]$ if and only if $xb = a$. You should verify that if x is associated with $[[(a, b)]]$, then x is also associated with a rational number $[[(c, d)]]$ if and only if $(c, d) \in [[(a, b)]]$. That is, an integer is associated with at most one rational number. Note also that a rational number $[[(a, b)]]$ has an integer n associated with it if and only if b divides a, in the sense of Example 2, Article 6.1. Noting that any integer x is surely associated with the rational number $[[(x, 1)]]$, we conclude that any integer x is associated with a unique equivalence class in Q, a class we will denote by $[[x]]$, so that the mapping $x \rightarrow [[x]]$ of Z into Q is well defined. Furthermore, this mapping is one to one and not onto (you should supply a precise description of the subset of Q constituting the image of this mapping). Finally, the mapping preserves both addition and multiplication; that is, $[[x_1]] + [[x_2]] = [[x_1 + x_2]]$ and $[[x_1]] \cdot [[x_2]] = [[x_1 x_2]]$ for any integers x_1 and x_2. Thus the image of the mapping $x \rightarrow [[x]]$ is a subset of Q (closed under addition and multiplication, as you can verify; see Exercise 8), which, for all intents and purposes, is identical to Z. Hence Z may be regarded as a subset of Q in exactly the same sense in which we previously observed N to be a subset of Z (recall the lengthy discussion between Theorems 2 and 3, earlier in this article).

We are left with the final problem of defining an ordering on Q. Before addressing this matter, let us first make a remark pertaining to generalization of the part of the construction of Q we've seen thus far. Recall that the $(Z, +, \cdot)$ is a particular example of an algebraic structure known as an integral domain, that is, a commutative ring with unity having no zero divisors (recall the discussions following Theorems 3 and 5). From a course in abstract algebra you will learn that the process of passing from integers to quotients of integers can be generalized. In fact, any integral domain D can be "embedded" in a unique smallest field F containing D as a subdomain; this F is called the *field of quotients* of D. Viewed in this more general context, the field of rationals is the field of quotients of the integral domain of integers.

Finally, let us deal with the issue of order in $\mathbf{Q}$. We do this by noting that the subset $\mathbf{Q}^+$ of $\mathbf{Q}$ defined by $\mathbf{Q}^+ = \{[[(a, b)]] \,|\, a, b \in \mathbf{Z}, ab > 0\}$ satisfies the properties of $\mathscr{P}$, the positive part of an ordered field, in Definition 1, Article 9.2. Once again, verification of this fact is left to you in Exercise 9.

With this, all the properties of ordered fields listed in Article 9.2 can now be seen as valid in $\mathbf{Q}$. We remind you of the deficiency in $\mathbf{Q}$, discussed in Article 9.3 (recall Example 3 of that article), that causes us to carry our construction beyond $\mathbf{Q}$. The ordered field $(\mathbf{Q}, +, \cdot)$ is incomplete, in the sense of Definition 4, Article 9.3. In Article 10.3 we will outline a construction of a *complete* ordered field, the real numbers $\mathbf{R}$, that can be built from $\mathbf{Q}$ using equivalence classes of *Cauchy sequences*. As in the two constructions of this article, well-definedness of operations will be an important issue; analogous to those two constructions we will see that $\mathbf{R}$ contains a substructure that is essentially identical to $\mathbf{Q}$.

Exercises

★1. Prove Theorem 2(b); that is, prove that the operation of multiplication on $\mathbf{Z}$, as defined in Definition 1(b), is well defined.

2. This exercise relates to the "embedding" of $\mathbf{N}$ in $\mathbf{Z}$, outlined in the text following the proof of Theorem 2.

(a) Prove that the mapping $n \to [n]$ of $\mathbf{N}$ into $\mathbf{Z}$ is one to one.

(b) Prove that the mapping of $\mathbf{N}$ into $\mathbf{Z}$ described in (a) is not onto. Prove, in addition, that an equivalence class $[(p, q)]$ is in the image of this mapping if and only if $p > q$.

(c) Prove that the mapping described in (a) "preserves the operations" of addition and multiplication in $\mathbf{N}$; that is $[n_1] + [n_2] = [n_1 + n_2]$ and $[n_1][n_2] = [n_1 n_2]$ for any positive integers n_1 and n_2.

★(d) Prove that the subset $\mathbf{Z}^+ = \{[(p, q)] \,|\, p \in \mathbf{N}, q \in \mathbf{N}, \ p > q\}$ is closed under addition and multiplication.

3. Verify the following algebraic properties for $\mathbf{Z}$:

(a) Closure, associativity, and commutativity for addition

(b) Additive cancellation

★(c) Distributivity of multiplication over addition

(d) Closure, associativity, commutativity and identity for multiplication

(e) (i) For all $a \in \mathbf{Z}, (-1)a = -a$

    (ii) For all $a, b \in \mathbf{Z}, a(-b) = -(ab) = (-a)b$

    (iii) For all $a \in \mathbf{Z}, -(-a) = a$

    (iv) For all $a, b \in \mathbf{Z}, (-a)(-b) = ab$

(f) The results of Theorem 9, Article 10.1, generalized to $\mathbf{Z}$ (dropping, however, any assumptions about order relationships between integers a, b, and c).

4. *(a)*   Prove that the relation $<$ from Definition 2 is well defined. That is, prove that if $(a, b) \sim (a', b')$ and $(c, d) \sim (c', d')$, where all the variables involved represent positive integers, then $a + d < b + c$ if and only if $a' + d' < b' + c'$.

(b)   In **Z**, prove that:

(i) $1 > 0$

$\star$*(ii)*   If $x \in \mathbf{Z}$, $x = [(a, b)]$, then $x > 0$ if and only if $a > b$, $x < 0$ if and only if $a < b$ and $x = 0$ if and only if $a = b$

(iii)   If $x \in \mathbf{Z}$, then $x > 0$ if and only if $-x < 0$

(iv)   If $x, y \in \mathbf{Z}$, then $x < y$ if and only if $-y < -x$

(v)   If $x, y \in \mathbf{Z}$, then $x < y$ if and only if $y - x > 0$; $x = y$ if and only if $y - x = 0$

5. *(a)*   Generalize part (c) of Theorem 8, Article 10.1, to **Z**; that is, prove that the relation $<$, defined on **Z** in Definition 2, is transitive.

(b)   Generalize Theorem 10, Article 10.1, to **Z**; that is, prove the trichotomy property for the relation $<$ on **Z**.

(c)   Prove parts (b)(c)(d) of Theorem 6.

(d)   Generalize parts (a)(b)(c) of Exercise 6, Article 10.1, to **Z** [adding, however, whatever additional hypotheses might be necessary in (b)].

6. *(a)*   Prove that there is no integer x such that $0 < x < 1$. [*Hint:* Apply the well-ordering principle to the set $\{x \in \mathbf{Z} \mid 0 < x < 1\}$ under the assumption that this set is nonempty. Keep in mind the result in Theorem 6(a).]

(b)   Prove that there is no integer between x and $x + 1$, for any integer x. [*Hint:* Use an argument by cases, approaching the case $x > 0$ by induction.)

7. Prove that the operations of addition and multiplication on **Q**, from Definition 3, are well defined.

8. Prove that the mapping $x \to [[x]]$ of **Z** into **Q**, defined in the discussion following Definition 3 (see the fourth paragraph following Definition 3) is one to one, not onto, and preserves the operations of addition and multiplication. Prove that the image of this mapping, a proper subset of **Q**, is closed under the operations of addition and multiplication in **Q**.

9. Prove that the subset $\mathbf{Q}^+$ of **Q**, defined by $\mathbf{Q}^+ = \{[[(a, b)]] \mid a, b \in \mathbf{Z}, ab > 0\}$ satisfies the conditions of Definition 1, Article 9.2, for the positive part of an ordered field.

10. Using Articles 9.1 and 9.2, make a list of algebraic and order properties that are valid in the structure $(\mathbf{Q}, +, \cdot)$, by virtue of the fact that this structure is an ordered field.

10.3   Outline of the Construction of the Reals

We now deal with the problem of constructing **R** from **Q**. The difficulties in presenting this material are pedagogical as well as mathematical. As has happened at several previous stages of the text (e.g., Articles 6.4 and 8.3), we have a situation in which the details of the mathematics we would like to present are, in all likelihood, slightly beyond the level of experience of most readers. Specifically, a full understanding of the construction of **R** from **Q**, by using equivalence classes of Cauchy sequences, requires experience and well-developed facility in working with properties of sequences, and especially a working knowledge of the definitions of convergent sequence and Cauchy sequence. In truth, most students who are ever going to go through all the details of this construction should probably do so after their course in advanced calculus.

For these reasons, we place even less emphasis in this article than before on providing full proofs of most theorems. For the more readily accessible arguments, we strike a balance between proofs given in the text and those left as exercises. In the case of a number of either very detailed and lengthy or quite technical proofs, we give only an outline or some discussion of the proof. If highly motivated, you may take this as a challenge to your proof-writing ability, whereas if you are more casual in your approach, then you should only try to follow the main lines of the development.

So let us begin our sketch of the construction of **R**; we start with some heuristics. Think of a familiar irrational number such as π. A familiar characteristic of this number is its nonterminating, nonrepeating decimal expansion that begins 3.14159. One way to think of the number π, using rational numbers only, is as the limit of the sequence $x_1 = 3.1$, $x_2 = 3.14$, $x_3 = 3.141$, and so on. This example illustrates the idea of an irrational number as the limit of a sequence of rational numbers, and so introduces us to the basic idea behind the construction of the reals from the rationals by way of sequences. But, of course, the rules of the game do not permit us to work back from a known irrational number to a sequence of rationals. We must proceed outward from the rational number system, with no a priori knowledge of any other type of number. The idea that should motivate us, however, is this. It seems from the preceding example that there are sequences of rationals that "want to" converge but have nothing to converge to in the system **Q**. Theorem 1, one of the few we prove in this article, gives us an initial handle on precisely which sequences of rationals "seem to want" to converge. First, let us formulate a definition of a convergent sequence of rational numbers.

DEFINITION 1

A sequence $\{q_n\}$ of rational numbers is said to **converge** to the rational number q, denoted $q_n \to q$, if and only if, to every positive rational number ε, there corresponds a positive integer N such that $|q_n - q| < \varepsilon$ whenever $n \in \mathbf{N}$ with $n \geq N$.

THEOREM 1

If $\{q_n\}$ is a convergent sequence of rational numbers, then $\{q_n\}$ satisfies the condition: To every positive rational number ε, there corresponds a positive integer N such that $|q_m - q_n| < \varepsilon$ whenever $m, n \in \mathbf{N}$ with $m, n \geq N$.

Proof   Let ε be an arbitrary positive rational number. We must prove that there exists a positive integer N such that, for any $m, n \in \mathbf{N}$ with $m, n \geq N$, we have $|q_m - q_n| < \varepsilon$. According to the hypothesis of convergence, say to a rational number q, we may assert that, corresponding to the given ε, divided by 2, there is a positive integer N_0 such that, for any integers m and n greater than or equal to N_0, we have both $|q_m - q| < \varepsilon/2$ and $|q_n - q| < \varepsilon/2$. Letting the desired N equal this N_0, we note that $|q_m - q_n| = |(q_m - q) + (q - q_n)| \leq |q_m - q| + |q - q_n| < \varepsilon/2 + \varepsilon/2 = \varepsilon$, whenever $m, n \in \mathbf{N}$ with $m, n \geq N$, as desired. $\square$

DEFINITION 2
A sequence of rational numbers satisfying the property derived in Theorem 1 is called a **Cauchy sequence** of rational numbers.

Intuitively, Cauchy sequences are sequences whose terms "eventually" all become closer and closer to one another (in comparison to a convergent sequence, whose terms eventually all become arbitrarily close to a particular number). Theorem 1 tells us that any sequence of rational numbers that converges to a rational number must have this Cauchy property. The example given earlier, involving π, provides a clue that there are Cauchy sequences of rationals that do not converge to rationals. It suggests, furthermore, that if sequences of rationals are going to converge to something outside $\mathbf{Q}$ (something that doesn't exist in our discussion as yet, but that it is our goal to construct), then the only sequences that "have a prayer" of doing so are Cauchy sequences.

Hence we are motivated to begin our construction by considering the collection $\mathfrak{C}$ of all Cauchy sequences of rational numbers. We make $\mathfrak{C}$ into an algebraic structure by defining operations of addition and multiplication in componentwise fashion. That is, the nth term of the sum (respectively, product) of two sequences in $\mathfrak{C}$ is the sum (respectively, product) of the respective nth terms. In order for these operations on $\mathfrak{C}$ to be meaningful, we need to be certain that the result of combining two elements of $\mathfrak{C}$ is an element of $\mathfrak{C}$ (we are, of course, referring here to the issue of *closure*). Toward this end, we have Theorem 2.

THEOREM 2
If $\{a_n\}$ and $\{b_n\}$ are Cauchy sequences of rationals, so are the sequences $\{a_n + b_n\}$, $\{a_n b_n\}$ and $\{-a_n\}$. Also, any constant sequence is Cauchy, including the sequences $\{0, 0, 0, \ldots\}$ and $\{1, 1, 1, \ldots\}$.

We begin here to give only comments on proofs, rather than the proofs themselves, of most theorems. In reference to Theorem 2 we note that a necessary lemma for proving closure under multiplication is the fact that every Cauchy sequence of rationals is bounded in $\mathbf{Q}$ [see Exercise 1(a)]. That is, if $\{q_n\}$ is Cauchy, then there exists a rational number B such that $|q_n| \leq B$ for all $n \in \mathbf{N}$. We remark also that once Theorem 2 is known, it is relatively easy to see that the algebraic structure $(\mathfrak{C}, +, \cdot)$ satisfies all except possibly Axiom 10 of the axioms for a field. In fact, it is clear that Axiom 10 is not satisfied, because $\{1/n\} \in \mathfrak{C}$, while the only possible candidate for its multiplicative inverse, namely, $\{n\}$, is not in $\mathfrak{C}$. Sequences containing some (but <u>not</u> all) zero terms also present difficulties, in connection with Axiom 10. Any such sequence is not the additive identity sequence (all of whose terms are zero), but its product with any other sequence clearly will not equal the multiplicative identity sequence (a constant sequence of 1's), and so any such sequence fails to have a multiplicative inverse in $\mathfrak{C}$. Hence it is clear that the structure $(\mathfrak{C}, +, \cdot)$ is not itself a candidate for the complete ordered field that we seek.

There is another difficulty with the structure $\mathfrak{C}$, yet another reason that $(\mathfrak{C}, +, \cdot)$ cannot be the structure we are seeking. This problem, however, turns out to be part of the solution, since it suggests how we might build another structure from $\mathfrak{C}$. If we have it in mind to identify irrational numbers with Cauchy sequences of rationals that do not converge to rationals (this, indeed, is our basic premise), then we must note the following. Clearly there may be many distinct Cauchy sequences that "seem to want" to converge to the same (irrational) number. Consider, for example, our sequence of decimal approximations to π, described at the outset of this article. We may easily generate a countably infinite number of different, but "equivalent" Cauchy sequences, one in fact for each positive integer n, by changing the nth term of the given sequence and leaving all other terms unchanged. If our original Cauchy sequence seemed to want to converge to π, then surely all these new sequences, each of which differs from the original in only a single term, must seem to want to converge to π also. The answer to this problem, which amazingly turns out to be the solution to our other problems as well, is to define an equivalence relation on $\mathfrak{C}$ and to deal with *equivalence classes of Cauchy sequences*, rather than with Cauchy sequences themselves. Denoting by **R** this collection of equivalence classes of Cauchy sequences, we announce at this (admittedly premature) stage that this **R** is going to turn out to be the underlying set for the real number field! Let us now proceed with a careful outline of the details.

DEFINITION 3

A sequence $\{z_n\}$ of rational numbers is said to be a **null sequence** if and only if to every positive rational number ε, there corresponds a positive integer N such that $|z_n| < \varepsilon$ whenever $n \in \mathbf{N}$ with $n \geq N$.

In other words, a null sequence of rationals is simply a sequence of rationals that converges to zero; the sequence $\{1/n\}$ is a familiar example. We now apply the concept of null sequence to aid in formulating the desired equivalence relation on $\mathfrak{C}$. The idea is this: If two sequences of rationals seem to want to converge to the same number (whether or not rational),

what should be true about the componentwise difference of the two sequences? Those of you whose immediate reaction is "null sequence" are
"right on the money"! We now have a way of characterizing, in a manner
that operates entirely within **Q**, our intuitive, but vague, idea of two sequences of rationals seeming to want to converge to the same number (possibly not rational). We formalize this in Definition 4.

DEFINITION 4
Define a relation $\sim$ on the set $\mathfrak{C}$ of all Cauchy sequences of rational numbers,
by the rule $\{a_n\} \sim \{b_n\}$ if and only if the sequence $\{a_n - b_n\}$ of componentwise
differences is a null sequence.

THEOREM 3
The relation $\sim$ is an equivalence relation on $\mathfrak{C}$.

As indicated earlier, we denote by **R** the collection of all equivalence
classes generated on $\mathfrak{C}$ by $\sim$. Also, we denote by $[a_n]$ the equivalence class
determined by the sequence $\{a_n\}$. The proof of Theorem 3 is an easy exercise [see Exercise 2(a)] for anyone with any experience whatsoever in working with sequences. Recalling the process used in Article 10.2 to construct
Z from **N** and **Q** from **Z**, the next step should be evident; it is time to
define operations of addition and multiplication on **R**.

DEFINITION 5
We define operations of "addition" and "multiplication," denoted $+$ and $\cdot$ respectively, on **R**, as follows. Let $[a_n]$ and $[b_n]$ be elements of **R**. Then we define:

(a)   The **sum** $[a_n] + [b_n]$ to be $[a_n + b_n]$, and
(b)   The **product** $[a_n][b_n]$ to be $[a_n b_n]$.

If we have done our job well thus far in this chapter, you should be at
least one move ahead of the discussion at this stage and thinking about
what must clearly be the next step. We must prove that $+$ and $\cdot$, as defined
in Definition 5, are well-defined operations. That is, we must show that if
$[a_n] = [a'_n]$ and $[b_n] = [b'_n]$, then $[a_n + b_n] = [a'_n + b'_n]$ and $[a_n b_n] = [a'_n b'_n]$.
More specifically, we need the following result.

THEOREM 4
Let $[a_n]$, $[b_n]$, $[a'_n]$, and $[b'_n]$ be elements of **R**. Then if $\{a_n - a'_n\}$ and $\{b_n - b'_n\}$
are null sequences, we have:

(a) $\{(a_n + b_n) - (a'_n + b'_n)\}$ is a null sequence, and
(b) $\{a_n b_n - a'_n b'_n\}$ is a null sequence.

The proof of Theorem 4, which we again do not include in the text,
should be a reasonable exercise [see Exercise 2(b)] for those who are at-

tempting to fill in the proofs; (b) is by far the less routine and we include hints for the proof in the statement of the exercise.

At this point we have constructed the object we've been looking for, but we are far from finished. In fact, there are four major steps remaining. You should stop for a moment and think through what those four steps are. Let us now resume and begin to present, with most details omitted, the four steps.

THEOREM 5

The system ($\mathbf{R}$, $+$, $\cdot$) is a field.

Remarks on the proof   Most parts of the verification of Theorem 5 (i.e., all field axioms except the multiplicative inverse axiom) are routine and are left to you in Exercise 3(a). We do note, however, in reference to Axiom 4, that the additive identity for $\mathbf{R}$ is the equivalence class consisting of all the null sequences of rational numbers [you should verify in Exercise 3(b) that the collection of all null sequences does indeed constitute an equivalence class]. This fact is important in understanding why the multiplicative inverse axiom is satisfied in $\mathbf{R}$. Suppose $[a_n]$, for instance, is a nonzero equivalence class in $\mathbf{R}$. We claim that $[a_n]$ has a multiplicative inverse $[b_n]$ in $\mathbf{R}$. That is, there exists a Cauchy sequence $\{b_n\}$ such that $[a_n b_n] = [1]$, in other words, such that $\{1 - a_n b_n\}$ is a null sequence. The fact that $[a_n]$ is nonzero means that $\{a_n\}$ is not a null sequence. This means that there exists a positive rational ε such that infinitely many terms of the sequence are $\geq \varepsilon$ in absolute value. In symbols, $\exists \varepsilon > 0$ (ε rational) such that, for any $N \in \mathbf{N}$, there exists $n \in \mathbf{N}$ such that $n > N$ and $|a_n| \geq \varepsilon$. Combining this with the fact that $\{a_n\}$ is Cauchy, we can prove that there exists a positive integer N_0 such that $|a_m| > \varepsilon/2$ for all $m \in \mathbf{N}$ such that $m > N_0$. An immediate consequence of this fact is that $a_m \neq 0$ for all but (at most) finitely many terms of the sequence, specifically, $a_m \neq 0$ whenever $m > N_0$. We are now ready to define the sequence $\{b_n\}$. Let $b_n = 0$ if $n \leq N_0$ and let $b_n = 1/a_n$ if $n \geq N_0$. Clearly the product sequence $\{a_n b_n\}$ has values 0 for $n \leq N_0$ and 1 for $n > N_0$, so that the sequence $\{1 - a_n b_n\}$, having all terms beyond the N_0th equal to zero, is clearly a null sequence, as desired. One final remark about this verification: We must, of course, prove specifically that the sequence $\{b_n\}$, as we've defined it, determines an equivalence class in $\mathbf{R}$. For this we need that $\{b_n\}$ is Cauchy. You should be able to fill in this detail [see Exercise 3(c)], if you wish to do so.   □

So ($\mathbf{R}$, $+$, $\cdot$) is a field, modulo, of course, verification of all the details of Theorem 5. Before addressing the matters of ordering and completeness, let us consider in exactly what sense $\mathbf{Q}$ can be regarded as a subset of $\mathbf{R}$. We say that a rational number q is *associated with* the real number $[q_n]$ if and only if the sequence $\{q_n - q\}$ is null. Note that if q is associated with the equivalence class containing the sequence $\{q_n\}$, then q is associated with the real number $[q'_n]$ if and only if $\{q_n - q'_n\}$ is a null sequence; that is, $\{q_n\}$ is equivalent to $\{q'_n\}$. Noting that any rational q is surely associated with the real number $[q] = [\{q, q, q, \ldots\}]$, we conclude that each rational number is associated with a unique equivalence class in **R**, so that the mapping $q \to [q]$ is well defined. You should be familiar by now with the litany of details that should be verified, in reference to the mapping $q \to [q]$. This mapping is one to one, not onto, and preserves addition and multiplication; its image is a subset of **R** that is closed under addition and multiplication (see Exercise 4).

We deal next with the matter of ordering. In order that $(\mathbf{R}, +, \cdot)$ be established to be an ordered field, we must specify the subset of **R** that will serve as $\mathscr{P}$, the positive part of **R**. It turns out that the definition of $\mathscr{P}$ is not especially intuitive. Recall, from the discussion of the proof of Theorem 5, that any nonnull Cauchy sequence has the property that the set of all terms of the sequence, after some specific term, is "bounded away" from zero by some specific positive rational number ($\varepsilon/2$ in the context of that discussion). More formally, if $\{a_n\}$ is a nonnull Cauchy sequence of rationals, then there exists a positive rational number ε and a positive integer N such that $|a_n| \geq \varepsilon$ for all $n \geq N$. This provides the idea for the correct definition of positivity in **R**.

DEFINITION 6
An element $[a_n]$ of **R** is said to be **positive** if and only if there exists a positive rational number ε and a positive integer N such that $a_n \geq \varepsilon$ for all $n \geq N$.

As usual, we must worry about well-definedness. Specifically, we should verify that if $\{a_n\}$ and $\{a'_n\}$ are equivalent Cauchy sequences, then $\{a_n\}$ satisfies the property in Definition 6 if and only if $\{a'_n\}$ does (see Exercise 5). Following this, we need to verify that the set $\mathscr{P}$ of all positive elements satisfies the requirements of Definition 1, Article 9.2. This done, the conclusion that $(\mathbf{R}, +, \cdot)$ is an ordered field is justified.

The final step is the verification of completeness. This is technically the most complicated part of the entire development, and we continue here to omit most of the details of the proof. Let us, however, look for a moment at the main lines of the argument. As we have learned to do, we begin by asking ourselves, "What must we prove?" The answer to this question, of course, is contained in the definition of completeness. We must let X be a nonempty subset of **R** that is bounded above in **R**. We must show that X has a least upper bound in **R**; that is, we must prove existence of a real number l satisfying the two defining properties of the least upper bound in an ordered field (recall Definition 4, Article 9.3). Now the fact that X is bounded above in **R** means that there exists a real number $[a_n]$ such that every element $[x_n]$ of X satisfies $[x_n] \leq [a_n]$; that is, $[a_n - x_n]$ is positive in the sense of Definition 6. It follows that there is an integer $[k]$ (i.e., the equivalence class containing the constant sequence with all terms equal to the integer k) such that $[x_n] \leq [k]$ for all $[x_n] \in X$. This k is an upper bound in $\mathbf{R}$ for X; our goal is to produce a <u>least</u> upper bound for X. Such an object, being an element of $\mathbf{R}$, may be determined by specifying a Cauchy sequence $\{q_n\}$ of rationals with appropriate properties. The following procedure can be shown to yield such a sequence. For each positive integer m, let t_m be the smallest integer such that the real (in fact, rational) number determined by the constant sequence $\{t_m/2^m, t_m/2^m, t_m/2^m, \ldots\}$ is an upper bound for X. The fact that such an integer exists, for each $m \in \mathbf{N}$, depends on the well-ordering principle for $\mathbf{N}$; the existence of the integer upper bound $[k]$, alluded to earlier, comes into play in this verification. Next, define a sequence $\{q_n\}$ by letting $q_n = t_n/2^n$ for each $n \in \mathbf{N}$; let $l = [q_n]$. It can be proved that $\{q_n\}$ is a Cauchy sequence of rationals, so that $l \in \mathbf{R}$. Finally, it can be shown that l satisfies the two conditions required to conclude that l is the least upper bound for the given X. Subject to rigorous verification of all the details just outlined, we are able to conclude Theorem 6.

THEOREM 6
The ordered field $(\mathbf{R}, +, \cdot)$ is complete.

In fact, much more can be proved in reference to the real number field, including a theorem asserting uniqueness of a complete ordered field. Specifically, it can be shown that any complete ordered field must be *order isomorphic to* (i.e., for all intents and purposes in an algebraic sense, *the same as*) $\mathbf{R}$. As indicated earlier, we will not pursue uniqueness of a complete ordered field in this text.

Recalling that $\mathbf{Q}$ turned out to be the "smallest" field containing $\mathbf{Z}$, you may wonder whether $\mathbf{R}$ has that same relationship to $\mathbf{Q}$. The answer is "no." The subset $\mathbf{Q}[\sqrt{2}] = \{a + b\sqrt{2} \,|\, a, b \in \mathbf{Q}\}$ is a field (under the usual operations of addition and multiplication inherited from $\mathbf{R}$) properly contained in $\mathbf{R}$ and properly containing $\mathbf{Q}$. The structure of fields such as $Q[\sqrt{2}]$, known as *subfields* of $\mathbf{R}$, is commonly studied in the portion of an introductory abstract algebra course devoted to field theory.

Having fought your way through the outlined construction of $\mathbf{R}$, and also being familiar with the manner in which the complex number field is built from $\mathbf{R}$ (recall Article 9.4), you may wish to spend a few moments comparing the two constructions. Such a comparison should remove any doubt that such descriptive terms as "real" and "imaginary," in reference to these number systems, are anything other than historical accidents.

Finally, it may be recalled, from Definition 5 and Theorem 1, Article 9.3, that the real number field is Archimedean ordered. Basically, this means that, given any positive real numbers a and b with $a < b$, a sufficient number of additions of a to itself will eventually exceed b. When this concept was introduced, in Article 9.3, we promised to provide an example of a non-Archimedean ordered field. Such a field is presented in our concluding example.

EXAMPLE 1   Consider the algebraic structure $\mathbf{R}[x]$ of all polynomials in the single indeterminate x with real coefficients. It can be proved that $(\mathbf{R}[x], +, \cdot)$ is an integral domain (recall terminology introduced in Article 10.2), under the operations of ordinary addition and multiplication of polynomials. Hence we may use the construction described in Article 10.2 (in building $\mathbf{Q}$ from $\mathbf{Z}$) to pass from $\mathbf{R}[x]$ to $\mathbf{R}(x)$, the field of quotients of $\mathbf{R}[x]$, which turns out to be representable as the familiar collection of all rational functions in x with real coefficients. We may introduce an ordering in $\mathbf{R}[x]$ by calling a polynomial positive if the coefficient of its highest-degree term is positive. This ordering may be extended to $\mathbf{R}(x)$ by declaring a rational function $p(x)/q(x)$ to be positive in case the product $p(x)q(x)$ is a positive polynomial. This ordering on $\mathbf{R}(x)$ is non-Archimedean, since, for example, no finite number of additions of the constant polynomial 1 to itself will ever exceed the positive polynomial x. $\square$

Exercises

1. This exercise relates to the proof of Theorem 2.

★*(a)*   Prove that every Cauchy sequence of rational numbers is bounded.

(b)   Prove that if $\{a_n\}$ and $\{b_n\}$ are Cauchy sequences of rational numbers, then $\{a_n + b_n\}$ and $\{-a_n\}$ are also Cauchy sequences. Prove also that any constant sequence of rationals is Cauchy.

(c)   Use the result in (a) to prove that if $\{a_n\}$ and $\{b_n\}$ are Cauchy sequences of rationals, then $\{a_n b_n\}$ is Cauchy. (*Note:* For any positive integers m and n, $a_m b_m - a_n b_n = a_m b_m - a_n b_m + a_n b_m - a_n b_n$. Use the boundedness of both sequences and the triangle inequality.)

2. *(a)*   Prove Theorem 3; that is, prove that relation $\sim$ defined as $\mathfrak{C}$ is an equivalence relation.

(b)   Prove Theorem 4(a); that is, prove that addition on $\mathbf{R}$ is a well-defined operation.

(c)   Prove Theorem 4(b); that is, prove that multiplication on $\mathbf{R}$ is well defined. (*Note:* Follow the hints given for Exercise 1(c).]

3. *(a)*   Verify, in detail, all field axioms, except Axiom 10, for the structure $(\mathbf{R}, +, \cdot)$.

(b)   Prove that the collection of all null sequences of rational numbers constitutes an equivalence class in $\mathbf{R}$, by using the two steps:

(i)   Any two null sequences are equivalent.

(ii)   Any sequence equivalent to a null sequence is itself null.

(c)   Prove that the sequence $\{b_n\}$, defined in the verification of Axiom 10 for $(\mathbf{R}, +, \cdot)$, (cf., Remarks on the proof of Theorem 5), is a Cauchy sequence. (*Hint:*

You need to use both the fact that $\{a_n\}$ is Cauchy and the fact that $\{a_n\}$ is eventually bounded away from zero.)

4. Prove that the mapping $q \to [q]$ of **Q** into **R**, defined in the paragraph following the proof of Theorem 5, is one to one, not onto, and preserves addition and multiplication in **Q**. Prove also that the image of this mapping, a proper subset of **R**, is closed under addition and multiplication.

5. Prove that the definition of positivity in **R**, given in Definition 6, is well defined (see the precise formulation of well-definedness in this context following Definition 6).

6. Prove that any real number x lies between two consecutive integers; that is, prove that, given $x \in \mathbf{R}$, there corresponds an integer n such that $n - 1 \le x < n$. (*Hints:* First, use the Archimedean property of **R** to prove that x must necessarily lie between two integers, say, m and p. Having accomplished this, use the well-ordering principle for **N** to show that x lies between two consecutive integers in the set $\{m, m + 1, \ldots, m + (p - m)\}$.)

Answers and Solutions to Selected Exercises

Article 1.1

1. (b) $B = \{-\frac{3}{2}\}$ (i) $I = \{1, 2\}$ (m) $M = \{-5, -1, (1 \pm \sqrt{22})/3\}$.
2. (a) **R**   (e) $[-\frac{4}{5}, \frac{3}{2}]$ (m) **C**   (n) **R**.
3. (a) (i) well defined   (ii) not well defined.
4. (c) $-16, 32, -64, 128, -256$.
7. (b) for **Z**, we may say that there exist real numbers a, b, and c such that $a \in \mathbf{Z}$, $c \in \mathbf{Z}$, and $a < c < b$, but $b \notin \mathbf{Z}$. The same characterization may be used for **Q**, replacing **Z** by **Q**. The statement is clearly true in both cases.
9. (a) (ii) $\mathscr{P}(S) = \{\varnothing, \{a\}, \{b\}, \{c\}, \{d\}, \{a, b\}, \{a, c\}, \{a, d\}, \{b, c\}, \{b, d\}, \{c, d\}, \{a, b, c\}, \{a, b, d\}, \{a, c, d\}, \{b, c, d\}, S\}$.
10. If $A \in A = \{Y | Y \notin Y\}$, then, by definition of A, we have $A \notin A$, a contradiction. On the other hand, if $A \notin A$, then, again, by definition of A, it must not be the case that $A \notin A$; that is, $A \in A$, again, a contradiction. The discovery, in 1901, of this paradox by the British mathematician and philosopher, Bertrand Russell, had devastating effects in the mathematical world and brought about essential changes of direction in the developing field of set theory.   □

Article 1.2

1. (c) $A \cup A' = U$ (k) $A \triangle A = \varnothing$ (l) $C \triangle C' = U$.
2. (b) (d) $(A \cap C)' = \{1, 2, 3, 4, 5, 6, 7, 8, 10\} = A' \cup C'$ (k) (n) $(A \cup B) \cap C = \{9\} = (A \cap C) \cup (B \cap C)$.
3. (c) (d) $(A \cup C) - (A \cap C) = \{1, 2, 4, 7, 8\} = A \triangle C$.   (j) (k) $(C - B) \cap (C - A) = \{2, 4, 8\} = C - (B \cup A)$.
4. (f) $A \times (B \cup C) = \{(1, 2), (1, 3), (1, 4), (1, 5), (1, 6), (1, 8), (1, 9), (1, 10), (7, 2), (7, 3), (7, 4), (7, 5), (7, 6), (7, 8), (7, 9), (7, 10), (9, 2), (9, 3), (9, 4), (9, 5), (9, 6), (9, 8), (9, 9), (9, 10)\}$.

6. (a) (j) $A \cap C = [2, 4] = C - A'$,   (f) $A - C = (4, 9)$,
(g) $C - A = [-1, 2)$

7. (c) $A - B = (-\infty, -3]$ (d) $A \triangle B = (-\infty, -3] \cup (6, \infty)$
(l) $(A \triangle B) \triangle C = (-\infty, -4] \cup (-3, 1) \cup (3, 6] \cup [7, \infty)$.

8. (c) $D \cap A' = \emptyset$ (i) $(D \cap A) \cup (D \cap A') = D$.

10. (b) $(-\infty, -6] \cup [8, \infty)$ (e) $(-\infty, -3) \cup (-3, 3) \cup (3, \infty)$.

11. (a) $[-2, -1] \cup [1, 2]$.

12. (c) (i) $C \cap E = \{f \mid f$ is the function $f(x) = x^2 + 3x$ with domain **R**$\}$
(iv) $A \cap D = D$.

Article 1.3

2. (b) Let $A = \{2, 3, 10\}$ and $B = \{1, 3, 8, 10\}$. Then $\{1, 3, 4, 5, 6, 7, 8, 9, 10\} = \{2\}' = (A - B)' \neq A - B' = \{3, 10\}$.   (g) Let $X = \{4, 7\}$, $A = \{1, 4, 7, 9\}$, $B = \{2, 4, 6, 9\}$. Then $X \subseteq A$, but $X \cup (A \cap B) = \{4, 7, 9\} \neq \{4, 9\} = (X \cup A) \cap B$.

4. (a) For example, we might try $A = \{3, 4, 5, 8, 10\}$, $B = \{1, 4, 5, 9\}$, and $X = \{2, 5, 6, 7\}$. Then $A \cap X = \{5\} = B \cap X$, but $A \cap X' = \{3, 4, 8, 10\} \neq \{1, 5, 9\} = B \cap X'$. Or else, we could let $A = \{6, 8, 9\}$, $B = \{2, 6, 8, 10\}$, and $X = \{1, 2, 9, 10\}$. Then $A \cap X' = \{6, 8\} = B \cap X'$, but $A \cap X = \{9\}$, whereas $B \cap X = \{2, 10\}$. The example seems to indicate that if A and B are distinct and $A \cap X = B \cap X$, then $A \cap X'$ can't equal $B \cap X'$, and vice versa.
(b) An elegant formulation of the idea described informally in (a) is this: "For any sets A, B, and X, if $A \cap X = B \cap X$ and $A \cap X' = B \cap X'$, then $A = B$." If this conversion is not intuitively evident to you, you will learn logical principles in Chapters 2 and 3, by which you will be able to make such conversions yourself systematically.

7. (b) $X \cap (Y \cup Z) = (X \cap Y) \cup (X \cap Z) = (-\infty, -4) \cup (7/2, \infty)$.

10. (f) True   (j) True.

Article 1.5

1. (i) 1   (m) 32   (n) 2   (p) 4.

5. (b) 56 three-person committees and 56 five-person committees.

6. (b) $4 \times 4 \times 4 \times 4 \times 12 = 3072$.

9. (b) There are $2^{10} = 1024$ possible choices for both A and B, for a combined total of $(1024)^2 = 1,048,576$.

12. (a) $3^9 = 19,683$ (b) $3^6 = 729$.

Article 2.1

1. (c) a statement   (i) a statement only in a specific context   (k) not a statement.

4. (d) p: the sum of two even integers is even (true), q: the product of two odd integers is odd (true); $p \wedge \sim q$ is false.   (f) (g) p: April is the name of a month (true), q: September is the name of a month (true), r: Wednesday is the name of a month (false); in (f), $\sim(p \wedge q \wedge r)$ is true; in (g), $\sim p \wedge \sim q \wedge \sim r$ is false.

Article 2.2

3. (*a*) (*iv*) I pass the course and (still) do not make the dean's list.   (*vi*) If I pass the course, then I make the dean's list.   (*b*) (*ii*) $q \vee \sim r$ ($\sim q \to \sim r$ is also a correct representation)   (*iv*) $q \to p$ ($\sim p \to \sim q$ is also a correct representation).

4. (*c*) p: $2 = 5$ (false), q: $4 + 5 = 9$ (true), r: $5^2 = 25$ (true); $(\sim p \vee q) \to \sim r$ is false. (*f*) (*h*) p: $\int_{-\pi}^{\pi} \sin x \, dx = 0$ (true), q: $d/dx(2^x) = x2^{x-1}$ (false), r: $\ln 6 = (\ln 2)(\ln 3)$ (false); in (f), $(p \wedge \sim q) \to r$ is false; in (h), $p \to (r \to q)$ is true.

Article 2.3

4. (*a*) (*i*) converse: $r \to (p \wedge q)$; contrapositive: $\sim r \to (\sim p \vee \sim q)$; inverse: $(\sim p \vee \sim q) \to \sim r$.   (*b*) (*iii*) inverse (*vii*) original.   (*d*) (*ii*) converse: If $\sin(\pi/3) = \frac{1}{2}$, then $2 < 4$ and $5 + 5 = 10$; inverse: If either $2 \geq 4$ or $5 + 5 \neq 10$, then $\sin(\pi/3) \neq \frac{1}{2}$; contrapositive: If $\sin(\pi/3) \neq \frac{1}{2}$, then either $2 \geq 4$ or $5 + 5 \neq 10$; negation: $2 < 4$ and $5 + 5 = 10$, but $\sin(\pi/3) \neq \frac{1}{2}$. □

5. (*b*) $\sim q \to \sim r$ (*e*) $(r \to q) \to p$.

7. (*b*) (*i*) In (*a′*), p is stronger than q, due to its stronger conclusion; in (*b′*), p is stronger than q, due to its weaker hypothesis.   (*ii*) In (*a′*), p and q are both true; in (*b′*), p is false and q is true.   (*iii*) Our answers to (*ii*) are consistent with our answers to (*i*). The fact that p is stronger than q, in (*a′*) and (*b′*) excludes only the possibility "p true-q false."

10. (*b*) (*ii*) $\sim p \vee \sim q \vee r$.

Article 2.4

4. p: I keep my job, q: Smith is retained, r: You recommend Smith's firing. The argument has the form $[(\sim q \to \sim p) \wedge (\sim q \to r)] \to (\sim r \to p)$, an invalid argument (consider the case: r false, p false, and q true).

8. A: $p \to q$ is a tautology, B: $q \to p$ is a tautology, C: $p \Leftrightarrow q$ is a tautology. The argument has the form $[(A \to (B \Leftrightarrow C)) \wedge (A \wedge \sim C)] \to \sim B$, a valid argument.

Article 3.1

2. (*g*) $\{4, 5, 6, 7\}$ (*k*) U (*l*) $\varnothing$ (*s*) U.

4. (*a*) (*i*) both equal $\{1, 2, 3, 8, 9, 10\}$.

Article 3.2

1. (*d*) All easy problems are solvable.   (*i*) Some unsolvable problems are not mathematics problems.
2. (*c*) $(\exists x)(p(x) \land \sim r(x))$ (*i*) $(\forall x)(r(x) \rightarrow (p(x) \land \sim q(x)))$.
3. (*c*) (*i*) F   (*ii*) T   (*iii*) T   (*iv*) F   (*v*) T   (*vi*) F   (*d*) (*i*) T
   (*ii*) T   (*iii*) T   (*iv*) F   (*v*) T   (*vi*) T.
9. (*a*) $(\forall x)(p(x) \Leftrightarrow q(x))$ (*b*) $P = Q$ (*c*) $P = Q$ if and only if $(P' \cup Q) \cap (P \cup Q') = U$, for any sets P and Q.
11. (*a*) (*b*) (*d*) (*e*) p implies q; s and t are equivalent.

Article 3.3

1. (*c*) All women are either not young or not athletes.   (*g*) Some athletes are either not young or are men and no men are athletes.
4. (*c*) $(\exists x)(\sim p(x) \land \sim q(x))$ (*h*) $(\exists x)((p(x) \land \sim q(x)) \lor (\sim p(x) \land q(x)))$.
5. (*c*) $(\exists x)(p(x) \land \sim q(x) \land \sim r(x))$.
6. (*d*) Prove that there exists a function f such that f has a relative maximum or minimum at $x = 0$, but $f'(0)$ does not equal zero.
9. (*b*) $0 = x^2 + 8x + 16 = (x + 4)^2$. Hence if $x^2 + 8x + 16 = 0$, then $x = -4$, so that there is at most one solution. Substituting -4 for x in $x^2 + 8x + 16$ yields $(-4)^2 + 8(-4) + 16 = 0$, so that, in fact, there is exactly one solution, $x = -4$, as desired.

Article 3.4

1. (*b*) proposition   (*f*) propositional function of two variables.
2. (*e*) There exists x such that, for every y and z, $p(x, y, z)$.
4. (*c*) Everyone has someone to whom they are a friend, who is not a friend in return.   (*g*) Everyone is his own friend.
7. (*a*) (*v*) -8 divides 0 (true)   (*xi*) For any integers m and n, if m divides n, then n divides m (false).
9. (*b*) There exists a real number x such that $xy = x$ for every real number y (true—let $x = 0$).   (*g*) To every positive real number μ, there corresponds at least one positive integer n such that $1/n < \mu$.
10. (*a*) $(\exists x)(\forall y)(x \le y)$ (false).   (*d*) $(\forall x \in \mathbf{Q'})(\forall y \in \mathbf{Q'})(\exists z \in \mathbf{Q'})(x < z < y)$ (true).

Article 3.5

3. $p(x)$: x is a good citizen, $q(x)$: x registers to vote, $r(x)$: x does community service, $s(x)$; x is lazy; the argument has the form: $P \subseteq Q$, $Q \cap R \neq \emptyset$, $R \cap S = \emptyset$, therefore $P \cap S' \neq \emptyset$. This is invalid, as demonstrated by the substitutions $U = \{1, 2, 3, 4, 5\}$, $P = \{1, 2\}$, $Q = \{1, 2, 3\}$, $R = \{3, 4\}$, $S = \{1, 2, 5\}$.

7. $p(x)$: X is a field, $q(x)$: X is a ring, $r(x)$: X is an integral domain; this argument has the form: $P \subseteq Q$, $Q \cap R \neq \varnothing$, $R \cap P' \neq \varnothing$, therefore $Q \cap P' \neq \varnothing$. The argument is invalid. Let $U = \{1, 2, 3, 4, 5\}$, $P = \{1, 2\}$, $Q = \{1, 2\}$, $R = \{2, 3, 4\}$.

Article 4.1

2. (a) Proof   Assume $X \subseteq Y$ and $X \subseteq Z$. To prove $X \subseteq Y \cap Z$, let x be an arbitrary element of X. We must prove $x \in Y \cap Z$; that is, $x \in Y$ and $x \in Z$. Now since $x \in X$ and $X \subseteq Y$, we have $x \in Y$. Similarly, since $x \in X$ and $X \subseteq Z$, we have $x \in Z$. Hence $x \in Y$ and $x \in Z$ so $x \in Y \cap Z$, as desired.   □

7. (b) Proof   Assume $B' \subseteq A'$. We must prove $A \subseteq B$. Now, by 7(a), since $B' \subseteq A'$, then $A'' \subseteq B''$. But since $A = A''$ and $B = B''$ [by Exercise 6(a)(iii)], this leads to $A \subseteq B$, our desired conclusion.   □

9. (a) Proof $\Rightarrow$ Assume $A \cap B = U$. We must prove $A = U$ and $B = U$. For the first of these, note that $A \subseteq U$ is always true so that we need only establish the reverse containment $U \subseteq A$. To do this, let $x \in U$. Since $U = A \cap B$, then $x \in A \cap B$. Since $x \in A \cap B$, then $x \in A$ and $x \in B$ so that, in particular, $x \in A$. An identical argument verifies that $U \subseteq B$, so that $U = B$, as well. $\Leftarrow$ Assume $A = U$ and $B = U$. To prove $A \cap B = U$, let $x \in U$; we must show $x \in A \cap B$; that is, $x \in A$ and $x \in B$. Now since $x \in U$ and $U = A$, then $x \in A$. Since $x \in U$ and $U = B$, then $x \in B$. Hence $x \in A$ and $x \in B$, as desired.   □

(*Note:* An alternative presentation of the argument is "assume $A = U$ and $B = U$. Then $A \cap B = U \cap U = U$.")

Article 4.2

1. and 2. (b) union $= \mathbf{N}$, intersection $= \{1\} = A_1$; increasing.   (c) union $= \mathbf{N} = A_1$, intersection $= \varnothing$; decreasing.   (j) union $= \mathbf{R}$, intersection $= (-\infty, 1] = A_1$; increasing.   (k) union $= (-\infty, -1) = A_1$, intersection $= \varnothing$; decreasing.

5. (b) Proof   Assume $\{A_k | k = 1, 2, \ldots\}$ is a decreasing family. We may prove the desired equality by proving mutual inclusion, where we note that $\supseteq$ follows immediately from Exercise 4(a). To prove $\subseteq$, let x be an arbitrary element of $\bigcup_{k=1}^{\infty} A_k$; we must prove $x \in A_1$. Now since $x \in \bigcup_{k=1}^{\infty} A_k$, then $x \in A_j$ for some $j \in \mathbf{N}$. If $j = 1$, we are finished. If $j > 1$, then $A_j \subseteq A_1$, by the "decreasing" hypothesis. In that case $x \in A_j$ and $A_j \subseteq A_1$ together imply $x \in A_1$, our desired conclusion.   □

5. (e) (i) Proof   Let $x \in \bigcap_{k=m}^{\infty} A_k$. To prove $x \in \bigcap_{k=n}^{\infty} A_k$, we must prove $x \in A_h$ for every $h \geq n$. So assume $h \in \mathbf{N}$ and $h \geq n$. Since $m < n \leq h$, we have $h > m$. Since $x \in \bigcap_{k=m}^{\infty} A_k$, then $x \in A_k$ for every $k \geq m$; in particular $x \in A_h$. Since h was an arbitrarily chosen integer greater than or equal to m, we have established $x \in \bigcap_{k=n}^{\infty} A_k$, as desired.   □

6. (a) Yes. Let $A_k = (0, 1 + 1/k)$ for each $k = 1, 2, \ldots$. Then $\bigcap_{k=1}^{\infty} A_k = (0, 1]$. Note that this is not possible in a finite collection of sets.

7. (b) Proof   Assume C is a set satisfying $C \subseteq A_k$ for each $k = 1, 2, 3, \ldots$. To prove $C \subseteq \bigcap_{k=1}^{\infty} A_k$, let $x \in C$ and let j be an arbitrary positive integer; we must prove $x \in A_j$. Since $C \subseteq A_k$ for each $k = 1, 2, 3, \ldots$, then, in particular, $C \subseteq A_j$. Since $x \in C$ and $C \subseteq A_j$, we have $x \in A_j$. Since j was arbitrarily chosen, we have $x \in \bigcap_{k=1}^{\infty} A_k$, as desired. $\square$

Article 4.3

1. (a) (b) (iii) $\lim_{x \to 3} f(x) = \frac{24}{6} = 4$. Type I (i.e., continuous) at $a = 3$.
(viii) $\lim_{x \to 3} f(x) = \lim_{x \to 3} ((3 - x)/3x)(1/(x - 3)) = \lim_{x \to 3} (-\frac{1}{3}x) = -\frac{1}{9}$. Type II (i.e., not continuous) at $a = 3$ since f is not defined at 3.
2. (a) $\lim_{x \to 3} f(x)$ does not exist since $\lim_{x \to 3^-} f(x) = 9 \neq 1 = \lim_{x \to 3^+} f(x)$.
(b) $\lim_{x \to 3} f(x) = \lim_{x \to 3} (2x - 5) = 1$.
3. (a) (iii) Let ε be any specific positive real number less than or equal to B (i.e., B is the largest value of ε that could be used), say, $\varepsilon = B/2$. Let δ be an arbitrary positive real number. Then, for any nonzero x between $-\delta$ and δ, we have either $0 < x < \delta$ and $f(x) = 5x + B > B > B/2$, or else $-\delta < x < 0$ and $f(x) = 2x - B < -B < -B/2$. In either case $f(x)$ is not within a distance of $\varepsilon = B/2$ of $L = 0$. Surely then, corresponding to the given (specific) ε and an arbitrarily chosen positive δ, there can always be found x such that $0 < |x| < \delta$, whereas $|f(x)| \geq \varepsilon$.
4. (d) The graph of the tangent function tells us that $\lim_{x \to (\pi/2)^-} = \infty$, whereas $\lim_{x \to (\pi/2)^+} = -\infty$.
5. (a) Let $\varepsilon = \frac{1}{2}$ and let $\delta > 0$ be given. Corresponding to this arbitrarily chosen δ, there clearly exists a positive integer n such that both $2/(4n + 1)\pi$ and $2/(4n + 3)\pi$ are less than δ. If $x = 2/(4n + 1)\pi$, then $1/x = (4n + 1)\pi/2$ so that $\sin(1/x) = \sin[(4n + 1)\pi/2] = 1$. If $x = 2/(4n + 3)\pi$, then $1/x = (4n + 3)\pi/2$ so that $\sin(1/x) = \sin[(4n + 3)\pi/2] = -1$. We conclude that, in any neighborhood of $a = 0$ (no matter how narrow), there exist values of x for which $\sin(1/x) = 1$ and $\sin(1/x) = -1$. Thus it is impossible, given an ε neighborhood of $L = 0$ with $\varepsilon < 1$, to find a δ neighborhood about $a = 0$ such that all positive values of x within that neighborhood have their corresponding $f(x)$ within ε of $L = 0$.
8. (b) (ii) $\lim_{x \to \infty} (x + 6)/(x^2 - 10) = \lim_{t \to 0} ((1/t) + 6)/((1/t^2) - 10) = \lim_{t \to 0} ((6t + 1)/t)(t^2/(1 - 10t^2)) = \lim_{t \to 0} (6t^2 + t)/(1 - 10t^2) = 0/1 = 0$.
(iii) $\lim_{x \to \infty} (x^2 - 2x + 3)/(2x^2 + 5x - 3) = \lim_{x \to \infty} [(1 - (3/x) + (3/x^2)]/[(2 + (5/x) - (3/x^2)] = (1 - 0 + 0)/(2 + 0 - 0) = \frac{1}{2}$.
(d) (i) $\lim_{x \to a} f(x) = \infty$ if and only if, corresponding to any $M > 0$, there exists $\delta > 0$ such that, whenever $0 < |x - a| < \delta$, then $f(x) \geq M$.

Article 5.1

2. (a) (i) Proof   Let x be an arbitrary real number. Then, $\cos^4 x - \sin^4 x = (\cos^2 x - \sin^2 x)(\cos^2 x + \sin^2 x) = (\cos^2 x - \sin^2 x)(1) = \cos^2 x - \sin^2 x = \cos 2x$. $\square$

3. (d) Proof   Let A be an arbitrary subset of U. Then, $A \bigtriangleup U = (A - U) \cup (U - A) = \emptyset \cup A' = A'$. $\square$

5. (a) (ii) Proof   Let A, B, and C be arbitrary sets. Then $(A \cup B) - C = (A \cup B) \cap C' = (A \cap C') \cup (B \cap C') = (A - C) \cup (B - C)$. $\square$

7. (a) Proof   Assume $n, k \in \mathbf{N}$ with $k \leq n$. Then $\binom{n}{k-1} + \binom{n}{k} = [n!/((k-1)!(n-k-1)!)] + [n!/k!(n-k)!] = [kn! + (n-k+1)n!]/[k!(n-k+1)!] = n!(k+n-k+1)/k!(n-k+1)! = (n+1)n!/k!(n+1-k)! = (n+1)!/k!(n+1-k)! = (n+1)!/k!(n+1-k)! = \binom{n+1}{k}$. $\square$

9. (b) Proof   Assume f and g are odd functions. To show $f + g$ is odd, we must show that $(f + g)(-x) = -(f + g)(x)$ for all $x \in \mathbf{R}$. So let $x \in \mathbf{R}$ be arbitrarily chosen. Then $(f + g)(-x) = f(-x) + g(-x) = -f(x) + (-(g(x))) = -(f(x) + g(x))$, as desired. Similarly, $(f - g)(-x) = f(-x) - g(-x) = -f(x) - (-g(x)) = -(f(x) - g(x)) = -((f - g)(x))$, as desired. Also, $(f \circ g)(-x) = f(g(-x)) = f(-g(x)) = -f(g(x)) = -(f \circ g)(x)$. Finally, $(fg)(-x) = f(-x)g(-x) = (-f(x))(-g(x)) = f(x)g(x) = (fg)(x)$, so that fg is even, as claimed. $\square$

12. (b) Proof   Rewrite $60 + 14x - 2x^2$ in the form $-2(x^2 - 7x + \frac{49}{4}) + (60 + \frac{49}{2}) = -2(x - \frac{7}{2})^2 + (\frac{169}{2})$. Clearly this expression assumes its maximum value of $\frac{169}{2}$ at $x = \frac{7}{2}$. $\square$

13. (d) We show the statement is false by displaying a counterexample. Let $U = \{1, 2, 3, 4, 5\}$, $A = \{1, 2, 5\}$, $B = \{3, 4\}$, $C = \{1, 2, 4\}$. Then $A \cap (B \cup C) = \{1, 2\}$, whereas $(A \cap B) \cup C = \{1, 2, 4\}$.

17. (a) Proof   Given $A = (a_{ij})_{m \times n}$ and $B = (b_{ij})_{m \times n}$, to prove $A = B$, we need only show that $a_{ij} = b_{ij}$ for all i, j satisfying $1 \leq i \leq m$, $1 \leq j \leq n$. So choose arbitrary integers h and k satisfying $1 \leq h \leq m$, $1 \leq k \leq n$. Now $A^t = (c_{ji})_{n \times m}$ and $B^t = (d_{ji})_{n \times m}$, where $c_{ji} = a_{ij}$ and $d_{ji} = b_{ij}$ for all i, j with $1 \leq i \leq m$, $1 \leq j \leq n$. Since $A^t = B^t$, we know that $c_{kh} = d_{kh}$. Hence $a_{hk} = c_{kh} = d_{kh} = b_{hk}$, and we have $a_{hk} = b_{hk}$, as desired. $\square$

(e) Proof   Let A and B be arbitrary symmetric square matrices, so that $A = A^t$ and $B = B^t$. To prove $A + B$ is symmetric, we need only show $(A + B)^t = A + B$. But $(A + B)^t = A^t + B^t = A + B$. $\square$

Article 5.2

2. (a) Proof   Let A and B be sets such that $A \subseteq B$. To prove $\mathscr{P}(A) \subseteq \mathscr{P}(B)$, let X be an arbitrary element of $\mathscr{P}(A)$. To prove $X \in \mathscr{P}(B)$, we must show $X \subseteq B$. Now since $X \in \mathscr{P}(A)$, we know $X \subseteq A$. Since $X \subseteq A$ and $A \subseteq B$, then $X \subseteq B$ (by Example 7, Article 4.1), our desired conclusion. $\square$

5. (b) Apply the criterion in (a) with $h = k = 1$, $f(x) = 1 + (1/(x - 1))$. Assume $x \neq 1$, $x \neq 0$. Then $f(-x + 1) = 1 + (1/((-x + 1) - 1)) = 1 - (1/x) = 2 - [1 + ((1/(x + 1) - 1))] = 2 - f(x + 1)$.

9. (a) Proof   To prove $[0, 1]$ is convex, let $x, y \in [0, 1]$ and let t be a real number satisfying $0 \leq t \leq 1$. Then $tx \geq 0$, $1 - t \geq 0$, and $y \geq 0$, so that $tx + (1 - t)y \geq 0$. Also, since $0 \leq x \leq 1$, then $tx \leq t$ and since $0 \leq y \leq 1$, then $(1 - t)y \leq 1 - t$. Hence $tx + (1 - t)y \leq t + (1 - t) = 1$. Thus $0 \leq tx + (1 - t)y \leq 1$, as desired. $\square$

Article 5.3

4. (a) Proof   Let X, A, and B be sets such that $X \subseteq B$. To prove $X \cup (A \cap B) \subseteq (X \cup A) \cap B$, let $x \in X \cup (A \cap B)$. To prove $x \in (X \cup A) \cap B$, we must prove $x \in (X \cup A)$ and $x \in B$. Since $x \in X \cup (A \cap B)$, then either $x \in X$ or $x \in A \cap B$. We divide the argument into cases. *Case I:* If $x \in X$, then $x \in X \cup A$ since $X \subseteq X \cup A$. Since $X \subseteq B$ and $x \in X$, then $x \in B$, so that our desired conclusion holds in this case. *Case II:* If $x \in A \cap B$, then $x \in A$ so that $x \in X \cup A$. Furthermore, $x \in A \cap B$ implies $x \in B$. Again, we have our desired conclusion in this case. Since these cases are exhaustive, our theorem is proved. □

7. (b) Proof   Let A, B, and X be arbitrary sets. Then $A = A \cap U = A \cap (X \cup X') = (A \cap X) \cup (A \cap X') = (B \cap X) \cup (B \cap X') = B \cap (X \cup X') = B \cap U = B$. □

10. (a) Proof   Let x, $y \in \mathbf{R}$. Let $x' = (x + y)/2$ and $y' = (x - y)/2$. By Exercise 9(g, h), using specialization, we have $\sin(x' + y') - \sin(x' - y') = 2 \cos x' \cos y'$. Resubstituting, this becomes $\sin x - \sin y = 2 \cos((x + y)/2) \sin((x - y)/2)$, as desired. □

12. (b) (ii) Proof   Let x, $y \in \mathbf{R}$ and consider the cases $x < y$, $x = y$, and $x > y$. If $x < y$, then $(\frac{1}{2})(x + y + |x - y|) = (\frac{1}{2})(x + y + y - x) = (\frac{1}{2})(2y) = y = x \vee y$. If $x = y$, then $(\frac{1}{2})(x + y + |x - y|) = (\frac{1}{2})(x + x) = (\frac{1}{2})(2x) = x = x \vee y$. If $x > y$, then $(\frac{1}{2})(x + y + |x - y|) = (\frac{1}{2})(x + y + x - y) = (\frac{1}{2})(2x) = x = x \vee y$. □

13. (c) Proof   Given diagonal matrices A and B, to prove $AB = C = (c_{ij})_{n \times n}$ is diagonal, we must prove that if $i \neq j$, then $c_{ij} = 0$. So let i and j be arbitrary, distinct integers between 1 and n, inclusive; note that $c_{ij} = \sum_{k=1}^{n} a_{ik} b_{kj}$. Now since $i \neq j$, then for each $k = 1, 2, \ldots, n$, either $k \neq i$ or $k \neq j$. If $k \neq i$, then $a_{ik} = 0$ (since A is diagonal), whereas if $k \neq j$, then $b_{kj} = 0$ (since B is diagonal). In either case we have that the product $a_{ik} b_{kj} = 0$, so that the sum used to compute c_{ij} is the sum of n zeros and so equals zero, as desired. □

Article 5.4

3. (b) Proof   Define S in the usual manner.   (i) Clearly $1 \in S$ since $(1)(2) = 2 = (1)(2)(3)/3$.   (ii) Assume $m \in S$. To prove $m + 1 \in S$, note that $\sum_{k=1}^{m+1} k(k + 1) = \sum_{k=1}^{m} k(k + 1) + (m + 1)(m + 2) = (\frac{1}{3})m(m + 1)(m + 2) + (m + 1)(m + 2) = (\frac{1}{3})[m(m + 1)(m + 2) + 3(m + 1)(m + 2)] = (\frac{1}{3})(m + 1)(m + 2)(m + 3)$, as desired. □.

7. (d) Proof   Define S in the usual manner.   (i) $1 \in S$ since $x - y$ divides $x - y$.   (ii) Assume $m \in S$. To prove $m + 1 \in S$, we must prove $x - y$ divides $x^{m+1} - y^{m+1}$. Now $x^{m+1} - y^{m+1} = x(x^m - y^m) + (xy^m - y^{m+1}) = x(x^m - y^m) + y^m(x - y)$. Since $x - y$ divides $x^m - y^m$ (by induction hypothesis), then $x - y$ divides $x(x^m - y^m)$. Also, $x - y$ clearly divides $y^m(x - y)$. Hence $x - y$ divides the indicated sum, so that $x - y$ divides $x^{m+1} - y^{m+1}$, as required. □

8. (b) Proof   Let $S = \{n \in \mathbf{N} \mid n \geq 10 \text{ and } n^3 < 2^n\}$. Clearly $10 \in S$, since $1000 < 1024$. So assume $m \in S$. To prove $m + 1 \in S$, we must prove $(m + 1)^3 < 2^{m+1}$. Now $(m + 1)^3 = m^3 + 3m^2 + 3m + 1$. Since $m \geq 10$, then

$3m^2 + 3m + 1 < 3m^2 + 3m^2 + 3m^2 = 9m^2 < m(m^2) = m^3$. Hence
$m^3 + 3m^2 + 3m + 1 < m^3 + m^3 < 2^m + 2^m = 2(2^m) = 2^{m+1}$, as required. □

12. (a) Proof   "If $m \in \emptyset$, then $m + 1 \in \emptyset$" is true since "$m \in \emptyset$" is false for any $m \in N$. □

Article 6.1

3. (b) (i) $[\sim(p \leftrightarrow q)] \leftrightarrow [p \leftrightarrow \sim q]$. You should verify, by using the truth table, that this statement form is a tautology.

4. (a) Proof   Let X, Y, and Z be sets. We establish equality by proving mutual inclusion. Let $t \in (X \cup Y) \times Z$. Then $t = (p, q)$ where $p \in X \cup Y$ and $q \in Z$. Now $p \in X \cup Y$ means either $p \in X$ or $p \in Y$. In the case $p \in X$, we have $t = (p, q) \in X \times Z \subseteq (X \times Z) \cup (Y \times Z)$. If $p \in Y$, then $t = (p, q) \in Y \times Z \subseteq (X \times Z) \cup (Y \times Z)$. These two cases are exhaustive and, in either case, we have $t \in (X \times Z) \cup (Y \times Z)$, as desired. Conversely, suppose $t \in (X \times Z) \cup (Y \times Z)$, so that either $t \in (X \times Z)$ (in which case $t = (x, z_1)$ where $x \in X$ and $z_1 \in Z$) or $t \in (Y \times Z)$ [so that $t = (y, z_2)$ where $y \in Y$ and $z_2 \in Z$]. In the first case $t = (x, z_1)$ where $x \in X \subseteq X \cup Y$ and $z_1 \in Z$. In the second case $t = (y, z_2)$ where $y \in Y \subseteq X \cup Y$ and $z_2 \in Z$. In either case $t \in (X \cup Y) \times Z$, as desired. □

6. (b) Proof   Assume S is a convex subset of $\mathbf{R}$. To prove S is an interval, suppose x, y, and z are real numbers with $x < y < z$, $x \in S$, and $z \in S$. We must prove $y \in S$. Now, by (a), there must exist a real number t, with $0 < t < 1$, such that $z = tx + (1 - t)y$. Since S is convex, then for any $x, z \in S$ and $t \in (0, 1)$, we may conclude $tx + (1 - t)y \in S$. Hence $z = tx + (1 - t)y \in S$, as desired. □

9. (b) A real number a is <u>not</u> a point of accumulation of S if and only if $\exists \delta > 0$ such that $N'(a; \delta) \cap S = \emptyset$; in other words, there exists a δ neighborhood of the point a containing no points of S other than, possibly, a itself. To prove that 2 is not a point of accumulation of $S = (0, 1) \cup \{2\}$, let $\delta = \frac{1}{2}$ (or any other specific positive real number less than 1). Clearly $N(2, \frac{1}{2}) = (\frac{3}{2}, \frac{5}{2})$ contains no points of S, other than 2 itself, as required.

13. (b) Proof   Let $\varepsilon > 0$ be given. We must produce $\delta > 0$ such that, whenever $0 < |x| < \delta$, then $|g(x)| < \varepsilon$. Let $\delta = \varepsilon$. Suppose now that x is a real number satisfying $0 < |x| < \delta$. If x is irrational, then $|g(x)| = 0 < \varepsilon$. If x is rational, then $|g(x)| = |x| < \delta < \varepsilon$, so that $|g(x)| < \varepsilon$. In either case we have the desired conclusion. □

Article 6.2

1. (e) Proof   Let A, B, and C be sets. Let $t \in (A \times C) - (B \times C)$. To prove $t \in (A - B) \times C$, we must prove that there exist $x \in A - B$ and $y \in C$ such that $t = (x, y)$. Now $t \in (A \times C) - (B \times C)$ means $t \in A \times C$ so $\exists x \in A$, $y \in C$ such that $t = (x, y)$. We will be finished if we can prove $x \notin B$, so that

$x \in A - B$. To do this, suppose x were an element of B. Then we would have $t = (x, y) \in B \times C$, contradicting the fact that $t \in (A \times C) - (B \times C)$. Hence $x \notin B$, so $x \in A - B$ and $t \in (A - B) \times C$, as desired. $\square$

(g) Proof   Let A and B be subsets of U such that $A' \cup B = U$. To prove $A \subseteq B$, let $x \in A$. Hence $x \notin A'$. If $x \notin B$, then $x \notin A' \cup B$. This contradicts the hypothesis $A' \cup B = U$ (which says that every element of U is either in B or in A'). $\square$

8. Proof   Suppose $f'(x_0) \neq 0$. Then since $f'(x_0)$ exists, we may assert that either $f'(x_0) > 0$ or $f'(x_0) < 0$. If $f'(x_0) > 0$, then by Exercise 16(c), Article 6.1, there exists a neighborhood $N(x_0; \delta)$ such that if $x \in N(x_0; \delta)$ and $x < x_0$, then $f(x) < f(x_0)$ and if $x \in N(x_0; \delta)$ and $x > x_0$, then $f(x) > f(x_0)$. This contradicts the hypothesis that f has a relative maximum at x_0. A similar argument can be formulated to reach a contradiction in the case $f'(x_0) < 0$. $\square$

9. (c) Proof   If B were a subset of C, we would have $A \subseteq B$ and $B \subseteq C$, so that $A \subseteq C$, contradicting part of the hypothesis. $\square$

10. (d) Proof   If not, then both $\sqrt{2} + x$ and $\sqrt{2} - x$ are rational, so that their sum $2\sqrt{2}$ is rational. But by (c), since $2 \in \mathbf{Q}$ and $\sqrt{2} \notin \mathbf{Q}$, $2\sqrt{2} \notin \mathbf{Q}$, so that we have a contradiction. $\square$

11. (c) Proof   If $\varnothing$ is not open, then $\exists x \in \varnothing$ and $\delta > 0$ such that $N(x; \delta)$ is not a subset of $\varnothing$. But the statement "$\exists x \in \varnothing$" is false, so we have a contradiction. $\square$

15. (b) Proof   Assume A, B, and C are sets with $A \subseteq B$ and $B \subseteq C$. If $A \nsubseteq C$, then there exists an element $x \in A$ such that $x \notin C$. Now this x is either in B or not in B. If $x \in B$, then the fact that $x \in B$, but $x \notin C$ contradicts $B \subseteq C$. If $x \notin B$, then the fact that $x \in A$, but $x \notin B$ contradicts the fact that $A \subseteq B$. In either case we arrive at a contradiction, so that our assumption $A \nsubseteq C$ must be incorrect, as desired. (Compare this proof with the proof in Example 7, Article 4.1.) $\square$

Article 6.3

1. (c) Proof $\sqrt{(4x + 36)} = x + 8 \Rightarrow 4x + 36 = (x + 8)^2 = x^2 + 16x + 64 \Rightarrow x^2 + 12x + 28 = 0 \Rightarrow x = -6 \pm 2\sqrt{2}$. Hence $-6 + 2\sqrt{2}$ and $-6 - 2\sqrt{2}$ are the only possible solutions. Substitution shows that only $-6 + 2\sqrt{2}$ is an actual solution. (*Note:* In substituting, we must compare $2 + 2\sqrt{2}$ with $2\sqrt{(3 + 2\sqrt{2})}$ (equal, since both are positive and both have square $12 + 8\sqrt{2}$) and $2 - 2\sqrt{2}$ with $2\sqrt{(3 - 2\sqrt{2})}$ [negatives of each other, since both have square $12 - 8\sqrt{2}$, but $2 - 2\sqrt{2} < 0$, whereas $2\sqrt{(3 - 2\sqrt{2})} > 0$]. $\square$

4. (b) Proof   First, note that $X = \varnothing$ satisfies the statement $A \cap X = X$ for all sets A in U. For uniqueness, suppose X is any set satisfying "$A \cap X = X$ for all subsets A of U." In particular (using specialization), letting $A = \varnothing$, we have $\varnothing \cap X = X$. But again, it is known that $\varnothing = \varnothing \cap X$ so that we have $\varnothing = \varnothing \cap X = X$, so that $X = \varnothing$, our desired conclusion. $\square$

6. (c) Proof   First, it is clear that if $x_n \to x$, then x is a cluster point of $\{x_n\}$. In detail, let $\varepsilon > 0$ and $N \in \mathbf{N}$ be given; we must produce $m > N$ such that $|x_n - x| < \varepsilon$. Now since $x_n \to x$, then corresponding to this ε, there exists a

positive integer M, such that $|x_n - x| < \varepsilon$ whenever $n \geq M$. Hence, for the desired m, simply choose a positive integer larger than both N and M, and note that $|x_m - x| < \varepsilon$, as desired. For uniqueness, suppose x' is another cluster point of $\{x_n\}$. Let $\varepsilon > 0$ be given. We will show $|x - x'| < \varepsilon$, so that $x = x'$, by Example 5, Article 6.2. Since $x_n \to x$, then corresponding to this ε, divided by 2, $\exists N \in \mathbf{N}$ such that $|x_n - x| < \varepsilon/2$ whenever $n \geq N$. Since x' is a cluster point of $\{x_n\}$, then corresponding again to $\varepsilon/2$ <u>and</u> the preceding N, there exists $p \geq N$ such that $|x_p - x'| < \varepsilon/2$. Note that $|x_p - x| < \varepsilon/2$ since $p \geq N$. Hence $|x - x'| = |x - x_p + x_p - x'| \leq |x - x_p| + |x_p - x'| < \varepsilon/2 + \varepsilon/2 = \varepsilon$, as desired. $\square$

7. (c) Proof   Assume S_1 and S_2 are both bounded above in $\mathbf{R}$. To prove that $S_1 \cup S_2$ is bounded above in $\mathbf{R}$, we must show that there exists $M \in \mathbf{R}$ such that $x \leq M$ for all $x \in S_1 \cup S_2$. Now we know that $\exists M_1 \in \mathbf{R}$ such that $x \leq M_1$ for all $x \in S_1$ and $\exists M_2 \in \mathbf{R}$ such that $x \leq M_2$ for all $x \in S_2$. Let $M = \max\{M_1, M_2\}$. If $x \in S_1 \cup S_2$, then either $x \in S_1$ (in which case $x \leq M_1 \leq M$, as desired), or else $x \in S_2$ (so that $x \leq M_2 \leq M$, again, as desired). $\square$

10. (a) See the proof of Theorem 1, Article 9.3.
   (e) Proof   Assume $u = \text{lub } S$ and $u \notin S$. We must show that every neighborhood $N(u; \varepsilon)$ of u contains a point of S other than u itself. So let $\varepsilon > 0$ be given. By (ii) of the definition of lub, there exists $y \in S$ such that $y > u - \varepsilon$, so that $u - \varepsilon < y \leq u$ and $y \in N(u; \varepsilon)$. Clearly $u \neq y$ since $u \notin S$ and $y \in S$. $\square$
   For the example, let $S = [1, 2] \cup \{3\}$. Then $3 = \text{lub } S$, but 3 is clearly not a point of accumulation of S.

Article 7.1

2. (a) R_5 contains the ordered pairs $(4, -\frac{3}{2})$, $(8, -2)$, $(\frac{31}{10}, 0)$, $(4, \frac{7}{2})$, and (π, π), among many others.

3. (a) R is transitive if and only if
   $(\forall x)(\forall y)(\forall z)[((x, y) \in R \wedge (y, z) \in R) \Rightarrow ((x, z) \in R)]$; R is antisymmetric if and only if $(\forall x)(\forall y)[((x, y) \in R \wedge (y, x) \in R) \Rightarrow (x = y)]$.   (b) R is not reflexive on A if and only if $(\exists x \in A)((x, x) \notin R)$; R is not symmetric if and only if $(\exists x)(\exists y)[(x, y) \in R \wedge (y, x) \notin R]$; R is not transitive if and only if $(\exists x)(\exists y)(\exists z)[(x, y) \in R \wedge (y, z) \in R \wedge (x, z) \notin R]$; R is not antisymmetric if and only if $(\exists x)(\exists y)[(x, y) \in R \wedge (y, x) \in R \wedge (x \neq y)]$.

5. (a) R_{18} is symmetric only (if $y = 1/x$, then $x = 1/y$). It is not reflexive ($2 \neq \frac{1}{2}$, e.g.), not transitive (since $3 = 1/(\frac{1}{3})$ and $(\frac{1}{3}) = \frac{1}{3}$, but $3 \neq \frac{1}{3}$), and clearly not antisymmetric.   (b) R_{20} is reflexive (since $|x - x| = 0 \leq 1$ for any $x \in \mathbf{R}$), symmetric (following from the fact that $|x - y| = |y - x|$), not transitive (since, e.g., $|2.5 - 2| \leq 1$ and $|3.2 - 2.5| \leq 1$, but $|3.2 - 2| > 1$), and not antisymmetric [since (3, 2) and (2, 3) are both in R_{20}, but $3 \neq 2$].

10. (c) Proof $\Rightarrow$ Assume R is symmetric. We prove $R = R^{-1}$ by mutual inclusion. First, let $(x, y) \in R$. By symmetry, $(y, x) \in R$ so that $(x, y) \in R^{-1}$ and $R \subseteq R^{-1}$. The reverse inclusion is proved in an identical manner. $\Leftarrow$ Conversely, suppose

$R = R^{-1}$. To prove R is symmetric, let $(x, y) \in R$. Then $(y, x) \in R^{-1} = R$, so $(y, x) \in R$, as desired. $\square$

11. (c) $[1] = \{1, 3\}$, $[2] = \{2, 3\}$, $[3] = \{1, 2, 3\}$, $[4] = \{5\}$, $[5] = \{4\}$.

Article 7.2

2. (b) S_2 is an equivalence relation. It is reflexive since everyone has the same biological parents as himself or herself. It is symmetric: If x and y have the same biological parents, so do y and x. It is transitive, for if x and y have the same biological parents and y and z have the same biological parents, then x and z have the same biological parents.

4. (a) (i) $q = 4, r = 1$ (iv) $q = -4, r = 3$ (c) For $m_1 = 13$ and $d = 5$, we have $q_1 = 2$ and $r_1 = 3$. For $m_2 = -17$, $d = 5$, we have $q_2 = -4$ and $r_2 = 3$. Note that $r_1 = 3 = r_2$, not unexpected since m_1 and m_2 are congruent modulo 5 in this case. For $m_1 = 8$ and $d = 5$, we have $q_1 = 1$ and $r_1 = 3$. For $m_2 = -3$, $d = 5$, we have $q_2 = -1$ and $r_2 = 2$. Note that $r_1 = 3, r_2 = 2$, so $r_1 \neq r_2$, as we expect in this case, since this m_1 and m_2 are not congruent modulo 5. $\square$

7. Proof   (Reflexive) Let $m, n \in \mathbf{Q}$, with $n \neq 0$. Clearly $(m, n) \sim (m, n)$, since $mn = nm$. (Symmetric) Let $m, n, p, q \in \mathbf{Q}$, with $n \neq 0$ and $q \neq 0$, and assume $(m, n) \sim (p, q)$, so that $mq = np$. To prove $(p, q) \sim (m, n)$, we need only show $pn = qm$, clearly true since $pn = np = mq = qm$, using commutativity. (Transitive) Assume $m, n, p, q, r, s \in \mathbf{Q}$, with $n \neq 0$, $q \neq 0$, $s \neq 0$, with $(m, n) \sim (p, q)$ and $(p, q) \sim (r, s)$. To prove $(m, n) \sim (r, s)$, we must prove $ms = nr$. By our assumptions, we have $mq = np$ and $ps = qr$. Multiplying the first equation by s and the second by n, we get $mqs = nps = nqr$, so that $msq = nrq$. Since $q \neq 0$, we may cancel it to get $ms = nr$, as required. $\square$

8. (d) <u>Ordered pair example</u> for (R, NS, NT): Let $S = \{1, 2, 3\}$, $R_1 = \{(1, 1), (2, 2), (3, 3), (1, 2), (2, 3), (3, 2), (1, 3), (3, 1)\}$. R_1 is clearly (R, NS) and is also (NT) since $(2, 3) \in R_1$ and $(3, 1) \in R_1$, but $(2, 1) \notin R_1$. <u>Rule example</u> for (R, NS, NT): Let $S = \mathbf{R} - \{0\}$ and $R_2 = \{(x, y) \mid y \neq 2x\}$. Now R_2 is reflexive since $x \in S$ implies $x \neq 0$ so that $x \neq 2x$. R_2 is not symmetric since $(6, 3) \in R_2$, but $(3, 6) \notin R_2$. Finally, R_2 is not transitive, because $(6, 3) \in R_2$ and $(3, 12) \in R_2$, but $(6, 12) \notin R_2$.

9. (a) (v) NR, S, NT

Article 7.3

1. (c) $A/E_3 = \{\{a, b\}, \{c, e\}, \{d, f\}\}$

2. (b) $A/\mathscr{P}_2 = \{(a, a), (b, b), (c, c), (d, d), (e, e), (f, f), (c, d), (d, c), (c, f), (f, c), (d, f), (f, d)\}$.

3. (b) $\mathscr{P} = \{\{\text{odd integers}\}, \{\text{even integers}\}\}$, a two-celled partition of $\mathbf{Z}$.
(j) The partition has infinitely many cells. The cell containing a function $y = f(x)$ contains precisely those functions whose functional values differ from those of f at only a finite number of points.

4. (*c*) Proof   Assume $[x] = [y]$. Then $y \in [x]$, so that $x \mathrel{E} y$. Conversely, suppose $x \mathrel{E} y$ and let $w \in [y]$. Then $y \mathrel{E} w$. Since $x \mathrel{E} y$, we have $x \mathrel{E} w$, so that $w \in [x]$ and $[y] \subseteq [x]$. The reverse inclusion is proved in identical fashion. $\square$

Article 7.4

1. (*c*) 2 is a lower bound and 60 an upper bound for $\{4, 6, 10\}$, which has neither a greatest nor a least element.
6. (*a*) $M \vee N$ is simply the union $M \cup N$, by Exercise 5(*a*).
7. (*a*) (*iii*) lub $C_3 = \{1, 3, 5, 7, \ldots\}$, which is also the greatest element of C_3. Also, glb $C_3 = \emptyset$. Note that C_3 has no least element.
8. (*b*) (*i*) Proof   Given the hypotheses $[M_1] = [M_2]$ and $[N_1] = [N_2]$, suppose $[M_1] \leq [N_1]$. Then $n(M_2) = n(M_1) \leq n(N_1) = n(N_2)$, so that $n(M_2) \leq n(N_2)$, as desired. The implication $\Leftarrow$ follows in a similar manner. $\square$

Article 8.1

1. (*c*) (*ii*) r_2 is not a function since the ordered pair $(0, y) \in r_2$, for any $y \in \mathbf{R}$.
4. (*e*) j is not one to one since $j(0) = j(1) = j(-1) = 0$.
9. (*c*) Proof   Note first that f is a mapping of A into B, and i_X is a mapping of X into A, so that $f \circ i_X$ is a mapping of X into B. By definition of restriction, $f/_X$ is a mapping of X into B, also. Hence $f \circ i_X$ and $f/_X$ have the same domain and codomain. To prove equality of mappings, we need only prove that $(f \circ i_X)(x) = (f/_X)(x)$, for each $x \in X$. Letting x be an arbitrary element of X, we note that $(f \circ i_X)(x) = f(i_X(x)) = f(x) = (f/_X)(x)$, as desired. $\square$
10. (*e*) Proof   By definition of composition, dom $(g \circ f) = \{x \in \text{dom } f \mid f(x) \in \text{dom } g\}$. Since dom $f = A$ and dom $g = C$, this translates to $\{x \mid x \in A \text{ and } f(x) \in C\}$. Since rng $f \subseteq C$, we have that $x \in A$ implies $f(x) \in C$, so that $\{x \mid x \in A \text{ and } f(x) \in C\} = \{x \mid x \in A\} = A$. Hence dom $(g \circ f) = A$, as desired. Suppose now that $z \in \text{rng } (g \circ f)$, so that $z = (g \circ f)(x)$ for some $x \in A$. Hence $z = g(f(x))$ for some $x \in A$. Since $f(x) \in \text{rng } f$ and rng $f \subseteq C$, then $f(x) \in C$ and $z = g(c)$ for some $c \in C$ [namely; $c = f(x)$]. Since g maps C into D, then $z = g(c) \in D$. Hence rng $(g \circ f) \subseteq D$. $\square$
13. (*a*) Proof   If $g: C \to B$ is an extension of $f: A \to B$, then $f \subseteq g$, by definition. To prove $A \subseteq C$, let a be an arbitrary element of A. Since $A = \text{dom } f$, then $(a, f(a)) \in f$. Since $f \subseteq g$, we have $(a, f(a)) \in g$, so that $a \in \text{dom } g$. Since $C = \text{dom } g$, we conclude $a \in C$, as desired. $\square$

Article 8.2

2. (*b*) Since $f(x) = (x^2 - x - 12)/(x - 4) = x + 3$, for all $x \in \text{dom } f$, then f is clearly injective [recall Exercise 6(*b*), Article 5.2]. However, since $7 \notin \text{im } f$, then im $f \subset \mathbf{R}$, so that f is not surjective, and hence is not bijective.
(*k*) $\tan^{-1}$ is defined as the inverse of the tangent function, restricted to

$(-\pi/2, \pi/2)$. The latter is one to one over that interval and has range **R**. Hence $\tan^{-1}$ is one to one, but since its image equals $(-\pi/2, \pi/2) \subset [-\pi/2, \pi/2]$, the mapping $f: \mathbf{R} \to [-\pi/2, \pi/2]$ is not onto.

3. (c) Proof $\Rightarrow$ Suppose $g \circ f: X \to Z$ is a surjection. Then g is surjective, by Theorem 2(d). $\Leftarrow$ Conversely, suppose g is surjective. Then f and g are both surjective so that $g \circ f$ is surjective, by Theorem 2(a). $\square$

4. (b) (ii) Define $f: \mathbf{R} \to \mathbf{R}$ by $f(x) = 2x - 3$ and $g: \mathbf{R} \to \mathbf{R}$ by $g(x) = \sin x$. Note that f is clearly bijective. But the mapping $g \circ f: \mathbf{R} \to \mathbf{R}$, $(g \circ f)(x) = \sin(2x - 3)$ has range $[-1, 1]$, a proper subset of the range **R**, and so is not surjective, and consequently is not bijective.

7. (a) (iii) Given $f: \mathbf{R} \to \mathbf{R}$, $f(x) = 3x - 7$, we have $f^{-1}([-7, 2]) = [0, 3]$.
(b) (iv) $f^{-1}(\{e, 0\}) = \{A, C, D, E, G, H\}$.   (c) (iii) $x \in f^{-1}([-1, 1]) \Leftrightarrow$
$-1 \le (x + 1)^2 \le 1 \Leftrightarrow 0 \le (x + 1)^2 \le 1 \Leftrightarrow -1 \le x + 1 \le 1 \Leftrightarrow -2 \le x \le 0$.
Hence $f^{-1}([-1, 1]) = [-2, 0]$.

9. (a) (i) Proof Let $x \in f^{-1}(N_1 \cup N_2)$. Then $f(x) \in N_1 \cup N_2$, that is, either $f(x) \in N_1$ or $f(x) \in N_2$. If $f(x) \in N_1$, then $x \in f^{-1}(N_1) \subseteq f^{-1}(N_1) \cup f^{-1}(N_2)$, so $x \in f^{-1}(N_1) \cup f^{-1}(N_2)$, as desired. Similarly, if $f(x) \in N_2$, then $x \in f^{-1}(N_2) \subseteq f^{-1}(N_1) \cup f^{-1}(N_2)$, so $x \in f^{-1}(N_1) \cup f^{-1}(N_2)$, again, as desired. Conversely, suppose $x \in f^{-1}(N_1) \cup f^{-1}(N_2)$. Then either $x \in f^{-1}(N_1)$ or $x \in f^{-1}(N_2)$. If $x \in f^{-1}(N_1)$, then $f(x) \in N_1 \subseteq N_1 \cup N_2$ so that $x \in f^{-1}(N_1 \cup N_2)$. An identical argument leads to the same conclusion [i.e., $x \in f^{-1}(N_1 \cup N_2)$] in case $x \in f^{-1}(N_2)$. $\square$

12. (a) Proof $\Rightarrow$ Assume $f(f^{-1}(Y)) = Y$ and let $y \in Y$. To prove $y \in \text{rng } f$, we must prove $y = f(x)$ for some $x \in A$. Now $y \in Y = f(f^{-1}(Y))$ so $y \in f(f^{-1}(Y))$; that is, $y = f(x)$ for some $x \in f^{-1}(Y)$. But $f^{-1}(Y) \subseteq A$ and so $y = f(x)$ for some $x \in A$, as desired. Conversely, assume $y \in \text{rng } f$. Since we know $f(f^{-1}(Y)) \subseteq Y$ in general [by using Theorem 5(a)], we need only prove $Y \subseteq f(f^{-1}(Y))$. So let $y \in Y$. To show $y \in f(f^{-1}(Y))$, we must show $y = f(x)$ for some $x \in f^{-1}(Y)$. Now $y \in Y$ and $Y \subseteq \text{rng } f$ means $y \in \text{rng } f$, so that $y = f(x)$ for some $x \in A$. Now $f(x) = y \in Y$ so $f(x) \in Y$ so that this x, in fact, is contained in $f^{-1}(Y)$. Hence $y = f(x)$ for some $x \in f^{-1}(Y)$, as required. As to the consistency between this result and Theorem 5(d), note that $f(f^{-1}(Y)) = Y$ for all subsets Y of $B \Leftrightarrow Y \subseteq \text{rng } f$ for all subsets Y of $B \Leftrightarrow B \subseteq \text{rng } f \Leftrightarrow B = \text{rng } f \Leftrightarrow f$ is onto. $\square$

14. (c) Proof Assume f is one to one. If (b) has been proved, we need only prove $f(M_1 - M_2) \subseteq f(M_1) - f(M_2)$ in order to establish equality. Hence let $y \in f(M_1 - M_2)$. Then $y = f(x)$ for some $x \in M_1 - M_2$. To prove $y \in f(M_1) - f(M_2)$, we must show that $y \in f(M_1)$, but $y \notin f(M_2)$. Now since $y = f(x)$, where $x \in M_1 - M_2 \subseteq M_1$, we know that $y \in f(M_1)$. Proceeding indirectly, suppose $y \in f(M_2)$. Then $y = f(m)$ for some $m \in M_2$. Hence we have $y = f(x) = f(m)$, where $m \in M_2$ and $x \in M_1 - M_2$ so that $x \notin M_2$. Thus $x \neq m$. But $f(x) = f(m)$ and $x \neq m$ contradicts the one-to-one property of f. $\square$

Article 8.3

1. (c) Proof The mapping $f: (0, 1) \to (7, 13)$ given by $f(x) = 6x + 7$ is clearly a one-to-one mapping of $(0, 1)$ onto $(7, 13)$. $\square$

2. (*a*) Proof   Suppose $\emptyset$ is not finite, that is, $\emptyset$ is infinite. Then there exists a proper subset X of $\emptyset$ such that $X \cong \emptyset$. But the statement $X \subset \emptyset$ implies $\exists x \in \emptyset$ such that $x \in \emptyset X$. The statement "$\exists x \in \emptyset$" is a contradiction. $\square$

6. (*c*) Proof   By the hypotheses, there exists a one-to-one mapping f of A_1 onto B_1 and there exist bijections g and h of A_2 onto A_1 and B_2 onto B_1, respectively. We must produce a one-to-one mapping F of A_2 onto B_2. To do this, let $F = h^{-1} \circ f \circ g$. Clearly F is a mapping from A_2 into B_2. Since h^{-1}, f, and g are all one to one, F is one to one [recall Theorem 2(*a*), Article 8.2], as required. $\square$
This result says that the relation $\le$ is a well-defined relation on equivalence classes of sets identified with one another by the equivalence relation $\cong$. Viewing $\le$ as a relation on equivalence classes of sets, rather than on sets, Schroeder-Bernstein says that if $[A] \le [B]$ and if $[B] \le [A]$, then $[A] = [B]$, the requirement for antisymmetry.

Article 8.4

1. (*c*) Proof $x \in B \cap (\bigcup_{\lambda \in I} A_\lambda) \Leftrightarrow x \in B$ and $x \in \bigcup_{\lambda \in I} A_\lambda \Leftrightarrow x \in B$ and $x \in A_\lambda$ for some $\lambda \in I \Leftrightarrow$ [this step follows from the logical principle stated in Exercise 11(*c*), Article 3.3] $x \in B \cap A_\lambda$ for some $\lambda \in I \Leftrightarrow x \in \bigcup_{\lambda \in I} (B \cap A_\lambda)$. $\square$

4. (*b*) Proof $x \in f^{-1}(B_\mu)$ if and only if $f(x) \in \bigcap_{\mu \in J} B_\mu \Leftrightarrow f(x) \in \bigcap_{\mu \in J} B_\mu$ for all $\mu \in J \Leftrightarrow x \in f^{-1}(B_\mu)$ for all $\mu \in J \Leftrightarrow x \in \bigcap_{\mu \in J} f^{-1}(B_\mu)$. $\square$

Article 9.1

2. (*b*) Proof   Suppose y and z are both multiplicative inverses of a nonzero $x \in F$. Then $y = 1 \cdot y = (yx)y = (zx)y = z(xy) = z \cdot 1 = z$, so that $y = z$, as required. $\square$

5. (*b*) False; in the field $(\mathbf{R}, +, \cdot)$, $-1 = (-1)^{-1}$, but $-1 \ne 1$.   (*c*) False; in the field $\mathbf{Z}_2$, $1 = -1$, since $1 + 1 = 0$.

10. (*a*) False; $a = 2$ has no square root in the field $(\mathbf{Q}, +, \cdot)$. Also, in the field $(\mathbf{Z}_7, +, \cdot)$, 0, 1, 2, and 4 are the only squares.

Article 9.2

1. (*a*) Proof   We proceed by induction on n. Let S consist of precisely those positive integers for which the desired result is true. We claim $S = \mathbf{N}$. (i) $1 \in S$ since $x \in F$, $x \ne 0$, implies $x^2 \in \mathscr{P}$, by Theorem 1(*c*).   (ii) Assume $m \in S$. To prove $m + 1 \in S$, let $x \in S$, $x \ne 0$; we must show $x^{2(m+1)} \in \mathscr{P}$. Now $x^{2(m+1)} = x^{2m+2} = x^{2m}x^2$, where we note that $x^{2m} \in \mathscr{P}$ by induction hypothesis, whereas $x^2 \in \mathscr{P}$ by Theorem 1(*c*). Hence the product is in $\mathscr{P}$, by (*b*) of Definition 1. $\square$

3. (*b*) (*v*) Proof   Assume $x, y, a \in F$ with $x \le y$ and $a \le 0$. To prove $ax \ge ay$, we must prove that either $ax - ay \in \mathscr{P}$ or $ax = ay$. By hypothesis, we have that either $y - x \in \mathscr{P}$ or $y = x$ and either $-a \in \mathscr{P}$ or $a = 0$. Now if $a = 0$ or

$y = x$, then clearly $ax = ay$. So assume $y - x \in \mathscr{P}$ and $-a \in \mathscr{P}$. Then the product $(y - x)(-a) \in \mathscr{P}$. But $(y - x)(-a) = (-a)(y) + (-a)(-x) = ax - ay$, so $ax - ay \in \mathscr{P}$, as desired. $\square$

4. (b) (i) Proof   Let $a, b \in F$ with $a \geq 0$, $b \geq 0$. Then $a^2 < b^2 \Leftrightarrow 0 < b^2 - a^2 \Leftrightarrow 0 < (b - a)(b + a) \Leftrightarrow b - a > 0$. The last step follows since $b + a > 0$, by (a) of Definition 1, since, necessarily, either $a > 0$ or $b > 0$ (otherwise $a = 0$ and $b = 0$, contradicting $a^2 < b^2$). $\square$

5. (a) (ii) Proof   The result is clearly true if $x = 0$, so assume $x \neq 0$. Then $|x|^2 = |x^2|$, by Theorem 5(b) (using specialization, with $x = y$). But $x^2 > 0$, by Theorem 1(c), so that $|x^2| = x^2$, by Definition 4. Hence $|x|^2 = x^2$, as desired. $\square$

6. (a) (iii) Proof   Given $x, y \in F$ with $y \neq 0$, we have $|x/y| = |x(1/y)|$ [by Theorem 5(b)] $= |x|(1/|y|)$ [by (ii) of this exercise] $= |x|/|y|$. $\square$

Article 9.3

1. (e) Proof   Let $S = (3, 4) \cup \{6\}$. To prove $3 = $ glb S, note first that $3 \leq x$ for all $x \in S$. For if $x = 6$, then $3 < 6 = x$, whereas if $x \in (3, 4)$, then $3 < x < 4$ so that, in particular, $3 \leq x$. For part (b) of Definition 3, let $\varepsilon > 0$ be given. Let $k = \min \{\frac{1}{2}, \varepsilon/2\}$. Then, $3 < 3 + k < 4$ so that $y = 3 + k \in S$ and $y = 3 + k \leq 3 + \varepsilon/2 < 3 + \varepsilon$, as required. To prove $6 = $ lub S, note first that if $x \in S$, then either $3 < x < 4$ (so that $x < 6$) or $x = 6$. Hence $x \leq 6$ for all $x \in S$, so that (a) of Definition 3 is satisfied. For (b) of Definition 3, let $\varepsilon > 0$ be given. Then $6 \in S$ and $6 - \varepsilon < 6$, as desired. $\square$

4. (c) Proof   Let $y = $ lub T; then $t \leq y$ for all $t \in T$. Since $S \subseteq T$, then $s \leq y$ for all $s \in S$. Now let $x = $ lub S. If $x > y$, then $\varepsilon = x - y > 0$ and, by (b) of Definition 3, there must exist $s' \in S$ such that $s' > s - \varepsilon$. But then $s' > x - \varepsilon = x - (x - y) = y$. But $s' \in S$ and $s' > y$ contradicts our earlier conclusion that $s \leq y$ for all $s \in S$. Hence our supposition $x > y$ must be false, so that $x \leq y$; that is, lub $S \leq $ lub T, as desired. $\square$

6. Proof   Let S be a nonempty subset of F which is bounded below in F, say, by B. Then $B \leq x$ for all $x \in S$. Consider the set $T = \{-x \mid x \in S\}$. Letting $y \in T$, we note that $y = -x$ for some $x \in S$, so that $y = -x \leq -B$ for all $y \in T$; that is, $-B$ is an upper bound for T. By completeness of F, T has a least upper bound in F, call it u. Now $-u \in F$, since F is a field, and by Exercise 5(a), $-u = $ glb $\{-x \mid x \in T\}$. But clearly $\{-x \mid x \in T\} = S$ (you should verify this), so that $-u = $ glb S and S has the greatest lower bound in F. $\square$

Article 9.4

1. (g) $8i/17$ (i.e., $x = 0$, $y = \frac{8}{17}$).

3. (a) $z = (-\frac{16}{25}) + (-\frac{13}{25})i$.

6. (b) Proof   Let $z_1 = x_1 + y_1 i$, $z_2 = x_2 + y_2 i$. Since z_1 and z_2 are both real, then $y_1 = y_2 = 0$. Now $z_1 z_2 = (x_1 + y_1 i)(x_2 + y_2 i) = (x_1 x_2 - y_1 y_2) + (x_1 y_2 - x_2 y_1)i = (x_1 x_2 - (0 \cdot 0)) + (x_1 \cdot 0 - x_2 \cdot 0)i = x_1 x_2 = \text{Re}(z_1)\,\text{Re}(z_2)$. $\square$

Article 10.1

1. (b) $x^1 = x$; $x^n = x(x^{n-1})$ if $n > 1$.

3. (b) Proof   Let $S = \{m \in \mathbf{N} \,|\, \sigma(m) = 1 + m\}$. Clearly $1 \in S$, since when $m = 1$, then $\sigma(m) = m + 1 = 1 + 1 = 1 + m$. Next, assume $p \in S$ so that $\sigma(p) = 1 + p$. We must prove that $\sigma(p) = p + 1 \in S$; that is, $(p + 1) + 1 = 1 + (p + 1)$. But $(p + 1) + 1 = (1 + p) + 1$ (by induction hypothesis and well-definedness of addition) $= 1 + (p + 1)$ (by associativity).   □

6. (a) Proof   Given $a, b, c \in \mathbf{N}$ with $a + c < b + c$. Suppose that $a < b$ is false. Then, by Theorem 10, we must have $b < a$ or $b = a$. If $b < a$, then $b + c < a + c$, by Theorem 8(g), whereas if $b = a$, then $b + c = a + c$, by the well-definedness of addition. The conclusion in either of these cases contradicts the hypothesis $a + c < b + c$.   □

8. (a) Proof   Let S be a subset of $\mathbf{N}$ satisfying (i) $1 \in S$ and (ii) for all $m \in \mathbf{N}$, if $m \in S$, then $m + 1 \in S$; we claim $S = \mathbf{N}$. For if not, then $\mathbf{N} - S \neq 0$, and so, by the well-ordering principle, $\mathbf{N} - S$ contains a least element, call it m_0. Now clearly $m_0 > 1$, since $1 \in S$ (by (i)) and $m_0 \in \mathbf{N} - S$, so that $m_0 - 1 \in \mathbf{N}$. Since $m_0 - 1 < m_0$ and m_0 is the least element of $\mathbf{N} - S$, then $m_0 - 1 \in S$. Hence, by (ii), $m_0 = (m_0 - 1) + 1 \in S$, contradicting the fact that $m_0 \in \mathbf{N} - S$.   □

Article 10.2

1. Proof   Assume $(a, b) \sim (a', b')$ and $(c, d) \sim (c', d')$, where all symbols represent elements of $\mathbf{N}$. To show $(ac + bd, ad + bc) \sim (a'c' + b'd', a'd' + b'c')$, we must prove that $ac + bd + a'd' + b'c' = ad + bc + a'c' + b'd'$. We use the following two lemmas, whose simple proofs are left to you. *Lemma 1:* If $(a, b) \sim (a', b')$, then $a < a' \Leftrightarrow b < b'$. *Lemma 2:* If $(a, b) \sim (a', b')$, and $a < a'$, then $a' - a = b' - b$. Assume without loss of generality that $c < c'$, so that $d < d'$ by Lemma 1. Then $ac + bd + a'd' + b'c' = ac + b'c' + a'd' + bd = (a + b')c + (a' + b)d + b'(c' - c) + a'(d' - d) = (a' + b)c + (a + b')d + b'(d' - d) + a'(c' - c) = bc + ad + b'd' + a'c' = ad + bc + a'c' + b'd'$, as desired. The second equality in the preceding string follows by adding $b'c + a'd$ to both sides and using additive cancellation [Theorem 5(d), Article 10.1].   □

2. (d) Proof   Let $[(p, q)]$ and $[(r, s)]$ be elements of $\mathbf{Z}^+$, so that $p > q$ and $r > s$. We claim that $[(p, q)] + [(r, s)] \in \mathbf{Z}^+$ and $[(p, q)] \cdot [(r, s)] \in \mathbf{Z}^+$; that is, $p + r > q + s$ and $pr + qs > ps + qr$, respectively. The former is true, by Exercise 6, Article 10.1. For the latter, we note that $pr + qs = ps + qr + (p - q)(r - s)$, where $(p - q)(r - s) \in \mathbf{N}$, by (b) of the corollary to Theorem 3, Article 10.1, since $p - q \in \mathbf{N}$ and $r - s \in \mathbf{N}$ (because $p > q$ and $r > s$). Hence, by Definition 2, Article 10.1, we conclude $pr + qs > ps + qr$, as desired.   □

3. (c) Proof   Let $x = [(p, q)]$, $y = [(r, s)]$, and $z = [(t, u)]$. Then $x(y + z) = [(p, q)] \cdot [(r + t, s + u)] = [(p(r + t) + q(s + u), p(s + u) + q(r + t))] = [(pr + qs) + (pt + qu), (ps + qr) + (pu + qt)] = [(pr + qs, ps + qr)] + [(pt + qu, pu + qt)] = xy + xz$, as desired.   □

4. (b) (ii) Proof   Given $x = [(a, b)]$, assume $x > 0$; that is, $[(1, 1)] < [(a, b)]$ so that, by Definition 2, we have $1 + b < 1 + a$. By Exercise 6(a), Article 10.1, we have $b < a$ or $a > b$, as desired. The converse follows by reversing each of the preceding steps. Next, we note that $x < 0 \Leftrightarrow [(a, b)] < [(1, 1)] \Leftrightarrow a + 1 < b + 1 \Leftrightarrow a < b$, where the final step follows from Exercise 6(a), Article 10.1, and Theorem 8(g), Article 10.1. Finally, $x = 0 \Leftrightarrow [(a, b)] = [(1, 1)] \Leftrightarrow a + 1 = b + 1 \Leftrightarrow a = b$. Note that the last equivalence follows from the well-definedness of addition (in the direction $\Leftarrow$) and additive cancellation (for $\Rightarrow$). $\quad\square$

Article 10.3

1. (a) Proof   Let $\{p_m: m = 1, 2, \ldots\}$ be a Cauchy sequence of rational numbers. Corresponding to the positive rational number 1, there exists a positive integer N such that $|p_m - p_N| < 1$, whenever $m \geq N$. Since $|x| - |y| \leq |x - y|$ for any x and y, we have $|p_m| - |p_N| \leq |p_m - p_N| < 1$, so that $|p_m| \leq 1 + |p_N|$ for all $m \geq N$. Letting $B = \max\{|p_1|, |p_2|, \ldots, |p_{m-1}|, 1 + |p_N|\}$, we have $|p_m| \leq B$, as desired. $\quad\square$

List of Symbols

Symbol	Meaning
$a \in A, x \notin X$	Set membership and nonmembership, p. 4
$\{a, b, c, d, e\}$	Roster description of a finite set, p. 4
$\{x \mid p(x)\}$	Rule description of a set, p. 5
$\{a, b, \ldots, y, z\}$	Pattern description of a finite set, p. 6
$\{a, b, c, \ldots\}$	Pattern description of an infinite set, p. 6
U	Universal set or domain of discourse, p. 6
N, Z, Q, R, C	Positive integers, integers, rationals, reals, complex numbers (resp.), p. 7
$[a, b], (a, \infty),$ etc.	Various types of intervals in **R**, p. 8
$\varnothing, \{a\}$	Empty set, a single-element set, p. 9
$\square$	End of solution to example or proof of theorem, p. 10
$A = B, A \neq B$	Set theoretic equality, nonequality, p. 10
$A \subseteq B, A \nsubseteq B$	Subset relation and its negation, p. 11
$A \subset B, A \not\subset B$	Proper subset relation and its negation, p. 12
$\mathscr{P}(A)$	Power set, i.e., set of all subsets of A, p. 13
$A \cap B, A \cup B$	Intersection and union of sets, p. 16
A'	Complement of a set, p. 18
$A - B$	Set theoretic difference, p. 19
$A \triangle B$	Symmetric difference, p. 20
(a, b)	Ordered pair, p. 21
$A \times B$	Cartesian product of sets, p. 22
$n(S)$	Number of elements in a set, p. 43
$\{x_1, x_2, \ldots, x_k\}$	Generic set containing k elements, p. 43
$n!$	n factorial, p. 46
$P(n, k)$	Permutations of n objects, k at a time, p. 46
$C(n, k)$	Combinations of n objects, k at a time, p. 47
$\binom{n}{k}$	Binomial coefficient, "n choose k," p. 50

$\sim$, $\wedge$, $\vee$	Logical negation, conjunction, disjunction connectives, p. 56
$\rightarrow$, $\leftrightarrow$	Conditional, biconditional connectives, p. 61
$/$	Sheffer stroke, p. 76
$p(x)$, $q(x, y)$, $r(x, y, z)$	Propositional function in one or more variables, p. 82
$\forall$, $\exists$	Universal, existential quantifiers (resp.), p. 88
$\exists!$	"There exists a unique . . . ," p. 100
$\mathscr{A} = \{A_i \| i \in \mathbf{N}\}$	Countably infinite collection of sets, p. 124
$\bigcup\limits_{i=1}^{\infty} A_i$, $\bigcap\limits_{i=1}^{\infty} A_i$	Countably infinite union and intersection, p. 125
$\lim_{x \to a} f(x)$	Limit, as x approaches a, of $f(x)$, p. 129
$A = (a_{ij})_{m \times n}$	Matrix A with m rows, n columns, p. 158
A^t, $\|A\|$	Transpose of matrix A, determinant of A, p. 158
$\Sigma_{k=1}^{n} x_k$	Sum of n numbers of a given form, p. 181
$N(x; \delta)$	δ neighborhood of a real number x, p. 191
(m, n)	Greatest common divisor of integers m and n, p. 218
I_X	Identity relation on a set X, p. 232
$x \equiv y \bmod m$	Congruence modulo m, p. 232
$R, S, T, AS,$ NR, NS, NT	Reflexive, symmetric, etc., properties, p. 232
R^{-1}	Inverse of a relation R, p. 233
$[x]$	Equivalence class determined by x, p. 238
$\mathfrak{P}$	Partition of a set, p. 240
$A/\mathfrak{P}$	The equivalence relation determined on a set A by a partition $\mathfrak{P}$, p. 241
A/E	Set of all equivalence classes induced on a set A by an equivalence relation E, p. 243
$(A, \leq)$	Partially ordered set (poset), p. 245
$y = f(x)$	Functional notation, p. 253
$f\colon A \to B$	Function (or mapping) from domain A to codomain B, p. 256
f^{-1}	Inverse relation to a function f, p. 258
f/X	Restriction of a mapping, p. 260
i_X	Inclusion mapping, p. 260
$g \circ f$	Composition of functions or mappings, p. 260
$f(M)$, $f^{-1}(N)$	Image and inverse image of a set, p. 270
$A \cong B$, $A \not\cong B$	Numerical equivalence of sets and its negation, pp. 277–78
$\mathscr{N}_0$	Aleph-naught, i.e., the cardinal number of any countably infinite set, p. 283
c	Cardinal number of the continuum, p. 283
$A \leq B$, $A < B$	Cardinal number of A is less than or equal to (resp., less than) cardinal number of B, p. 284
$\mathscr{A} = \{A_\lambda \| \lambda \in l\}$	Arbitrary collection of sets, p. 290

$\bigcup_{\lambda \in I} A_\lambda, \bigcap_{\lambda \in I} A_\lambda$	Arbitrary union and intersection (resp.), p. 290
$\prod_{\lambda \in I} A_\lambda$	Direct product of an arbitrary collection, p. 291
$(F, +, \cdot)$	A field F, p. 295
$0, 1, -a, a^{-1}$	Additive and multiplicative identities, additive and multiplicative inverses of an element a, in a field, p. 295
$(\mathbf{Z}_m, +, \cdot)$	The integers modulo m, p. 297
$\mathbf{R}[x]$	Algebraic structure of all polynomials in variable x, with real coefficients, p. 298
$(F, \mathscr{P})$	Ordered field F with positive part $\mathscr{P}$, p. 304
$|x|$	Absolute value of x, in an ordered field, p. 307
$d(x, y)$	Distance from x to y, in an ordered field, p. 308
$\mathrm{Re}(z), \mathrm{Im}(z)$	Real and imaginary parts of a complex number z, p. 32
$z^*, |z|$	Complex conjugate and modulus of a complex number z, p. 322
$z = re^{i\theta}$	Polar form of a complex number z, p. 325
$\sigma(m)$	Successor of a positive integer m, p. 331

Index